APPLIED ELASTICITY

APPLIED ELASTICITY

CHI-TEH WANG, Sc.D.

New York   Toronto   London

McGRAW-HILL BOOK COMPANY, INC.

1953

THE MAPLE PRESS COMPANY, YORK, PA.

PREFACE

During the past seven years, the author has been giving courses in the theory of elasticity to graduate engineering students at New York University. This book is an outgrowth of these lectures. In preparing these lecture notes, the author had two objectives in mind: first, to provide the student with the necessary fundamental knowledge of the theory so that he will be able to formulate any problem occurring in the classical theory of elasticity; second, to acquaint him with the most useful analytical and numerical methods so that after the problem is formulated, the student will be able to solve it by one of these methods.

The author has found that the students, while taking a course in the theory of elasticity, are often studying advanced calculus concurrently. Therefore, in presenting the material, the mathematics is kept at a level which does not presume a thorough background in advanced calculus. Whenever higher mathematics is involved, it will be derived where it is first encountered. It is hoped, however, that the restriction to the elementary mathematics will result in no undue sacrifice of rigor.

As this book is intended mainly for engineers, an attempt is made to emphasize the physical meanings of the notations and mathematical relationships occurring in the subject. Since it is the engineer's task to furnish necessary information and data to the designer within a limited period of time, several of the most powerful numerical methods are discussed in detail. Whenever an exact solution is intractable by other means, these numerical methods usually yield an approximate solution with sufficient accuracy for engineering applications.

Suitable acknowledgments to sources are made throughout this volume, but the author's chief debt is to Professors S. Timoshenko, R. V. Southwell, and I. S. Sokolnikoff, whose work influenced the selection of topics covered in this book. The author is indebted to many of his students, particularly to Frank Lane and Robert J. Vaccaro, who read the complete manuscript and made many corrections and suggestions. To Professor E. Reissner of the Massachusetts Institute of Technology, the author is grateful for his valuable criticisms. The author wishes to take this opportunity to thank Professor F. K. Teichmann, chairman of the Department of Aeronautics at New York University, for his unfailing cooperation. To his wife Julia, the author is indebted for her long and persevering efforts in encouraging his completion of this manuscript. To Jane, a young lady of six, who so often and so cheerfully sacrificed her weekend playtime to "let Dad finish his work," this book is humbly dedicated.

C. T. Wang

CONTENTS

CHAPTER 1

ANALYSIS OF STRESS

1.1. Definition and Notation of Stress. When a body is under the action of external forces, it undergoes distortion and the effect of the forces is transmitted throughout the body. Across any small internal plane area of the body, forces are exerted by the part of the body on one side of the area upon the part of the body on the other side. The term *stress* denotes internal force per unit area. Let us assume that the material is continuous. Then the stress at any point across a small area ΔA can be defined by the limiting equation

$$\text{Stress} = \lim_{\Delta A \to 0} \frac{\Delta F}{\Delta A}$$

where ΔF is the internal force on the area ΔA surrounding the given point. The justification of the assumption of continuity of material will be discussed later.

Passing through a given point, infinitely many planes may be drawn. Take, as an example, the case of a bar under simple tension. In Fig. 1.1, we have drawn two planes passing through the point P. Although the resultant forces acting on these planes are the same, the stresses on these planes are different because the areas and the inclinations of these planes are different. Therefore, for a complete description of a stress, we have to specify not only its magnitude, direction, and sense but also the surface upon which it acts. Consequently, stress is described by *tensors*, because in addition to its magnitude, direction, and sense, which define a *vector*, it depends on another vector, which represents the surface upon which it acts. Referring to an arbitrarily chosen set of rectangular cartesian coordinate axes, a force is completely determined by its components in the directions of these axes. A convenient way of describing these components is the single-subscript notation, wherein F_x, F_y, F_z denote, respectively, the x, y, z component of the force. This notation, however, is not sufficient to describe a stress completely because in this case we have to designate also the surface on which it acts. A surface may be designated by a subscript which gives the direction of its normal. For example, a plane parallel to the yz plane has its normal in the x direction, so that we may use the subscript x to denote the yz plane. The stress at a point on

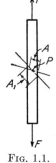

Fig. 1.1.

1

a surface may be resolved into two components—a *normal stress* perpendicular to the surface and a *shearing stress* acting in the plane of the surface. We shall denote the normal-stress component by the letter σ and the shearing-stress component by the letter τ. For a normal-stress component, the direction is already specified, and only one subscript is needed

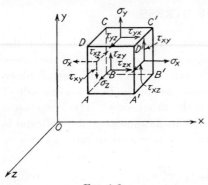

Fig. 1.2.

to denote the plane on which it acts. In the case of a shearing-stress component, it can again be resolved into two components in the directions of the coordinate axes in its plane, and we therefore need two subscripts for its description—one, say the first subscript, to denote the plane on which it acts, and the other, or the second subscript, to denote its direction. For example, the three stress components acting on a surface parallel to the yz plane will be denoted by σ_x, τ_{xy}, τ_{xz} according to this notation. Through a point in a body we can construct three orthogonal coordinate planes on which we have nine stress components. The notation of other stress components is shown in Fig. 1.2.

Let us next define the sign convention. A normal stress is defined as positive if it is a *tensile* stress, *i.e.*, if it is directed away from the surface upon which it acts. If it is directed toward the surface, it is called a *compressive* stress and is defined as negative. Since a tensile stress is always directed away from the surface, on a surface such as $A'B'C'D'$ in Fig. 1.2, it is positive when it is in the positive direction of the coordinate axis, while on such a surface as $ABCD$, it is positive when opposite to the positive direction of the coordinate axis. In view of this, we shall define the positive directions of the shearing stresses as follows: on any surface where the tensile stress is in the positive direction of the coordinate axis, such as $A'B'C'D'$, the shearing stresses are positive if they are in the positive directions of the other two coordinate axes. If the tensile stress is opposite to the positive axis, the positive directions of the shearing stresses are also opposite to the positive axes. Following this rule the positive directions of the stress components acting on the right, front, or top side of the cubic element in Fig. 1.2 coincide with the positive directions of the coordinate axes. The positive directions are all reversed if we are considering the left, rear, or bottom side of this element.

1.2. Differential Equations of Equilibrium. A body is said to be in *equilibrium* when, under the action of external forces, it is at rest or moving in a straight line with constant velocity. There are, in general, two kinds of external forces which may act on a body. They are the *surface forces* and the *body forces*. A force such as the hydrostatic pressure, which is distributed over the surface of a body, is called a surface force. Such forces as the gravitational and centrifugal forces, which are distributed over the volume of the body, are called body forces. A surface force is given in terms of force per unit area, and a body force is given in terms of force per unit volume. To distinguish these forces, we shall use the symbols $\bar{X}$, $\bar{Y}$, $\bar{Z}$ to denote the x, y, z components of a surface force and the symbols X, Y, Z to denote the x, y, z components of a body force.

Before we proceed to derive the equilibrium equations, we shall first explain the method of writing the stress components on the various surfaces of an infinitesimal element. Let us take an elementary block of unit

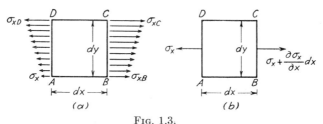

Fig. 1.3.

length with a cross-sectional area $dx\,dy$. In general, the stresses in a body vary from point to point. Consider the simple case where the element is subjected to tensile stresses in the x direction only (Fig. 1.3a). Let us denote the stress at A by σ_x. Since dx is an infinitesimal linear element, we may write the stress at B, σ_{xB}, as the sum of σ_x and the small variation of stress from A to B. From the well-known rules in the differential calculus, this small variation may be obtained by multiplying the rate of change of σ_x with respect to x at A by the length AB, namely,

$$\sigma_{xB} = \sigma_x + \frac{\partial \sigma_x}{\partial x}\,dx \qquad (1.1)$$

In (1.1) the partial derivative sign is used because σ_x varies not only with respect to x but also with respect to y. Similarly, the stresses at D and C may be written as

$$\sigma_{xD} = \sigma_x + \frac{\partial \sigma_x}{\partial y}\,dy \qquad (1.2)$$

$$\sigma_{xC} = \sigma_{xB} + \frac{\partial \sigma_{xB}}{\partial y}\,dy$$

$$= \left(\sigma_x + \frac{\partial \sigma_x}{\partial x}\,dx\right) + \frac{\partial}{\partial y}\left(\sigma_x + \frac{\partial \sigma_x}{\partial x}\,dx\right)dy$$

$$= \sigma_x + \frac{\partial \sigma_x}{\partial x}\,dx + \frac{\partial \sigma_x}{\partial y}\,dy \qquad (1.3)$$

Since dx and dy are infinitesimal quantities, their squares and products are very small compared with the quantities themselves. As a result, in Eq. (1.3) the term $(\partial^2\sigma_x/\partial x\,\partial y)\,dx\,dy$ has been neglected as it is small in comparison with the terms $(\partial\sigma_x/\partial x)\,dx$ or $(\partial\sigma_x/\partial y)\,dy$. Terms containing small quantities of higher degrees are called higher-order terms, and they can be neglected in the presence of terms containing small quantities of lower degree.

Equations (1.1) to (1.3) can also be explained by means of Taylor's expansion in the differential calculus. Consider an arbitrary function $f(x,y)$. Let the value of this function at $x = x_0$, $y = y_0$ be $f(x_0,y_0)$ or f_0. Then, expanding $f(x_0 + dx, y_0 + dy)$ in terms of Taylor's series, we find that the value of the function at $x = x_0 + dx$, $y = y_0 + dy$ is

$$f(x_0 + dx,\, y_0 + dy) = f_0 + \left(\frac{\partial f}{\partial x}\right)_0 dx + \left(\frac{\partial f}{\partial y}\right)_0 dy + \frac{1}{2}\left(\frac{\partial^2 f}{\partial x^2}\right)_0 dx^2$$
$$+ \frac{1}{2}\left(\frac{\partial^2 f}{\partial y^2}\right)_0 dy^2 + \left(\frac{\partial^2 f}{\partial x\,\partial y}\right)_0 dx\,dy + \cdots$$

where $(\partial f/\partial x)_0$, $(\partial f/\partial y)_0$, etc., denote the values of the first partial derivatives at x_0, y_0. If we let $f(x,y) = \sigma_x$, $dy = 0$ and neglect higher-order terms, we arrive at Eq. (1.1). Similarly, by letting $dx = 0$ and neglecting higher-order terms, we obtain Eq. (1.2). By retaining both dx and dy and neglecting higher-order terms, we obtain Eq. (1.3).

When higher-order terms are neglected, we find that the stresses over the faces AD and BC are distributed in a linear manner. Hence, the force acting on the face AD is

$$F_1 = \frac{1}{2}\left(\sigma_x + \sigma_x + \frac{\partial\sigma_x}{\partial y}\,dy\right)dy = \sigma_x\,dy + \frac{1}{2}\frac{\partial\sigma_x}{\partial y}\,dy^2$$

Similarly, the force acting on the face BC is

$$F_2 = \frac{1}{2}\left(\sigma_x + \frac{\partial\sigma_x}{\partial x}\,dx + \sigma_x + \frac{\partial\sigma_x}{\partial x}\,dx + \frac{\partial\sigma_x}{\partial y}\,dy\right)dy$$
$$= \sigma_x\,dy + \frac{\partial\sigma_x}{\partial x}\,dx\,dy + \frac{1}{2}\frac{\partial\sigma_x}{\partial y}\,dy^2$$

The resultant force acting on the element $ABCD$ is therefore

$$\Sigma F = F_2 - F_1 = \frac{\partial\sigma_x}{\partial x}\,dx\,dy$$

If we assume that the mean stress on AD is σ_x and is acting at the center of the face, then the mean stress acting on BC will be $\sigma_x + (\partial\sigma_x/\partial x)\,dx$. So far as the resultant force is concerned, this second state of stress distribution gives identically the same result as the first stress state. The derivation of the equilibrium equations is based mainly on these result-ants. For the purpose of deriving the equilibrium equations, we may therefore consider the second state of simplified stress distribution instead of the more detailed first state.

Figure 1.4 shows the same element subjected to a general system of positive two-dimensional stresses, as well as body forces, according to the simplified mode of representation. By two-dimensional stress system we mean that in such a case σ_x, σ_y, τ_{xy}, and τ_{yx} are independent of z and the other stress components are zero. The body forces X and Y are assumed to be independent of z, and Z is zero. Such a state of stress is called *plane*

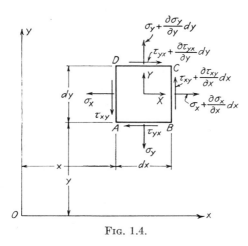

FIG. 1.4.

stress. Summing all forces in the x direction, the condition $\Sigma F_x = 0$ gives

$$\left(\sigma_x + \frac{\partial \sigma_x}{\partial x}\,dx\right)dy - \sigma_x\,dy + \left(\tau_{yx} + \frac{\partial \tau_{yx}}{\partial y}\,dy\right)dx - \tau_{yx}\,dx + X\,dx\,dy = 0$$

Collecting terms, we obtain

$$\left(\frac{\partial \sigma_x}{\partial x} + \frac{\partial \tau_{yx}}{\partial y} + X\right)dx\,dy = 0$$

Since $dx\,dy$ is not necessarily zero, the condition $\Sigma F_x = 0$ necessitates

$$\frac{\partial \sigma_x}{\partial x} + \frac{\partial \tau_{yx}}{\partial y} + X = 0 \tag{1.4}$$

Similarly from $\Sigma F_y = 0$, we obtain

$$\frac{\partial \tau_{xy}}{\partial x} + \frac{\partial \sigma_y}{\partial y} + Y = 0 \tag{1.5}$$

Equations (1.4) and (1.5) are the two-dimensional differential equations of equilibrium in cartesian coordinates.

In the general case of an elementary block under a system of positive three-dimensional stresses, we can show that the differential equations of equilibrium in cartesian coordinates are the following:

$$\frac{\partial \sigma_x}{\partial x} + \frac{\partial \tau_{yx}}{\partial y} + \frac{\partial \tau_{zx}}{\partial z} + \overset{\circ}{X} = 0$$

$$\frac{\partial \tau_{xy}}{\partial x} + \frac{\partial \sigma_y}{\partial y} + \frac{\partial \tau_{zy}}{\partial z} + \overset{\circ}{Y} = 0 \qquad (1.6)$$

$$\frac{\partial \tau_{xz}}{\partial x} + \frac{\partial \tau_{yz}}{\partial y} + \frac{\partial \sigma_z}{\partial z} + \overset{\circ}{Z} = 0$$

Referring again to Fig. 1.4, and taking moments about 0, we obtain from the condition $\Sigma M_0 = 0$ that

$$(\sigma_x \, dy)\left(y + \frac{dy}{2}\right) - \left(\sigma_x + \frac{\partial \sigma_x}{\partial x} \, dx\right) dy \left(y + \frac{dy}{2}\right) - (\tau_{xy} \, dy)x$$

$$+ \left(\tau_{xy} + \frac{\partial \tau_{xy}}{\partial x} \, dx\right) dy \, (x + dx) - (\sigma_y \, dx)\left(x + \frac{dx}{2}\right)$$

$$+ \left(\sigma_y + \frac{\partial \sigma_y}{\partial y} \, dy\right) dx \left(x + \frac{dx}{2}\right) + (\tau_{yx} \, dx)y$$

$$- \left(\tau_{yx} + \frac{\partial \tau_{yx}}{\partial y} \, dy\right) dx \, (y + dy) - (X \, dx \, dy)\left(y + \frac{dy}{2}\right)$$

$$+ (Y \, dx \, dy)\left(x + \frac{dx}{2}\right) = 0$$

where the counterclockwise moments are taken positive. Collecting terms and neglecting the higher-order terms, we have

$$(\tau_{xy} - \tau_{yx}) \, dx \, dy - \left(\frac{\partial \sigma_x}{\partial x} + \frac{\partial \tau_{yx}}{\partial y} + X\right) y \, dx \, dy$$

$$+ \left(\frac{\partial \tau_{xy}}{\partial x} + \frac{\partial \sigma_y}{\partial y} + Y\right) x \, dx \, dy = 0 \quad (1.7)$$

From Eqs. (1.4) and (1.5), we see that the terms in the second and third parentheses of Eq. (1.7) are zero. Since $dx \, dy$ is not necessarily zero, Eq. (1.7) reduces to

$$\tau_{xy} - \tau_{yx} = 0$$

or

$$\tau_{xy} = \tau_{yx} \qquad (1.8)$$

In the general three-dimensional case, by taking moments of the forces acting on the elementary block with respect to the z, y, and x axes, respectively, we can prove that

$$\tau_{xy} = \tau_{yx} \qquad \tau_{xz} = \tau_{zx} \qquad \tau_{yz} = \tau_{zy} \qquad (1.9)$$

Equations (1.9) show that the shearing-stress components are symmetrical. In Sec. 1.1, we mentioned that there are nine different stress components acting on the three coordinate planes at any point in a body. Now we find that out of the six shearing-stress components only three are independent. Since the stress components τ_{xy} and τ_{yx}, τ_{xz} and τ_{zx}, and τ_{yz} and τ_{zy} are equal to each other, we shall make no distinction between them from now on.

Problem 1. Derive Eq. (1.3) by writing σ_{xC} in terms of σ_{xD} and the stress variation at D instead of writing it in terms of σ_{xB} and the stress variation at B as was carried out in the text.

Problem 2. Verify Eqs. (1.6).

Problem 3. Verify Eqs. (1.9).

Problem 4. Show that the shearing-stress components will not be symmetrical, *i.e.*, that Eqs. (1.9) are no longer valid, when "body moments" are present. We find such an example in the case where an elastic body contains a large number of evenly distributed small magnetized particles and therefore each element in the body is influenced by a moment due to the magnetic field.

1.3. Specification of Stress at a Point. We shall now proceed to show that the state of stress within a body is completely determined when we know the values of the six stress components at each point. Let us consider again the simpler case of plane stress. Knowing the stress components σ_x, σ_y, τ_{xy} at any point of the body, we shall show that the stress acting on any plane through this point perpendicular to the xy plane and inclined to the x and y axes can be calculated. Let O be an arbitrary point in a stressed body and σ_x, σ_y, and τ_{xy} the stress components at O

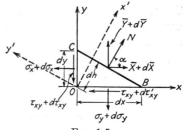

FIG. 1.5.

(Fig. 1.5). To find the stress on another plane through O and inclined to the x and y axes, we take a plane BC parallel to it and at an infinitesimal distance dh from O, so that this latter plane together with the coordinate planes forms a small triangular prism OBC. Since the stresses vary continuously over the volume of the body, the mean stress components acting on OC will be $\sigma_x + d\sigma_x$ and $\tau_{xy} + d\tau_{xy}$ and the stress components acting on OB will be $\sigma_y + d\sigma_y$ and $\tau_{xy} + d\tau'_{xy}$. If we denote $\bar{X}$ and $\bar{Y}$ as the x and y components of the stress on the plane parallel to BC through O, the corresponding stress components on BC may be written as $\bar{X} + d\bar{X}$ and $\bar{Y} + d\bar{Y}$. As the element is made smaller and smaller, these stress components will then approach those acting on planes through O. In other words, as $dh \to 0$, $d\sigma_x$, $d\sigma_y$, $d\tau_{xy}$, $d\tau'_{xy}$, and $d\bar{X}$ and $d\bar{Y}$ all approach zero as a limit.

Consider the equilibrium of the prismatical element. The forces acting on the element can be obtained by multiplying the mean stress components by the respective areas of the surfaces upon which they act. Let N be the normal to the plane BC, and denote the cosines of the angles between the normal N and the axes x and y by

$$\cos Nx = l \qquad \cos Ny = m$$

N is taken positive when it is directed outward from the element. Then, if A denotes the area of the side BC of the element, the areas of OC and OB are Al and Am, respectively. The condition $\Sigma F_x = 0$ gives

$$(\bar{X} + d\bar{X})A - (\sigma_x + d\sigma_x)Al - (\tau_{xy} + d\tau'_{xy})Am - X(\tfrac{1}{2} A\, dh) = 0 \quad (1.10)$$

where X is the x component of the body force. Upon dividing by A and passing to the limit as $dh \to 0$, Eq. (1.10) becomes

$$\bar{X} = l\sigma_x + m\tau_{xy} \tag{1.11}$$

Similarly, the condition $\Sigma F_y = 0$ gives

$$\bar{Y} = l\tau_{xy} + m\sigma_y \tag{1.12}$$

Thus, if the stress components σ_x, σ_y, and τ_{xy} at a point are given, the components of stress at the point on any plane defined by the direction cosines l and m can be calculated from Eqs. (1.11) and (1.12).

If we introduce a new system of coordinate axes x' and y' and let x' be in the direction of N, the stress components on the plane BC in terms of σ and τ can be easily obtained from $\bar{X}$ and $\bar{Y}$ as follows,

$$\begin{aligned}
\sigma_{x'} &= l\bar{X} + m\bar{Y} = l^2\sigma_x + m^2\sigma_y + 2lm\tau_{xy} \\
\tau_{x'y'} &= l\bar{Y} - m\bar{X} = (l^2 - m^2)\tau_{xy} + lm(\sigma_y - \sigma_x)
\end{aligned} \tag{1.13}$$

where $l = \cos x'x$ and $m = \cos x'y$. Equations (1.13) establish the laws of transformation of the stress components under an orthogonal transformation of coordinate axes in the two-dimensional case.

In the general three-dimensional stress system, the equations corresponding to Eqs. (1.11) and (1.12) are

$$\begin{aligned}
\bar{X} &= l\sigma_x + m\tau_{xy} + n\tau_{zx} \\
\bar{Y} &= l\tau_{xy} + m\sigma_y + n\tau_{yz} \\
\bar{Z} &= l\tau_{zx} + m\tau_{yz} + n\sigma_z
\end{aligned} \tag{1.14}$$

where $\bar{X}$, $\bar{Y}$, and $\bar{Z}$ are the x, y, and z components of the stress on an arbitrary plane with a normal N and $l = \cos Nx$, $m = \cos Ny$, $n = \cos Nz$. It can be shown that the three-dimensional equations governing the transformation of coordinate axes are

$$\sigma_{x'} = l_1{}^2\sigma_x + m_1{}^2\sigma_y + n_1{}^2\sigma_z + 2l_1m_1\tau_{xy} + 2m_1n_1\tau_{yz} + 2n_1l_1\tau_{zx}$$
$$\sigma_{y'} = l_2{}^2\sigma_x + m_2{}^2\sigma_y + n_2{}^2\sigma_z + 2l_2m_2\tau_{xy} + 2m_2n_2\tau_{yz} + 2n_2l_2\tau_{zx}$$
$$\sigma_{z'} = l_3{}^2\sigma_x + m_3{}^2\sigma_y + n_3{}^2\sigma_z + 2l_3m_3\tau_{xy} + 2m_3n_3\tau_{yz} + 2n_3l_3\tau_{zx} \qquad (1.15)$$
$$\tau_{x'y'} = l_1l_2\sigma_x + m_1m_2\sigma_y + n_1n_2\sigma_z + (l_1m_2 + m_1l_2)\tau_{xy}$$
$$+ (m_1n_2 + n_1m_2)\tau_{yz} + (n_1l_2 + l_1n_2)\tau_{zx}$$
$$\tau_{y'z'} = l_2l_3\sigma_x + m_2m_3\sigma_y + n_2n_3\sigma_z + (l_2m_3 + m_2l_3)\tau_{xy}$$
$$+ (m_2n_3 + n_2m_3)\tau_{yz} + (n_2l_3 + l_2n_3)\tau_{zx}$$
$$\tau_{z'x'} = l_3l_1\sigma_x + m_3m_1\sigma_y + n_3n_1\sigma_z + (l_3m_1 + m_3l_1)\tau_{xy}$$
$$+ (m_3n_1 + n_3m_1)\tau_{yz} + (n_3l_1 + l_3n_1)\tau_{zx}$$

where the direction cosines l, m, n between the new coordinate axes x', y', z' and the original coordinate axes x, y, z are defined in the following table:

	x	y	z
x'	l_1	m_1	n_1
y'	l_2	m_2	n_2
z'	l_3	m_3	n_3

From the above table we see that $l_1 = \cos x'x$, $m_2 = \cos y'y$, etc.

Since the transformation of coordinates is orthogonal, the direction cosines are related by equations of the types

$$l_1{}^2 + l_2{}^2 + l_3{}^2 = 1$$
$$l_1{}^2 + m_1{}^2 + n_1{}^2 = 1$$
$$l_1l_2 + m_1m_2 + n_1n_2 = 0 \qquad (1.16)$$
$$l_1m_1 + l_2m_2 + l_3m_3 = 0$$

Adding the first three equations of (1.15) and making use of the orthogonality relations (1.16), we find

$$\sigma_x + \sigma_y + \sigma_z = \sigma_{x'} + \sigma_{y'} + \sigma_{z'} \qquad (1.17)$$

In other words, the quantity $\sigma_x + \sigma_y + \sigma_z$ is invariant with respect to orthogonal transformations of coordinates.

Problem 1. Show that the following quantities are invariant:

a. $\sigma_x\sigma_y + \sigma_y\sigma_z + \sigma_z\sigma_x - \tau_{xy}{}^2 - \tau_{yz}{}^2 - \tau_{zz}{}^2$

b. $\sigma_x\sigma_y\sigma_z + 2\tau_{xy}\tau_{yz}\tau_{zx} - \sigma_x\tau_{yz}{}^2 - \sigma_y\tau_{zx}{}^2 - \sigma_z\tau_{yz}{}^2$

Problem 2. Verify Eqs. (1.14) and (1.15).

1.4. Principal Stresses and the Mohr Diagram. If we let α be the angle between the normal N and the x axis, we have then $l = \cos \alpha$ and $m = \sin \alpha$. Expressions (1.13) for the normal and shearing components of stress on the surface BC may be written as

$$\sigma_{x'} = \sigma_x \cos^2 \alpha + \sigma_y \sin^2 \alpha + 2\tau_{xy} \sin \alpha \cos \alpha \qquad (1.18)$$
$$\tau_{x'y'} = \tau_{xy}(\cos^2 \alpha - \sin^2 \alpha) + (\sigma_y - \sigma_x) \sin \alpha \cos \alpha \qquad (1.19)$$

It is evident that the values of $\sigma_{x'}$ and $\tau_{x'y'}$ vary with respect to the angle α, and for certain values of α, $\sigma_{x'}$ may attain a maximum or minimum value. From the differential calculus, we know that such values of α may be determined from the condition $d\sigma_{x'}/d\alpha = 0$. Differentiating $\sigma_{x'}$ as given by Eq. (1.18) with respect to α and equating the result to zero, we obtain

$$2(\sigma_y - \sigma_x) \sin \alpha \cos \alpha + 2\tau_{xy}(\cos^2 \alpha - \sin^2 \alpha) = 0 \qquad (1.20)$$

or
$$\tan 2\alpha = \frac{2 \sin \alpha \cos \alpha}{\cos^2 \alpha - \sin^2 \alpha} = \frac{2\tau_{xy}}{\sigma_x - \sigma_y} \qquad (1.21)$$

Since $\tan 2\alpha = \tan (\pi + 2\alpha)$, from Eq. (1.21) two perpendicular directions can be found, and it can be shown that $\sigma_{x'}$ is a maximum along one of the directions and a minimum along the other one. These directions are called *principal directions* and the corresponding normal stresses the *principal stresses*. Comparing Eq. (1.19) with (1.20), we see that on the planes perpendicular to these directions the shearing stresses are zero. The magnitudes of the principal stresses may be obtained by substituting the values of α given by (1.21) into Eq. (1.18). With some transformation, we obtain

$$\sigma_1 = \sigma_{\max} = \frac{\sigma_x + \sigma_y}{2} + \sqrt{\left(\frac{\sigma_x - \sigma_y}{2}\right)^2 + \tau_{xy}^2}$$
$$\sigma_2 = \sigma_{\min} = \frac{\sigma_x + \sigma_y}{2} - \sqrt{\left(\frac{\sigma_x - \sigma_y}{2}\right)^2 + \tau_{xy}^2} \qquad (1.22)$$

In terms of the principal stresses, Eqs. (1.18) and (1.19) may be simplified to yield

$$\sigma_{x'} = \sigma_1 \cos^2 \alpha + \sigma_2 \sin^2 \alpha$$
$$\tau_{x'y'} = \tfrac{1}{2}(\sigma_2 - \sigma_1) \sin 2\alpha \qquad (1.23)$$

The variation of $\sigma_{x'}$ and $\tau_{x'y'}$, as we vary the angle α, can be represented by means of a graph known as *Mohr's circle*. For convenience we shall rewrite Eqs. (1.23) in the following form:

$$\sigma_{x'} = \frac{\sigma_1 + \sigma_2}{2} + \frac{\sigma_1 - \sigma_2}{2} \cos 2\alpha$$
$$\tau_{x'y'} = -\frac{\sigma_1 - \sigma_2}{2} \sin 2\alpha \qquad (1.24)$$

The Mohr's circle may be constructed as follows: From an arbitrary point O on the horizontal axis we lay off segments OA and OB equal, respectively, to σ_1 and σ_2 in directions to agree with the sign of these stresses (Fig. 1.6). In the figure, both σ_1 and σ_2 are assumed positive or tensile stresses. If they are compressive or negative, points A and B will be on the left side of O. From a point C bisecting AB we draw a circle with radius CA. This circle is the so-called Mohr's circle, which gives us graphically the results contained in Eqs. (1.24) and in addition enables us to visualize and to determine other useful stress relations.

In the usual case, however, the principal stresses are not given. Under such conditions the construction of Mohr's circle may proceed as follows: Let σ_x, σ_y, τ_{xy} be the given stress components. On the horizontal axis, lay off OF and OF' equal to σ_x and σ_y. At F we lay off a distance perpendicular to OF and equal to τ_{xy}, thus obtaining D. Similarly, at F' we lay off $F'D'$ equal to τ_{xy} and in the opposite direction to FD. Draw the straight line DD', which intersects the horizontal axis at C. With C as a center and CD as radius, the Mohr's circle as shown in Fig. 1.6 can again be drawn. From the Mohr's circle we can find the principal stresses which are equal to OA and OB.

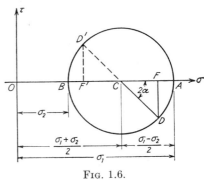

FIG. 1.6.

In order to find the stresses on any plane BC whose normal makes an angle α with the stress σ_x (Fig. 1.5), we measure from the axis CA an angle equal to 2α and obtain the point D on the circle. From the figure,

$$OF = OC + CF = \frac{\sigma_1 + \sigma_2}{2} + \frac{\sigma_1 - \sigma_2}{2} \cos 2\alpha = \sigma_{x'}$$

$$DF = CD \sin 2\alpha = \frac{\sigma_1 - \sigma_2}{2} \sin 2\alpha = -\tau_{x'y'}$$

Comparing with Eqs. (1.24), we see that the coordinates of point D give the stress components on the plane BC.

It may be noted that the angle may be measured in either clockwise or counterclockwise direction without affecting the numerical values of the results. A sign convention[1] may be set up for the shearing stresses in connection with the use of Mohr's circle. We are not, however, going to present it here because, so far as practical application is concerned, the directions of shearing stresses are usually of little interest.

A number of important conclusions follow directly from an inspection of Mohr's circle:

1. Taking the angle to be $\pi + 2\alpha$ instead of 2α, that is, by prolonging the radius CD to the point D', the stresses on the plane perpendicular to BC (Fig. 1.5) are obtained. This shows that the shearing stresses on two

[1] See S. Timoshenko and J. N. Goodier, "Theory of Elasticity," 2d ed., p. 15, McGraw-Hill Book Company, Inc., New York, 1951.

perpendicular planes are numerically equal as we have proved previously [Eqs. (1.8), (1.9)].

2. As α varies, the sum of normal stresses on mutually perpendicular planes is a constant since $OF' + OF = 2OC$. Hence we have

$$\sigma_1 + \sigma_2 = \sigma_{x'} + \sigma_{y'}$$

which is the two-dimensional case of Eq. (1.17).

3. The maximum shearing stress equals the radius of the Mohr's circle and acts on planes inclined at 45° to the principal directions. Hence

$$\tau_{\max} = \frac{\sigma_1 - \sigma_2}{2} = \sqrt{\left(\frac{\sigma_x - \sigma_y}{2}\right)^2 + \tau_{xy}{}^2} \qquad (1.25)$$

The corresponding normal stresses on planes of maximum shear are equal to each other and are equal to

$$\sigma_{x'} = \sigma_{y'} = \frac{\sigma_1 + \sigma_2}{2} = \frac{\sigma_x + \sigma_y}{2} \qquad (1.26)$$

Let us now extend our discussion to the case of the three-dimensional stress system. We shall show that there exist three mutually perpendicular principal planes on which the three normal stress components have stationary values (maximum, minimum, or minimax), while the shearing-stress components on these planes are zero. These normal stresses are the principal stresses. Let us consider the normal stress on a plane perpendicular to the x' axis. From (1.15), we find

$$\sigma_{x'} = l^2\sigma_x + m^2\sigma_y + n^2\sigma_z + 2lm\tau_{xy} + 2mn\tau_{yz} + 2nl\tau_{zx} \qquad (1.27)$$

where l, m, n are direction cosines of x' with respect to the x, y, z axes, respectively. But l, m, n in the above equation are not independent, since they must satisfy the equation

$$l^2 + m^2 + n^2 = 1 \qquad (1.28)$$

Therefore, we may regard l, m in Eq. (1.27) as independent variables which may be given arbitrary values and $\sigma_{x'}$, n as functions of l and m.

To determine the direction cosines of the plane on which $\sigma_{x'}$ has a stationary value, we let

$$\frac{\partial \sigma_{x'}}{\partial l} = 0 \qquad \frac{\partial \sigma_{x'}}{\partial m} = 0$$

Carrying out the differentiation and rearranging the terms, we obtain

$$l\sigma_x + m\tau_{xy} + n\tau_{zx} + (l\tau_{zx} + m\tau_{yz} + n\sigma_z)\frac{\partial n}{\partial l} = 0$$

$$l\tau_{xy} + m\sigma_y + n\tau_{yz} + (l\tau_{zx} + m\tau_{yz} + n\sigma_z)\frac{\partial n}{\partial m} = 0 \qquad (1.29)$$

Now, by partially differentiating (1.28) with respect to l and m, we have

$$l + n\frac{\partial n}{\partial l} = 0 \qquad m + n\frac{\partial n}{\partial m} = 0 \qquad (1.30)$$

Substituting these relations into (1.29), we find that (1.29) may be written in the form

$$\frac{l\sigma_x + m\tau_{xy} + n\tau_{zx}}{l} = \frac{l\tau_{xy} + m\sigma_y + n\tau_{yz}}{m} = \frac{l\tau_{zx} + m\tau_{yz} + n\sigma_z}{n} \tag{1.31}$$

But, from (1.14)

$$l\sigma_x + m\tau_{xy} + n\tau_{zx} = \bar{X}$$
$$l\tau_{xy} + m\sigma_y + n\tau_{yz} = \bar{Y}$$
$$l\tau_{zx} + m\tau_{yz} + n\sigma_z = \bar{Z}$$

With these relations, Eqs. (1.31) become

$$\frac{\bar{X}}{l} = \frac{\bar{Y}}{m} = \frac{\bar{Z}}{n} \tag{1.32}$$

Equations (1.32) show that on a plane for which $\sigma_{x'}$ has a stationary value the resultant stress has components in the directions x, y, z proportional to l, m, n, the direction cosines of the normal to the plane. This means that the resultant stress on such a plane is purely normal. We have therefore proved that on the plane for which $\sigma_{x'}$ has a stationary value the shearing stress is zero and the plane is a principal plane.

To show there exist three principal planes, we let

$$\frac{\bar{X}}{l} = \frac{\bar{Y}}{m} = \frac{\bar{Z}}{n} = \sigma$$

The magnitude of the principal stress is then

$$l\bar{X} + m\bar{Y} + n\bar{Z} = l(l\sigma) + m(m\sigma) + n(n\sigma) = (l^2 + m^2 + n^2)\sigma = \sigma \tag{1.33}$$

Let us now rewrite Eqs. (1.31) into the following form:

$$l(\sigma_x - \sigma) + m\tau_{xy} + n\tau_{zx} = 0$$
$$l\tau_{xy} + m(\sigma_y - \sigma) + n\tau_{yz} = 0 \tag{1.34}$$
$$l\tau_{zx} + m\tau_{yz} + n(\sigma_z - \sigma) = 0$$

Equations (1.34) may now be regarded as equations for the determination of the direction cosines l, m, n of the principal planes. Since $l^2 + m^2 + n^2 = 1$, then l, m, n cannot vanish simultaneously. Equations (1.34) are homogeneous linear equations in l, m, n and will give solutions different from zero only if the determinant of these equations is zero. Calculating this determinant and equating it to zero results in the following cubic equation in σ:

$$\sigma^3 - (\sigma_x + \sigma_y + \sigma_z)\sigma^2 + (\sigma_x\sigma_y + \sigma_y\sigma_z + \sigma_x\sigma_z - \tau_{xy}{}^2 - \tau_{yz}{}^2 - \tau_{zx}{}^2)\sigma$$
$$- (\sigma_x\sigma_y\sigma_z + 2\tau_{xy}\tau_{yz}\tau_{zx} - \sigma_x\tau_{yz}{}^2 - \sigma_y\tau_{zx}{}^2 - \sigma_z\tau_{xy}{}^2) = 0 \tag{1.35}$$

The three roots of this equation give the values of the three principal stresses. By substituting each of these stresses in Eqs. (1.34) and using (1.28), we can find three sets of direction cosines for the three principal planes. We may note here that the determination of the principal stresses must be independent of the directions of the coordinate axes x, y, z. Therefore the factors in parentheses in (1.35) must be independent of any change of directions of coordinates and are invariants with respect to orthogonal transformation of coordinates.

Problem 1. Determine the principal stresses and the angle α if

$$\sigma_x = 6{,}250 \text{ psi} \qquad \sigma_y = -1{,}250 \text{ psi} \qquad \tau_{xy} = 6{,}500 \text{ psi}$$

Problem 2. Determine the maximum shearing stress, the corresponding normal stresses, and the angle α for the given state of stress in Prob. 1.

1.5. Boundary Conditions in Terms of Given Surface Forces. When a body, under external loads, is in equilibrium, we have already shown that the stress components must satisfy the differential equations of equilibrium at all points throughout the body.   These stress components vary over the volume of the body, and when we arrive at the outer surface, or the boundary, of the body, they must be in equilibrium with the given external forces there.   The external forces may therefore be considered as a continuation of the internal stress distribution.   The conditions of equilibrium at the boundary can be obtained from Eqs. (1.14) and are called the *boundary conditions* of the body in equilibrium.   If we denote the components of the surface forces per unit area at a point on the boundary by $\bar{X}$, $\bar{Y}$, $\bar{Z}$ and let l, m, n be the direction cosines of the normal N to the boundary, from Eqs. (1.14) we find our boundary conditions as

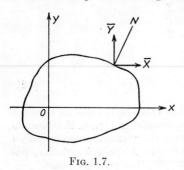

Fig. 1.7.

$$
\begin{aligned}
\bar{X} &= l\sigma_x + m\tau_{xy} + n\tau_{zx} \\
\bar{Y} &= l\tau_{xy} + m\sigma_y + n\tau_{yz} \\
\bar{Z} &= l\tau_{zx} + m\tau_{yz} + n\sigma_z
\end{aligned}
\tag{1.36}
$$

In the particular case of plane stress (Fig. 1.7) Eqs. (1.36) reduce to

$$
\bar{X} = l\sigma_x + m\tau_{xy} \qquad \bar{Y} = l\tau_{xy} + m\sigma_y
\tag{1.37}
$$

CHAPTER 2

ANALYSIS OF STRAIN

2.1. Strain Components. A body is said to be *strained* whenever the relative positions of points in the body are altered. Let us assume that the material is continuous. Then at any point in the body there is a particle of material. Let the coordinates of this particle before strain be x, y, z. After strain, the particle will undergo displacements u, v, w in the x, y, z directions and will now have the coordinates $x + u$, $y + v$, $z + w$. In general, the displacements u, v, w vary from point to point in the body and are therefore functions of x, y, z.

We shall begin our discussion of strain with the two-dimensional case, *i.e.*, the case of *plane strain*. By plane strain we mean that all the particles originally in a plane will remain in the same plane after strain. If we choose our coordinate axes so that the x and y axes are in the plane of

deformation, then we have $w = 0$ and u, v independent of z. Let us consider a small rectangular element $ABCD$ with sides dx and dy in the unstrained body (Fig. 2.1). After strain, the element is displaced to the position $A'B'C'D'$. We observe that there are two basic geometric deformations: one is a change in length of an originally straight line in a certain direction, and the other is a change in the value of a given angle. Accordingly, we shall classify *strain* into two kinds, *viz.*, the *longitudinal strain* and the *shearing strain*. The

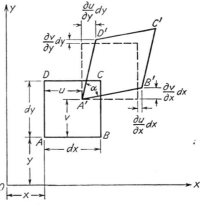

FIG. 2.1.

ratio of the change in length to the original length of a straight line element is defined as the *longitudinal strain*. Let us denote the longitudinal strain by the letter ϵ. For continuous material, ϵ at any point in a segment initially ΔL long may be defined by the limiting equation

$$\epsilon = \lim_{\Delta L \to 0} \frac{\Delta \delta}{\Delta L}$$

in which $\Delta \delta$ is the change in length of the given segment. The change in value of an originally right angle in the unstrained state is defined as the

15

shearing strain and will be denoted by γ. In the case of the rectangular element $ABCD$ as shown in Fig. 2.1, before strain, the length of AB is dx. After strain, A is displaced to A'. Let us denote the x, y components of the displacement of the particle at A by u and v. As u and v vary from point to point in the body, we may expand these quantities into Taylor's series as in the case of stress components. Neglecting higher-order terms, the displacements from B to B' can be written as $u + (\partial u/\partial x)\, dx$ and $v + (\partial v/\partial x)\, dx$. The x projection of $A'B'$ is therefore $dx + (\partial u/\partial x)\, dx$, and the y projection is $(\partial v/\partial x)\, dx$. The square of the length of $A'B'$ is

$$(A'B')^2 = \left(dx + \frac{\partial u}{\partial x}\, dx\right)^2 + \left(\frac{\partial v}{\partial x}\, dx\right)^2$$

The longitudinal strain component in the x direction, ϵ_x, is defined as the longitudinal strain of an element which is in the x direction before strain. We have, therefore,

$$\epsilon_x = \frac{A'B' - AB}{AB}$$

or

$$A'B' = (1 + \epsilon_x)AB = (1 + \epsilon_x)\, dx$$

Substituting the above expression into the expression for $(A'B')^2$ and dividing through by $(dx)^2$, we obtain

$$2\epsilon_x + \epsilon_x{}^2 = 2\frac{\partial u}{\partial x} + \left(\frac{\partial u}{\partial x}\right)^2 + \left(\frac{\partial v}{\partial x}\right)^2 \tag{2.1}$$

If we confine our attention to the case where the deformation of the body is very small, then ϵ and the derivatives of u and v are small quantities. The squares and products of these quantities are therefore negligible in comparison with the quantities themselves. Dropping these higher-order terms in Eq. (2.1), we have

$$\epsilon_x = \frac{\partial u}{\partial x}$$

Similarly the longitudinal-strain component in the y direction is $\partial v/\partial y$ or $\epsilon_y = \partial v/\partial y$.

In order to find the shearing strain, let us consider the distortion of a right angle in the unstrained state. The shearing strain γ_{xy} at a point is defined as the change in the value of the angle between the two elements originally parallel to the x and y axes at that point. Accordingly, γ_{xy} at the point A is the change of the angle between the element AB and AD. The displacement of the point B' in the y direction is $v + (\partial v/\partial x)\, dx$, and the displacement of the point D' in the x direction is $u + (\partial u/\partial y)\, dy$. Neglecting higher-order terms, we find that, owing to these displacements, the line AB after strain, or $A'B'$, is inclined to its unstrained direction by a small angle $\partial v/\partial x$ and the direction $A'D'$ is inclined to AD by the small angle $\partial u/\partial y$. From this we see that the right angle DAB between the elements AB and AD is diminished by the angle $(\partial v/\partial x) + (\partial u/\partial y)$. Hence

$$\gamma_{xy} = \frac{\partial v}{\partial x} + \frac{\partial u}{\partial y}$$

The strain components in the general three-dimensional case can be obtained in a similar manner. We get, in this case,

$$\epsilon_x = \frac{\partial u}{\partial x} \qquad \epsilon_y = \frac{\partial v}{\partial y} \qquad \epsilon_z = \frac{\partial w}{\partial z} \qquad \gamma_{xy} = \frac{\partial u}{\partial y} + \frac{\partial v}{\partial x} \qquad \gamma_{yz} = \frac{\partial v}{\partial z} + \frac{\partial w}{\partial y}$$

$$\gamma_{zx} = \frac{\partial w}{\partial x} + \frac{\partial u}{\partial z} \quad (2.2)$$

These six quantities, ϵ_x, ϵ_y, ϵ_z, γ_{xy}, γ_{yz}, γ_{zx}, are called the *components of strain*. From these formulas it is easy to see that the shearing strains are symmetrical, *viz.*,

$$\gamma_{xy} = \gamma_{yx} \qquad \gamma_{yz} = \gamma_{zy} \qquad \gamma_{zx} = \gamma_{xz}$$

We also observe from formulas (2.2) that, to any expressions of displacement u, v, w, we may add, respectively, the components

$$\bar{u} = a + by - cz \qquad \bar{v} = d - bx + ez \qquad \bar{w} = f + cx - ey$$

without changing the strain components. The constants a, d, f in the above expressions represent a translatory motion of the body, and the constants b, c, e represent rotation of the body around the coordinate axes. Since the displacements $\bar{u}$, $\bar{v}$, $\bar{w}$ represent the motion of the body as a whole and do not induce any strain in the body, we shall call them *rigid-body displacements*.

2.2. Specification of Strain at a Point. Given the three longitudinal-strain components and the three shearing-strain components at a point, it can be shown that the

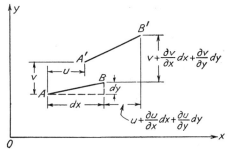

Fig. 2.2.

elongation in *any* direction and the distortion of the angle between *any* two perpendicular directions can be calculated.

Let us again consider the case of plane strain. Consider a small linear element AB in the unstrained body of length dL with the direction cosines l, m (Fig. 2.2). The projections of the element on the coordinate axes are $dx = l\,dL$, $dy = m\,dL$. After strain, AB is displaced to $A'B'$, and the displacement components of A are equal to u and v. Let the length of $A'B'$ be dL'. Since the element AB is originally inclined to the coordinate axes, following the same reasoning as in the derivation of Eq. (1.3), the displacement components of B' will then be

$$u + du = u + \frac{\partial u}{\partial x} dx + \frac{\partial u}{\partial y} dy$$

$$v + dv = v + \frac{\partial v}{\partial x} dx + \frac{\partial v}{\partial y} dy$$

(2.3)

Let ϵ be the longitudinal strain in the direction AB defined by

$$\epsilon = \frac{A'B' - AB}{AB} = \frac{dL' - dL}{dL}$$

or
$$dL' = (1 + \epsilon) dL$$

In terms of its projections we have

$$(A'B')^2 = (1 + \epsilon)^2 dL^2 = \left(dx + \frac{\partial u}{\partial x} dx + \frac{\partial u}{\partial y} dy \right)^2$$
$$+ \left(dy + \frac{\partial v}{\partial x} dx + \frac{\partial v}{\partial y} dy \right)^2 \quad (2.4)$$

Upon expanding, (2.4) becomes

$$dL^2 + 2\epsilon\, dL^2 + \epsilon^2\, dL^2 = dx^2 + dy^2$$
$$+ 2 \frac{\partial u}{\partial x} dx^2 + 2 \frac{\partial u}{\partial y} dx\, dy + 2 \frac{\partial v}{\partial x} dx\, dy + 2 \frac{\partial v}{\partial y} dy^2$$
$$+ \left(\frac{\partial u}{\partial x} \right)^2 dx^2 + \left(\frac{\partial u}{\partial y} \right)^2 dy^2 + \left(\frac{\partial v}{\partial x} \right)^2 dx^2 + \left(\frac{\partial v}{\partial y} \right)^2 dy^2 \quad (2.5)$$

Recalling that $dL^2 = dx^2 + dy^2$ and noting that, for infinitesimal deformation ϵ, $\dfrac{\partial u}{\partial x}, \dfrac{\partial u}{\partial y}, \dfrac{\partial v}{\partial x}, \dfrac{\partial v}{\partial y}$ are infinitesimal quantities and their squares can be neglected compared with the quantities themselves, Eq. (2.5) then becomes

$$\epsilon\, dL^2 = \frac{\partial u}{\partial x} dx^2 + \frac{\partial u}{\partial y} dx\, dy + \frac{\partial v}{\partial x} dx\, dy + \frac{\partial v}{\partial y} dy^2$$

or, after dividing through by dL^2,

$$\epsilon = \frac{\partial u}{\partial x} l^2 + \frac{\partial v}{\partial y} m^2 + \left(\frac{\partial u}{\partial y} + \frac{\partial v}{\partial x} \right) lm = l^2 \epsilon_x + m^2 \epsilon_y + lm \gamma_{xy} \quad (2.6)$$

where the relations $dx/dL = l$ and $dy/dL = m$ have been used.

If we denote by x' and y' the directions of the new coordinate axes, we obtain

$$\epsilon_{x'} = l^2 \epsilon_x + m^2 \epsilon_y + lm \gamma_{xy} \quad (2.7)$$

where we now have $l = \cos x'x$ and $m = \cos x'y$.

To find the shearing strain when referring to these new directions, let us consider two perpendicular elements OA and OB before deformation (Fig. 2.3). After deformation, OA and OB are displaced to $O'A'$ and $O'B'$, respectively. Let dL_1 and dL_2 be the original length of OA and OB and ϵ_1 and ϵ_2 be the longitudinal-strain components in the directions of OA and OB. Denote by l_1, m_1 and l_2, m_2 the direction cosines of OA and

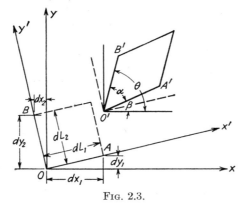

FIG. 2.3.

OB, respectively. Using Eqs. (2.3), we find that the direction cosines l_1', m_1' of $O'A'$ are

$$l_1' = \frac{dx_1 + du_1}{dL_1(1 + \epsilon_1)} = \frac{[1 + (\partial u/\partial x)]\,dx_1 + (\partial u/\partial y)\,dy_1}{dL_1(1 + \epsilon_1)}$$

$$= l_1\left(1 - \epsilon_1 + \frac{\partial u}{\partial x}\right) + m_1\frac{\partial u}{\partial y} \qquad (2.8)$$

$$m_1' = \frac{dy_1 + dv_1}{dL_1(1 + \epsilon_1)} = l_1\frac{\partial v}{\partial x} + m_1\left(1 - \epsilon_1 + \frac{\partial v}{\partial y}\right)$$

where, in obtaining the last step in the above formulas, we have carried out the division and then neglected the resulting higher-order terms. Similarly the direction cosines l_2' and m_2' of $O'B'$ are

$$l_2' = l_2\left(1 - \epsilon_2 + \frac{\partial u}{\partial x}\right) + m_2\frac{\partial u}{\partial y}$$

$$m_2' = l_2\frac{\partial v}{\partial x} + m_2\left(1 - \epsilon_2 + \frac{\partial v}{\partial y}\right) \qquad (2.9)$$

Let the angle between $O'A'$ and $O'B'$ be α. From Fig. 2.3, we see

$$\cos\alpha = \cos(\theta - \beta) = \cos\beta\cos\theta + \sin\beta\sin\theta = l_1'l_2' + m_1'm_2' \qquad (2.10)$$

Substituting into Eq. (2.10) the expressions of l_1', m_1', l_2', and m_2' as given by Eqs. (2.8) and (2.9) and neglecting the higher-order terms, we obtain

$$\cos\alpha = (l_1l_2 + m_1m_2)(1 - \epsilon_1 - \epsilon_2) + 2(l_1l_2\epsilon_x + m_1m_2\epsilon_y)$$
$$+ (l_1m_2 + l_2m_1)\gamma_{xy} \qquad (2.11)$$

From the definition of shearing strain, we have

$$\gamma_{x'y'} = \frac{\pi}{2} - \alpha$$

For small shearing strain, the angle $(\pi/2) - \alpha$ is small, and we have therefore

$$\gamma_{x'y'} = \frac{\pi}{2} - \alpha \cong \sin\left(\frac{\pi}{2} - \alpha\right) = \cos \alpha$$

Since $l_1 l_2 + m_1 m_2 = \cos AOB = \cos(\pi/2) = 0$, substitution of (2.11) into the above expression gives

$$\gamma_{x'y'} = 2(l_1 l_2 \epsilon_x + m_1 m_2 \epsilon_y) + (l_1 m_2 + l_2 m_1)\gamma_{xy} \tag{2.12}$$

Equations (2.7) and (2.12) thus verify our statement that in the case of plane strain the longitudinal- and shearing-strain components in any other direction can be calculated if ϵ_x, ϵ_y, and γ_{xy} are known. Since $l_2 = \cos y'x = \cos(\pi - x'y) = -\cos x'y = -m_1$, and

$$m_2 = \cos y'y = \cos x'x = l_1$$

Eq. (2.12) may be written as

$$\gamma_{x'y'} = (l_1^2 - m_1^2)\gamma_{xy} + 2l_1 m_1(\epsilon_y - \epsilon_x) \tag{2.13}$$

If we compare Eqs. (2.7) and (2.13) with Eqs. (1.13), we see that Eqs. (2.7) and (2.13) become exactly the same as Eqs. (1.13) with ϵ replaced by σ and γ replaced by 2τ. If we write $\gamma = 2\gamma'$, then all our discussion on principal stress holds true also for principal strain in terms of ϵ_x, ϵ_y, and γ'_{xy}. Therefore, we can construct Mohr's circle for strain exactly the same way as the Mohr's circle for stress.

In the general three-dimensional case, if, as before, we define the direction cosines by the following table,

	x	y	z
x'	l_1	m_1	n_1
y'	l_2	m_2	n_2
z'	l_3	m_3	n_3

the formulas of transformation of strain components can be shown to be of the following form:

$$\epsilon_{x'} = l_1^2 \epsilon_x + m_1^2 \epsilon_y + n_1^2 \epsilon_z + l_1 m_1 \gamma_{xy} + m_1 n_1 \gamma_{yz} + n_1 l_1 \gamma_{zx}$$

$$\epsilon_{y'} = l_2^2 \epsilon_x + m_2^2 \epsilon_y + n_2^2 \epsilon_z + l_2 m_2 \gamma_{xy} + m_2 n_2 \gamma_{yz} + n_2 l_2 \gamma_{zx}$$

$$\epsilon_{z'} = l_3^2 \epsilon_x + m_3^2 \epsilon_y + n_3^2 \epsilon_z + l_3 m_3 \gamma_{xy} + m_3 n_3 \gamma_{yz} + n_3 l_3 \gamma_{zx}$$

$$\gamma_{x'y'} = 2l_1 l_2 \epsilon_x + 2m_1 m_2 \epsilon_y + 2n_1 n_2 \epsilon_z + (l_1 m_2 + m_1 l_2)\gamma_{xy}$$
$$+ (m_1 n_2 + n_1 m_2)\gamma_{yz} + (n_1 l_2 + l_1 n_2)\gamma_{zx} \tag{2.14}$$

$$\gamma_{y'z'} = 2l_2 l_3 \epsilon_x + 2m_2 m_3 \epsilon_y + 2n_2 n_3 \epsilon_z + (l_2 m_3 + m_2 l_3)\gamma_{xy}$$
$$+ (m_2 n_3 + n_2 m_3)\gamma_{yz} + (n_2 l_3 + l_2 n_3)\gamma_{zx}$$

$$\gamma_{z'x'} = 2l_3 l_1 \epsilon_x + 2m_3 m_1 \epsilon_y + 2n_3 n_1 \epsilon_z + (l_3 m_1 + m_3 l_1)\gamma_{xy}$$
$$+ (m_3 n_1 + n_3 m_1)\gamma_{yz} + (n_3 l_1 + l_3 n_1)\gamma_{zx}$$

Adding the first three equations of (2.14) and recalling the conditions of orthogonality (1.16), we can prove that the sum of the longitudinal-strain components is also an invariant with respect to transformations from one set of rectangular axes to another, *viz.*,

$$\epsilon_{x'} + \epsilon_{y'} + \epsilon_{z'} = \epsilon_x + \epsilon_y + \epsilon_z \tag{2.15}$$

Problem. Prove that the following quantities are also invariant:

a. $\epsilon_x \epsilon_y + \epsilon_y \epsilon_z + \epsilon_z \epsilon_x - \frac{1}{4}(\gamma_{xy}^2 + \gamma_{yz}^2 + \gamma_{zx}^2)$

b. $\epsilon_x \epsilon_y \epsilon_z + \frac{1}{4}(\gamma_{xy}\gamma_{yz}\gamma_{zx} - \epsilon_x \gamma_{yz}^2 - \epsilon_y \gamma_{zx}^2 - \epsilon_z \gamma_{xy}^2)$

2.3. Compatibility Equations. Reverting now to the expressions of the strain components in terms of the components of displacement, Eqs. (2.2), we observe that the six strain components are expressed in terms of three displacement components. These equations may be regarded as a system of partial differential equations for the determination of the displacements u, v, w when the strain components ϵ_x, ϵ_y, ϵ_z, γ_{xy}, γ_{yz}, and γ_{zx} are given functions of x, y, z. Since there are six equations for three unknown functions, we cannot expect in general that these equations will possess a solution if the strain components are arbitrarily prescribed. Thus, there must be some conditions to be imposed on the strain components in order that these six equations will give a set of single-valued continuous solutions for the three displacement components. The fact that the strain components cannot be prescribed arbitrarily can be seen from the following geometrical considerations: Imagine that an elastic body is subdivided into a number of small cubic elements before deformation. Now suppose that each element is subjected to an arbitrary deformation. After the deformation, these elements become parallelepipeds, and it may happen that it is impossible to arrange the parallelepipeds to form a continuous distorted body. To ensure that these parallelepipeds form a continuous body, the strain components for each element must satisfy certain relations. We shall now proceed to investigate these relations.

Differentiating γ_{xy} with respect to x and y from the expression

$$\gamma_{xy} = \frac{\partial u}{\partial y} + \frac{\partial v}{\partial x}$$

we have

$$\frac{\partial^2 \gamma_{xy}}{\partial x\, \partial y} = \frac{\partial^2}{\partial x\, \partial y}\frac{\partial u}{\partial y} + \frac{\partial^2}{\partial x\, \partial y}\frac{\partial v}{\partial x}$$

Since u and v are single-valued continuous functions, we may rewrite the above expression into the following form:

$$\frac{\partial^2 \gamma_{xy}}{\partial x\, \partial y} = \frac{\partial^2}{\partial y^2}\frac{\partial u}{\partial x} + \frac{\partial^2}{\partial x^2}\frac{\partial v}{\partial y} \tag{2.16}$$

But $\epsilon_x = \partial u/\partial x$, and $\epsilon_y = \partial v/\partial y$.   Hence (2.16) becomes

$$\frac{\partial^2 \epsilon_x}{\partial y^2} + \frac{\partial^2 \epsilon_y}{\partial x^2} = \frac{\partial^2 \gamma_{xy}}{\partial x \, \partial y} \tag{2.17}$$

Now if we differentiate γ_{xy} with respect to x and z and γ_{zx} with respect to y and x and add the resulting expressions, we have

$$\frac{\partial^2 \gamma_{xy}}{\partial x \, \partial z} + \frac{\partial^2 \gamma_{zx}}{\partial y \, \partial x} = \frac{\partial^2}{\partial x \, \partial z}\left(\frac{\partial u}{\partial y} + \frac{\partial v}{\partial x}\right) + \frac{\partial^2}{\partial y \, \partial x}\left(\frac{\partial w}{\partial x} + \frac{\partial u}{\partial z}\right)$$

Again, recognizing the fact that u, v, w are single-valued continuous functions, we may rewrite the above expressions as follows:

$$2\frac{\partial^2}{\partial y \, \partial z}\frac{\partial u}{\partial x} + \frac{\partial^2}{\partial x^2}\left(\frac{\partial v}{\partial z} + \frac{\partial w}{\partial y}\right) = 2\frac{\partial^2 \epsilon_x}{\partial y \, \partial z} + \frac{\partial^2 \gamma_{yz}}{\partial x^2}$$

or
$$2\frac{\partial^2 \epsilon_x}{\partial y \, \partial z} = \frac{\partial}{\partial x}\left(-\frac{\partial \gamma_{yz}}{\partial x} + \frac{\partial \gamma_{zx}}{\partial y} + \frac{\partial \gamma_{xy}}{\partial z}\right) \tag{2.18}$$

Further relations can be written down at once by the method of "cyclic permutation."   Collecting our results, we find that, in all, six relations have to be satisfied by the strain components, *viz.*,

$$\begin{aligned}
\frac{\partial^2 \epsilon_x}{\partial y^2} + \frac{\partial^2 \epsilon_y}{\partial x^2} &= \frac{\partial^2 \gamma_{xy}}{\partial x \, \partial y} \qquad & 2\frac{\partial^2 \epsilon_x}{\partial y \, \partial z} &= \frac{\partial}{\partial x}\left(-\frac{\partial \gamma_{yz}}{\partial x} + \frac{\partial \gamma_{zx}}{\partial y} + \frac{\partial \gamma_{xy}}{\partial z}\right) \\[2mm]
\frac{\partial^2 \epsilon_y}{\partial z^2} + \frac{\partial^2 \epsilon_z}{\partial y^2} &= \frac{\partial^2 \gamma_{yz}}{\partial y \, \partial z} & 2\frac{\partial^2 \epsilon_y}{\partial z \, \partial x} &= \frac{\partial}{\partial y}\left(\frac{\partial \gamma_{yz}}{\partial x} - \frac{\partial \gamma_{zx}}{\partial y} + \frac{\partial \gamma_{xy}}{\partial z}\right) \\[2mm]
\frac{\partial^2 \epsilon_z}{\partial x^2} + \frac{\partial^2 \epsilon_x}{\partial z^2} &= \frac{\partial^2 \gamma_{zx}}{\partial z \, \partial x} & 2\frac{\partial^2 \epsilon_z}{\partial x \, \partial y} &= \frac{\partial}{\partial z}\left(\frac{\partial \gamma_{yz}}{\partial x} + \frac{\partial \gamma_{zx}}{\partial y} - \frac{\partial \gamma_{xy}}{\partial z}\right)
\end{aligned} \tag{2.19}$$

These differential equations are known as *compatibility equations* for strain.   They must be satisfied by the strain components to ensure the existence of single-valued continuous functions u, v, w connected with the strain components by Eqs. (2.2).

Problem 1.   Show that

$$\epsilon_x = k(x^2 + y^2) \qquad \epsilon_y = ky^2 \qquad \gamma_{xy} = 2kxy \qquad \epsilon_z = \gamma_{yz} = \gamma_{zx} = 0$$

where k is a small constant, is a possible state of strain while

$$\epsilon_x = kz(x^2 + y^2) \qquad \epsilon_y = ky^2 z \qquad \gamma_{xy} = 2kxyz \qquad \epsilon_z = \gamma_{yz} = \gamma_{zx} = 0$$

is not a possible one.

Problem 2.   An elastic solid is heated nonuniformly to a temperature distribution $T(x,y,z)$, where $T(x,y,z)$ is a function of x, y, z.   If each element in the body has unrestrained thermal expansion, the strain components will be

$$\epsilon_x = \epsilon_y = \epsilon_z = \alpha T \qquad \gamma_{xy} = \gamma_{yz} = \gamma_{zx} = 0$$

where α is the coefficient of thermal expansion and is a constant. Prove that this can occur only when T is a linear function of x, y, z.

Problem 3. Determine the relations among the constants A_0, A_1, B_0, B_1, C_0, C_1, C_2 so that the following is a possible system of strains: $\quad a \quad b \quad \alpha \quad \beta \quad A \quad B \quad C$

$$\epsilon_x = A_0 + A_1(x^2 + y^2) + (x^4 + y^4)$$
$$\epsilon_y = B_0 + B_1(x^2 + y^2) + (x^4 + y^4)$$
$$\gamma_{xy} = C_0 + C_1xy(x^2 + y^2 + C_2)$$
$$\epsilon_z = \gamma_{yz} = \gamma_{zx} = 0$$

Ans. $A_1 + B_1 - 2C_2 = 0$, $C_1 = 4$

$$b + \beta - 2c = 0 \qquad B = 4$$

CHAPTER 3

STRESS-STRAIN RELATIONS AND THE GENERAL EQUATIONS OF ELASTICITY

3.1. Idealization of Engineering Materials. In order to subject the behavior of engineering materials to a mathematical analysis, it will be necessary to introduce some idealization on the properties of the materials. In the theory of elasticity, as in other branches of mathematical physics, we are confronted at the outset by two conflicting requirements. On the one hand, we desire our theory to predict as much as possible the behavior of real materials under the action of applied forces. On the other hand, the theory must be simple enough mathematically so that it can be applied to a wide range of problems with a possibility of solving the resulting equations.

It is known that every solid body deforms under the action of applied forces. To every kind of stress there is a corresponding strain. If the stresses are not too great, the strained body will recover its original shape and size when the stresses are removed. The property which a body possesses of recovering from strain is called *elasticity*. We call a body *perfectly elastic* if it recovers completely. If the body does not recover completely, the strain that remains when the stress is removed is called *permanent set* and the body is said to be in a *plastic state*. If forces are applied to any solid body and these forces are gradually increased, it is observed experimentally that until some definite limit in the magnitude of these forces is reached the body will be perfectly elastic. The limit is called the *elastic limit*. Beyond this elastic limit, the material will be in the plastic state, and permanent set will be produced. In the theory of elasticity we shall assume that the material is perfectly elastic, *i.e.*, we shall limit our attention to the behavior of the material before the elastic limit is reached.

We shall further assume the material to be *continuous, homogeneous,* and *isotropic*. By continuous material we mean a material having the nature of a structureless mass. An elastic body is said to be homogeneous if the elastic properties are the same throughout the body, *i.e.*, are independent of the location. If the elastic properties of the body are the same in all directions about any given point, then the body is said to be isotropic. In the analysis of stress and strain as carried out in Chaps. 1 and 2, we have already used the assumption of continuity of material, while the

24

assumptions of homogeneity and isotropy are not necessary until we attempt to develop relations between stresses and strains.

Most engineering materials are formed of either crystalline substances such as brass or small fibers such as timber. Our assumptions obviously conflict with our knowledge of real materials. However, the dimensions of most crystals and fibers are so small in comparison with the dimensions of the entire body that the behavior of the material on the average appears to justify the assumption of continuity and homogeneity. In the case of crystalline materials, the crystals are usually so chaotically distributed that the body as a whole is isotropic. It may be remarked that the process of rolling frequently produces a definite orientation of crystals, so that many rolled metals are *anisotropic*. Such a structural material as wood, for example, is definitely anisotropic, and the elastic properties of wood in the direction of the grain differ greatly from those in the direction perpendicular to the annual rings. In assuming isotropic material we shall of course exclude the treatment of engineering structures made of these materials.

3.2. Generalized Hooke's Law. All stressed bodies are strained. The first formulation of a relation between the deformation and the applied force was due to Hooke. Hooke's law of proportionality between the forces and displacements can be rendered freely as "Extension is proportional to force," and it refers to the average extension of a thin rod when the latter is subjected to a tensile stress. If we consider a thin rod with cross-sectional area A subjected to tensile force F, and if we assume that the tensile stress σ is uniformly distributed over the area of the cross section, Hooke's law may be written in the following form:

$$\sigma = c\epsilon \tag{3.1}$$

where c is a constant and ϵ is the longitudinal strain.

A natural generalization of Hooke's law immediately suggests itself, *viz.*, when more than one strain component exists and when the elastic limit is not exceeded, then at every point of the medium *each of the six stress components may be expressed as a linear function of the six components of strain, and conversely.* This last statement is called the *generalized Hooke's law.* Expressed mathematically, we have the six "stress-strain" equations of the type

$$\sigma_x = c_{11}\epsilon_x + c_{12}\epsilon_y + c_{13}\epsilon_z + c_{14}\gamma_{xy} + c_{15}\gamma_{yz} + c_{16}\gamma_{zx} \tag{3.2}$$

or, conversely, the six "strain-stress" equations of the type

$$\epsilon_x = c'_{11}\sigma_x + c'_{12}\sigma_y + c'_{13}\sigma_z + c'_{14}\tau_{xy} + c'_{15}\tau_{yz} + c'_{16}\tau_{zx} \tag{3.3}$$

where $c_{11}, \ldots, c'_{11}, \ldots$ define the elastic properties of the material. For homogeneous materials, $c_{11}, \ldots, c'_{11}, \ldots$ are constants independent of x, y, z. Given the six equations of type (3.2), we can deduce the six equations of type (3.3), and vice versa.

Whether (3.2) or (3.3) be adopted as the generalized statement of Hooke's law, 36 constants are apparently involved. However, these 36 constants are not all independent, and we shall now proceed to show that for *isotropic* materials they can be reduced to only two independent ones.

First we shall show that the directions of the principal stresses coincide with the directions of the principal strains. Let 1, 2, 3 be the principal directions of *strain*. The shearing-strain components referring to these directions are therefore zero,[1] and from Eqs. (3.2) we have

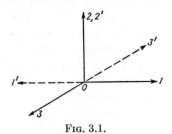

FIG. 3.1.

$$\tau_{12} = c_{41}\epsilon_1 + c_{42}\epsilon_2 + c_{43}\epsilon_3 \qquad (3.4)$$

Introduce the coordinate system $1'$, $2'$, $3'$ which is obtained from the 1, 2, 3 system by rotating the 1, 2, 3 axes through an angle of 180° about the 2 axis (Fig. 3.1). The $1'$ and $3'$ axes will then be directed in the opposite directions of the 1 and 3 axes, respectively, and the 2 and $2'$ axes coincide. Define the direction cosines of $1'$, $2'$, and $3'$ by the following table:

	1	2	3
$1'$	l_1	m_1	n_1
$2'$	l_2	m_2	n_2
$3'$	l_3	m_3	n_3

These direction cosines then have the following values:

$$l_1 = n_3 = \cos 180° = -1 \qquad m_2 = \cos 0° = 1$$

and
$$l_2 = l_3 = m_1 = m_3 = n_1 = n_2 = \cos 90° = 0$$

For isotropic materials the elastic constants such as c_{41}, c_{42}, and c_{43} should not change with the directions. Since the new coordinate axes are also in the principal directions of strain, referring to these new directions, Eq. (3.4) becomes

$$\tau_{1'2'} = c_{41}\epsilon_{1'} + c_{42}\epsilon_{2'} + c_{43}\epsilon_{3'} \qquad (3.5)$$

From the formulas for the transformation of stress components, Eqs. (1.15), we find that $l_1 m_2$ is the only nonzero product of the direction cosines, and

$$\tau_{1'2'} = l_1 m_2 \tau_{12} = -\tau_{12} \qquad (3.6)$$

From the formulas for the transformation of strain components, Eqs. (2.14), we find

$$\epsilon_{1'} = l_1^2 \epsilon_1 = \epsilon_1 \qquad \epsilon_{2'} = m_2^2 \epsilon_2 = \epsilon_2 \qquad \epsilon_{3'} = n_3^2 \epsilon_3 = \epsilon_3 \qquad (3.7)$$

[1] See the discussions in Sec. 2.2, p. 20, and Sec. 1.4, pp. 10, 13.

Combining with Eqs. (3.6) and (3.7), we see that Eq. (3.5) becomes

$$-\tau_{12} = c_{41}\epsilon_1 + c_{42}\epsilon_2 + c_{43}\epsilon_3 \tag{3.8}$$

By comparing Eq. (3.8) with Eq. (3.4), we find that the terms on the right side of Eq. (3.8) are identical to those on the right side of Eq. (3.4). We obtain therefore $\tau_{12} = -\tau_{12}$, which is not possible unless

$$\tau_{12} = 0 \tag{3.9}$$

Similarly, we can show that $\tau_{23} = \tau_{31} = 0$. This means that if 1, 2, 3 are the principal directions of strain, the shearing-stress components referred to this coordinate system are zero; in other words, 1, 2, 3 are also the principal directions of *stress*.

With the preceding proof, we shall henceforth make no distinction between the principal directions of stress and the principal directions of strain. Referring to these principal directions, Eqs. (3.2) become

$$\begin{aligned}
\sigma_1 &= c_{11}\epsilon_1 + c_{12}\epsilon_2 + c_{13}\epsilon_3 \\
\sigma_2 &= c_{21}\epsilon_1 + c_{22}\epsilon_2 + c_{23}\epsilon_3 \\
\sigma_3 &= c_{31}\epsilon_1 + c_{32}\epsilon_2 + c_{33}\epsilon_3
\end{aligned} \tag{3.10}$$

We observe that the constant c_{ij} represents the elastic property of the material relating the stress in the i direction to the strain in the j direction. From the consideration of isotropy, the effect of an extension ϵ_1 on the stress σ_1 must be the same as the effect of ϵ_2 on σ_2 and the effect of ϵ_3 on σ_3. Thus we have $c_{11} = c_{22} = c_{33}$. Likewise, because of isotropy, the effect on σ_1 of extensions ϵ_2 and ϵ_3 must be indistinguishable. Thus, $c_{12} = c_{13}$. Similarly, we can show that $c_{21} = c_{23}$ and $c_{31} = c_{32}$. Moreover, the effect on σ_1 of ϵ_2 or ϵ_3 must be identical to the effect on σ_2 of ϵ_1 or ϵ_3, and the effect of ϵ_1 or ϵ_3 on σ_2 must be the same as that of ϵ_1 or ϵ_2 on σ_3. Therefore, we find

$$c_{11} = c_{22} = c_{33} \qquad c_{12} = c_{21} = c_{13} = c_{31} = c_{23} = c_{32} \tag{3.11}$$

From (3.11), we observe that, by referring to the principal axes, we need be concerned only with two elastic constants. Denote these two constants by a and b. Equations (3.10) then become

$$\sigma_1 = a\epsilon_1 + b(\epsilon_2 + \epsilon_3) \qquad \sigma_2 = a\epsilon_2 + b(\epsilon_1 + \epsilon_3) \qquad \sigma_3 = a\epsilon_3 + b(\epsilon_1 + \epsilon_2) \tag{3.12}$$

By letting $a - b = 2\mu$ and $b = \lambda$ and denoting

$$e = \epsilon_1 + \epsilon_2 + \epsilon_3$$

we may rewrite Eqs. (3.12) in the following form:

$$\sigma_1 = \lambda e + 2\mu\epsilon_1 \qquad \sigma_2 = \lambda e + 2\mu\epsilon_2 \qquad \sigma_3 = \lambda e + 2\mu\epsilon_3 \tag{3.13}$$

The constants λ and μ were introduced by G. Lamé and are usually referred to as the constants of Lamé.

Equations (3.13) give us the relations between the principal stress components and the principal strain components. The stress-strain relations referring to an arbitrary system of cartesian coordinate axes may be obtained by using the formulas for the transformation of stress and strain components. Let x, y, z be such an arbitrary system of coordinate axes with the direction cosines defined as follows:

	1	2	3
x	l_1	m_1	n_1
y	l_2	m_2	n_2
z	l_3	m_3	n_3

Since 1, 2, 3 are principal directions, the shearing stresses and shearing strains referring to these directions are zero. From the formulas for the transformation of stress components, we obtain

$$\sigma_x = l_1{}^2\sigma_1 + m_1{}^2\sigma_2 + n_1{}^2\sigma_3 \qquad \tau_{xy} = l_1 l_2 \sigma_1 + m_1 m_2 \sigma_2 + n_1 n_2 \sigma_3 \quad (3.14)$$

Similarly, from the formulas for the transformation of strain components we obtain

$$\epsilon_x = l_1{}^2\epsilon_1 + m_1{}^2\epsilon_2 + n_1{}^2\epsilon_3 \qquad \gamma_{xy} = 2(l_1 l_2 \epsilon_1 + m_1 m_2 \epsilon_2 + n_1 n_2 \epsilon_3) \quad (3.15)$$

Substitution of Eqs. (3.13) into Eqs. (3.14) results in the following:

$$\sigma_x = (l_1{}^2 + m_1{}^2 + n_1{}^2)\lambda e + 2\mu(l_1{}^2\epsilon_1 + m_1{}^2\epsilon_2 + n_1{}^2\epsilon_3)$$
$$\tau_{xy} = (l_1 l_2 + m_1 m_2 + n_1 n_2)\lambda e + 2\mu(l_1 l_2 \epsilon_1 + m_1 m_2 \epsilon_2 + n_1 n_2 \epsilon_3) \quad (3.16)$$

In Chap. 2, we have proved that the sum of longitudinal-strain components is an invariant with respect to orthogonal transformation of coordinates. Hence

$$e = \epsilon_1 + \epsilon_2 + \epsilon_3 = \epsilon_x + \epsilon_y + \epsilon_z$$

Recalling that

$$l_1{}^2 + m_1{}^2 + n_1{}^2 = 1 \qquad l_1 l_2 + m_1 m_2 + n_1 n_2 = 0$$

and using the relations given by Eqs. (3.15), Eqs. (3.16) become

$$\sigma_x = \lambda e + 2\mu\epsilon_x \qquad \tau_{xy} = \mu\gamma_{xy} \qquad (3.17)$$

where we now have $e = \epsilon_x + \epsilon_y + \epsilon_z$. Similar relations can be obtained in an analogous manner for the other stress components, and we arrive at the following six relations, which are the generalized Hooke's law for isotropic materials referring to any arbitrary cartesian coordinates x, y, z:

$$\begin{aligned}
\sigma_x &= \lambda e + 2\mu\epsilon_x & \tau_{xy} &= \mu\gamma_{xy} \\
\sigma_y &= \lambda e + 2\mu\epsilon_y & \tau_{yz} &= \mu\gamma_{yz} \\
\sigma_z &= \lambda e + 2\mu\epsilon_z & \tau_{zx} &= \mu\gamma_{zx}
\end{aligned} \qquad (3.18)$$

Solving the first three equations in (3.18) for ϵ_x, ϵ_y, ϵ_z, we find

$$\epsilon_x = \frac{\lambda + \mu}{\mu(3\lambda + 2\mu)} \sigma_x - \frac{\lambda}{2\mu(3\lambda + 2\mu)} (\sigma_y + \sigma_z)$$

$$\epsilon_y = \frac{\lambda + \mu}{\mu(3\lambda + 2\mu)} \sigma_y - \frac{\lambda}{2\mu(3\lambda + 2\mu)} (\sigma_z + \sigma_x) \qquad (3.19)$$

$$\epsilon_z = \frac{\lambda + \mu}{\mu(3\lambda + 2\mu)} \sigma_z - \frac{\lambda}{2\mu(3\lambda + 2\mu)} (\sigma_x + \sigma_y)$$

3.3. Generalized Hooke's Law in Terms of Engineering Elastic Constants. Let us consider an elementary block with sides parallel to the coordinate axes and submitted to the action of normal stress σ_x uniformly distributed over two opposite sides, but with no other stresses on the six faces. In such a case, the ratio of stress to strain is called the *modulus of elasticity in tension*. For most engineering materials, the modulus of elasticity in tension is equal to that in compression and we shall give it the shortened name modulus of elasticity. We shall denote the modulus of elasticity by the letter E. The modulus of elasticity was first introduced by Young and is often called the *Young's modulus*. Expressed symbolically, we have

$$\epsilon_x = \frac{\sigma_x}{E} \qquad (3.20)$$

From experimental results it is observed that extension of the element in the x direction is accompanied by lateral contractions in the y and z directions, and we have

$$\epsilon_y = \epsilon_z = -\nu\epsilon_x = -\nu\frac{\sigma_x}{E} \qquad (3.21)$$

in which ν is a constant called *Poisson's ratio*.

From the generalized Hooke's law, we see that, under this system of stresses, Eqs. (3.19) are reduced to

$$\epsilon_x = \frac{\lambda + \mu}{\mu(3\lambda + 2\mu)} \sigma_x \qquad \epsilon_y = \epsilon_z = -\frac{\lambda}{2\mu(3\lambda + 2\mu)} \sigma_x$$

By comparison with Eqs. (3.20) and (3.21), we find that

$$E = \frac{\mu(3\lambda + 2\mu)}{\lambda + \mu} \qquad \nu = \frac{\lambda}{2(\lambda + \mu)} \qquad (3.22)$$

The ratio between the shearing-stress component and its corresponding shearing-strain component is called the *modulus of elasticity in shear*, or the *modulus of rigidity*, and is denoted by the letter G. That is,

$$G = \frac{\tau}{\gamma} \qquad (3.23)$$

From Eqs. (3.18), we see that $G = \mu$. As we have observed that for isotropic materials there are only two independent elastic constants, there must therefore exist a relation between the three constants E, ν, G. Solving for μ from Eqs. (3.22), we find

$$G = \frac{E}{2(1 + \nu)} \tag{3.24}$$

In terms of these engineering elastic constants, the generalized Hooke's law may be written as

$$\epsilon_x = \frac{1}{E}[\sigma_x - \nu(\sigma_y + \sigma_z)] \qquad \gamma_{xy} = \frac{\tau_{xy}}{G} = \frac{2(1+\nu)}{E}\tau_{xy}$$

$$\epsilon_y = \frac{1}{E}[\sigma_y - \nu(\sigma_z + \sigma_x)] \qquad \gamma_{yz} = \frac{\tau_{yz}}{G} = \frac{2(1+\nu)}{E}\tau_{yz} \tag{3.25}$$

$$\epsilon_z = \frac{1}{E}[\sigma_z - \nu(\sigma_x + \sigma_y)] \qquad \gamma_{zx} = \frac{\tau_{zx}}{G} = \frac{2(1+\nu)}{E}\tau_{zx}$$

Or, in terms of strain components, these equations become

$$\sigma_x = \frac{\nu E}{(1+\nu)(1-2\nu)}e + \frac{E}{1+\nu}\epsilon_x \qquad \tau_{xy} = G\gamma_{xy} = \frac{E}{2(1+\nu)}\gamma_{xy}$$

$$\sigma_y = \frac{\nu E}{(1+\nu)(1-2\nu)}e + \frac{E}{1+\nu}\epsilon_y \qquad \tau_{yz} = G\gamma_{yz} = \frac{E}{2(1+\nu)}\gamma_{yz} \tag{3.26}$$

$$\sigma_z = \frac{\nu E}{(1+\nu)(1-2\nu)}e + \frac{E}{1+\nu}\epsilon_z \qquad \tau_{zx} = G\gamma_{zx} = \frac{E}{2(1+\nu)}\gamma_{zx}$$

In the case of plane stress, we let $\sigma_z = \tau_{yz} = \tau_{zx} = 0$ in Eqs. (3.25) and obtain the strain-stress relations as follows:

$$\epsilon_x = \frac{1}{E}(\sigma_x - \nu\sigma_y)$$

$$\epsilon_y = \frac{1}{E}(\sigma_y - \nu\sigma_x)$$

$$\epsilon_z = -\frac{\nu}{E}(\sigma_x + \sigma_y) \tag{3.27}$$

$$\gamma_{xy} = \frac{\tau_{xy}}{G}$$

The relations between stress and strain are

$$\sigma_x = \frac{E}{1 - \nu^2}(\epsilon_x + \nu\epsilon_y)$$

$$\sigma_y = \frac{E}{1 - \nu^2}(\epsilon_y + \nu\epsilon_x) \tag{3.28}$$

$$\tau_{xy} = G\gamma_{xy}$$

In the case of plane strain, we let $\epsilon_z = \gamma_{yz} = \gamma_{zx} = 0$ in Eqs. (3.26) and find the stress-strain relations to be as follows:

$$\sigma_x = \frac{E}{(1 + \nu)(1 - 2\nu)}[(1 - \nu)\epsilon_x + \nu\epsilon_y]$$

$$\sigma_y = \frac{E}{(1 + \nu)(1 - 2\nu)}[\nu\epsilon_x + (1 - \nu)\epsilon_y] \qquad (3.29)$$

$$\sigma_z = \frac{\nu E}{(1 + \nu)(1 - 2\nu)}(\epsilon_x + \epsilon_y)$$

$$\tau_{xy} = G\gamma_{xy}$$

The strain-stress relations become

$$\epsilon_x = \frac{1 + \nu}{E}[(1 - \nu)\sigma_x - \nu\sigma_y]$$

$$\epsilon_y = \frac{1 + \nu}{E}[(1 - \nu)\sigma_y - \nu\sigma_x] \qquad (3.30)$$

$$\gamma_{xy} = \frac{\tau_{xy}}{G}$$

Comparing Eqs. (3.27), (3.28), (3.29), and (3.30), it is evident that if we assume a state of plane stress, we need not have a corresponding plane-strain state and conversely, if we assume a state of plane strain, we need not have a corresponding plane-stress state.

Adding the first three equations of (3.25) or (3.26), we obtain the following relation between the volume expansion e and the sum of normal stress Θ,

$$e = \frac{1 - 2\nu}{E}\Theta \qquad (3.31)$$

where $\Theta = \sigma_x + \sigma_y + \sigma_z$. In the case of a uniform hydrostatic pressure of the amount p we have

$$\sigma_x = \sigma_y = \sigma_z = -p$$

and Eq. (3.31) gives

$$e = -\frac{3(1 - 2\nu)}{E}p \qquad (3.32)$$

which represents the relation between unit expansion e and hydrostatic pressure p. The quantity $E/3(1 - 2\nu)$ is called the *modulus of volume expansion*, or *bulk modulus*.

3.4. Formulation of Elasticity Problems. The object of a problem in elasticity is usually to find the stress distribution in an elastic body, and in some cases to find the strain at any point due to given body forces and given conditions at the boundary of the body. To determine the stress at a point, we must find the six stress components. These six stress components satisfy the three equations of equilibrium. Since three equations are not sufficient to solve for six unknowns, we introduce the six strain components and at the same time we have the six relations defining the strain components in terms of the three displacement components and the six stress-strain relations. Thus we have altogether 15 unknowns and 15 equations. This system of equations is generally sufficient for the solution of an elasticity problem.

If we are interested in finding only the stress components in a body, we may reduce the system of equations to six equations with six unknown stress components. Since the displacement components are not to be found in this case, the compatibility equations must be satisfied to ensure the existence of single-valued displacements. Let us take, for instance, the compatibility equation

$$\frac{\partial^2 \epsilon_y}{\partial z^2} + \frac{\partial^2 \epsilon_z}{\partial y^2} = \frac{\partial^2 \gamma_{yz}}{\partial y \, \partial z} \tag{3.33}$$

From Eqs. (3.25), using the notation $\Theta = \sigma_x + \sigma_y + \sigma_z$, we find

$$\epsilon_y = \frac{1}{E}\left[(1 + \nu)\sigma_y - \nu\Theta\right] \qquad \epsilon_z = \frac{1}{E}\left[(1 + \nu)\sigma_z - \nu\Theta\right] \qquad \gamma_{yz} = \frac{2(1 + \nu)\tau_{yz}}{E}$$

Substituting these expressions into (3.33), we obtain

$$(1 + \nu)\left(\frac{\partial^2 \sigma_y}{\partial z^2} + \frac{\partial^2 \sigma_z}{\partial y^2}\right) - \nu\left(\frac{\partial^2 \Theta}{\partial z^2} + \frac{\partial^2 \Theta}{\partial y^2}\right) = 2(1 + \nu)\frac{\partial^2 \tau_{yz}}{\partial y \, \partial z} \tag{3.34}$$

From the third and second equations of (1.6), we have

$$\frac{\partial \tau_{yz}}{\partial y} = -\frac{\partial \sigma_z}{\partial z} - \frac{\partial \tau_{zx}}{\partial x} - Z \tag{3.35}$$

$$\frac{\partial \tau_{yz}}{\partial z} = -\frac{\partial \sigma_y}{\partial y} - \frac{\partial \tau_{xy}}{\partial x} - Y \tag{3.36}$$

Differentiating Eq. (3.35) with respect to z and Eq. (3.36) with respect to y, and adding them together, we obtain

$$2\frac{\partial^2 \tau_{yz}}{\partial y \, \partial z} = -\frac{\partial^2 \sigma_y}{\partial y^2} - \frac{\partial^2 \sigma_z}{\partial z^2} - \frac{\partial}{\partial x}\left(\frac{\partial \tau_{xy}}{\partial y} + \frac{\partial \tau_{zx}}{\partial z}\right) - \frac{\partial Y}{\partial y} - \frac{\partial Z}{\partial z}$$

or combining with the first equation of (1.6), *viz.*,

$$\frac{\partial \tau_{xy}}{\partial y} + \frac{\partial \tau_{zx}}{\partial z} = -\frac{\partial \sigma_x}{\partial x} - X$$

we find

$$2\frac{\partial^2 \tau_{yz}}{\partial y \, \partial z} = \frac{\partial^2 \sigma_x}{\partial x^2} - \frac{\partial^2 \sigma_y}{\partial y^2} - \frac{\partial^2 \sigma_z}{\partial z^2} + \frac{\partial X}{\partial x} - \frac{\partial Y}{\partial y} - \frac{\partial Z}{\partial z}$$

Substituting this in Eq. (3.34), we obtain

$$(1 + \nu)\left(\nabla^2\Theta - \nabla^2\sigma_x - \frac{\partial^2 \Theta}{\partial x^2}\right) - \nu\left(\nabla^2\Theta - \frac{\partial^2 \Theta}{\partial x^2}\right) = (1 + \nu)\left(\frac{\partial X}{\partial x} - \frac{\partial Y}{\partial y} - \frac{\partial Z}{\partial z}\right) \tag{3.37}$$

where to simplify the writing we have used the symbol

$$\nabla^2 = \frac{\partial^2}{\partial x^2} + \frac{\partial^2}{\partial y^2} + \frac{\partial^2}{\partial z^2}$$

From the other two compatibility equations of the type (3.33), two analogous equations to (3.37) can be obtained. Adding these three equations together, we find

$$\nabla^2\Theta = -\frac{1+\nu}{1-\nu}\left(\frac{\partial X}{\partial x} + \frac{\partial Y}{\partial y} + \frac{\partial Z}{\partial z}\right)$$

Substituting this expression for $\nabla^2\Theta$ into Eq. (3.37), we obtain finally

$$\nabla^2\sigma_x + \frac{1}{1+\nu}\frac{\partial^2\Theta}{\partial x^2} = -\frac{\nu}{1-\nu}\left(\frac{\partial X}{\partial x} + \frac{\partial Y}{\partial y} + \frac{\partial Z}{\partial z}\right) - 2\frac{\partial X}{\partial x} \qquad (3.38)$$

By substituting $\nabla^2\Theta$ into the other two equations, we can obtain three equations of the type (3.38). In a similar manner, the remaining three compatibility equations can be transformed into equations of the following form:

$$\nabla^2\tau_{yz} + \frac{1}{1+\nu}\frac{\partial^2\Theta}{\partial y\,\partial z} = -\left(\frac{\partial Z}{\partial y} + \frac{\partial Y}{\partial z}\right) \qquad (3.39)$$

Collecting our results, we find the following six equations for the six unknown stress components:

$$
\begin{aligned}
\nabla^2\sigma_x + \frac{1}{1+\nu}\frac{\partial^2\Theta}{\partial x^2} &= -\frac{\nu}{1-\nu}\left(\frac{\partial X}{\partial x} + \frac{\partial Y}{\partial y} + \frac{\partial Z}{\partial z}\right) - 2\frac{\partial X}{\partial x} \\
\nabla^2\sigma_y + \frac{1}{1+\nu}\frac{\partial^2\Theta}{\partial y^2} &= -\frac{\nu}{1-\nu}\left(\frac{\partial X}{\partial x} + \frac{\partial Y}{\partial y} + \frac{\partial Z}{\partial z}\right) - 2\frac{\partial Y}{\partial y} \\
\nabla^2\sigma_z + \frac{1}{1+\nu}\frac{\partial^2\Theta}{\partial z^2} &= -\frac{\nu}{1-\nu}\left(\frac{\partial X}{\partial x} + \frac{\partial Y}{\partial y} + \frac{\partial Z}{\partial z}\right) - 2\frac{\partial Z}{\partial z} \\
\nabla^2\tau_{xy} + \frac{1}{1+\nu}\frac{\partial^2\Theta}{\partial x\,\partial y} &= -\left(\frac{\partial X}{\partial y} + \frac{\partial Y}{\partial x}\right) \\
\nabla^2\tau_{yz} + \frac{1}{1+\nu}\frac{\partial^2\Theta}{\partial y\,\partial z} &= -\left(\frac{\partial Y}{\partial z} + \frac{\partial Z}{\partial y}\right) \\
\nabla^2\tau_{zx} + \frac{1}{1+\nu}\frac{\partial^2\Theta}{\partial z\,\partial x} &= -\left(\frac{\partial Z}{\partial x} + \frac{\partial X}{\partial z}\right)
\end{aligned}
\qquad (3.40)
$$

The original 15 equations can also be reduced to 3 equations in terms of the three displacement components. From the generalized Hooke's law (3.26), we have

$$\sigma_x = \lambda e + 2G\epsilon_x \qquad \tau_{xy} = G\gamma_{xy} \qquad \tau_{zx} = G\gamma_{zx}$$

where $\lambda = \nu E/(1+\nu)(1-2\nu)$. Substituting these relations into the first equation of (1.6), we find

$$\lambda\frac{\partial e}{\partial x} + G\left(2\frac{\partial\epsilon_x}{\partial x} + \frac{\partial\gamma_{xy}}{\partial y} + \frac{\partial\gamma_{zx}}{\partial z}\right) + X = 0 \qquad (3.41)$$

and if we substitute for the strain component the expressions (2.1), *viz.*,

$$\epsilon_x = \frac{\partial u}{\partial x} \qquad \epsilon_y = \frac{\partial v}{\partial y} \qquad \epsilon_z = \frac{\partial w}{\partial z} \qquad \gamma_{xy} = \frac{\partial u}{\partial y} + \frac{\partial v}{\partial x} \qquad \gamma_{yz} = \frac{\partial v}{\partial z} + \frac{\partial w}{\partial y} \qquad \gamma_{zx} = \frac{\partial w}{\partial x} + \frac{\partial u}{\partial z}$$

we find that (3.41) can be written in the form

$$(\lambda + G)\frac{\partial e}{\partial x} + G\nabla^2 u + X = 0$$

where $e = (\partial u/\partial x) + (\partial v/\partial y) + (\partial w/\partial z)$. The other two equations can be transformed in a similar manner.

Thus the three equations of equilibrium, expressed in terms of displacements, are

$$(\lambda + G) \frac{\partial e}{\partial x} + G\nabla^2 u + X = 0$$

$$(\lambda + G) \frac{\partial e}{\partial y} + G\nabla^2 v + Y = 0 \qquad (3.42)$$

$$(\lambda + G) \frac{\partial e}{\partial z} + G\nabla^2 w + Z = 0$$

Substituting Eqs. (3.26) and (2.1) into the boundary conditions (1.36), we find

$$\bar{X} = \lambda el + G \left(l\frac{\partial u}{\partial x} + m\frac{\partial u}{\partial y} + n\frac{\partial u}{\partial z} \right) + G \left(l\frac{\partial u}{\partial x} + m\frac{\partial v}{\partial x} + n\frac{\partial w}{\partial x} \right)$$

$$\bar{Y} = \lambda em + G \left(l\frac{\partial v}{\partial x} + m\frac{\partial v}{\partial y} + n\frac{\partial v}{\partial z} \right) + G \left(l\frac{\partial u}{\partial y} + m\frac{\partial v}{\partial y} + n\frac{\partial w}{\partial y} \right) \qquad (3.43)$$

$$\bar{Z} = \lambda en + G \left(l\frac{\partial w}{\partial x} + m\frac{\partial w}{\partial y} + n\frac{\partial w}{\partial z} \right) + G \left(l\frac{\partial u}{\partial z} + m\frac{\partial v}{\partial z} + n\frac{\partial w}{\partial z} \right)$$

Instead of prescribing the distribution of the surface forces on the boundary, the boundary conditions of an elasticity problem could also be given in terms of the displacements u, v, w on the bounding surface. Or we may be given the boundary condition that, on part of the boundary surface, surface force is prescribed and, on the other part, the displacements are prescribed. Equations (3.42) together with the boundary conditions completely define the three displacement components u, v, w. It may be noted that we need not adjoin the compatibility equations, for the only purpose of the latter is to impose restrictions on the strain components which shall ensure the single-valued continuous displacements u, v, and w.

3.5. Strain Energy.

When an elastic body is under the action of external forces, the body deforms and work is done by these forces. If a strained, perfectly elastic body is allowed to recover slowly to its unstrained state, it is capable of giving back all the work done by these external forces. For this reason the work done in straining such a body may be regarded as energy stored in the body and is called the *strain energy*.

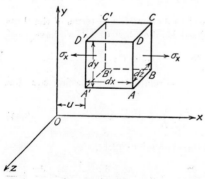

Fig. 3.2.

In order to calculate the amount of strain energy stored in a strained body, let us consider the work done by the stresses acting on the surface of an elementary rectangular block of dimensions dx, dy, dz inside the body. Let us first assume that the element is acted on by σ_x only (Fig. 3.2). If we denote the x component of the displacement of the face $A'B'C'D'$ by u, the corresponding displacement of $ABCD$ will be $u + (\partial u/\partial x)\, dx$. On $A'B'C'D'$, the force $\sigma_x\, dy\, dz$ and the displacement u are in opposite directions, while on $ABCD$ they are in the same direction. During the deformation the stress component σ_x increases from zero to some value σ_x while the displacement u increases from zero to the value u. Thus, work is done by the force acting on $ABCD$ and is done on the force acting on $A'B'C'D'$. The net work done, or the work stored in the element, is therefore

$$\int_{\sigma_x=0}^{\sigma_x=\sigma_x} \sigma_x \, d\left(u + \frac{\partial u}{\partial x} \, dx\right) dy \, dz - \int_{\sigma_x=0}^{\sigma_x=\sigma_x} \sigma_x \, du \, dy \, dz$$

$$= \int_{\sigma_x=0}^{\sigma_x=\sigma_x} \sigma_x \, d\left(\frac{\partial u}{\partial x}\right) dx \, dy \, dz$$

From the definition of ϵ_x and Hooke's law, $\partial u/\partial x = \epsilon_x = \sigma_x/E$, we have therefore

$$\int_{\sigma_x=0}^{\sigma_x=\sigma_x} \frac{\sigma_x}{E} \, d\sigma_x \, dx \, dy \, dz = \frac{\sigma_x{}^2}{2E} \, dx \, dy \, dz = \frac{1}{2} \sigma_x \epsilon_x \, dx \, dy \, dz$$

The strain energy stored in the element $dx \, dy \, dz$ is thus

$$dU = \tfrac{1}{2}\sigma_x \epsilon_x \, dx \, dy \, dz$$

Now assume that the element is under the action of both σ_x and σ_y. Let the action take place in the following order: First, σ_x is increased from zero to the value σ_x while σ_y remains zero; then, with σ_x remaining constant, σ_y is increased from zero to the value σ_y. When $\sigma_y = 0$, the work done by σ_x is the same as previously calculated. Since $\epsilon_x = \sigma_x/E$ in this case, we have therefore

$$dU_1 = \frac{1}{2E} \sigma_x{}^2 \, dx \, dy \, dz$$

While σ_x is increased from zero to the value σ_x, ϵ_y is also increased from zero to $-\nu\sigma_x/E$. But no work is done corresponding to the displacement produced by this part of ϵ_y because σ_y is zero during the process. With the value of σ_y increasing from zero to σ_y, there will be a corresponding increase of ϵ_y which is equal to σ_y/E. This part of ϵ_y will contribute to the strain energy of the amount

$$dU_2 = \frac{1}{2E} \sigma_y{}^2 \, dx \, dy \, dz$$

At the same time, owing to σ_y the value of ϵ_x increases from σ_x/E to $(\sigma_x - \nu\sigma_y)/E$. While ϵ_x is increasing, σ_x remains constant. The work done by this *constant* value of σ_x is therefore

$$dU_3 = \frac{(\sigma_x \, dy \, dz)(-\nu\sigma_y \, dx)}{E} = -\frac{\nu}{E} \sigma_x \sigma_y \, dx \, dy \, dz$$

In the above formula the factor $\tfrac{1}{2}$ is not included because σ_x remains constant during the change in ϵ_x. Thus the total strain energy accumulated in the element is

$$dU = dU_1 + dU_2 + dU_3 = \frac{1}{2E} (\sigma_x{}^2 + \sigma_y{}^2 - 2\nu\sigma_x\sigma_y) \, dx \, dy \, dz$$

With this system of stresses, we have from Hooke's law

$$\epsilon_x = \frac{1}{E} (\sigma_x - \nu\sigma_y) \qquad \epsilon_y = \frac{1}{E} (\sigma_y - \nu\sigma_x)$$

It is easy to verify that dU may be written in the following form:

$$dU = \tfrac{1}{2}(\sigma_x\epsilon_x + \sigma_y\epsilon_y) \, dx \, dy \, dz \tag{3.44}$$

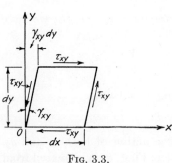

Fig. 3.3.

If we assume that the stresses are applied in a different order, we can prove that the strain energy stored in the body will be exactly the same. That is, the strain energy depends only on the final state of the stress and is independent of the manner in which the stresses are applied.

Now let us consider the element under the action of the shearing stress τ_{xy}. We see from Fig. 3.3 that the force is $\tau_{xy} \, dx \, dz$ and the displacement in the direction of the force is $\gamma_{xy} \, dy$. The strain energy is then

$$dU = \tfrac{1}{2}(\tau_{xy} \, dx \, dz)(\gamma_{xy} \, dy) = \tfrac{1}{2}\tau_{xy} \, \gamma_{xy} \, dx \, dy \, dz \tag{3.45}$$

From Hooke's law we see that the normal stresses will not produce any shearing strain and the shearing stresses will not produce any longitudinal strain. Thus if the element $dx \, dy \, dz$ is under the action of σ_x, σ_y, and τ_{xy} simultaneously, the amount of strain energy stored in the element can be obtained by adding the expressions (3.44) and (3.45), *viz.*,

$$\begin{aligned} dU = \tfrac{1}{2}(\sigma_x\epsilon_x + \sigma_y\epsilon_y \\ + \tau_{xy}\gamma_{xy}) \, dx \, dy \, dz \end{aligned} \tag{3.46}$$

This is the expression for strain energy stored in the element $dx \, dy \, dz$ under plane stress.

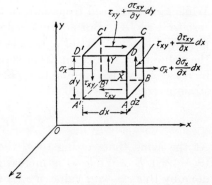

Fig. 3.4.

The same expression for strain energy (3.46) is obtained if we allow the stresses to vary in the element (Fig. 3.4). Assume that the element is under the action of the stress components σ_x and τ_{xy} and the body forces X, Y. During the deformation, σ_x and τ_{xy} increase from zero to some value σ_x and τ_{xy} while the displacements u and v increase correspondingly. The work done on the element is then

$$dU = \int \left(\sigma_x + \frac{\partial \sigma_x}{\partial x} \, dx \right) d \left(u + \frac{\partial u}{\partial x} \, dx + \frac{1}{2} \frac{\partial u}{\partial y} \, dy \right) dy \, dz$$

$$- \int \sigma_x \, d \left(u + \frac{1}{2} \frac{\partial u}{\partial y} \, dy \right) dy \, dz$$

$$+ \int \left(\tau_{xy} + \frac{\partial \tau_{xy}}{\partial y} \, dy \right) d \left(u + \frac{1}{2} \frac{\partial u}{\partial x} \, dx + \frac{\partial u}{\partial y} \, dy \right) dx \, dz$$

$$- \int \tau_{xy} \, d \left(u + \frac{1}{2} \frac{\partial u}{\partial x} \, dx \right) dx \, dz$$

$$+ \int \left(\tau_{xy} + \frac{\partial \tau_{xy}}{\partial x} \, dx \right) d \left(v + \frac{\partial v}{\partial x} \, dx + \frac{1}{2} \frac{\partial v}{\partial y} \, dy \right) dy \, dz$$

$$- \int \tau_{xy} \, d \left(v + \frac{1}{2} \frac{\partial v}{\partial y} \, dy \right) dy \, dz$$

$$+ \int X \, d \left(u + \frac{1}{2} \frac{\partial u}{\partial x} \, dx + \frac{1}{2} \frac{\partial u}{\partial y} \, dy \right) dx \, dy \, dz$$

$$+ \int Y \, d \left(v + \frac{1}{2} \frac{\partial v}{\partial x} \, dx + \frac{1}{2} \frac{\partial v}{\partial y} \, dy \right) dx \, dy \, dz$$

$$= \int \sigma_x \, d \left(\frac{\partial u}{\partial x} \right) dx \, dy \, dz + \int \tau_{xy} \, d \left(\frac{\partial u}{\partial y} + \frac{\partial v}{\partial x} \right) dx \, dy \, dz$$

$$+ \int \left(\frac{\partial \sigma_x}{\partial x} + \frac{\partial \tau_{xy}}{\partial y} + X \right) du \, dx \, dy \, dz$$

$$+ \int \left(\frac{\partial \tau_{xy}}{\partial x} + Y \right) dv \, dx \, dy \, dz \qquad (3.47)$$

where the limits of integration are from $u = 0$, $v = 0$ to the values u and v corresponding to σ_x and τ_{xy}, and the higher-order terms involving $dx^2 \, dy \, dz$ and $dx \, dy^2 \, dz$ are neglected. Now with $\sigma_y = 0$, the equilibrium conditions are

$$\frac{\partial \sigma_x}{\partial x} + \frac{\partial \tau_{xy}}{\partial y} + X = 0 \qquad \frac{\partial \tau_{xy}}{\partial x} + Y = 0$$

and therefore the last two integrals in (3.47) vanish. This indicates that the total work done by these stress variations is zero. Noting that $\partial u / \partial x = \epsilon_x$ and

$$\frac{\partial u}{\partial y} + \frac{\partial v}{\partial x} = \gamma_{xy}$$

(3.47) becomes

$$dU = \int \sigma_x \, d\epsilon_x \, dx \, dy \, dz + \int \tau_{xy} \, d\gamma_{xy} \, dx \, dy \, dz$$

Carrying out the integration, we find

$$dU = \tfrac{1}{2} (\sigma_x \epsilon_x + \tau_{xy} \gamma_{xy}) \, dx \, dy \, dz$$

which is the same as the case in which the stress variations were not considered.

The strain energy stored in the element $dx \, dy \, dz$ under a general three-dimensional stress system can be found in a similar manner, and we obtain in this case

$$dU = \tfrac{1}{2} (\sigma_x \epsilon_x + \sigma_y \epsilon_y + \sigma_z \epsilon_z + \tau_{xy} \gamma_{xy} + \tau_{yz} \gamma_{yz} + \tau_{zx} \gamma_{zx}) \, dx \, dy \, dz \quad (3.48)$$

The total strain energy stored in a deformed elastic body, U, can be found by integrating dU over the whole volume V, namely,

$$U = \tfrac{1}{2} \iiint\limits_{V} (\sigma_x \epsilon_x + \sigma_y \epsilon_y + \sigma_z \epsilon_z + \tau_{xy} \gamma_{xy} + \tau_{yz} \gamma_{yz} + \tau_{zx} \gamma_{zx}) \, dx \, dy \, dz \quad (3.49)$$

Using the strain-stress relations, Eqs. (3.25), the above formula for U can be expressed in terms of stress components only.   The formula (3.49) becomes in this case

$$U = \iiint_V \left[\frac{1}{2E} (\sigma_x{}^2 + \sigma_y{}^2 + \sigma_z{}^2) - \frac{\nu}{E} (\sigma_x\sigma_y + \sigma_y\sigma_z + \sigma_z\sigma_x) \right.$$

$$\left. + \frac{1}{2G} (\tau_{xy}{}^2 + \tau_{yz}{}^2 + \tau_{zx}{}^2) \right] dx\, dy\, dz \quad (3.50)$$

In the case of plane stress, $\sigma_z = \tau_{yz} = \tau_{zx} = 0$, and we have

$$U = \frac{1}{2} \iiint_V \left[\frac{1}{E} (\sigma_x{}^2 + \sigma_y{}^2 - 2\nu\sigma_x\sigma_y) + \frac{1}{G} \tau_{xy}{}^2 \right] dx\, dy\, dz \quad (3.51)$$

Or we may express U in terms of strain components only by using the stress-strain relations.   In this case, we find

$$U = \frac{E}{2(1 + \nu)} \iiint_V \left[\frac{\nu}{1 - 2\nu} e^2 + (\epsilon_x{}^2 + \epsilon_y{}^2 + \epsilon_z{}^2) \right.$$

$$\left. + \frac{1}{2} (\gamma_{xy}{}^2 + \gamma_{yx}{}^2 + \gamma_{zz}{}^2) \right] dx\, dy\, dz \quad (3.52)$$

In the case of plane stress, by using (3.28), we have

$$U = \frac{E}{2(1 + \nu)} \iiint_V \left[\frac{1}{1 - \nu} (\epsilon_x{}^2 + \epsilon_y{}^2 + 2\nu\epsilon_x\epsilon_y) + \frac{1}{2} \gamma_{xy}{}^2 \right] dx\, dy\, dz \quad (3.53)$$

3.6. Existence and Uniqueness of Solution.   From the set of equations together with the boundary conditions, we can prove not only that there exists a solution but also that the solution is unique, *i.e.*, there exists only one state of stress under a given external loading.   The rigorous proofs of the existence of solutions are due to Korn[1] and Lichtenstein.[2]   These proofs, however, are too lengthy to be included in this volume.   We shall prove here only the uniqueness theorem,[3] which can be stated as follows: If, in addition to the body forces, either the surface forces or the surface displacements are given on the boundary of an elastic body, there exists only one form of equilibrium in the sense that the distribution of stresses and strains in the body is determined uniquely.   In proving the above theorem, we must remember that we are dealing with elasticity problems

---

[1] A. Korn, Über die Lösung des Grundproblems des Elastizitätstheorie, *Math. Ann.*, Vol. 75, pp. 497–544, 1914.

[2] L. Lichtenstein, Über die erste Randwertaufgabe der Elastizitätstheorie, *Math. Z.*, Vol. 20, pp. 21–28, 1924.

[3] G. Kirchhoff, "Vorlesungen über Math. Phys. Mechanik," 3d ed., Leipzig, 1883.

with infinitesimal strains and displacements. If the strains or displacements are not infinitesimal, the solution may not be unique, as will be shown in the later chapters where problems concerning elastic stability are discussed.

In order to establish the uniqueness of solution of the boundary-value problems, let us assume that it is possible to obtain solutions

$$\sigma'_x, \sigma'_y, \ldots, u', v', w'$$

and

$$\sigma''_x, \sigma''_y, \ldots, u'', v'', w''$$

which satisfy the 15 elasticity equations and the boundary conditions. Then, for the first state of stress, the equations

$$\frac{\partial \sigma'_x}{\partial x} + \frac{\partial \tau'_{xy}}{\partial y} + \frac{\partial \tau'_{zx}}{\partial z} + X = 0$$

$$\cdots \cdots \cdots \cdots \cdots \cdots$$

$$\cdots \cdots \cdots \cdots \cdots \cdots$$

are satisfied as well as the following boundary conditions,

$$\bar{X} = l\sigma'_x + m\tau'_{xy} + n\tau'_{zx}$$

$$\cdots \cdots \cdots \cdots \cdots$$

$$\cdots \cdots \cdots \cdots \cdots$$

if the surface forces are prescribed, or

$$u = u'$$

$$\cdots \cdots$$

$$\cdots \cdots$$

if the boundary displacements are prescribed. For the second state of stress, we have

$$\frac{\partial \sigma''_x}{\partial x} + \frac{\partial \tau''_{xy}}{\partial y} + \frac{\partial \tau''_{zx}}{\partial z} + X = 0$$

$$\cdots \cdots \cdots \cdots \cdots \cdots$$

$$\cdots \cdots \cdots \cdots \cdots \cdots$$

$$\bar{X} = l\sigma''_x + m\tau''_{xy} + n\tau''_{zx}$$

$$\cdots \cdots \cdots \cdots \cdots$$

$$\cdots \cdots \cdots \cdots \cdots$$

or

$$u = u''$$

$$\cdots \cdots \cdots$$

$$\cdots \cdots \cdots$$

By subtraction, because of the linear character of the equations, we find that the stress distribution defined by the differences $\sigma'_x - \sigma''_x$, $\sigma'_y - \sigma''_y$, ... satisfies the equations

$$\frac{\partial(\sigma'_x - \sigma''_x)}{\partial x} + \frac{\partial(\tau'_{xy} - \tau''_{xy})}{\partial y} + \frac{\partial(\tau'_{zx} - \tau''_{zx})}{\partial z} = 0$$

. . . .

$$0 = l(\sigma'_x - \sigma''_x) + m(\tau'_{xy} - \tau''_{xy}) + n(\tau'_{zx} - \tau''_{zx})$$

. . . .

. . . .

Thus we have a new "difference" stress distribution in which all external forces and boundary displacements vanish.

If there is no external force or boundary displacements, there will be no work done. From the law of conservation of energy, the strain energy stored in the body will be zero. Now, from formula (3.52), we observe that the strain energy is a quadratic function of the strain components. If any strain component is different from zero, the strain energy will have a positive definite value. It cannot vanish unless all the strain components vanish. Therefore, if the strain energy stored in the body is zero, the strain components, and consequently the stress components, must be zero everywhere in the body, and the body is in an unstressed state. Consequently for the "difference" stress state, $\sigma'_x - \sigma''_x$, $\sigma'_y - \sigma''_y$, . . . must be zero and the two solutions must be identical, and there exists one unique solution as far as stresses and strains are concerned. As for the displacements, they are uniquely determined if the boundary displacements are prescribed. If the boundary forces are prescribed, the displacements will be determined up to within the quantities representing rigid-body motions.

In proving the uniqueness theorem, we have assumed that the displacements u, v, w are single-valued functions and that there are no initial stresses. In the cases in which there are initial stresses, if the principle of superposition can be applied, the deformations and stresses proposed by external forces are not affected by initial stresses and can be calculated in exactly the same manner as if there were no initial stresses. The total stresses will be the algebraic sum of the stresses produced by the external forces and the initial stresses. In cases when the principle of superposition is not applicable, such as the bending of a prismatical bar under axial tension or compression, the stresses produced by the external loads cannot be determined without knowing the initial stresses.

3.7. Saint-Venant's Principle. In the application of the theory of elasticity to engineering problems, we shall often refer to a principle due to Saint-Venant, the essence of which can be stated as follows: If a system of forces acting on a small portion of the surface of an elastic body is replaced by another statically equivalent system of forces acting on the same portion of the surface, this redistribution of loading produces substantial changes in the stresses only in the immediate neighborhood of the loading and the stresses are essentially the same in the parts of the body which are at large distances in comparison with the linear dimensions of the surface on which the forces are changed. By "statically equivalent systems" we mean that the two distributions of forces have the same resultant force and moment.

In the solution of practical problems, if the boundary conditions are prescribed according to the exact distribution of the forces, the problems may sometimes be so complicated mathematically as to defy solution. Frequently by modifying the boundary conditions slightly, the solution becomes possible, and we can obtain in this way a solution which gives essentially the same stress distribution in a large part of the elastic body as in the actual case. Therefore, by means of Saint-Venant's principle, we are allowed to simplify the solution of the problem by altering the boundary conditions as long as the systems of applied forces are statically equivalent. Furthermore, in many practical problems, the exact distribution of forces on the boundary is not known, but the statically equivalent loading can be easily determined. In these cases, we may proceed to solve the problem with this statically equivalent system of boundary forces, and from Saint-Venant's principle we know that in this way we shall obtain a satisfactory approximate solution.

CHAPTER 4

PLANE-STRESS AND PLANE-STRAIN PROBLEMS

4.1. The Governing Differential Equations. To solve the general equation (3.40) or (3.42) with boundary conditions which prescribe the values of either the stress or the displacement is the basic problem in the theory of elasticity. The solution of this general system of equations is, however, often too difficult to carry out. Fortunately, for many problems which are of practical interest, some simplifying assumptions can be made regarding the stress distribution or strain distribution, and solutions can then be carried out in a relatively simple manner.

Let us consider a long prismatical cylinder under the action of lateral loads uniformly distributed along the axis (Fig. 4.1). Assume that the

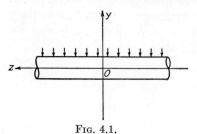

FIG. 4.1.

body force Z is zero, while X and Y are functions of x and y only. We find that in this case the deformation of a large portion of the body at some distance away from the ends is independent of the z coordinates and the displacements u and v are functions of x and y only. If the ends of the cylinder are prevented from moving in the z direction, then w is zero there. At the mid-section of the cylinder, by symmetry w must also be zero. We may therefore make the approximate assumption that w is zero at every cross section of the cylinder. In such a case, the strain components

$$\epsilon_x = \frac{\partial u}{\partial x} \qquad \epsilon_y = \frac{\partial v}{\partial y} \qquad \gamma_{xy} = \frac{\partial u}{\partial y} + \frac{\partial v}{\partial x}$$

are functions of x and y only and the strain components

$$\epsilon_z = \frac{\partial w}{\partial z} \qquad \gamma_{xz} = \frac{\partial w}{\partial x} + \frac{\partial u}{\partial z} \qquad \gamma_{yz} = \frac{\partial v}{\partial z} + \frac{\partial w}{\partial y}$$

vanish. We have therefore a state of *plane strain*.

From Hooke's law, Eqs. (3.29), we find that in this case the stress components σ_x, σ_y, σ_z, τ_{xy} are functions of x and y only and τ_{yz} and τ_{zx} are zero everywhere. Hence, the equilibrium equations become

$$\frac{\partial \sigma_x}{\partial x} + \frac{\partial \tau_{xy}}{\partial y} + X = 0 \qquad \frac{\partial \tau_{xy}}{\partial x} + \frac{\partial \sigma_y}{\partial y} + Y = 0 \qquad (4.1)$$

There are two important practical cases of body forces, *viz.*, gravitational force and centrifugal force. For the present we shall limit our attention to the cases where the body forces are gravitational forces only and later in this chapter shall discuss the cases where the body forces are centrifugal forces. When the body forces are gravitational forces only, we may write $X = \rho g_x$ and $Y = \rho g_y$, where ρ is the mass density of the material and g_x, g_y are the x and y components of the gravitational acceleration, respectively. Equations (4.1) then become

$$\frac{\partial \sigma_x}{\partial x} + \frac{\partial \tau_{xy}}{\partial y} + \rho g_x = 0 \qquad \frac{\partial \sigma_y}{\partial y} + \frac{\partial \tau_{xy}}{\partial x} + \rho g_y = 0 \qquad (4.2)$$

Equations (4.2) are satisfied if we introduce a stress function $\psi(x,y)$ such that

$$\sigma_x = \frac{\partial^2 \psi}{\partial y^2} \qquad \sigma_y = \frac{\partial^2 \psi}{\partial x^2} \qquad \tau_{xy} = -\frac{\partial^2 \psi}{\partial x\,\partial y} - \rho g_x y - \rho g_y x \qquad (4.3)$$

If the gravitational force is neglected, we have obviously

$$\sigma_x = \frac{\partial^2 \psi}{\partial y^2} \qquad \sigma_y = \frac{\partial^2 \psi}{\partial x^2} \qquad \tau_{xy} = -\frac{\partial^2 \psi}{\partial x\,\partial y} \qquad (4.4)$$

Our problem thus reduces to the determination of the stress function ψ with appropriate boundary conditions. Once the stress function is obtained, the stresses can be determined from formulas (4.3) or (4.4).

When we are solving for the stresses, the compatibility equations (2.19) must be used. By examining these equations, we find the only compatibility equation which is not identically satisfied is

$$\frac{\partial^2 \epsilon_x}{\partial y^2} + \frac{\partial^2 \epsilon_y}{\partial x^2} = \frac{\partial^2 \gamma_{xy}}{\partial x\,\partial y} \qquad (4.5)$$

In the case of plane strain, the strain-stress relations are

$$\epsilon_x = \frac{1+\nu}{E}[(1-\nu)\sigma_x - \nu\sigma_y]$$

$$\epsilon_y = \frac{1+\nu}{E}[(1-\nu)\sigma_y - \nu\sigma_x] \qquad (4.6)$$

$$\gamma_{xy} = \frac{2(1+\nu)}{E}\tau_{xy}$$

Substituting these relations into (4.5) and dropping a common factor, we have

$$\frac{\partial^2}{\partial y^2}[(1-\nu)\sigma_x - \nu\sigma_y] + \frac{\partial^2}{\partial x^2}[(1-\nu)\sigma_y - \nu\sigma_x] = 2\frac{\partial^2 \tau_{xy}}{\partial x\,\partial y} \qquad (4.7)$$

If we express the stress components in terms of the stress function according to (4.3) or (4.4), Eq. (4.7) becomes

$$\frac{\partial^4 \psi}{\partial x^4} + 2\frac{\partial^4 \psi}{\partial x^2\,\partial y^2} + \frac{\partial^4 \psi}{\partial y^4} = 0 \tag{4.8}$$

which is the governing equation for ψ. Since

$$\frac{\partial^4}{\partial x^4} + 2\frac{\partial^4}{\partial x^2\,\partial y^2} + \frac{\partial^4}{\partial y^4} = \left(\frac{\partial^2}{\partial x^2} + \frac{\partial^2}{\partial y^2}\right)^2 = (\nabla^2)^2$$

Eq. (4.8) may be written as

$$\nabla^4 \psi = 0$$

The operator $\nabla^2 = (\partial^2/\partial x^2) + (\partial^2/\partial y^2)$ is called the *Laplace* or *harmonic* operator, and Eq. (4.8) is called a *biharmonic equation*.

Next let us examine the case where the ends of the cylinder are free to expand. In such a case, we may assume that the longitudinal strain ϵ_z is a constant. Such a state may be called that of *generalized plane strain*. From Eq. (3.25), we find

$$\sigma_z = \nu(\sigma_x + \sigma_y) + E\epsilon_z \tag{4.9}$$

and

$$\epsilon_x = \frac{1+\nu}{E}\left[(1-\nu)\sigma_x - \nu\sigma_y\right] - \nu\epsilon_z$$

$$\epsilon_y = \frac{1+\nu}{E}\left[(1-\nu)\sigma_y - \nu\sigma_x\right] - \nu\epsilon_z \tag{4.10}$$

$$\gamma_{xy} = \frac{2(1+\nu)}{E}\tau_{xy}$$

where ϵ_z is a constant. Substituting (4.10) into Eq. (4.5) and simplifying, we again obtain Eq. (4.8) as our governing differential equation. With σ_x and σ_y determined, the constant value of ϵ_z can be found from the condition that the resultant force in the z direction acting on the ends of the cylinder is zero, *viz.*,

$$\iint\sigma_z\,dx\,dy = 0 \tag{4.11}$$

In the case of a long cylinder where the strain distribution is essentially plane, the dimension of the elastic body in the z direction is large compared with the other dimensions. Now let us consider the other extreme in which the dimension of the body in the z direction is very small, *viz.*, the case of a thin, flat plate. Assume that the plate is under the action of forces applied at the boundary, parallel to the plane of the plate and distributed uniformly over its thickness (Fig. 4.2). Assume also that the body force Z is zero, while X and Y are functions of x and y only. We see that

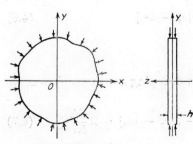

Fig. 4.2.

the surfaces of the plate $z = \pm h/2$ will be free of external forces and the stress components σ_z, τ_{xz}, τ_{yz} are zero there. If the plate is thin, without substantial error, we can assume that these components are zero throughout the thickness of the plate and the other three stress components σ_x, σ_y, τ_{xy} remain practically constant over the thickness of the plate. We have therefore in this case a state of *plane stress*, namely, $\sigma_z = \tau_{xz} = \tau_{yz} = 0$ and σ_x, σ_y, τ_{xy} are functions of x, y only. In this case, the equilibrium equations become again those given by (4.1) or (4.2), and we may again introduce the same stress function ψ to satisfy these equations.

The strain-stress relations become now

$$\epsilon_x = \frac{1}{E}(\sigma_x - \nu\sigma_y) \qquad \epsilon_y = \frac{1}{E}(\sigma_y - \nu\sigma_x) \qquad \gamma_{xy} = \frac{\tau_{xy}}{G} = \frac{2(1+\nu)}{E}\tau_{xy} \qquad (4.12)$$

Substituting these relations and those given by (4.3) into Eq. (4.5), we find again Eq. (4.8) as the governing equation for the stress function ψ.

In examining Eqs. (2.19), we find that, by assuming $\sigma_z = \tau_{xz} = \tau_{yz} = 0$ and σ_x, σ_y, τ_{xy} independent of z, in addition to Eq. (4.5), three other compatibility equations are to be satisfied. They are

$$\frac{\partial^2\epsilon_z}{\partial x^2} = 0 \qquad \frac{\partial^2\epsilon_z}{\partial y^2} = 0 \qquad \frac{\partial^2\epsilon_z}{\partial x\,\partial y} = 0 \qquad (4.13)$$

Integrating these equations, we obtain

$$\epsilon_z = -\frac{\nu}{E}(\sigma_x + \sigma_y) = ax + by + c$$

where a, b, c are constants of integration. This condition, however, will not be in general satisfied in the plane-stress problems by solving Eq. (4.8). Evidently the solution given by (4.8) cannot be exact because not all the compatibility equations are satisfied. An exact solution which satisfies all the compatibility equations can be obtained if we again assume $\sigma_z = \tau_{xz} = \tau_{yz} = 0$ but do not require σ_x, σ_y, τ_{xy} to be independent of z. In such a case, it can be shown[1] that if the body forces are neglected and if the external loads are distributed symmetrically with respect to the middle plane of the plate, the stress function ψ defined by Eq. (4.4) will have the following form,

$$\psi = \psi_1 - \frac{\nu}{2(1+\nu)}(\nabla^2\psi_1)z^2$$

where ψ_1 satisfies Eq. (4.8). For a thin plate, z is usually very small, and the second term in the above expression can be neglected. Therefore, although the solutions given by Eq. (4.8) do not satisfy all the compatibility equations, nevertheless they give good approximations to the thin-plate problems.

From the above formulation we find that for plane-stress problems, plane-strain problems, and generalized plane-strain problems, if the

[1] S. Timoshenko and J. N. Goodier, "Theory of Elasticity," 2d ed., pp. 241–244, McGraw-Hill Book Company, Inc., New York, 1951.

body force is the gravitational force only, the stress function is governed by the same differential equation. The only difference among these cases is that, after the stress components are obtained, in the case of plane strain, the strain components must be calculated from Eqs. (4.6), in the case of generalized plane strain, they must be calculated from Eqs. (4.10), while in the case of plane stress, they must be calculated from (4.12). The fact that the stress components can all be expressed in terms of a single stress function was first recognized by Airy,[1] and the stress function ψ is commonly known as *Airy's stress function*.

4.2. Bending of a Narrow Cantilever of Rectangular Cross Section under an End Load. As a first example, we shall attempt a rigorous solution for a cantilever beam of narrow rectangular cross section under an end load P. With its width h small compared with the depth d, the loaded beam (Fig. 4.3) may be regarded as an example in plane stress. The boundary conditions are that the upper and lower edges are free from load and the resultant shearing force at $x = 0$ is equal to P. If P is large compared with ρg, the gravitational force can be neglected.

From the static considerations we see that the bending moment at any section will be proportional to x and the stress component σ_x at any point of the section will be proportional to y. Accordingly we shall assume for a trial that

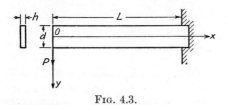

$$\sigma_x = \frac{\partial^2 \psi}{\partial y^2} = c_1 xy$$

where c_1 is some constant. Integrating, we find

$$\psi = \frac{c_1}{6} xy^3 + yf_1(x) + f_2(x)$$

Fig. 4.3.

where $f_1(x)$ and $f_2(x)$ are unknown functions of x. Substitution of the above expression into the governing equation (4.8),

$$\nabla^4 \psi = 0$$

results in

$$y \frac{d^4 f_1}{dx^4} + \frac{d^4 f_2}{dx^4} = 0$$

Since f_1 and f_2 are functions of x alone, the second term in the above equation is independent of y. But this equation must be satisfied for all values of x and y in the beam. This is possible only if

$$\frac{d^4 f_1}{dx^4} = 0 \quad \text{and} \quad \frac{d^4 f_2}{dx^4} = 0$$

or $f_1 = c_2 x^3 + c_3 x^2 + c_4 x + c_5 \qquad f_2 = c_6 x^3 + c_7 x^2 + c_8 x + c_9$

---

[1] G. B. Airy, *Brit. Assoc. Rept.*, 1862.

where $c_2, c_3, \ldots, c_9$ are constants of integration. Therefore, we have

$$\psi = \frac{c_1}{6} xy^3 + y(c_2 x^3 + c_3 x^2 + c_4 x + c_5) + c_6 x^3 + c_7 x^2 + c_8 x + c_9 \quad (4.14)$$

Neglecting the gravitational force, we obtain from (4.4)

$$\sigma_y = \frac{\partial^2 \psi}{\partial x^2} = 6(c_2 y + c_6)x + 2(c_3 y + c_7)$$

$$\tau_{xy} = -\frac{\partial^2 \psi}{\partial x\, \partial y} = -\frac{c_1}{2} y^2 - 3c_2 x^2 - 2c_3 x - c_4$$

The boundary conditions require that $\sigma_y = 0$ on $y = \pm d/2$, or

$$6\left(c_2 \frac{d}{2} + c_6\right)x + 2\left(c_3 \frac{d}{2} + c_7\right) = 0$$

$$6\left(-c_2 \frac{d}{2} + c_6\right)x + 2\left(-c_3 \frac{d}{2} + c_7\right) = 0$$

These equations must be valid for all values of x between 0 and L; it follows therefore that

$$c_2 \frac{d}{2} + c_6 = 0 \qquad c_3 \frac{d}{2} + c_7 = 0$$

$$-c_2 \frac{d}{2} + c_6 = 0 \qquad -c_3 \frac{d}{2} + c_7 = 0$$

Solving, we find $c_2 = c_3 = c_6 = c_7 = 0$. Thus,

$$\tau_{xy} = -\frac{c_1}{2} y^2 - c_4$$

To satisfy the condition that $\tau_{xy} = 0$ on $y = \pm d/2$, we must have

$$-\frac{c_1}{8} d^2 - c_4 = 0 \qquad \text{or} \qquad c_4 = -\frac{c_1 d^2}{8}$$

On the loaded end of the beam the sum of the distributed shearing forces must be equal to P. Hence

$$-\int_{-d/2}^{+d/2} \tau_{xy} h\, dy = \int_{-d/2}^{d/2} \frac{c_1}{8} h(4y^2 - d^2)\, dy = P$$

from which
$$c_1 = -\frac{12P}{d^3 h}$$

Noting that $I = d^3 h/12$ is the moment of inertia of the cross section, the final expressions for the stress components are therefore

$$\sigma_x = -\frac{Pxy}{I} \qquad \sigma_y = 0 \qquad \tau_{xy} = -\frac{P}{2I}\left(\frac{d^2}{4} - y^2\right) \quad (4.15)$$

This coincides completely with the elementary solution as given in books on the strength of materials. From this solution, we see that the distribution of the shearing force at the ends must be according to the parabolic law and that σ_x at the built-in end must vary linearly with y. The solution, therefore, is exact only when the boundary forces are so given. If the boundary forces are given in any other manner, this solution will not be an exact one; but by virtue of Saint-Venant's principle, it does represent the stress distribution for some cross section at a large distance from the ends. We notice that in the expression for ψ, the constants c_5, c_8, and c_9 are not determined by the boundary conditions. Their determination is actually irrelevant to the problem because the stress components do not depend on them.

With the stress components determined, we can now find the displacements in the beam. From the definitions of strain components and Hooke's law, we have

$$\frac{\partial u}{\partial x} = \epsilon_x = \frac{\sigma_x}{E} = -\frac{Pxy}{EI}$$

$$\frac{\partial v}{\partial y} = \epsilon_y = -\frac{\nu\sigma_x}{E} = \frac{\nu Pxy}{EI} \tag{4.16}$$

$$\frac{\partial u}{\partial y} + \frac{\partial v}{\partial x} = \gamma_{xy} = \frac{2(1+\nu)\tau_{xy}}{E} = -\frac{(1+\nu)P}{EI}\left(\frac{d^2}{4} - y^2\right)$$

Integrating the first two equations, we obtain

$$u = -\frac{P}{2EI}x^2y + g_1(y) \qquad v = \frac{\nu P}{2EI}xy^2 + g_2(x)$$

where $g_1(y)$ and $g_2(x)$ are some functions of y and x, respectively. Substituting these expressions into the third equation of (4.16), we find

$$\frac{dg_1}{dy} - \frac{P}{EI}\left(1 + \frac{\nu}{2}\right)y^2 = -\frac{dg_2}{dx} + \frac{P}{2EI}x^2 - \frac{(1+\nu)P}{4EI}d^2$$

We note that the terms on the left of the equal sign are functions of y alone and the terms on the right side are functions of x alone. A function of x can be equal to a function of y for all values of x and y only when they are both equal to a constant, say a_1. Thus

$$\frac{dg_1}{dy} = \frac{P}{EI}\left(1 + \frac{\nu}{2}\right)y^2 + a_1 \qquad \frac{dg_2}{dx} = \frac{P}{2EI}x^2 - \frac{(1+\nu)P}{4EI}d^2 - a_1$$

Integrating, we have

$$g_1(y) = \frac{P}{3EI}\left(1 + \frac{\nu}{2}\right)y^3 + a_1y + a_2$$

$$g_2(x) = \frac{P}{6EI}x^3 - \frac{(1+\nu)P}{4EI}d^2x - a_1x + a_3$$

where a_2 and a_3 are constants of integration. The displacements u and v are therefore

$$u = -\frac{P}{2EI}x^2y + \frac{P}{3EI}\left(1 + \frac{\nu}{2}\right)y^3 + a_1y + a_2$$

$$v = \frac{\nu P}{2EI}xy^2 + \frac{P}{6EI}x^3 - \frac{(1 + \nu)P}{4EI}d^2x - a_1x + a_3$$

Assume that the point $(x = L, y = 0)$ is fixed. The boundary conditions are then $u = v = \partial v/\partial x = 0$ at $x = L, y = 0$. We find by substitution,

$$a_1 = \frac{PL^2}{2EI} - \frac{(1 + \nu)Pd^2}{4EI} \qquad a_2 = 0 \qquad a_3 = \frac{PL^3}{3EI}$$

and

$$u = -\frac{P}{2EI}x^2y + \frac{P}{3EI}\left(1 + \frac{\nu}{2}\right)y^3 + \frac{P}{2EI}\left[L^2 - (1 + \nu)\frac{d^2}{2}\right]y$$

$$v = \frac{\nu P}{2EI}xy^2 + \frac{P}{6EI}x^3 - \frac{PL^2}{2EI}x + \frac{PL^3}{3EI}$$

The equation of the deflection curve is given by the expression of v at $y = 0$; namely,

$$(v)_{y=0} = \frac{Px^3}{6EI} - \frac{PL^2x}{2EI} + \frac{PL^3}{3EI}$$

The curvature of the deflection curve is

$$\frac{1}{R} \cong \left(\frac{d^2v}{dx^2}\right)_{y=0} = \frac{Px}{EI} = \frac{M}{EI}$$

where R is the radius of curvature and $M = Px$ is the bending moment at the section x. This is the well-known Bernoulli-Euler's formula in the elementary theory of bending. Now consider a plane section $x = c$, before the bending, where c is a constant. After the bending, a point (x,y) on the plane $x = c$ is displaced to $x' = c + u$, $y' = y + v$. The equation of the resulting surface is therefore

$$x' = c + \frac{P}{2EI}\left[L^2 - c^2 - (1 + \nu)\frac{d^2}{2}\right](y' - v) + \frac{P}{3EI}\left(1 + \frac{\nu}{2}\right)(y' - v)^3$$

which is substantially a plane surface if c is small compared with L, that is, if the section is far away from the built-in end. Now near the built-in end, the surface is obviously not a plane surface. However, if the beam is under the action of a bending moment only, it can be shown (see Sec. 9.1) that a plane section before bending indeed continues to be a plane after bending.

Problem 1. Let the load acting on the cantilever beam shown in Fig. 4.3 be a uniformly distributed load with an intensity of p instead of the concentrated load. Find the stress function and the stress components. The boundary conditions are that $\sigma_y = -p$ on $y = -d/2$, $\sigma_y = 0$ on $y = d/2$, $\tau_{xy} = 0$ on $y = \pm d/2$, and $\int_{-d/2}^{d/2} \sigma_x \, dy = \int_{-d/2}^{d/2} \sigma_x y \, dy = 0$ at $x = 0$. *Hint:* Take as a trial function

$$\tau_{xy} = -\frac{\partial^2 \psi}{\partial x \, \partial y} = x f(y)$$

Ans. $\psi = -px^2 \left(\dfrac{y^3}{d^3} - \dfrac{3y}{4d} + \dfrac{1}{4} \right) + \dfrac{pd^2}{5} \left(\dfrac{y^5}{d^5} - \dfrac{y^3}{2d^3} \right) + c_1 x + c_2 y + c_3$

Problem 2. If the load acting on the cantilever beam shown in Fig. 4.3 is a distributed load varying linearly with respect to x, we have the case of a vertical cantilever loaded by hydrostatic pressure. Denote the density of the liquid by ρ. Assume that the boundary conditions are $\sigma_y = -\rho x$ on $y = d/2$, $\sigma_y = 0$ on $y = -d/2$, $\tau_{xy} = 0$ on $y = \pm d/2$, $\sigma_x = 0$ at $x = 0$, and $\int_{-d/2}^{d/2} \tau_{xy} \, dy = 0$. Find the stress function and the stress components. *Hint:* Take as a trial function $\sigma_x = \partial^2 \psi / \partial y^2 = x^3 f_1(y) + x f_2(y)$.

Ans. $\psi = \dfrac{\rho x^3}{12d^3} (4y^3 - 3d^2 y - d^3) - \dfrac{\rho x y}{80d^3} (16y^4 - 8d^2 y^2 + d^4) + c_1 x + c_2 y + c_3$

Problem 3. A triangular plate, with narrow rectangular cross section and uniform thickness, is under the action of a uniformly distributed load p along its top edge as shown in Fig. 4.4. Verify that the stress function

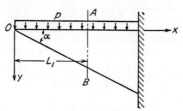

Fig. 4.4.

$$\psi = \frac{p \cot \alpha}{2(1 - \alpha \cot \alpha)} \left[-x^2 \tan \alpha + xy + (x^2 + y^2) \left(\alpha - \arctan \frac{y}{x} \right) \right]$$

satisfies the governing differential equation and the boundary conditions. For the particular case of $\alpha = 30°$, examine how the normal stress is distributed over the cross section AB and how it compares with the stress determined by the simple bending formula $\sigma_x = Mc/I$.

4.3. General Equations in Cylindrical Coordinates.

In discussing problems with circular boundaries, it is more convenient to use the *cylindrical coordinates* r, θ, z. In the case of plane-stress or plane-strain problems, we have $\tau_{rz} = \tau_{\theta z} = 0$ and the other stress components as functions of r and θ only. Hence the cylindrical coordinates reduce to the polar coordinates in this case. Consider the equilibrium of a small element $ABCD$ as shown in Fig. 4.5a. The radial components of the forces due to $\sigma_r + (\partial \sigma_r / \partial r) \, dr$ and σ_r are

$$\left(\sigma_r + \frac{\partial \sigma_r}{\partial r}\, dr\right)(r + dr)\, d\theta - \sigma_r r\, d\theta$$

The radial components of the forces due to $\sigma_\theta + (\partial \sigma_\theta / \partial \theta)\, d\theta$, σ_θ, $\tau_{r\theta} + (\partial \tau_{r\theta} / \partial \theta)\, d\theta$, and $\tau_{r\theta}$ can be seen from Fig. 4.5b as

$$-\left(\sigma_\theta + \frac{\partial \sigma_\theta}{\partial \theta}\, d\theta\right) dr \sin \frac{d\theta}{2} - \sigma_\theta\, dr \sin \frac{d\theta}{2} + \left(\tau_{r\theta} + \frac{\partial \tau_{r\theta}}{\partial \theta}\, d\theta\right) dr \cos \frac{d\theta}{2}$$

$$- \tau_{r\theta}\, dr \cos \frac{d\theta}{2}$$

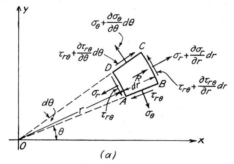

(a)

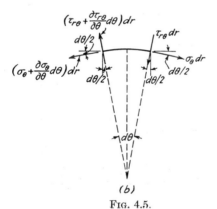

(b)

Fɪɢ. 4.5.

Since $d\theta$ is small, the above expression becomes

$$-\left(\sigma_\theta + \frac{\partial \sigma_\theta}{\partial \theta}\, d\theta\right) dr \frac{d\theta}{2} - \sigma_\theta\, dr \frac{d\theta}{2} + \left(\tau_{r\theta} + \frac{\partial \tau_{r\theta}}{\partial \theta}\, d\theta\right) dr - \tau_{r\theta}\, dr$$

Let F_r, F_θ be the components of the body force per unit volume in the radial and tangential directions, respectively. Summing up the above radial components of the forces, neglecting small quantities of higher order, and dividing through by the elementary area $r\, dr\, d\theta$, we obtain the equation of equilibrium in the radial direction as follows:

$$\frac{\partial \sigma_r}{\partial r} + \frac{1}{r} \frac{\partial \tau_{r\theta}}{\partial \theta} + \frac{\sigma_r - \sigma_\theta}{r} + F_r = 0$$

The equation of equilibrium in the tangential direction can be obtained in a similar manner. Corresponding to Eqs. (4.1), the equilibrium equations for plane problems in cylindrical coordinates are

$$\frac{\partial \sigma_r}{\partial r} + \frac{1}{r}\frac{\partial \tau_{r\theta}}{\partial \theta} + \frac{\sigma_r - \sigma_\theta}{r} + F_r = 0$$

$$\frac{1}{r}\frac{\partial \sigma_\theta}{\partial \theta} + \frac{\partial \tau_{r\theta}}{\partial r} + \frac{2\tau_{r\theta}}{r} + F_\theta = 0$$

(4.17)

If the body forces are neglected, we observe that Eqs. (4.17) will be identically satisfied with the introduction of the stress function ψ defined by

$$\sigma_r = \frac{1}{r}\frac{\partial \psi}{\partial r} + \frac{1}{r^2}\frac{\partial^2 \psi}{\partial \theta^2}$$

$$\sigma_\theta = \frac{\partial^2 \psi}{\partial r^2}$$

(4.18)

$$\tau_{r\theta} = \frac{1}{r^2}\frac{\partial \psi}{\partial \theta} - \frac{1}{r}\frac{\partial^2 \psi}{\partial r\, \partial \theta} = -\frac{\partial}{\partial r}\left(\frac{1}{r}\frac{\partial \psi}{\partial \theta}\right)$$

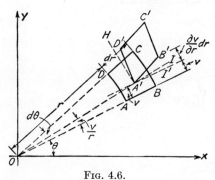

FIG. 4.6.

Now let us derive the compatibility equation for plane problems in cylindrical coordinates. Referring to Fig. 4.6, let $A'B'C'D'$ be the position of the element $ABCD$ after strain. Let u, v be the displacements of the point A, in the radial and tangential directions, respectively. Then the displacements of B are $u + (\partial u/\partial r)\, dr$ and $v + (\partial v/\partial r)\, dr$, and the square of the length $A'B'$ is

$$(A'B')^2 = \left(dr + \frac{\partial u}{\partial r}\, dr\right)^2 + \left(\frac{\partial v}{\partial r}\, dr\right)^2$$

By definition,

$$A'B' = (1 + \epsilon_r)AB = (1 + \epsilon_r)\, dr$$

By neglecting higher-order terms, we find

$$\epsilon_r = \frac{\partial u}{\partial r}$$

The longitudinal-strain component in the tangential direction depends on both u and v. Before strain, $AD = r\, d\theta$. After strain, owing to the displacement u, the length of AD becomes $(r + u)\, d\theta$. At the same time the point A' has undergone a tangential displacement v and the point D' a tangential displacement $v + (\partial v/r\, d\theta)\, r\, d\theta$. Hence

$$(A'D')^2 = [(1 + \epsilon_\theta)r \, d\theta]^2 = \left[(r + u) \, d\theta + \frac{\partial v}{r \, d\theta} r \, d\theta \right]^2 + \left(\frac{\partial u}{r \, d\theta} r \, d\theta \right)^2$$

Neglecting high-order terms, we obtain

$$\epsilon_\theta = \frac{u}{r} + \frac{1}{r} \frac{\partial v}{\partial \theta}$$

Let us now consider the shearing strain. The angle between the directions AB and $A'B'$, or angle $B'A'I'$, is $\partial v/\partial r$, and the angle between AD and $A'D'$, or angle $D'A'H = \partial u/r \, \partial \theta$. The change in the angle DAB, or the shearing strain $\gamma_{r\theta}$, is therefore

$$\gamma_{r\theta} = \angle D'A'H + \angle B'A'I = \angle D'A'H + \angle B'A'I' - \angle IA'I'$$

$$= \frac{\partial u}{r \, \partial \theta} + \frac{\partial v}{\partial r} - \frac{v}{r}$$

Collecting our results, we have

$$\epsilon_r = \frac{\partial u}{\partial r} \qquad \epsilon_\theta = \frac{u}{r} + \frac{1}{r} \frac{\partial v}{\partial \theta} \qquad \gamma_{r\theta} = \frac{1}{r} \frac{\partial u}{\partial \theta} + \frac{\partial v}{\partial r} - \frac{v}{r} \qquad (4.19)$$

Eliminating u and v from (4.19), it is easy to verify that the compatibility equation now becomes

$$\frac{\partial^2 \epsilon_\theta}{\partial r^2} + \frac{\partial^2 \epsilon_r}{r^2 \, \partial \theta^2} + \frac{2}{r} \frac{\partial \epsilon_\theta}{\partial r} - \frac{1}{r} \frac{\partial \epsilon_r}{\partial r} = \frac{\partial^2 \gamma_{r\theta}}{r \, \partial r \, \partial \theta} + \frac{1}{r^2} \frac{\partial \gamma_{r\theta}}{\partial \theta} \qquad (4.20)$$

Let us now consider the case of plane stress. The stress-strain relations in polar coordinates can be found by substituting the subscript r for x and θ for y in Eq. (4.12), which gives

$$\epsilon_r = \frac{1}{E} (\sigma_r - \nu\sigma_\theta)$$

$$\epsilon_\theta = \frac{1}{E} (\sigma_\theta - \nu\sigma_r) \qquad (4.21)$$

$$\gamma_{r\theta} = \frac{1}{G} \tau_{r\theta} = \frac{2(1 + \nu)}{E} \tau_{r\theta}$$

Substitution of these relations into (4.20) gives

$$\frac{\partial^2}{\partial r^2} (\sigma_r - \nu\sigma_\theta) + \frac{\partial^2}{r^2 \, \partial \theta^2} (\sigma_\theta - \nu\sigma_r) + \frac{2}{r} \frac{\partial}{\partial r} (\sigma_\theta - \nu\sigma_r) - \frac{1}{r} \frac{\partial}{\partial r} (\sigma_r - \nu\sigma_\theta)$$

$$= 2(1 + \nu) \frac{\partial^2 \tau_{r\theta}}{r \, \partial r \, \partial \theta} + 2(1 + \nu) \frac{1}{r^2} \frac{\partial \tau_{r\theta}}{d\theta} \qquad (4.22)$$

where the factor $1/E$ has been canceled. In terms of the stress function ψ as defined by (4.18), the compatibility equation becomes

$$\left(\frac{\partial^2}{\partial r^2} + \frac{1}{r} \frac{\partial}{\partial r} + \frac{1}{r^2} \frac{\partial^2}{\partial \theta^2} \right) \left(\frac{\partial^2 \psi}{\partial r^2} + \frac{1}{r} \frac{\partial \psi}{\partial r} + \frac{1}{r^2} \frac{\partial^2 \psi}{\partial \theta^2} \right) = 0 \qquad (4.23)$$

Equation (4.23) is the governing differential equation for the stress function ψ. Since $\dfrac{\partial^2}{\partial r^2} + \dfrac{1}{r}\dfrac{\partial}{\partial r} + \dfrac{1}{r^2}\dfrac{\partial^2}{\partial \theta^2}$ represents the Laplace operator ∇^2 in polar coordinates, Eq. (4.23) is merely Eq. (4.8) in polar coordinates. It is therefore also the governing equation for plane-strain and generalized plane-strain problems.

Problem 1. Show that the stress function ψ as defined by (4.18) is actually the *same* ψ as defined by (4.4).

Problem 2. The relation between polar and cartesian coordinates is given by

$$r^2 = x^2 + y^2 \qquad \theta = \arctan \frac{y}{x}$$

Prove that
$$\frac{\partial^2 \psi}{\partial x^2} + \frac{\partial^2 \psi}{\partial y^2} = \frac{\partial^2 \psi}{\partial r^2} + \frac{1}{r}\frac{\partial^2 \psi}{\partial r} + \frac{1}{r^2}\frac{\partial^2 \psi}{\partial \theta^2}$$

and therefore $\left(\dfrac{\partial^2}{\partial r^2} + \dfrac{1}{r}\dfrac{\partial}{\partial r} + \dfrac{1}{r^2}\dfrac{\partial^2}{\partial \theta^2}\right)\left(\dfrac{\partial^2 \psi}{\partial r^2} + \dfrac{1}{r}\dfrac{\partial \psi}{\partial r} + \dfrac{1}{r^2}\dfrac{\partial^2 \psi}{\partial \theta^2}\right) = 0$ is the biharmonic equation $\dfrac{\partial^4 \psi}{\partial x^4} + 2\dfrac{\partial^4 \psi}{\partial x^2 \partial y^2} + \dfrac{\partial^4 \psi}{\partial y^4} = 0$ in polar coordinates.

4.4. Thick Cylinder under Uniform Pressure. Shrink and Force Fits.

Let us consider a thick cylinder submitted to uniform pressure on the inner and outer surfaces (Fig. 4.7). Let a and b be the inner and outer radii of the cylinder and p_i and p_o be the internal and external pressures, respectively. Then the boundary conditions are

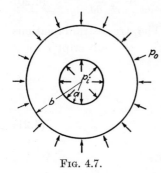

FIG. 4.7.

$$\sigma_r = -p_i \qquad \text{at } r = a$$
$$\sigma_r = -p_o \qquad \text{at } r = b \tag{4.24}$$

From the boundary conditions, we see that the stress distribution in this case will be symmetrical with respect to the axis through the center of the cylinder perpendicular to the xy plane. Thus the stress function ψ does not depend on θ and is a function of r only. The compatibility equation (4.23) then becomes

$$\left(\frac{d^2}{dr^2} + \frac{1}{r}\frac{d}{dr}\right)\left(\frac{d^2\psi}{dr^2} + \frac{1}{r}\frac{d\psi}{dr}\right) = 0$$

or

$$\frac{d^4\psi}{dr^4} + \frac{2}{r}\frac{d^3\psi}{dr^3} - \frac{1}{r^2}\frac{d^2\psi}{dr^2} + \frac{1}{r^3}\frac{d\psi}{dr} = 0 \tag{4.25}$$

Equation (4.25) is a *homogeneous linear differential* equation which can be solved by introducing a new variable ξ such that $\xi = \log r$ where "log" denotes natural logarithm. Then

$$\frac{d\psi}{dr} = \frac{d\psi}{d\xi}\frac{d\xi}{dr} = \frac{1}{r}\frac{d\psi}{d\xi}$$

$$\frac{d^2\psi}{dr^2} = \frac{d}{dr}\left(\frac{d\psi}{dr}\right) = \frac{1}{r^2}\left(\frac{d^2\psi}{d\xi^2} - \frac{d\psi}{d\xi}\right)$$

$$\frac{d^3\psi}{dr^3} = \frac{1}{r^3}\left(\frac{d^3\psi}{d\xi^3} - 3\frac{d^2\psi}{d\xi^2} + 2\frac{d\psi}{d\xi}\right)$$

$$\frac{d^4\psi}{dr^4} = \frac{1}{r^4}\left(\frac{d^4\psi}{d\xi^4} - 6\frac{d^3\psi}{d\xi^3} + 11\frac{d^2\psi}{d\xi^2} - 6\frac{d\psi}{d\xi}\right)$$

Substituting, Eq. (4.25) becomes

$$\frac{d^4\psi}{d\xi^4} - 4\frac{d^3\psi}{d\xi^3} + 4\frac{d^2\psi}{d\xi^2} = 0$$

which is an ordinary differential equation with constant coefficients of which the solution is well known. The general solution is

$$\psi = c_1\xi e^{2\xi} + c_2 e^{2\xi} + c_3\xi + c_4$$

or
$$\psi = c_1 r^2 \log r + c_2 r^2 + c_3 \log r + c_4 \qquad (4.26)$$

where c_1, c_2, c_3, and c_4 are constants of integration. From (4.26), the stress components are

$$\sigma_r = \frac{1}{r}\frac{d\psi}{dr} = c_1(1 + 2\log r) + 2c_2 + \frac{c_3}{r^2}$$

$$\sigma_\theta = \frac{d^2\psi}{dr^2} = c_1(3 + 2\log r) + 2c_2 - \frac{c_3}{r^2}$$

$$\tau_{r\theta} = 0$$

In the above expressions for the stresses, we have three constants of integration, while there are only two boundary conditions. To determine these constants uniquely, let us examine the displacements. Now, in the case of axial symmetry, the expressions for the strain components are

$$\epsilon_r = \frac{du}{dr} \qquad \epsilon_\theta = \frac{u}{r} \qquad \gamma_{r\theta} = \frac{dv}{dr} - \frac{v}{r}$$

If the ends of the cylinder are free to expand, we shall prove later that $\sigma_z = 0$ and the stress-strain relations given by (4.21) should be used. Hence

$$\frac{du}{dr} = \frac{1}{E}(\sigma_r - \nu\sigma_\theta) \qquad \text{and} \qquad \frac{u}{r} = \frac{1}{E}(\sigma_\theta - \nu\sigma_r)$$

From the first equation we find by integration

$$Eu = c_1[r(1 - 3\nu) + 2(1 - \nu)(r\log r - r)]$$

$$+ 2c_2(1 - \nu)r - c_3(1 + \nu)\frac{1}{r} + c_5$$

where c_5 is a constant of integration.   From the second equation we have

$$Eu = c_1[r(3 - \nu) + 2r(1 - \nu) \log r] + 2c_2(1 - \nu)r - c_3(1 + \nu)\frac{1}{r}$$

In order that these two expressions for u be the same, we must have

$$c_1 = 0\dagger \qquad \text{and} \qquad c_5 = 0$$

and
$$Eu = 2c_2(1 - \nu)r - c_3(1 + \nu)\frac{1}{r} \tag{4.27}$$

It may be pointed out that for such a problem with rotational symmetry, instead of solving Eq. (4.25), we may proceed directly from the equilibrium equation (4.17) and define the stress function in a different manner as is carried out in Sec. 4.6.   Then by solving a compatibility equation for the rotational symmetrical case we shall obtain expressions for the stresses where c_1 is automatically zero.

The boundary conditions (4.24) now become

$$2c_2 + \frac{c_3}{a^2} = -p_i \qquad 2c_2 - \frac{c_3}{b^2} = -p_o$$

Solving, we have

$$2c_2 = \frac{p_i a^2 - p_o b^2}{b^2 - a^2} \qquad c_3 = \frac{a^2 b^2 (p_o - p_i)}{b^2 - a^2} \tag{4.28}$$

The stress components are therefore

$$\sigma_r = \frac{a^2 b^2 (p_o - p_i)}{b^2 - a^2}\frac{1}{r^2} + \frac{p_i a^2 - p_o b^2}{b^2 - a^2}$$

$$\sigma_\theta = - \frac{a^2 b^2 (p_o - p_i)}{b^2 - a^2}\frac{1}{r^2} + \frac{p_i a^2 - p_o b^2}{b^2 - a^2} \tag{4.29}$$

We see from (4.29) that the sum $\sigma_r + \sigma_\theta$ is independent of r and is constant through the thickness of the wall of the cylinder.   If the ends of the cylinder are free to expand, then

$$\epsilon_z = \text{constant}$$

and from the stress-strain relations we find

$$\sigma_z = \nu(\sigma_r + \sigma_\theta) + E\epsilon_z = C$$

where C is a constant to be determined from the condition that the resultant forces are zero on the ends, *viz.*

$$\int_a^b \sigma_z 2\pi r \, dr = \pi C(b^2 - a^2) = 0$$

From which we find

$$C = \sigma_z = 0$$

† If the stress-strain relations for plane strain or generalized plane strain are used instead of those for plane stress, we will arrive at the same conclusion that c_1 must be zero.

Consequently, in finding the strain components, the stress-strain relations for plane stress should be used.

Equations (4.24) and (4.26) can be used to study the stresses in the case of *shrink* or *force fits*. There are many practical cases where it is desirable to force or shrink an external member on a shaft or wheel. The inner diameter of the external member is usually made slightly less than the external diameter of the shaft or wheel. If the external cylinder is expanded by heating, slipped over the shaft or wheel, and then allowed to cool, we obtain a *shrink fit*. Steel tires for locomotives are shrunk onto the wheels. *Force fits* are obtained by pressing the hub onto the shaft. In either case, once the two parts are fitted together, they exert on one another a pressure sufficient to prevent any relative movement, and it is often required to find the pressure which will be entailed by a given difference in diameter, or *interference*.

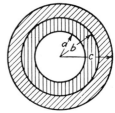

Fig. 4.8.

Suppose that two cylinders are engaged by shrink fit or force fit so that, after assembly, the inner cylinder has radii a and b and the outer cylinder has radii b and c (Fig. 4.8). When $a = 0$, this gives us the case of a cylinder shrunk on a solid shaft.

Now let p be the radial pressure between the two cylinders. If these cylinders were disengaged, the inner cylinder would evidently expand and the external cylinder would contract. By the principle of superposition, the removal of the pressure p is equivalent to the imposition of a negative p on the outer surface of the inner cylinder and on the inner surface of the outer cylinder. Thus, if we let $p_i = 0$, $p_o = -p$, and $r = b$ in (4.27) and (4.28), we obtain the increase in the external radius of the inner cylinder, which is

$$u_1 = \frac{bp}{E_1(b^2 - a^2)}\left[(1 + \nu_1)a^2 + (1 - \nu_1)b^2\right]$$

where E_1, ν_1 pertain to the material of the inner cylinder. Similarly, the radial displacement of the inner surface of the outer cylinder can be found by substituting $p_i = -p$, $p_o = 0$, $r = c$ and changing the symbols a and b in (4.28) to b and c, respectively. Hence

$$u_2 = -\frac{bp}{E_2(c^2 - b^2)}\left[(1 + \nu_2)c^2 + (1 - \nu_2)b^2\right]$$

where E_2, ν_2 pertain to the material of the outer cylinder.

The inner cylinder, after disengagement, will therefore have an external radius $b + u_1$, while the outer cylinder will have an internal radius $b + u_2$. The difference in diameter, corresponding to a radial pressure p, after disengagement is given by

$$\delta = 2(u_1 - u_2)$$

$$= 2bp \left[\frac{(1 + \nu_1)a^2 + (1 - \nu_1)b^2}{E_1(b^2 - a^2)} + \frac{(1 + \nu_2)c^2 + (1 - \nu_2)b^2}{E_2(c^2 - b^2)} \right]$$

When both cylinders are made of the same material, we have

$$\delta = \frac{4b^3(c^2 - a^2)}{(b^2 - a^2)(c^2 - b^2)} \frac{p}{E}$$

For a cylinder shrunk on a solid shaft, $a = 0$, and the above formula reduces to

$$\delta = \frac{4bc^2}{c^2 - b^2} \frac{p}{E}$$

If the magnitude of σ_r or σ_θ in the cylinders after engagement is specified, the value of p can be determined from (4.29) and then δ from the above formulas. The application of the formulas to the design of big guns has been discussed in detail by Southwell.[1]

Problem 1. A cylinder, 4 in. internal diameter and 1 in. thick, has an external sleeve 1 in. thick shrunk on it. The shrinkage is such that, when the internal fluid pressure is applied, the maximum *shear* stress both in the tube and sleeve is 16,000 psi. Calculate the fluid pressure, and determine the pressure between the sleeve and cylinder when the fluid pressure is absent.

Ans. 15,880 psi; 2,880 psi

Problem 2. A tube whose external and internal diameters are 18 in. and 12 in., respectively, has another tube 3 in. thick shrunk onto it. The internal diameter of this outer tube is machined to be 0.05 in. less than the external diameter of the inner tube. If the tubes are made of steel with $E = 30 \times 10^6$ psi, determine the expressions for the stresses developed in the inner tube.

4.5. The Effect of Small Circular Holes in Strained Plates. Stress Concentration. Consider a flat plate subjected to a certain stress distribution. If we drill a circular hole through it at some point, a redistribution of stress will result, involving large additional stress in the immediate neighborhood of the hole. The high *stress concentration* at the edge of a circular hole is of much practical importance, for example, in the problem of flaws in otherwise continuous material and holes in ship's decks and airplane fuselages.

If the hole is small, its effect will be negligible at a distance of a few diameters from its edge. Thus points at such distances may be regarded as at infinity. We shall first solve the problem of a small hole in an infinite plate, and from that result the error in regarding a finite plate as infinite can be ascertained.

[1] R. V. Southwell, "Theory of Elasticity," 2d ed., pp. 408–423, Oxford University Press, London and New York, 1941.

Let us assume that the plate is subjected to a uniform tensile stress S in the x direction.   We shall take the origin of coordinates at the center

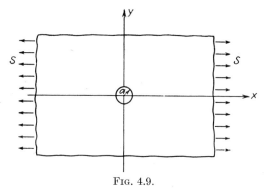

FIG. 4.9.

hole.   In the absence of any hole, we have obviously

$$\sigma_x = S \qquad \sigma_y = \tau_{xy} = 0$$

which may be derived from the stress function

$$\psi_1 = \tfrac{1}{2} S y^2$$

Note that ψ_1 satisfies the biharmonic equation and is therefore the exact solution.   In terms of cylindrical coordinates, since $y = r \sin \theta$, we have

$$\psi_1 = \tfrac{1}{2} S r^2 \sin^2 \theta = \tfrac{1}{4} S r^2 (1 - \cos 2\theta)$$

from which it follows

$$\sigma_{r_1} = \frac{1}{r} \frac{\partial \psi_1}{\partial r} + \frac{1}{r^2} \frac{\partial^2 \psi_1}{\partial \theta^2} = \frac{1}{2} S(1 + \cos 2\theta)$$

$$\sigma_{\theta_1} = \frac{\partial^2 \psi_1}{\partial r^2} = \frac{1}{2} S(1 - \cos 2\theta) \qquad (4.30)$$

$$\tau_{r\theta_1} = - \frac{\partial}{\partial r} \left(\frac{1}{r} \frac{\partial \psi_1}{\partial \theta} \right) = - \frac{1}{2} S \sin 2\theta$$

When a hole of radius a is drilled through the plate, the boundary conditions become

$$\sigma_r = \tau_{r\theta} = 0 \qquad \text{at } r = a$$

and $\sigma_r = \sigma_{r_1}$, $\sigma_\theta = \sigma_{\theta_1}$, $\tau_{r\theta} = \tau_{r\theta_1}$ at $r = \infty$.   Guided by the expression of ψ_1, we shall assume a trial stress function of the form

$$\psi = f_1(r) + f_2(r) \cos 2\theta$$

where $f_1(r)$ and $f_2(r)$ are unknown functions of r.   Substituting into the biharmonic equation

$$\left(\frac{\partial^2}{\partial r^2} + \frac{1}{r} \frac{\partial}{\partial r} + \frac{1}{r^2} \frac{\partial^2}{\partial \theta^2} \right) \left(\frac{\partial^2 \psi}{\partial r^2} + \frac{1}{r} \frac{\partial \psi}{\partial r} + \frac{1}{r^2} \frac{\partial^2 \psi}{\partial \theta^2} \right) = 0$$

and noting that the resulting equation must be satisfied for all values of θ, we find that $f_1(r)$ and $f_2(r)$ must satisfy the following ordinary differential equations:

$$\left(\frac{d^2}{dr^2} + \frac{1}{r}\frac{d}{dr}\right)\left(\frac{d^2f_1}{dr^2} + \frac{1}{r}\frac{df_1}{dr}\right) = 0 \qquad (4.31)$$

$$\left(\frac{d^2}{dr^2} + \frac{1}{r}\frac{d}{dr} - \frac{4}{r^2}\right)\left(\frac{d^2f_2}{dr^2} + \frac{1}{r}\frac{df_2}{dr} - \frac{4f_2}{r^2}\right) = 0 \qquad (4.32)$$

The general solution of Eq. (4.31) has been found in the previous section as

$$f_1(r) = c_1 r^2 \log r + c_2 r^2 + c_3 \log r + c_4$$

Equation (4.32) can again be reduced to a differential equation with constant coefficients by introducing the new variable ξ such that $\xi = \log r$ as in the solution of Eq. (4.25). By such a transformation, we find that the general solution of (4.32) is

$$f_2(r) = c_5 r^2 + c_6 r^4 + \frac{c_7}{r^2} + c_8$$

The stress function is therefore

$$\psi = (c_1 r^2 \log r + c_2 r^2 + c_3 \log r + c_4) + \left(c_5 r^2 + c_6 r^4 + \frac{c_7}{r^2} + c_8\right)\cos 2\theta$$

where $c_1, c_2, \ldots, c_8$ are constants of integration. The corresponding stress components are

$$\sigma_r = c_1(1 + 2\log r) + 2c_2 + \frac{c_3}{r^2} - \left(2c_5 + \frac{6c_7}{r^4} + \frac{4c_8}{r^2}\right)\cos 2\theta$$

$$\sigma_\theta = c_1(3 + 2\log r) + 2c_2 - \frac{c_3}{r^2} + \left(2c_5 + 12c_6 r^2 + \frac{6c_7}{r^4}\right)\cos 2\theta$$

$$\tau_{r\theta} = \left(2c_5 + 6c_6 r^2 - \frac{6c_7}{r^4} - \frac{2c_8}{r^2}\right)\sin 2\theta$$

At $r = a$, the boundary condition requires that $\sigma_r = \tau_{r\theta} = 0$ for all values of θ; and at $r = \infty$, $\sigma_r = \sigma_{r_1}$, $\sigma_\theta = \sigma_{\theta_1}$, $\tau_{r\theta} = \tau_{r\theta_1}$. From the condition that σ_r, σ_θ, and $\tau_{r\theta}$ must remain finite for infinite r, we have

$$c_1 = c_6 = 0$$

From the other boundary conditions, we find

$$2c_2 + \frac{c_3}{a^2} = 0 \qquad 2c_5 + \frac{6c_7}{a^4} + \frac{4c_8}{a^2} = 0 \qquad 2c_5 - \frac{6c_7}{a^4} - \frac{2c_8}{a^2} = 0$$

$$2c_5 = -\frac{S}{2} \qquad 2c_2 = \frac{S}{2}$$

The solutions of these equations are

$$c_2 = \frac{S}{4} \qquad c_3 = -\frac{a^2}{2} S \qquad c_5 = -\frac{S}{4} \qquad c_7 = -\frac{a^4}{4} S \qquad c_8 = \frac{a^2}{2} S$$

The stress components are therefore

$$\sigma_r = \frac{S}{2}\left(1 - \frac{a^2}{r^2}\right) + \frac{S}{2}\left(1 + \frac{3a^4}{r^4} - \frac{4a^2}{r^2}\right)\cos 2\theta$$

$$\sigma_\theta = \frac{S}{2}\left(1 + \frac{a^2}{r^2}\right) - \frac{S}{2}\left(1 + \frac{3a^4}{r^4}\right)\cos 2\theta \qquad (4.33)$$

$$\tau_{r\theta} = -\frac{S}{2}\left(1 - \frac{3a^4}{r^4} + \frac{2a^2}{r^2}\right)\sin 2\theta$$

From the above formulas, it is evident that maximum σ_θ occurs at the ends of the diameter of the hole perpendicular to the direction of the tension. Substituting $r = a$ and $\theta = \pi/2$ or $3\pi/2$ into the expression for σ_θ, we find that the maximum value of σ_θ is $3S$. Thus for a flat plate containing a small hole under the action of uniform tensile stress S at the edge, the maximum tensile stress becomes three times the value of the uniform stress.

Now let us examine the error involved in assuming an infinite plate. On the cross section of the plate through the center of the hole and perpendicular to the x axis, we have $\theta = \pi/2$ and, from (4.33),

$$\sigma_\theta = \frac{S}{2}\left(2 + \frac{a^2}{r^2} + \frac{3a^4}{r^4}\right) \qquad \tau_{r\theta} = 0$$

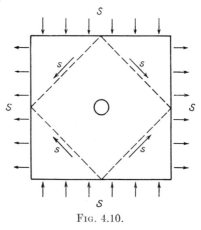

Fig. 4.10.

We see that as r increases, σ_θ rapidly approaches the value of S. At a distance of $10a$ from the center of the hole, the terms containing r in the value of σ_θ, which are the stresses due to the hole, have only about $\frac{1}{200}$ of their value at the edge of the hole. Hence, we are justified in regarding a distance of five diameters from the center of a hole as practically an infinite distance away.

Now let us consider the problem of a small circular hole in a flat plate under uniform shearing stress S. From our previous study on combined stresses, we note that by imposing a uniform tensile stress S in the x direction and a uniform compressive stress S in the y direction, we obtain a uniform shearing stress S on the diagonal planes, Fig. 4.10. Now, owing to a uniform compression in the y direction, we have

$$\sigma_r = -\frac{S}{2}\left(1 - \frac{a^2}{r^2}\right) - \frac{S}{2}\left(1 + \frac{3a^4}{r^4} - \frac{4a^2}{r^2}\right)\cos 2\left(\theta - \frac{\pi}{2}\right)$$

$$\sigma_\theta = -\frac{S}{2}\left(1 + \frac{a^2}{r^2}\right) + \frac{S}{2}\left(1 + \frac{3a^4}{r^4}\right)\cos 2\left(\theta - \frac{\pi}{2}\right)$$

$$\tau_{r\theta} = \frac{S}{2}\left(1 - \frac{3a^4}{r^4} + \frac{2a^2}{r^2}\right)\sin 2\left(\theta - \frac{\pi}{2}\right)$$

Superposing this stress system on that given by (4.33), we find

$$\sigma_r = S\left(1 + \frac{3a^4}{r^4} - \frac{4a^2}{r^2}\right)\cos 2\theta$$

$$\sigma_\theta = -S\left(1 + \frac{3a^4}{r^4}\right)\cos 2\theta \tag{4.34}$$

$$\tau_{r\theta} = -S\left(1 - \frac{3a^4}{r^4} + \frac{2a^2}{r^2}\right)\sin 2\theta$$

It is easy to see that at $r = \infty$, $\theta = \pi/4$, $\sigma_r = \sigma_\theta = 0$, and $\tau_{r\theta} = -S$. The maximum magnitude of σ_θ is $4S$ and occurs at the points $r = a$ and $\theta = 0$, $\pi/2$, π, $3\pi/2$. Hence, for a large plate under pure shear, the maximum tangential stress in the plate is four times the value of the applied shear.

The stresses in an infinite plate with an elliptical hole were first discussed by Inglis[1] and among others by Muschelisvili.[2] The solution of Muschelisvili will be discussed in Sec. 8.11. If one of the principal axes of the elliptical hole coincides with the direction of the tension S, the stresses at the ends of the axis of the hole perpendicular to the direction of the tension are

$$\sigma = S\left(1 + 2\frac{a}{b}\right) \tag{4.35}$$

where $2a$ is the axis of ellipse perpendicular to the tension and $2b$ is the other axis. When $a = b$, $\sigma = 3S$, which is the maximum stress when the hole is circular. If the ratio a/b is very large, the maximum stress at the edge of the hole becomes very large and there is a high stress concentration. This explains why cracks perpendicular to the directions of the applied forces tend to spread. To stop the spreading of the cracks, we may drill holes at their ends to reduce the high stress concentration.

Problem 1. A plate is under uniform tension at infinity, that is, $\sigma_x = \sigma_y = S$ at $r = \infty$. Find the stress distribution in the plate and the maximum stress due to the

---

[1] C. E. Inglis, Stresses in a Plate Due to the Presence of Cracks and Sharp Corners, *Trans. Inst. Naval Arch. (London)*, 1913.

[2] N. Muschelisvili, *Bull. acad. sci. Russ.*, Vol. xiii, p. 663, 1919.

presence of a small circular hole by using formulas (4.33) and the method of super-position.

Ans. $\sigma_r = S\left(1 - \dfrac{a^2}{r^2}\right),\ \sigma_\theta = S\left(1 + \dfrac{a^2}{r^2}\right),\ \tau_{\theta r} = 0,\ \sigma_{\max} = 2S$

Problem 2. Show that the solution of the above problem can also be obtained from formulas (4.29).

Hint: First show that the condition $\sigma_x = \sigma_y = S$ is equivalent to $\sigma_r = -p_o = S$. Then let $b = \infty$ and $p_i = 0$.

4.6. Stresses in Rotating Disks and Cylinders. The stress produced in a disk rotating at high speed is important in many practical instances, among which is the design of disk wheels in steam and gas turbines. The stresses due to tangential forces being transmitted are usually small in these cases, and the large stresses are due to the centrifugal forces of the rotating disk. Let us first consider the case of a thin disk with constant thickness. The body force is now the centrifugal force, which is

$$F_r = \rho\omega^2 r$$

where ρ is the mass density of the material of the disk and ω is the angular velocity. It is evident that the stress distribution in the disk must be symmetrical with respect to the axis of rotation. The equilibrium equation is therefore

$$\frac{d\sigma_r}{dr} + \frac{\sigma_r - \sigma_\theta}{r} + \rho\omega^2 r = 0$$

or

$$\frac{d}{dr}(r\sigma_r) - \sigma_\theta + \rho\omega^2 r^2 = 0 \tag{4.36}$$

It is easy to verify that the above equation is satisfied if we introduce a stress function ψ such that

$$r\sigma_r = \psi \qquad \sigma_\theta = \frac{d\psi}{dr} + \rho\omega^2 r^2 \tag{4.37}$$

In the case of rotational symmetry, u is a function of r only, and $v = 0$ From (4.19), we have

$$\epsilon_r = \frac{du}{dr} \qquad \epsilon_\theta = \frac{u}{r} \tag{4.38}$$

Eliminating u, we obtain a simplified compatibility equation for the case of rotational symmetry as

$$\frac{d}{dr}(r\epsilon_\theta) - \epsilon_r = 0$$

or

$$r\frac{d\epsilon_\theta}{dr} + \epsilon_\theta - \epsilon_r = 0 \tag{4.39}$$

Using Hooke's law (4.21) and the stress function ψ, we find that the above equation becomes

$$\frac{d^2\psi}{dr^2} + \frac{1}{r}\frac{d\psi}{dr} - \frac{\psi}{r^2} + (3 + \nu)\rho\omega^2 r = 0 \tag{4.40}$$

Or writing this in a different form,

$$\frac{d}{dr}\left[\frac{1}{r}\frac{d}{dr}(r\psi)\right] = -(3+\nu)\rho\omega^2 r$$

We observe that this differential equation can be solved by direct integration, which gives

$$\psi = -\frac{3+\nu}{8}\rho\omega^2 r^3 + c_1\frac{r}{2} + c_2\frac{1}{r}$$

where c_1 and c_2 are constants of integration. The corresponding stress components are

$$\sigma_r = \frac{\psi}{r} = -\frac{3+\nu}{8}\rho\omega^2 r^2 + \frac{c_1}{2} + \frac{c_2}{r^2}$$

$$\sigma_\theta = \frac{d\psi}{dr} + \rho\omega^2 r^2 = -\frac{1+3\nu}{8}\rho\omega^2 r^2 + \frac{c_1}{2} - \frac{c_2}{r^2}$$

For a solid disk of radius b with no external forces applied at the boundary, we have $\sigma_r = 0$ at $r = b$. Since these stresses cannot be infinite in the disk, $c_2 = 0$ and the boundary condition requires

$$-\frac{3+\nu}{8}\rho\omega^2 b^2 + \frac{c_1}{2} = 0$$

or

$$c_1 = \frac{3+\nu}{4}\rho\omega^2 b^2$$

The stress components are

$$\sigma_r = \frac{3+\nu}{8}\rho\omega^2(b^2 - r^2) \qquad \sigma_\theta = \frac{1}{8}\rho\omega^2[(3+\nu)b^2 - (1+3\nu)r^2] \qquad (4.41)$$

The maximum stress occurs at the center of the disk and is

$$\sigma_r = \sigma_\theta = \frac{3+\nu}{8}\rho\omega^2 b^2$$

If the disk has a circular hole of radius a at the center, the condition that no external forces are applied at the boundaries requires $\sigma_r = 0$ at $r = b$ and $r = a$. Thus

$$-\frac{3+\nu}{8}\rho\omega^2 b^2 + \frac{c_1}{2} + \frac{c_2}{b^2} = 0 \qquad -\frac{3+\nu}{8}\rho\omega^2 a^2 + \frac{c_1}{2} + \frac{c_2}{a^2} = 0$$

from which we find that

$$\frac{c_1}{2} = \frac{3+\nu}{8}\rho\omega^2(b^2 + a^2) \qquad c_2 = -\frac{3+\nu}{8}\rho\omega^2 a^2 b^2$$

so that the stress components are

$$\sigma_r = \frac{3 + \nu}{8} \rho\omega^2 \left(b^2 + a^2 - \frac{a^2 b^2}{r^2} - r^2 \right)$$

$$\sigma_\theta = \frac{3 + \nu}{8} \rho\omega^2 \left(b^2 + a^2 + \frac{a^2 b^2}{r^2} - \frac{1 + 3\nu}{3 + \nu} r^2 \right)$$

(4.42)

The maximum stress occurs at the inner boundary and is

$$\sigma_\theta = \frac{3 + \nu}{4} \rho\omega^2 b^2 \left(1 + \frac{1 - \nu}{3 + \nu} \frac{a^2}{b^2} \right)$$

If the circular hole is very small, $(a/b)^2$ is negligible compared with 1 and we find the maximum value of the stress is now twice that for a solid disk. That is, by making a small circular hole in a rotating disk, we shall double the maximum stress in the disk.

For the case of a rotating long circular shaft or cylinder, we may consider the problem to be one with plane strain. Hooke's law in this case is

$$\epsilon_r = \frac{1 + \nu}{E} [(1 - \nu)\sigma_r - \nu\sigma_\theta]$$

$$\epsilon_\theta = \frac{1 + \nu}{E} [(1 - \nu)\sigma_\theta - \nu\sigma_r]$$

(4.43)

$$\gamma_{r\theta} = \frac{2(1 + \nu)}{E} \tau_{r\theta}$$

Substituting into Eq. (4.38) and using the stress function defined by (4.37), we find that the compatibility equation becomes now

$$\frac{d^2\psi}{dr^2} + \frac{1}{r}\frac{d\psi}{dr} - \frac{\psi}{r^2} + \frac{3 - 2\nu}{1 - \nu} \rho\omega^2 r = 0$$

(4.44)

In problems where the gravitational force is the only body force, we find that the governing differential equations for plane stress and plane strain are the same. This is not the case when the body force includes the centrifugal force, as can be seen by comparing Eqs. (4.40) and (4.44). Integrating (4.44) as in the case of Eq. (4.40), we obtain

$$\psi = -\frac{1}{8}\frac{3 - 2\nu}{1 - \nu} \rho\omega^2 r^3 + \frac{c_1}{2} r + c_2 \frac{1}{r}$$

The corresponding stress components are

$$\sigma_r = \frac{\psi}{r} = -\frac{1}{8}\frac{3 - 2\nu}{1 - \nu} \rho\omega^2 r^2 + \frac{c_1}{2} + \frac{c_2}{r^2}$$

$$\sigma_\theta = \frac{d\psi}{dr} + \rho\omega^2 r^2 = -\frac{1}{8}\frac{1 + 2\nu}{1 - \nu} \rho\omega^2 r^2 + \frac{c_1}{2} - \frac{c_2}{r^2}$$

The constants of integration can be determined in the same manner as in the case of a thin disk. Thus, for a solid shaft of radius b, we have

$$\sigma_r = \frac{1}{8}\frac{3-2\nu}{1-\nu}\rho\omega^2(b^2 - r^2)$$

$$\sigma_\theta = \frac{1}{8}\frac{\rho\omega^2}{1-\nu}[(3-2\nu)b^2 - (1+2\nu)r^2]$$

(4.45)

For a tubular shaft with inner and outer radii a and b, we have

$$\sigma_r = \frac{1}{8}\frac{3-2\nu}{1-\nu}\rho\omega^2\left(b^2 + a^2 - \frac{a^2b^2}{r^2} - r^2\right)$$

$$\sigma_\theta = \frac{1}{8}\frac{3-2\nu}{1-\nu}\rho\omega^2\left(b^2 + a^2 + \frac{a^2b^2}{r^2} - \frac{1+2\nu}{3-2\nu}r^2\right)$$

(4.46)

The maximum stress for the solid shaft occurs at its center and is

$$\sigma_r = \sigma_\theta = \frac{1}{8}\frac{3-2\nu}{1-\nu}\rho\omega^2b^2$$

The maximum stress for the hollow shaft occurs at the inner surface and is

$$\sigma_\theta = \frac{1}{4}\frac{3-2\nu}{1-\nu}\rho\omega^2b^2\left(1 + \frac{1-2\nu}{3-2\nu}\frac{a^2}{b^2}\right)$$

We see again that the maximum stress is doubled when a solid shaft has a small hole drilled through its center.

In the above discussion, we have assumed that the stress σ_z in the shaft is so adjusted that there is no longitudinal extension ϵ_z. With $\epsilon_z = 0$, we have

$$\sigma_z = \nu(\sigma_r + \sigma_\theta)$$

Hence, in the case of a solid shaft,

$$\sigma_z = \frac{\nu\rho\omega^2}{4(1-\nu)}[(3-2\nu)b^2 - 2r^2]$$

(4.47)

and in the case of a tubular shaft,

$$\sigma_z = \frac{3-2\nu}{4(1-\nu)}\nu\rho\omega^2\left(b^2 + a^2 - \frac{2r^2}{3-2\nu}\right)$$

(4.48)

If the shaft is allowed to expand freely in the longitudinal direction, then there is a uniform extension ϵ_z in the shaft. The uniform longitudinal strain ϵ_z can be determined from the condition (4.11) that there is no resultant longitudinal force on the ends. Hence

$$\int_0^{2\pi}\int_a^b \sigma_z r\, d\theta\, dr = 0$$

where the lower limit a is zero in the case of a solid shaft and is equal to the inner radius for a tubular shaft. Since σ_z is independent of θ, the above condition can be written as

$$\int_a^b \sigma_z r \, dr = 0$$

Thus, in the case of a solid shaft,

$$\nu \int_a^b (\sigma_r + \sigma_\theta) r \, dr + E\epsilon_z \frac{b^2}{2} = 0$$

from which we obtain

$$\epsilon_z = -\frac{\nu}{2E} \rho\omega^2 b^2$$

and

$$\sigma_z = \frac{\nu\rho\omega^2}{4(1 - \nu)} (b^2 - 2r^2) \tag{4.49}$$

For a tubular shaft, we have

$$\nu \int_a^b (\sigma_r + \sigma_\theta) r \, dr + E\epsilon_z \frac{b^2 - a^2}{2} = 0$$

from which we obtain

$$\epsilon_z = -\frac{\nu}{2E} \rho\omega^2 (b^2 + a^2)$$

and

$$\sigma_z = \frac{\nu\rho\omega^2}{4(1 - \nu)} (b^2 + a^2 - 2r^2) \tag{4.50}$$

Problem 1. A thin disk with external radius b is shrunk onto an incompressible shaft of radius a, so that the normal pressure between the shaft and disk is p psi. Show that the angular velocity ω which will just cause the disk to become loose on the shaft is given by

$$\omega^2 = \frac{4p}{\rho(b^2 - a^2)} \frac{(1 + \nu)b^2 + (1 - \nu)a^2}{(3 + \nu)b^2 + (1 - \nu)a^2}$$

where a and b are measured in inches and ρ is the mass per cubic inch.

Problem 2. A thin circular disk of uniform thickness and of radius b is built up of two concentric portions, the surface of separation having a radius a. Find the minimum value of the radial pressure over the surface of separation when the disk is at rest, in order that the outer portion of the disk may not become loose upon the inner portion at an angular velocity ω.

Ans. $\frac{1}{8}(3 + \nu)\rho\omega^2(b^2 - a^2)$

Problem 3. A solid steel shaft 2 ft in diameter is rotating at a speed of 300 rpm. If the shaft is constrained at its ends so that it cannot expand or contract longitudinally, calculate the total longitudinal thrust over a cross section due to rotational stresses. The weight of the steel is 480 lb per cu ft, and $\nu = 0.3$.

Ans. 6,930 lb (tension)

Problem 4. Show that the problem of a thick tube under uniform pressure can also be solved by letting $\omega = 0$ and following the method of solution used in this section.

4.7. Rotating Disk of Variable Thickness. The method of the last section may be used to treat the problem of a rotating disk the thickness of which is a function of the distance r from the axis (Fig. 4.11). If we let σ_r and σ_θ denote the mean radial and tangential stresses at r, and h the variable thickness, the equation of equilibrium of such an element is

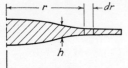

FIG. 4.11.

$$\frac{d}{dr}(hr\sigma_r) - h\sigma_\theta + \rho\omega^2hr^2 = 0 \qquad (4.51)$$

This equation is satisfied if we introduce a stress function ψ such that

$$hr\sigma_r = \psi \qquad h\sigma_\theta = \frac{d\psi}{dr} + \rho\omega^2hr^2 \qquad (4.52)$$

Using Hooke's law and the expressions (4.52), the compatibility equation (4.39) becomes

$$r^2\frac{d^2\psi}{dr^2} + \left(1 - \frac{r}{h}\frac{dh}{dr}\right)r\frac{d\psi}{dr} + \left(\nu\frac{r}{h}\frac{dh}{dr} - 1\right)\psi = -(3 + \nu)\rho\omega^2hr^3 \quad (4.53)$$

from which ψ can be found when h is given.

If the thickness of the disk varies according to the equation

$$h = cr^{-\beta}$$

where c is a constant and β is any number, Eq. (4.53) reduces to

$$r^2\frac{d^2\psi}{dr^2} + (1 + \beta)r\frac{d\psi}{dr} - (1 + \nu\beta)\psi = -(3 + \nu)\rho\omega^2cr^{3-\beta}$$

This equation can be reduced to an equation with constant coefficients by the substitution $\xi = \log r$. With the relations worked out in Sec. 4.4, we find the equation becomes

$$\frac{d^2\psi}{d\xi^2} + \beta\frac{d\psi}{d\xi} - (1 + \nu\beta)\psi = -(3 + \nu)\rho\omega^2ce^{(3-\beta)\xi}$$

The general solution is

$$\psi = c_1e^{q_1\xi} + c_2e^{q_2\xi} - \frac{3 + \nu}{8 - (3 + \nu)\beta}c\rho\omega^2e^{(3-\beta)\xi}$$

or

$$\psi = c_1r^{q_1} + c_2r^{q_2} - \frac{3 + \nu}{8 - (3 + \nu)\beta}c\rho\omega^2r^{3-\beta}$$

where q_1, q_2 are the roots of the equation

$$q^2 + \beta q - (1 + \nu\beta) = 0 \qquad (4.54)$$

The corresponding stress components are therefore

$$\sigma_r = \frac{\psi}{hr} = \frac{c_1}{c} r^{q_1+\beta-1} + \frac{c_2}{c} r^{q_2+\beta-1} - \frac{3+\nu}{8-(3+\nu)\beta} \rho\omega^2 r^2$$

$$\sigma_\theta = \frac{1}{h} \frac{\partial \psi}{\partial r} + \rho\omega^2 r^2 = \frac{c_1}{c} q_1 r^{q_1+\beta-1} + \frac{c_2}{c} q_2 r^{q_2+\beta-1} - \frac{1+3\nu}{8-(3+\nu)\beta} \rho\omega^2 r^2$$

From (4.54) we find

$$q = -\frac{\beta}{2} \pm \sqrt{\left(\frac{\beta}{2}\right)^2 + (1+\nu\beta)}$$

If we let q_2 be the smaller root and if β is positive, we have

$$(q_2 + \beta) = \frac{\beta}{2} - \sqrt{\left(\frac{\beta}{2}\right)^2 + (1+\nu\beta)}$$

since $\sqrt{(\beta/2)^2 + (1+\nu\beta)} > \beta/2$, $(q_2 + \beta)$ is always a negative quantity.

For a solid disk, if β is positive, we must have $c_2 = 0$ because otherwise σ_r and σ_θ would be infinite at the center of the disk. If there are no surface forces acting on the boundary, the condition $\sigma_r = 0$ at $r = b$ gives

$$\frac{c_1}{c} = \frac{3+\nu}{8-(3+\nu)\beta} \rho\omega^2 b^{3-q_1-\beta}$$

Hence

$$\sigma_r = \frac{3+\nu}{8-(3+\nu)\beta} \rho\omega^2 b^2 \left[\left(\frac{r}{b}\right)^{q_1+\beta-1} - \left(\frac{r}{b}\right)^2 \right]$$

$$\sigma_\theta = \frac{3+\nu}{8-(3+\nu)\beta} \rho\omega^2 b^2 \left[q_1 \left(\frac{r}{b}\right)^{q_1+\beta-1} - \frac{1+3\nu}{3+\nu} \left(\frac{r}{b}\right)^2 \right] \tag{4.55}$$

For a disk with uniform thickness, we have $\beta = 0$. From (4.54), we find $q_1 = 1$. Equations (4.55) thus reduce to Eqs. (4.41). For a disk with a central circular hole of radius a, the constants of integration can be determined in the same manner as in the previous section by the conditions that $\sigma_r = 0$ at both $r = b$ and $r = a$.

In designing a rotating disk, the criterion of the so-called "disk with uniform stress" has been proposed. According to such a proposal, the thickness h should be so proportioned that $\sigma_r = \sigma_\theta$ at every point in the disk. Substituting into Hooke's law (4.21), we find

$$\epsilon_r = \epsilon_\theta$$

The compatibility equation (4.39) becomes then

$$\frac{d\epsilon_\theta}{dr} = 0 \qquad \text{or} \qquad \epsilon_\theta = \text{constant}$$

From Hooke's law, it follows that σ_r and σ_θ are not only equal but constant throughout the disk.

Equation of equilibrium (4.51) reduces to

$$\sigma \frac{d(hr)}{dr} - \sigma h + \rho\omega^2 hr^2 = 0$$

where σ is the constant value of the stress. Carrying out the differentiation and combining, we find

$$\frac{1}{h}\frac{dh}{dr} = -\frac{\rho\omega^2}{\sigma} r$$

which, upon integration, gives

$$\log h = -\frac{\rho\omega^2}{2\sigma} r^2 + c_3$$

or $\qquad h = e^{-(\rho\omega^2 r^2/2\sigma)+c_3} = e^{c_3}e^{-(\rho\omega^2 r^2/2\sigma)} = c_4 e^{-(\rho\omega^2 r^2/2\sigma)}$ $\qquad$ (4.56)

where c_3 and c_4 are constants.

4.8. Thermal Stresses in Thin Disks and Long Cylinders. In previous discussions we have assumed that the state of strain is due solely to the applied forces. There are other causes because of which stresses may be set up in an elastic body. One of them is the unequal heating of different parts of the body. With a few exceptions, the elements of a body expand as the temperature is increased. If the element is allowed to expand freely, the body will be strained but there will not be any stress due to such an expansion. However, if the temperature rise in the body is not uniform and the body is continuous, the expansion of the elements cannot proceed freely and *thermal stresses* are produced. The problem of determining the thermal stresses in an elastic body due to a given temperature distribution finds many practical applications in machine design, such as in the design of steam and gas turbines and internal-combustion engines.

Let us consider first an unstrained elastic body with a uniform temperature T_0. Now imagine that the body is heated to some temperature T above T_0. The body will be stressed if T varies from point to point in the body. The strain of an element may be considered as consisting of two parts. One part is due to the expansion of the element because of the change of its temperature. If α is the *coefficient of linear expansion* of the material, which is defined as the change in length per unit length per degree rise in temperature, this part of longitudinal strain will be αT. There will be no shearing strains produced, because the expansion of a small element, due to change of temperature, will not produce angular distortion in an isotropic material. If the element is allowed to expand freely, this is the only component of strain and the element will not be stressed. Now, if the element is not allowed to expand freely, stresses will be produced and the total strain of the element must be the sum of that part due to the stresses and that due to the change of the temperature.

Referring to cartesian coordinates, if the stress components at the point are $\sigma_x, \sigma_y, \sigma_z, \tau_{xy}, \tau_{yz}, \tau_{zx}$, the strain components are therefore

$$\epsilon_x = \frac{1}{E}[\sigma_x - \nu(\sigma_y + \sigma_z)] + \alpha T \qquad \gamma_{xy} = \frac{1}{G}\tau_{xy}$$

$$\epsilon_y = \frac{1}{E}[\sigma_y - \nu(\sigma_x + \sigma_z)] + \alpha T \qquad \gamma_{yz} = \frac{1}{G}\tau_{yz} \qquad (4.57)$$

$$\epsilon_z = \frac{1}{E}[\sigma_z - \nu(\sigma_x + \sigma_y)] + \alpha T \qquad \gamma_{zx} = \frac{1}{G}\tau_{zx}$$

From the above formulas, we obtain the relations between stress and strain as follows,

$$\sigma_x = \lambda e + \frac{E}{1 + \nu}\epsilon_x - \frac{\alpha E T}{1 - 2\nu}$$

$$\sigma_y = \lambda e + \frac{E}{1 + \nu}\epsilon_y - \frac{\alpha E T}{1 - 2\nu} \qquad (4.58)$$

$$\sigma_z = \lambda e + \frac{E}{1 + \nu}\epsilon_z - \frac{\alpha E T}{1 - 2\nu}$$

where λ is equal to $\nu E/(1 + \nu)(1 - 2\nu)$ and $e = \epsilon_x + \epsilon_y + \epsilon_z$. The relations between τ and γ are the same as in the case when there are no thermal strains.

Now let us consider a thin circular disk with uneven temperature distribution. Assume the temperature T is a function of the radial distance r only. We have a case of plane stress with rotational symmetry. In terms of cylindrical coordinates, we find, from (4.57),

$$\epsilon_r = \frac{1}{E}(\sigma_r - \nu\sigma_\theta) + \alpha T \qquad \epsilon_\theta = \frac{1}{E}(\sigma_\theta - \nu\sigma_r) + \alpha T \qquad (4.59)$$

The equilibrium equation

$$\frac{d\sigma_r}{dr} + \frac{\sigma_r - \sigma_\theta}{r} = 0$$

is identically satisfied if we introduce the stress function ψ such that

$$\sigma_r = \frac{\psi}{r} \qquad \sigma_\theta = \frac{d\psi}{dr} \qquad (4.60)$$

Substituting (4.59) and (4.60) into the compatibility equation (4.39)

$$r\frac{d\epsilon_\theta}{dr} + \epsilon_\theta - \epsilon_r = 0$$

and simplifying, we find

$$\frac{d^2\psi}{dr^2} + \frac{1}{r}\frac{d\psi}{dr} - \frac{\psi}{r^2} = -\alpha E\frac{dT}{dr}$$

or

$$\frac{d}{dr}\left[\frac{1}{r}\frac{d}{dr}(r\psi)\right] = -\alpha E\frac{dT}{dr} \qquad (4.61)$$

This equation can be easily integrated, and the solution is

$$\psi = -\frac{\alpha E}{r} \int_a^r Tr\, dr + \frac{c_1 r}{2} + \frac{c_2}{r} \tag{4.62}$$

where the lower limit a in the integral can be chosen arbitrarily. For a disk with a hole, it may be the inner radius. For a solid disk we may take it as zero.

The stress components can now be found by substituting (4.62) into formulas (4.60). Hence

$$\sigma_r = -\frac{\alpha E}{r^2} \int_a^r Tr\, dr + \frac{c_1}{2} + \frac{c_2}{r^2}$$

$$\sigma_\theta = \alpha E\left(-T + \frac{1}{r^2}\int_a^r Tr\, dr\right) + \frac{c_1}{2} - \frac{c_2}{r^2}$$

For a solid disk, we must have finite stresses at the center, and therefore c_2 must be zero. If there is no external force applied at the boundary, $\sigma_r = 0$ at $r = b$. It follows then that

$$c_1 = \frac{2\alpha E}{b^2} \int_0^b Tr\, dr$$

The stress components are

$$\sigma_r = \alpha E\left(\frac{1}{b^2}\int_0^b Tr\, dr - \frac{1}{r^2}\int_0^r Tr\, dr\right)$$

$$\sigma_\theta = \alpha E\left(-T + \frac{1}{b^2}\int_0^b Tr\, dr + \frac{1}{r^2}\int_0^r Tr\, dr\right) \tag{4.63}$$

Consider, as an example, a thin disk which receives heat over its faces and rejects it at its circumference in such a way that the temperature at any point in the disk is essentially uniform through the thickness. If T_0 is the temperature at the edge of the disk and T_1 is the temperature at the center, the temperature rise at a radius r is given by

$$T = (T_1 - T_0) - (T_1 - T_0)\frac{r^2}{b^2}$$

Substituting the expression of T given by the above formula into Eqs. (4.63) and integrating, we obtain

$$\sigma_r = -\frac{1}{4}\alpha E(T_1 - T_0)\left(1 - \frac{r^2}{b^2}\right) \qquad \sigma_\theta = -\frac{1}{4}\alpha E(T_1 - T_0)\left(1 - \frac{3r^2}{b^2}\right)$$

If there is a circular hole of radius a at the center of the disk and the edges are free of external forces, we have

$$\sigma_r = 0 \qquad \text{at } r = b \text{ and } r = a$$

Then

$$\frac{c_1}{2} + \frac{c_2}{b^2} = \frac{\alpha E}{b^2} \int_a^b Tr \, dr \qquad \frac{c_1}{2} + \frac{c_2}{a^2} = 0$$

from which it follows that

$$\frac{c_1}{2} = \frac{\alpha E}{b^2 - a^2} \int_a^b Tr \, dr \qquad c_2 = -\frac{a^2 \alpha E}{b^2 - a^2} \int_a^b Tr \, dr$$

and
$$\sigma_r = \alpha E \left[-\frac{1}{r^2} \int_a^r Tr \, dr + \frac{1}{b^2 - a^2} \int_a^b Tr \, dr \right.$$
$$\left. -\frac{a^2}{r^2(b^2 - a^2)} \int_a^b Tr \, dr \right] \tag{4.64}$$

$$\sigma_\theta = \alpha E \left[-T + \frac{1}{r^2} \int_a^r Tr \, dr + \frac{1}{b^2 - a^2} \int_a^b Tr \, dr \right.$$
$$\left. -\frac{a^2}{r^2(b^2 - a^2)} \int_a^b Tr \, dr \right]$$

Let us now consider the thermal stresses in a long circular cylinder with a temperature distribution symmetrical about its axis. If the ends of the cylinder are restrained in such a way that $\epsilon_z = 0$, we have a plane-strain problem. In terms of cylindrical coordinates, the stress-strain relations are

$$\epsilon_r = \frac{1}{E} [\sigma_r - \nu(\sigma_\theta + \sigma_z)] + \alpha T$$

$$\epsilon_\theta = \frac{1}{E} [\sigma_\theta - \nu(\sigma_r + \sigma_z)] + \alpha T \tag{4.65}$$

$$\epsilon_z = \frac{1}{E} [\sigma_z - \nu(\sigma_r + \sigma_\theta)] + \alpha T$$

In the case of plain strain, $\epsilon_z = 0$, and the third equation of (4.65) gives

$$\sigma_z = \nu(\sigma_r + \sigma_\theta) - \alpha ET \tag{4.66}$$

Substituting (4.66) into the first two equations of (4.65), we obtain

$$\epsilon_r = \frac{1 + \nu}{E} [(1 - \nu)\sigma_r - \nu\sigma_\theta + \alpha ET]$$
$$\epsilon_\theta = \frac{1 + \nu}{E} [(1 - \nu)\sigma_\theta - \nu\sigma_r + \alpha ET] \tag{4.67}$$

Let us now substitute (4.67) and (4.60) into the compatibility equation (4.39); after some simplification we obtain

$$\frac{d^2\psi}{dr^2} + \frac{1}{r}\frac{d\psi}{dr} - \frac{\psi}{r^2} = -\frac{\alpha E}{1 - \nu}\frac{dT}{dr} \tag{4.68}$$

Comparing with Eq. (4.61), we find that these two equations are the same except the coefficient of dT/dr. The solution is therefore

$$\psi = -\frac{\alpha E}{1-\nu}\frac{1}{r}\int_a^r Tr\,dr + \frac{c_1 r}{2} + \frac{c_2}{r}$$

from which it follows that

$$\sigma_r = -\frac{\alpha E}{1-\nu}\frac{1}{r^2}\int_a^r Tr\,dr + \frac{c_1}{2} + \frac{c_2}{r^2}$$

For a solid cylinder, $c_2 = 0$ so that the stresses in the cylinder will be finite. On the outer surface $r = b$, $\sigma_r = 0$, and we find

$$c_1 = \frac{2\alpha E}{1-\nu}\frac{1}{b^2}\int_0^b Tr\,dr$$

The stress components are therefore

$$\sigma_r = \frac{\alpha E}{1-\nu}\left(\frac{1}{b^2}\int_0^b Tr\,dr - \frac{1}{r^2}\int_0^r Tr\,dr\right)$$
$$\sigma_\theta = \frac{\alpha E}{1-\nu}\left(-T + \frac{1}{b^2}\int_0^b Tr\,dr + \frac{1}{r^2}\int_0^r Tr\,dr\right) \tag{4.69}$$

and, from Eq. (4.66)

$$\sigma_z = \frac{\alpha E}{1-\nu}\left(\frac{2\nu}{b^2}\int_0^b Tr\,dr - T\right) \tag{4.70}$$

This is the normal stress distribution which must be applied to keep $\epsilon_z = 0$ throughout. If the cylinder has free ends, we can superpose on it a uniform axial stress $\sigma_z = c_3$ so that the resultant force on the ends is zero. Integrating, we find that the condition

$$\int_0^b \sigma_z 2\pi r\,dr = 0$$

gives

$$c_3 = \frac{2\alpha E}{b^2}\int_0^b Tr\,dr$$

In such a case, we have therefore

$$\sigma_z = \frac{\alpha E}{1-\nu}\left(\frac{2}{b^2}\int_0^b Tr\,dr - T\right) \tag{4.71}$$

In the case of a circular cylinder with a concentric circular hole, the constants of integration can be determined by the conditions that $\sigma_r = 0$ at $r = b$ and $r = a$. Then,

$$\frac{c_1}{2} + \frac{c_2}{b^2} = \frac{\alpha E}{1-\nu}\frac{1}{b^2}\int_a^b Tr\,dr \qquad \frac{c_1}{2} + \frac{c_2}{a^2} = 0$$

Solving, we have

$$\frac{c_1}{2} = \frac{\alpha E}{1 - \nu} \frac{1}{b^2 - a^2} \int_a^b Tr \, dr$$

$$c_2 = -\frac{\alpha E}{1 - \nu} \frac{a^2}{b^2 - a^2} \int_a^b Tr \, dr$$

With these constants, we find

$$\sigma_r = \frac{\alpha E}{1 - \nu} \frac{1}{r^2} \left(\frac{r^2 - a^2}{b^2 - a^2} \int_a^b Tr \, dr - \int_a^r Tr \, dr \right)$$

$$\sigma_\theta = \frac{\alpha E}{1 - \nu} \frac{1}{r^2} \left(\frac{r^2 + a^2}{b^2 - a^2} \int_a^b Tr \, dr + \int_a^r Tr \, dr - Tr^2 \right)$$

(4.72)

and if we add to σ_z the uniform stress so that the resultant axial force is zero,

$$\sigma_z = \frac{\alpha E}{1 - \nu} \left(\frac{2}{b^2 - a^2} \int_a^b Tr \, dr - T \right)$$

(4.73)

If T_1 is the temperature on the inner surface of the cylinder and T_0 is the temperature on the outer surface, in the case of a steady heat flow, the temperature rise T at any distance r from the center is

$$T = \frac{T_1 - T_0}{\log (b/a)} \log \frac{b}{r}$$

Substituting this into Eqs. (4.69) and (4.70), the thermal stresses **are**

$$\sigma_r = \frac{\alpha E(T_1 - T_0)}{2(1 - \nu) \log (b/a)} \left[- \log \frac{b}{r} - \frac{a^2(r^2 - b^2)}{r^2(b^2 - a^2)} \log \frac{b}{a} \right]$$

$$\sigma_\theta = \frac{\alpha E(T_1 - T_0)}{2(1 - \nu) \log (b/a)} \left[1 - \log \frac{b}{r} - \frac{a^2(r^2 + b^2)}{r^2(b^2 - a^2)} \log \frac{b}{a} \right]$$

$$\sigma_z = \frac{\alpha E(T_1 - T_0)}{2(1 - \nu) \log (b/a)} \left[1 - \log \frac{b}{r} - \frac{2a^2}{b^2 - a^2} \log \frac{b}{a} \right]$$

(4.74)

If T_1 is higher than T_0, the radial stress is compressive at all points and becomes zero at the inner and outer surfaces of the cylinder. The stress components σ_θ and σ_z have their largest numerical values at the inner and outer surfaces of the cylinder.

Problem 1. A thin uniform disk of radius b is enclosed in a heavy ring of the same material into which it just fits when the disk and ring are at a uniform temperature. If the heat is supplied over the faces of the disk and it is rejected at the circumference, the temperature rise at a distance r from the center is given by

$$T = (T_1 - T_0) - (T_1 - T_0) \frac{r^2}{b^2}$$

Assume that the ring takes up a uniform temperature T_0 but undergoes no appreciable strain due to the stresses set up. Show that the radial compressive stress in the disk at a radius r is

$$\frac{1}{4} E\alpha(T_1 - T_0) \left(\frac{3 - \nu}{1 - \nu} - \frac{r^2}{b^2}\right)$$

Problem 2. When an electric current generates heat at a uniform rate per unit volume within a long, straight solid conductor of radius b, it can be shown that the consequent rise of temperature inside the conductor at any radius r is given by the formula $T = \lambda(b^2 - r^2)$, where λ is a constant. Assuming that the elastic limit of stress is not exceeded and that there are no external forces resisting longitudinal or radial expansion, prove that the temperature distribution will give rise to the following stresses:

$$\sigma_r = -\frac{E\alpha\lambda}{4(1 - \nu)} (b^2 - r^2) \qquad \sigma_\theta = \frac{E\alpha\lambda}{4(1 - \nu)} (3r^2 - b^2) \qquad \sigma_z = \frac{E\alpha\lambda}{2(1 - \nu)} (2r^2 - b^2)$$

CHAPTER 5

TORSION OF VARIOUS-SHAPED BARS

5.1. Torsion of Prismatic Bars. To solve the general equations of elasticity together with the given boundary conditions, the direct method of solution may not always be possible. For the solution of many problems, the *inverse method* and the *semi-inverse method* have been found to be useful. In the inverse method, any functions satisfying the differential equations are examined to see what boundary conditions these functions will satisfy. In this way useful solutions may be obtained. In the semi-inverse method, first proposed by Saint-Venant, simplifying assumptions are made regarding the stress components or the displacements so that the differential equations are simplified to such an extent that they may be solved without too much mathematical difficulty. These simplifying assumptions will evidently limit the generality of the resulting solution, but they can usually be made in such a way that the required solution can still be obtained. For example, in the case of torsion of a prismatic bar, which we shall discuss, we shall assume the displacements u, v, w to be of certain form, thus reducing the governing equations to one differential equation. Owing to these assumptions,

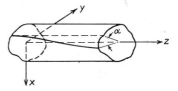

FIG. 5.1.

we shall be able to obtain not the solution for nonprismatic bars under torsion but only that for bars of constant cross section. The semi-inverse method has proved to be one of the most useful methods in solving elasticity problems.

Suppose that a prismatic bar, of length L, is fixed at one end in the xy plane, while the other end is acted upon by a couple whose moment lies along the z axis (Fig. 5.1). We assume that the fixed end is prevented from rotating but that both ends are allowed to extend or contract in the z direction. Under the action of the couple, the bar will be twisted, and the generators of the cylinder will be deformed into helical curves. The amount of rotation at any section will depend on the distance of the section from the fixed end. Since the deformation is small, it is reasonable to assume that the angle of twist α is proportional to the distance of the section from the fixed end. Thus

$$\alpha = \theta z \qquad (5.1)$$

where θ is the angle of twist per unit length. We shall assume that the angle of twist α is small. Consider a section of the bar which is at a distance z from the fixed end. A point P which has its coordinates x, y, z is displaced to $P'(x + u, y + v, z + w)$ after deformation. The projection of P' on the xy plane, P'_1, is shown in Fig. 5.2. Assume that in the xy plane P is rotated to P'_1 through the angle of twist α with $OP \cong OP'_1 = r$. If α is small, we have $\cos \alpha \cong 1$ and $\sin \alpha \cong \alpha$. Thus,

$$u = r \cos (\beta + \alpha) - r \cos \beta = r \cos \alpha \cos \beta - r \sin \alpha \sin \beta$$
$$- r \cos \beta \cong -y\alpha$$
$$v = r \sin (\beta + \alpha) - r \sin \beta = r \sin \alpha \cos \beta + r \cos \alpha \sin \beta$$
$$- r \sin \beta \cong x\alpha$$

Combining with (5.1), we obtain

$$u = -\theta yz \qquad v = \theta xz \tag{5.2}$$

which shall be our assumed form for u and v. For the present we shall make no assumptions about w, except that w is a function of x, y only and is independent of z. Thus, we may write

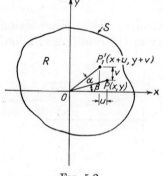

$$w = \theta\phi(x,y) \tag{5.3}$$

where $\phi(x,y)$ is some function of x and y. Since w defines the warping of the end surfaces, ϕ may be called a *warping function*. Our object is to determine whether or not the assumed displacements, together with some yet unknown function ϕ, will result in a system of stresses compatible with the given boundary conditions. The boundary

FIG. 5.2.

conditions in this case are that there should be only pure torsional moments on the two ends and no forces acting on the lateral surface of the bar.

The above values of the displacements give

$$\epsilon_x = \epsilon_y = \epsilon_z = \gamma_{xy} = 0 \qquad \gamma_{yz} = \theta\left(\frac{\partial\phi}{\partial y} + x\right) \qquad \gamma_{zx} = \theta\left(\frac{\partial\phi}{\partial x} - y\right) \tag{5.4}$$

whence it follows, from Eqs. (3.26), that

$$\sigma_x = \sigma_y = \sigma_z = \tau_{xy} = 0 \qquad \tau_{yz} = G\theta\left(\frac{\partial\phi}{\partial y} + x\right) \qquad \tau_{zx} = G\theta\left(\frac{\partial\phi}{\partial x} - y\right) \tag{5.5}$$

A substitution of these values in the equilibrium equations (3.42) shows that these equations will be satisfied if $\phi(x,y)$ satisfies the equation

$$\nabla^2\phi = \frac{\partial^2\phi}{\partial x^2} + \frac{\partial^2\phi}{\partial y^2} = 0 \tag{5.6}$$

throughout the cross section R of the bar, where $\nabla^2 = (\partial^2/\partial x^2) + (\partial^2/\partial y^2)$ is the Laplace operator.

Let us now investigate the boundary conditions. Since

$$\bar{X} = \bar{Y} = \bar{Z} = 0$$

on the lateral surface of the bar, the last equation in (1.36) becomes

$$\left(\frac{\partial \phi}{\partial x} - y\right) l + \left(\frac{\partial \phi}{\partial y} + x\right) m = 0 \qquad \text{on } S \tag{5.7}$$

where S is the boundary of the cross section of the bar. The other two equations in (1.36) are identically zero because of (5.5) and because on the lateral surface $n = \cos Nz = 0$.

On the other two bounding surfaces, *viz.*, the ends of the bar defined by the planes $z = 0$ and $z = L$, we must show that the distribution of stresses given by (5.5) is equivalent to a torsional couple and that there is no resultant force. The resultant force in the x direction is given by

$$\iint\limits_{R} \tau_{zx}\, dx\, dy = G\theta \iint\limits_{R} \left(\frac{\partial \phi}{\partial x} - y\right) dx\, dy \tag{5.8}$$

and this can be written as

$$G\theta \iint\limits_{R} \left\{ \frac{\partial}{\partial x}\left[x\left(\frac{\partial \phi}{\partial x} - y\right)\right] + \frac{\partial}{\partial y}\left[x\left(\frac{\partial \phi}{\partial y} + x\right)\right] \right\} dx\, dy \tag{5.9}$$

since

$$\frac{\partial}{\partial x}\left[x\left(\frac{\partial \phi}{\partial x} - y\right)\right] + \frac{\partial}{\partial y}\left[x\left(\frac{\partial \phi}{\partial y} + x\right)\right] = \left(\frac{\partial \phi}{\partial x} - y\right) + x\frac{\partial^2 \phi}{\partial x^2} + x\frac{\partial^2 \phi}{\partial y^2}$$

$$= \left(\frac{\partial \phi}{\partial x} - y\right) + x\left(\frac{\partial^2 \phi}{\partial x^2} + \frac{\partial^2 \phi}{\partial y^2}\right) = \left(\frac{\partial \phi}{\partial x} - y\right)$$

where the last step is achieved because $(\partial^2 \phi/\partial x^2) + (\partial^2 \phi/\partial y^2) = 0$ according to (5.6).

Now if f is any function of x and y, we have (Fig. 5.3)

$$\iint\limits_{R} \frac{\partial f}{\partial x}\, dx\, dy = \int \left(\int \frac{\partial f}{\partial x}\, dx\right) dy = \int (f_1 - f_2)\, dy$$

where f_1 is the value of f on the right side part of the boundary and f_2 is the value on the left side. The integration with respect to y now has to be carried out on the boundary curve from $y = y_A$ to $y = y_B$. If we integrate f along the curve following a counterclockwise direction, dy is positive on the right side of the boundary and is negative on the left side. As a result both $f_1 \, dy$ and $-f_2 \, dy$ become positive, and we may write

$$\iint\limits_{R} \frac{\partial f}{\partial x} \, dx \, dy = \oint_S f \, dy \tag{5.10}$$

Similarly,

$$\iint\limits_{R} \frac{\partial f}{\partial y} \, dx \, dy = - \oint_S f \, dx \tag{5.11}$$

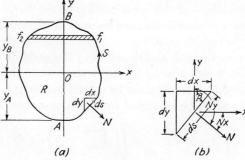

Fig. 5.3.

Using formulas (5.10) and (5.11), the expression (5.9) becomes

$$\oint_S \left[x\left(\frac{\partial \phi}{\partial x} - y\right) dy - x\left(\frac{\partial \phi}{\partial y} + x\right) dx \right]$$

$$= \oint_S x \left[\left(\frac{\partial \phi}{\partial x} - y\right) \frac{dy}{ds} - \left(\frac{\partial \phi}{\partial y} + x\right) \frac{dx}{ds} \right] ds \tag{5.12}$$

Since an outward normal N is defined as positive and the positive direction of s is counterclockwise, we have from Fig. 5.3b

$$l = \cos Nx = \frac{dx}{dN} = \frac{dy}{ds}$$

$$m = \cos Ny = \frac{dy}{dN} = \cos(\pi - \beta) = -\cos\beta = -\frac{dx}{ds} \tag{5.13}$$

Expression (5.12) then becomes

$$\oint_S x \left[\left(\frac{\partial \phi}{\partial x} - y\right) l + \left(\frac{\partial \phi}{\partial y} + x\right) m \right] ds = 0$$

The last step is obtained because $\{[(d\phi/dx) - y]l\} + \{[(\partial\phi/\partial y) + x]m\}$ is equal to zero on S according to (5.7). Thus, we have proved that

$$\iint\limits_{R} \tau_{zx} \, dx \, dy = 0$$

In a similar way, we can also show that the y component of the resultant force is zero, *i.e.*,

$$\iint_R \tau_{zy} \, dx \, dy = 0$$

so that the resultant force acting on the ends of the cylinder vanishes.

The resultant torsional moment T on the ends of the bar due to the assumed stress distribution is

$$T = \iint_R (x\tau_{yz} - y\tau_{zx}) \, dx \, dy$$

$$= G\theta \iint_R \left(x^2 + y^2 + x\frac{\partial \phi}{\partial y} - y\frac{\partial \phi}{\partial x} \right) dx \, dy \quad (5.14)$$

The integral appearing in (5.14) depends on the torsion function ϕ and hence on the cross section R of the bar. Letting

$$J = \iint_R \left(x^2 + y^2 + x\frac{\partial \phi}{\partial y} - y\frac{\partial \phi}{\partial x} \right) dx \, dy \quad (5.15)$$

we have

$$T = GJ\theta \quad (5.16)$$

where J is called *torsional constant*. Equation (5.16) shows that the torsional moment is proportional to the angle of twist per unit length, so that the product GJ provides a measure of the rigidity of a bar subjected to torsion and is called the *torsional rigidity* of the bar.

5.2. Torsion of Circular and Elliptical Bars. As formulated in the preceding section, the torsion problem is solved if we find the warping function $\phi(x,y)$ which satisfies the differential equation

$$\frac{\partial^2 \phi}{\partial x^2} + \frac{\partial^2 \phi}{\partial y^2} = 0 \quad (5.6)$$

inside the cross-sectional area, or domain, R and satisfies the condition

$$\left(\frac{\partial \phi}{\partial x} - y \right) l + \left(\frac{\partial \phi}{\partial y} + x \right) m = 0 \quad (5.7)$$

on the boundary S. Let us now show how the solution is found when the boundary is of special form.

The torsion of circular and elliptical bars was solved by the inverse method. The simplest solution of the Laplace equation is

$$\phi = \text{constant} = C \quad (5.17)$$

With $\phi = C$, the boundary condition (5.7) becomes

$$yl - xm = y\frac{dy}{ds} + x\frac{dx}{ds} = 0$$

i.e.,

$$\frac{d}{ds}\frac{x^2 + y^2}{2} = 0$$

or
$$x^2 + y^2 = \text{constant} \tag{5.18}$$

where x, y are the coordinates of any point on the boundary. From analytical geometry we know that (5.18) represents a circle with its center at the origin. Thus the function $\phi = C$ gives us the solution for the torsion of a circular bar. From (5.3), we have $w = \theta C$. If the boundary condition is $w = 0$ at $z = 0$, then $C = 0$. Therefore, a plane section of the cylinder normal to the z axis before torsion will remain plane after deformation. This is the assumption we usually make for such a solution in strength of materials. Examining (5.18), we see that this assumption is correct only when the boundary is a circle. For other sections, the assumption cannot be expected to be valid.

Let r_0 be the radius of the circle. From formula (5.15) if $\phi = C$, we have

$$J = \iint\limits_R (x^2 + y^2)\, dx\, dy = \tfrac{1}{2}\pi r_0^4$$

which is equal to the polar moment of inertia of the circular cross section, I_p. Thus, from (5.16),

$$T = GI_p\theta \tag{5.19}$$

and from (5.5), we obtain

$$\tau_{yz} = G\theta x = \frac{T}{I_p}x \qquad \tau_{zx} = -G\theta y = -\frac{T}{I_p}y \tag{5.20}$$

The resulting shearing stress at any point $P(x,y)$ is

$$\tau = \sqrt{\tau_{yz}^2 + \tau_{zx}^2} = \frac{T}{I_p}\sqrt{x^2 + y^2} = \frac{T}{I_p}r \tag{5.21}$$

where r is the distance of the point from the center of the circle and it is inclined to the x axis at an angle β with

$$\tan \beta = \frac{\tau_{yz}}{\tau_{zx}} = -\frac{x}{y}$$

Hence, the resultant shearing stress at any point is in the direction of the tangent of the circle passing through that point.

Next, let us examine the function

$$\phi = Axy \tag{5.22}$$

It is obvious that this function satisfies the Laplace equation. With ϕ in the form of (5.22), the boundary condition (5.7) after substitution becomes

$$(Ay - y)\frac{dy}{ds} - (Ax + x)\frac{dx}{ds} = 0 \qquad \text{or} \qquad \frac{d}{ds}\left(x^2 + \frac{1-A}{1+A}y^2\right) = 0$$

which, upon integration, gives

$$x^2 + \frac{1-A}{1+A}y^2 = \text{constant} \tag{5.23}$$

where x, y are the coordinates of any point on the boundary.

Now, the equation defining an ellipse with center at the origin is

$$x^2 + \frac{a^2}{b^2}y^2 = a^2 \tag{5.24}$$

where a and b represent the semiaxes. Comparing with (5.23), we find that these two equations are identical if

$$\frac{a^2}{b^2} = -\frac{A-1}{A+1}$$

or, by solving for A,

$$A = \frac{b^2 - a^2}{b^2 + a^2}$$

Therefore, the function

$$\phi = \frac{b^2 - a^2}{b^2 + a^2}xy \tag{5.25}$$

is the warping function for an elliptical cylinder under torsion. The torsional constant is

$$\begin{aligned}
J &= \iint_R (x^2 + y^2 + Ax^2 - Ay^2)\,dx\,dy \\
&= (A+1)\iint_R x^2\,dx\,dy + (1-A)\iint_R y^2\,dx\,dy \\
&= (A+1)I_y + (1-A)I_x \\
&= \frac{\pi a^3 b^3}{a^2 + b^2}
\end{aligned} \tag{5.26}$$

where I_y, I_x are the moments of inertia with respect to the y and x axes, respectively.

The shearing stresses at any point in the cross section are

$$\tau_{yz} = \frac{2Tx}{\pi a^3 b} \qquad \tau_{zx} = -\frac{2Ty}{\pi a b^3} \tag{5.27}$$

The resultant shearing stress at any point $P(x,y)$ is

$$\tau = \sqrt{\tau_{yz}^2 + \tau_{zx}^2} = \frac{2T}{\pi a^2 b^2} \sqrt{\frac{b^2 x^2}{a^2} + \frac{a^2 y^2}{b^2}} \tag{5.28}$$

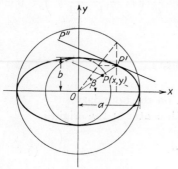

FIG. 5.4.

The maximum value of τ occurs at the extremity of the minor axis. To prove this, let us construct a series of ellipses inside the elliptical section. Let the semiaxes of these ellipses be a' and b' so that $a'/a = b'/b \leq 1$. The equations of these ellipses can be written in the parametric form as follows,

$$x = a' \cos \beta \qquad y = b' \sin \beta$$

where β is the angle as shown in Fig. 5.4. Substituting these equations into (5.28), we find that the resultant shearing stress at any point on these ellipses is

$$\begin{aligned}
\tau &= \frac{2T}{\pi a^2 b^2} \sqrt{b^2 \left(\frac{a'}{a}\right)^2 \cos^2 \beta + a^2 \left(\frac{b'}{b}\right)^2 \sin^2 \beta} \\
&= \frac{2T}{\pi a^2 b^2} \frac{a'}{a} \sqrt{b^2 \cos^2 \beta + a^2 \sin^2 \beta} \\
&= \frac{2T}{\pi a^2 b^2} \frac{a'}{a} \sqrt{b^2 + (a^2 - b^2) \sin^2 \beta}
\end{aligned}$$

If $a > b$, τ is maximum when $a' = a$ and $\beta = \pm \pi/2$. That is, $\tau_{\max}$ occurs at the extremity of the minor axis, and

$$\tau_{\max} = \frac{2T}{\pi a b^2} \tag{5.29}$$

For $a = b$, this formula reduces to (5.21), the formula for a circular bar. The direction of τ is given by the ratio of τ_{yz} to τ_{zx}. We see from formulas (5.27) that this ratio is proportional to y/x and hence is constant along the line OP. This means that the resultant shearing stress along any line OP has a constant direction which coincides with the direction of the tangent $P'P''$.

With the warping function (5.25) determined, the displacement w is easily found.

$$w = \theta \phi = \frac{T(b^2 - a^2)}{\pi a^3 b^3 G} xy \tag{5.30}$$

where the relation $\theta = T/GJ$ is used. The contour lines, defined by $w = \text{constant}$, are the hyperbolas shown in Fig. 5.5. If the cylinder is twisted by the torque T in the direction of the arrow shown in the figure, the convex portions of the cross section, *i.e.*, where w is positive, are indicated by solid lines and the concave portions, or where w is negative, are indicated by dotted lines. In the case of unrestrained ends, there are no normal stresses. If one end of the bar is restrained from warping such as in the case of a built-in end, however, normal stresses will be induced which are positive in one quadrant and negative in another one. These are similar to the stresses due to two equal and opposite bending moments and are therefore called the *bending stresses induced because of torsion.*

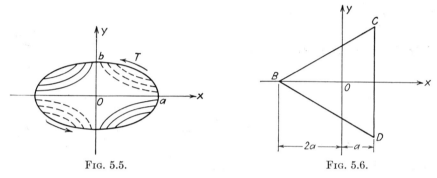

FIG. 5.5.   FIG. 5.6.

Problem. Show that the warping function $\phi = A(y^3 - 3x^2y)$ is the correct solution for an equilateral triangular bar under torsion (Fig. 5.6), where A is a constant to be determined. Find the torsional constant J and the maximum shearing stress. The equations of the boundary lines are

$$x - a = 0 \qquad \text{on } CD$$
$$x + 2a - \sqrt{3}\,y = 0 \qquad \text{on } BC$$
$$x + 2a + \sqrt{3}\,y = 0 \qquad \text{on } BD$$

Hint: First show that ϕ satisfies the differential equation. To show that ϕ satisfies the boundary conditions, determine the constant A on CD, and prove that, with this determined value of A and $y = \pm(x + 2a)/\sqrt{3}$, the boundary condition is satisfied on BC and BD. On CD, $l = 1$, $m = 0$. On BC, $l = \cos 120° = -\frac{1}{2}$, $m = \cos 30° = \sqrt{3}/2$. On BD, $l = \cos 240° = -\frac{1}{2}$, $m = \cos 150° = -\sqrt{3}/2$.

Ans. $A = -1/6a$, $J = 9\sqrt{3}\,a^4/5$. $\tau_{\max} = 3Ta/2J$. max τ occurs at $x = a$, $y = 0$

5.3. Torsion of Rectangular Bars. Let the sides of the rectangular cross section be $2a$ and $2b$, and let the origin be at the center of the rectangle with the coordinate axes parallel to its sides (Fig. 5.7). Our equations are, as before,

$$\frac{\partial^2\phi}{\partial x^2} + \frac{\partial^2\phi}{\partial y^2} = 0 \qquad\qquad (5.6)$$

over the whole rectangle and

$$\left(\frac{\partial\phi}{\partial x} - y\right)l + \left(\frac{\partial\phi}{\partial y} + x\right)m = 0 \qquad\qquad (5.7)$$

on the boundary. Now, on the boundary lines $x = \pm a$ or AB and CD we have $l = \pm 1$ and $m = 0$, and on the boundary lines BC and AD we have $l = 0$ and $m = \pm 1$. The boundary condition (5.7) may be rewritten as

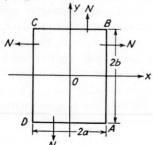

FIG. 5.7.

$$\frac{\partial \phi}{\partial x} = y \qquad \text{on } x = \pm a$$
$$\frac{\partial \phi}{\partial y} = -x \qquad \text{on } y = \pm b \tag{5.31}$$

These boundary conditions can be transformed into more convenient forms if we introduce a new function ϕ_1 such that

$$\phi = xy - \phi_1 \tag{5.32}$$

It is easy to verify that, in terms of ϕ_1, our governing equation is

$$\frac{\partial^2 \phi_1}{\partial x^2} + \frac{\partial^2 \phi_1}{\partial y^2} = 0 \tag{5.33}$$

over the whole rectangle and the boundary conditions become

$$\frac{\partial \phi_1}{\partial x} = 0 \qquad \text{on } x = \pm a \tag{5.34}$$

$$\frac{\partial \phi_1}{\partial y} = 2x \qquad \text{on } y = \pm b \tag{5.35}$$

We shall assume that the solution of Eq. (5.33) can be expressed in the form of an infinite series

$$\phi_1 = \sum_{n=0}^{\infty} X_n(x) Y_n(y) \tag{5.36}$$

where each term of the series satisfies the differential equation and $X_n(x)$ and $Y_n(y)$ are, respectively, functions of x alone and y alone. It is obvious that if the solution ϕ_1 cannot be expressed in the form of (5.36), we shall not be able to solve for the functions X_n and Y_n and have these functions satisfy the boundary conditions.

Substituting $X_n(x)$, $Y_n(y)$ in (5.33) and denoting the derivatives by primes, we obtain

$$X_n''(x) Y_n(y) + X_n(x) Y_n''(y) = 0 \qquad \text{or} \qquad \frac{X_n''(x)}{X_n(x)} = -\frac{Y_n''(y)}{Y_n(y)}$$

Since the expression on the left-hand side of the above equation is a function of x alone and the one on the right-hand side depends only on y, the equality can be fulfilled only if the expression on either side is equal to a constant; call it $-k_n^2$.† We are thus led to a pair of ordinary differential equations.

$$\frac{d^2 X_n}{dx^2} + k_n^2 X_n = 0 \quad \text{and} \quad \frac{d^2 Y_n}{dy^2} - k_n^2 Y_n = 0$$

These differential equations can be easily solved by the well-known methods of solving linear ordinary differential equations with constant coefficients. Their solutions are

$$X_n = c_1 \sin k_n x + c_2 \cos k_n x \tag{5.37}$$
$$Y_n = c_3 \sinh k_n y + c_4 \cosh k_n y \tag{5.38}$$

Now let us examine the boundary condition (5.35). First we observe that

$$\frac{\partial \phi_1}{\partial y} = \sum_{n=0}^{\infty} X_n(x) Y'_n(y) = 2x$$

must have the same value for $y = +b$ or $-b$. This condition can be satisfied if $Y'_n(y)$ are symmetric functions in y. Second, for $y = \pm b$, we have

$$\sum_{n=0}^{\infty} Y'_n(b) X_n(x) = 2x$$

This condition is satisfiable if $X_n(x)$ are antisymmetric functions in x. From these considerations, we find that $c_2 = c_4 = 0$. Now the condition (5.34) is satisfied if $X'_n(\pm a) = 0$ or

$$c_1 k_n \cos k_n a = 0$$

from which we find

$$k_n = \frac{(2n + 1)\pi}{2a}$$

Since c_1 and c_3 are arbitrary constants, we may write ϕ_1 in the following form,

$$\phi_1 = \sum_{n=0}^{\infty} A_n \sin k_n x \sinh k_n y \tag{5.39}$$

where $k_n = (2n + 1)\pi/2a$ and the constants A_n are to be determined so as to satisfy the boundary condition (5.35).

† The constant is taken as negative because otherwise the boundary conditions cannot be satisfied.

Differentiating ϕ_1 with respect to y, and substituting $y = \pm b$, we have from (5.35) that

$$2x = \sum_{n=0}^{\infty} A_n k_n \cosh k_n b \sin k_n x = \sum_{n=0}^{\infty} B_n \sin k_n x \qquad (5.40)$$

where to simplify the writing we have introduced the symbol

$$B_n = A_n k_n \cosh k_n b$$

The coefficients A_n can now be determined by utilizing the scheme used in expanding functions in Fourier series. If we multiply both sides of (5.40) by $\sin (2m + 1)\pi x/2a$ and integrate term by term with respect to x, recalling that

$$\sin k_n x \sin k_m x = \tfrac{1}{2}[\cos (k_n - k_m)x - \cos (k_n + k_m)x]$$
$$= \frac{1}{2}\left[\cos \frac{(n - m)\pi x}{a} - \cos \frac{(n + m + 1)\pi x}{a} \right]$$
$$\sin^2 k_m x = \frac{1}{2}\left[1 - \cos \frac{(2m + 1)\pi x}{2} \right]$$

we find

$$\int_{-a}^{a} \sin k_n x \sin k_m x \, dx = 0 \qquad \text{if } m \neq n$$
$$= a \qquad \text{if } m = n$$

and

$$\int_{-a}^{a} 2x \sin k_m x \, dx = \int_{-a}^{a} B_m \sin^2 k_m x \, dx$$

Upon evaluating the integrals in the above expression, we obtain

$$B_m = \frac{16(-1)^m a}{\pi^2 (2m + 1)^2} \qquad \text{or} \qquad A_n = \frac{32(-1)^n a^2}{\pi^3 (2n + 1)^3} \frac{1}{\cosh k_n b}$$

so that the solution is

$$\phi = xy - \phi_1$$
$$= xy - \frac{32a^2}{\pi^3} \sum_{n=0}^{\infty} \frac{(-1)^n}{(2n + 1)^3} \frac{1}{\cosh k_n b} \sin k_n x \sinh k_n y \qquad (5.41)$$

The torsional constant J can be evaluated from formula (5.15) as follows:

$$J = \int_{y=-b}^{y=b} \int_{x=-a}^{x=a} \left(x^2 + y^2 + x \frac{\partial \phi}{\partial y} - y \frac{\partial \phi}{\partial x} \right) dx \, dy$$
$$= \frac{8a^3 b}{3} \left[1 + \frac{96}{\pi^4} \sum_{n=0}^{\infty} \frac{1}{(2n + 1)^4} - \frac{384a}{\pi^5 b} \sum_{n=0}^{\infty} \frac{\tanh k_n b}{(2n + 1)^5} \right]$$

Since

$$\sum_{n=0}^{\infty} \frac{1}{(2n+1)^4} = \frac{\pi^4}{96}$$

we have the formula

$$J = 16a^3b \left[\frac{1}{3} - \frac{64a}{\pi^5 b} \sum_{n=0}^{\infty} \frac{\tanh k_n b}{(2n+1)^5} \right] = \kappa a^3 b \qquad (5.42)$$

For various b/a ratios, the corresponding values of κ are given in Table 5.1. The series in (5.42) can be written as

$$\sum_{n=0}^{\infty} \frac{\tanh k_n b}{(2n+1)^5} = \tanh \frac{\pi b}{2a} + \sum_{n=1}^{\infty} \frac{\tanh k_n b}{(2n+1)^5}$$

We note that $\sum_{n=1}^{\infty} \tanh k_n b/(2n+1)^5$ is less than $\sum_{n=1}^{\infty} 1/(2n+1)^5 = 0.0046$, while $\tanh (\pi b/2a) \geq 0.917$ if $b \geq a$. Thus, the first term of the series gives the value of the sum to within ½ per cent, and, for practical purposes, we can use the approximate formula

$$J = 16a^3b \left(\frac{1}{3} - \frac{64}{\pi^5} \frac{a}{b} \tanh \frac{\pi b}{2a} \right) \qquad (5.43)$$

With some calculation we find that the shearing stresses are given by the following formulas:

$$\tau_{zx} = \frac{T}{J} \left(\frac{\partial \phi}{\partial x} - y \right) = - \frac{16Ta}{J\pi^2} \sum_{n=0}^{\infty} \frac{(-1)^n}{(2n+1)^2} \frac{\sinh k_n y}{\cosh k_n b} \cos k_n x$$

$$\tau_{yz} = \frac{T}{J} \left(\frac{\partial \phi}{\partial y} + x \right) = \frac{T}{J} \left[2x - \frac{16a}{\pi^2} \sum_{n=0}^{\infty} \frac{(-1)^n}{(2n+1)^2} \frac{\cosh k_n y}{\cosh k_n b} \sin kx \right] \qquad (5.44)$$

Assuming that $b > a$, it can be shown that the maximum shearing stress is at the mid-points of the long sides $x = \pm a$ of the rectangle. Substituting $x = a$, $y = 0$ in (5.44), we find

$$\tau_{zx} = 0$$

and

$$\tau_{max} = \tau_{yz} = \frac{2Ta}{J} \left[1 - \frac{8}{\pi^2} \sum_{n=0}^{\infty} \frac{1}{(2n+1)^2 \cosh k_n b} \right] = \kappa_1 \frac{Ta}{J} \qquad (5.45)$$

The infinite series on the right side, which we denote by $\kappa_1/2$, converges very rapidly when $b > a$, and there is no difficulty in calculating τ_{max} with sufficient accuracy for any particular value of b/a. For various

b/a ratios, the corresponding values of κ_1 are included in Table 5.1. Substituting the values of J from (5.42) into (5.45), we have

$$\tau_{\max} = \kappa_2 \frac{T}{a^2 b} \tag{5.46}$$

where κ_2 is another numerical factor, several values of which are given in Table 5.1.

TABLE 5.1

b/a	κ	κ_1	κ_2
1.0	2.250	1.350	0.600
1.2	2.656	1.518	0.571
1.5	3.136	1.696	0.541
2.0	3.664	1.860	0.508
2.5	3.984	1.936	0.484
3.0	4.208	1.970	0.468
4.0	4.496	1.994	0.443
5.0	4.656	1.998	0.430
10.0	4.992	2.000	0.401
∞	5.328	2.000	0.375

The contour lines of the surface $w = $ constant can be easily plotted from the equation for ϕ. For a square bar, that is, $a = b$, the contour lines are shown in Fig. 5.8, where the solid lines represent positive w and the dotted lines negative w as defined in the previous section.

5.4. Membrane Analogy. From the example worked out in the previous

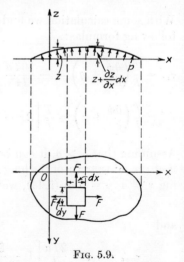

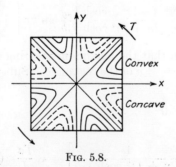

FIG. 5.8.

FIG. 5.9.

section, it becomes evident that a rigorous solution of the torsion problem for a bar with more complicated cross-sectional shape is likely to be very difficult. In developing approximate formulas for the torsional constants of many engineering sections, the so-called *membrane analogy* has proved very valuable. The membrane analogy is based on the mathematical analogy between the torsion problem and the behavior of a stretched elastic membrane subjected to a uniform lateral pressure.

Let a thin homogeneous membrane (Fig. 5.9) be stretched with uniform tension and fixed at its edge, which is a given curve in the x, y plane. When the membrane is subjected to a uniform lateral pressure p, it will undergo a small displacement z, where z is a function of x and y. Consider the equilibrium of an infinitesimal element $ABCD$ of the membrane after deformation. Let F be the uniform tension per unit length of the membrane. On the side AD, F is inclined at an angle β with respect to the axis. Since the deformation is small, $\beta \cong \partial z/\partial x$. The deflection z varies from point to point; therefore on the side BC, F is now inclined at an angle $\beta + (\partial \beta/\partial x)\, dx \cong (\partial z/\partial x) + (\partial^2 z/\partial x^2)\, dx$. Similarly, on the sides AB and CD, the tensile forces are inclined at the angles $\partial z/\partial y$ and $(\partial z/\partial y) + (\partial^2 z/\partial y^2)\, dy$, respectively. Summing up the z components of the forces acting on the four sides, we have

$$-(F\, dy)\,\frac{\partial z}{\partial x} + (F\, dy)\left(\frac{\partial z}{\partial x} + \frac{\partial^2 z}{\partial x^2}\, dx\right) - (F\, dx)\,\frac{\partial z}{\partial y}$$
$$+ (F\, dx)\left(\frac{\partial z}{\partial y} + \frac{\partial^2 z}{\partial y^2}\, dy\right) + p\, dx\, dy = 0$$

from which

$$\frac{\partial^2 z}{\partial x^2} + \frac{\partial^2 z}{\partial y^2} = -\frac{p}{F} \qquad \text{in } R \tag{5.47}$$

On the boundary, the deflection of the membrane is zero. The boundary condition is therefore

$$z = 0 \qquad \text{on } S \tag{5.48}$$

Now let us return to our torsion problem. The governing differential equation is

$$\frac{\partial^2 \phi}{\partial x^2} + \frac{\partial^2 \phi}{\partial y^2} = 0 \qquad \text{in } R \tag{5.6}$$

and the boundary condition is

$$\left(\frac{\partial \phi}{\partial x} - y\right) l + \left(\frac{\partial \phi}{\partial y} + x\right) m = 0 \qquad \text{on } S \tag{5.7}$$

Comparing these relations with (5.47) and (5.48), we find that apparently they are not analogous. However, they can be reduced to an analogous form if we introduce a new function $\psi(x,y)$ such that

$$\frac{\partial \phi}{\partial x} = \frac{\partial \psi}{\partial y} + y \qquad \frac{\partial \phi}{\partial y} = -\frac{\partial \psi}{\partial x} - x \tag{5.49}$$

From (5.49) we have

$$\frac{\partial^2 \phi}{\partial x^2} = \frac{\partial^2 \psi}{\partial x \, \partial y} \qquad \frac{\partial^2 \phi}{\partial y^2} = -\frac{\partial^2 \psi}{\partial y \, \partial x}$$

The differential equation (5.6) is identically satisfied, since

$$\frac{\partial^2 \phi}{\partial x^2} + \frac{\partial^2 \phi}{\partial y^2} = \frac{\partial^2 \psi}{\partial x \, \partial y} - \frac{\partial^2 \psi}{\partial y \, \partial x} = 0$$

That is, if ψ is defined as in (5.49) the equilibrium equations are satisfied identically.

In terms of ψ, the shearing stresses τ_{zx} and τ_{yz} are

$$\tau_{zx} = \frac{T}{J}\left(\frac{\partial \phi}{\partial x} - y\right) = \frac{T}{J}\frac{\partial \psi}{\partial y} \qquad \tau_{yz} = \frac{T}{J}\left(\frac{\partial \phi}{\partial y} + x\right) = -\frac{T}{J}\frac{\partial \psi}{\partial x} \quad (5.50)$$

If ψ is obtained, we can compute the shearing stresses by a simple differentiation. ψ is therefore the *stress function*, and the solution of ψ is equivalent to the solution of the stresses. In such a case, the compatibility equation must be used. With the stress system

$$\sigma_x = \sigma_y = \sigma_z = \tau_{xy} = 0$$

$$\tau_{zx} = \frac{T}{J}\frac{\partial \psi}{\partial y} \qquad \tau_{yz} = -\frac{T}{J}\frac{\partial \psi}{\partial x}$$

the corresponding strain components are

$$\epsilon_x = \epsilon_y = \epsilon_z = \gamma_{xy} = 0$$

$$\gamma_{zx} = \frac{T}{GJ}\frac{\partial \psi}{\partial y} \qquad \gamma_{yz} = -\frac{T}{GJ}\frac{\partial \psi}{\partial x}$$

Substituting into the compatibility equations (2.19), we find that the first three and the last equations are identically satisfied. The fourth and the fifth equations become

$$\frac{\partial}{\partial x}\left(-\frac{\partial \gamma_{yz}}{\partial x} + \frac{\partial \gamma_{zx}}{\partial y}\right) = 0 \qquad \frac{\partial}{\partial y}\left(\frac{\partial \gamma_{yz}}{\partial x} - \frac{\partial \gamma_{zx}}{\partial y}\right) = 0$$

Integrating, we have

$$-\frac{\partial \gamma_{yz}}{\partial x} + \frac{\partial \gamma_{zx}}{\partial y} = \text{constant} = c_1$$

This constant can be determined by substituting into the above equation

$$\gamma_{zx} = \frac{\tau_{zx}}{G} = \frac{T}{GJ}\left(\frac{\partial \phi}{\partial x} - y\right) \qquad \gamma_{yz} = \frac{\tau_{yz}}{G} = \frac{T}{GJ}\left(\frac{\partial \phi}{\partial y} + x\right)$$

from which we find

$$\frac{T}{GJ}\left(-\frac{\partial^2\phi}{\partial x\,\partial y}-1+\frac{\partial^2\phi}{\partial x\,\partial y}-1\right)=c_1$$

or $c_1 = -2T/GJ$. With this value of c_1, in terms of ψ, the above compatibility equation becomes

$$\frac{\partial^2\psi}{\partial x^2}+\frac{\partial^2\psi}{\partial y^2}=-2 \qquad \text{in } R \qquad (5.51)$$

which is the differential equation that ψ must satisfy. It may be pointed out that Eq. (5.51) is directly obtainable by differentiating Eqs. (5.49) and then eliminating ϕ between these equations. However, this will conceal the fact that (5.51) is actually the compatibility equation.

In terms of ψ, the boundary condition (5.8) becomes

$$\frac{\partial\psi}{\partial y}l-\frac{\partial\psi}{\partial x}m=0 \qquad \text{on } S$$

We have already shown in Sec. 5.1 that

$$l=\frac{dx}{dN}=\frac{dy}{ds} \qquad m=\frac{dy}{dN}=-\frac{dx}{ds} \qquad (5.13)$$

The boundary condition can therefore be written as

$$\frac{\partial\psi}{\partial y}\frac{dy}{ds}+\frac{\partial\psi}{\partial x}\frac{dx}{ds}=\frac{d\psi}{ds}=0$$

or
$$\psi=\text{constant}=c_2 \qquad \text{on } S \qquad (5.52)$$

We note that, in computing the stresses, only the derivatives of ψ are of interest and the value of the constant c_2 in (5.52) is irrelevant to the problem. For that reason, we may let $c_2 = 0$. Thus, the torsion problem is reduced to finding the function ψ such that

$$\frac{\partial^2\psi}{\partial x^2}+\frac{\partial^2\psi}{\partial y^2}=-2 \qquad \text{in } R \qquad (5.51)$$

$$\psi=0 \qquad \text{on } S \qquad (5.52)$$

Comparing these equations with the membrane equations, we see that they are exactly analogous if p/F is taken to be 2 and if the shape of the boundary of the membrane is the same as the cross section of the bar.

The membrane analogy is useful in the experimental determination of the stress function. The technique used to carry out such an experiment, as well as experiments according to other analogies, is discussed in detail in such books as "Handbook of Experimental Stress Analysis."[1]

[1] M. Hetenyi, "Handbook of Experimental Stress Analysis," pp. 700–751, John Wiley & Sons, Inc., New York, 1950.

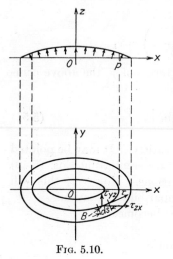

Fɪɢ. 5.10.

The membrane analogy not only is useful in actually determining the stress but also provides a visual picture of the stress distribution. Figure 5.10 represents such a membrane with the contour lines of the deflection surface plotted. Consider any point B on the membrane. Along the contour line, the deflection is constant, *i.e.*,

$$\frac{\partial z}{\partial s} = 0$$

From the analogy, we have

$$\frac{\partial \psi}{\partial s} = 0$$

Since

$$\frac{\partial \psi}{\partial s} = \frac{\partial \psi}{\partial y}\frac{dy}{ds} + \frac{\partial \psi}{\partial x}\frac{dx}{ds} = \frac{J}{T}\left(\tau_{zx}\frac{dy}{ds} - \tau_{yz}\frac{dx}{ds}\right) = \frac{J}{T}\left(\tau_{zx}\frac{dx}{dN} + \tau_{yz}\frac{dy}{dN}\right) = \frac{J}{T}\tau_{zN}$$

it follows that the component of the shearing stress normal to the contour line is zero. In other words, the shearing stress at a point B in the twisted bar is in the direction of the tangent to the contour line through this point. The magnitude of the resultant shearing stress τ at B can now be found from the following formula:

$$\tau = \tau_{yz}\frac{dy}{ds} + \tau_{zx}\frac{dx}{ds} = -\frac{T}{J}\left(\frac{\partial \psi}{\partial x}\frac{dx}{dN} + \frac{\partial \psi}{\partial y}\frac{dy}{dN}\right) = -\frac{T}{J}\frac{d\psi}{dN}$$

Thus the magnitude of the shearing stress at B is given by the slope of the membrane normal to the contour line, and therefore the maximum shearing stress occurs at the points where the contour lines are closest to each other. From the surface of the membrane, it can be seen that the maximum slope occurs on the boundary. It can therefore be concluded that the maximum shearing stresses also occur on the boundary of the bar.

We shall now proceed to derive the expression of the torsional constant J in terms of ψ. From formula (5.15),

$$J = \iint_R \left(x^2 + y^2 + x\frac{\partial \phi}{\partial y} - y\frac{\partial \phi}{\partial x}\right) dx\, dy$$

$$= -\iint_R \left(x\frac{\partial \psi}{\partial x} + y\frac{\partial \psi}{\partial y}\right) dx\, dy$$

$$= - \iint_R \left[\frac{\partial}{\partial x} (x\psi) + \frac{\partial}{\partial y} (y\psi) - 2\psi \right] dx\, dy$$

$$= - \oint_S x\psi\, dy + \oint_S y\psi\, dx + \iint_R 2\psi\, dx\, dy$$

$$J \quad = 2 \iint_R \psi\, dx\, dy \tag{5.53}$$

The last step was obtained because of Eq. (5.52), namely, $\psi = 0$ on S. From the membrane analogy, we see that the torsional constant J is equal to twice the volume bounded by the deflected membrane and the xy plane. In letting $c_2 = 0$ in (5.52), we contended that the value of c_2 is irrelevant to the problem. The calculation of J, however, apparently depends on the value of c_2. To explain this point, let us assume that c_2 is not zero and substitute $\psi_1 + c_2$ in the place of ψ in the next to the last step in (5.53). Since

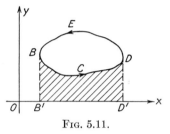

Fig. 5.11.

$\psi_1 + c_2 = c_2$ on the boundary, we have $\psi_1 = 0$ on S and ψ_1 is the same ψ as in the last step of (5.53). Thus

$$J = - \oint_S c_2 x\, dy + \oint_S c_2 y\, dx + \iint_R 2(\psi_1 + c_2)\, dx\, dy$$

From Fig. 5.11, we see that

$$\oint_S y\, dx = \int_{BCD} y\, dx + \int_{DEB} y\, dx$$
$$= \text{area } BCDD'B' - \text{area } BEDD'B'$$
$$= -A \tag{5.54}$$

where A is the area of the cross section. Similarly we can show $\oint_S x\, dy = A$. But $\iint_R dx\, dy = A$. Thus

$$J = -c_2 A - c_2 A + 2c_2 A + \iint_R 2\psi_1\, dx\, dy = \iint_R 2\psi_1\, dx\, dy$$

which is identical to formula (5.53).

5.5. Torsion of Thin Open Sections. Let us first consider the torsion of a bar with narrow rectangular cross section. From the membrane analogy, it is obvious that the effect of the short sides of the rectangle is only local. In formula (5.43), when b/a is large, we see that $\tanh (\pi b/2a)$ is approximately equal to 1 and the second term inside the parentheses becomes negligible. We have therefore

$$J \cong \frac{16a^3 b}{3}$$

In formula (5.45), when b/a is large, we see that

$$\cosh k_n b = \cosh \frac{(2n + 1)\pi}{2} \frac{b}{a}$$

is a large number and the sum of the infinite series becomes negligible. As a result, we obtain

$$\tau_{\max} \cong \frac{2Ta}{J} \tag{5.55}$$

With J determined, the angle of twist can be computed from the formula

$$\theta = \frac{T}{GJ} \tag{5.16}$$

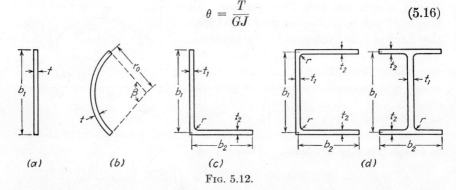

(a)   *(b)*   *(c)*   *(d)*

Fig. 5.12.

If we denote by b_1 and t the length and width of the rectangle (Fig. 5.12a), these formulas become

$$J \cong \frac{b_1 t^3}{3} \qquad \theta \cong \frac{3T}{b_1 t^3 G} \qquad \tau_{\max} \cong \frac{3T}{b_1 t^2} = G\theta t \tag{5.56}$$

As derived in the previous section, $\tau_{\max}$ is equal to the product of T/J and the maximum slope of the deflected membrane. In the case of a narrow rectangular section, from (5.55) and (5.56), we see that the maximum slope of the deflected membrane is $2a$ or t.

Let us compare the deflected membranes when the boundaries are as shown in Fig. 5.12a and b. It is apparent that the volumes under the membranes will be approximately the same if the cross-sectional areas are the same. Also, if t is small, the curvature of the shape in (b) can have only little effect on the maximum slope of the membrane. For that reason, we conclude that formula (5.56) can also be used for approximate solutions of other thin sections. Thus for such cross sections as shown in Fig. 5.12b, we merely have to replace b_1 in (5.56) by the developed length of the arc. In the case of a circular arc, the developed length is equal to $r_0 \beta$, where r_0 is the radius and β the angle subtended by the arc in radians.

For thin sections such as angles, channels, and I sections, the deflected membranes will behave as if they were stretched over several separate narrow rectangles.[1] Now J is equal to twice the volume bounded by the deflected membrane and the xy plane, and the maximum slope of the membrane is t_i where t_i is the larger of t_1 and t_2. We have, therefore, for the angle section (Fig. 5.12c),

$$J \cong \frac{b_1 t_1{}^3 + b_2 t_2{}^3}{3}$$

$$\theta \cong \frac{3T}{(b_1 t_1{}^3 + b_2 t_2{}^3)G} \qquad (5.57)$$

$$\tau_{\max} \cong G\theta t_i = \frac{3T t_i}{b_1 t_1{}^3 + b_2 t_2{}^3}$$

and for the channel and I section (Fig. 5.12d),

$$J \cong \frac{b_1 t_1{}^3 + 2b_2 t_2{}^3}{3}$$

$$\theta \cong \frac{3T}{(b_1 t_1{}^3 + 2b_2 t_2{}^3)G} \qquad (5.58)$$

$$\tau_{\max} \cong \frac{3T t_i}{b_1 t_1{}^3 + 2b_2 t_2{}^3}$$

It should be noted that a considerable stress concentration takes place at the reentrant corners, the magnitude of which depends on the radius of the fillets. For small radius of fillet (say $r = 0.1t$), Trefftz[2] obtained the following equation for the maximum stress at the fillet,

$$\tau_{\text{fillet}} = 1.74\tau_{\max} \sqrt[3]{\frac{t}{r}} \qquad (5.59)$$

where r is the radius of the fillet. Equation (5.59) is derived for an angle with equal thickness of flanges. In the case of two different thicknesses t_1 and t_2, the larger thickness must be used in the formula. The stress concentration at a reentrant corner has also been studied experimentally by using the soap-film analogy.[3] The ratio of $\tau_{\text{fillet}}/\tau_{\max}$ for several values of the ratio r/t are given in Table 5.2. For small radii of fillets, the experimental values of $\tau_{\text{fillet}}/\tau_{\max}$ are much smaller than those given by

[1] For a discussion of other approximate formulas, see G. W. Trayer and H. W. March, The Torsion of Members Having Sections Common in Aircraft Construction, *NACA Tech. Rept.* 334, 1929.

[2] E. Trefftz, Über die Wirkung ein Abrundung auf die Torsionspannungen in der innern Ecke eines Winkeleisens, *Z.A.M.M.*, Vol. 2, pp. 263–267, 1922.

[3] P. A. Cushman, "Shearing Stresses in Torsion and Bending by **Membrane** Analogy," doctoral dissertation, University of Michigan, 1932. Also *ASME Advance Paper*, June, 1932, meeting.

TABLE 5.2

r/t	$\frac{1}{8}$	$\frac{1}{4}$	$\frac{1}{2}$	1
$\tau_{\text{fillet}}/\tau_{\max}$	2.5	2.25	2.00	1.75

Eq. (5.59). This is probably due to the fact that it is difficult to obtain reliable values of τ_{fillet} for small radii of fillets.

5.6. Torsion of Thin Tubes. In terms of the stress function ψ, we have shown that on the boundary ψ must be a constant. When we have a solid section, we may let the constant be zero. When the section is bounded by two closed curves, as in Fig. 5.13, we shall again lose no generality by assuming that ψ vanishes on the outer boundary S_1 but we cannot assume it also vanishes on the inner boundary S_2, although we know that it has a constant value there. Because of this unknown constant, we need one additional equation to solve the problem. This additional equation may be obtained from the condition that the displacements must be single-valued.

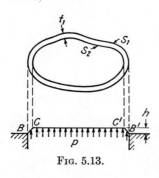

FIG. 5.13.

From Eqs. (5.5), we have

$$\tau_{zx} = G\theta\left(\frac{\partial\phi}{\partial x} - y\right) = G\left(\frac{\partial w}{\partial x} - \theta y\right) \quad \tau_{yz} = G\theta\left(\frac{\partial\phi}{\partial y} + x\right) = G\left(\frac{\partial w}{\partial y} + \theta x\right)$$

Let us now calculate the integral $\int\tau\,ds$ along the inner boundary.

$$\oint_{S_2}\tau\,ds = \oint_{S_2}\left(\tau_{zx}\frac{dx}{ds} + \tau_{yz}\frac{dy}{ds}\right)ds$$
$$= G\oint_{S_2}\left(\frac{\partial w}{\partial x}\,dx + \frac{\partial w}{\partial y}\,dy\right) + G\theta\oint_{S_2}(x\,dy - y\,dx)$$

From the condition that w is a single-valued function and the integration is taken round a closed curve, the first integral vanishes. As we have shown in Sec. 5.4, the second integral is equal to twice the area enclosed by S_2. Hence

$$\oint_{S_2}\tau\,ds = 2G\theta A_2 \tag{5.60}$$

where A_2 is the area enclosed by S_2.

Let us now return to the membrane analogy. If we replace the membrane inside S_2 by a weightless flat plate (Fig. 5.13), the equation of equilibrium of the plate is

$$\oint_{S_2}F\frac{\partial z}{\partial n}\,ds = pA_2 \tag{5.61}$$

where F, z are the surface tension and deflection of the membrane as defined in Sec. 5.4. Since

$$\frac{\partial z}{\partial n} = \frac{p}{2F} \frac{\partial \psi}{\partial n} = \frac{p}{2F} \frac{\tau}{G\theta}$$

we have from (5.61)

$$\oint_{S_2} F \frac{p}{2F} \frac{\tau}{G\theta} ds = pA_2 \qquad \text{or} \qquad \oint_{S_2} \tau \, ds = 2G\theta A_2$$

which we obtained as Eq. (5.60). Thus if we have a hollow section, we may consider the membrane as stretched over the outer boundary and a weightless flat plate on the inner boundary.

In Fig. 5.13, BB' and CC' are the levels of the outer and inner boundaries, and BC and $B'C'$ are the cross section of the membrane stretched between these boundaries. If the wall is thin, BC and $B'C'$ become approximately straight lines and the variation in slope of the membrane is negligible. This is equivalent to assuming that the shearing stresses are uniform across the thickness of the wall. If we denote by h the constant value of ψ on S_2, from the membrane analogy, h is the difference in levels of the two boundaries. Let t be the variable thickness of the wall. The shearing stress at any point is given by the slope of the membrane, or

$$\tau = \frac{Th}{Jt} \qquad \text{(5.62)}$$

The formula for J [Eq. (5.53)] must now be modified. In the derivation of Eqs. (5.10) and (5.11), the positive normal N has been taken outward from the cross section. With respect to the inner boundary, the same sign convention must be used, i.e., the positive direction is inward. To allow for this condition, we must change the sign of the line integrals in (5.10) and (5.11) when integrated along S_2. On S_1, we have $\psi = 0$, and on S_2 we have $\psi = h$. Therefore the formula (5.53) becomes

$$J = h \oint_{S_2} (x \, dy - y \, dx) + 2 \iint_R \psi \, dx \, dy \qquad \text{(5.63)}$$

where R denotes the area bounded between S_1 and S_2, or A_1. Because the section is thin, the value of ψ in the second integral can be replaced by its average value taken over S_1 and S_2, namely, $h/2$. We have, therefore,

$$J = 2h(A_2 + \tfrac{1}{2}A_1) = 2Ah$$

where A is the area enclosed by the mean line of the boundaries. Substituting into (5.62), we have

$$\tau = \frac{T}{2At} \qquad \text{(5.64)}$$

The angle of twist θ may be calculated from Eq. (5.60),

$$\oint_S \tau \, ds = \frac{T}{2A} \oint_S \frac{ds}{t} = 2G\theta A$$

from which we find

$$\theta = \frac{T}{4A^2G} \oint_S \frac{ds}{t} \tag{5.65}$$

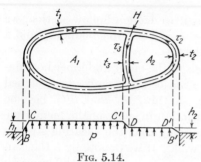

FIG. 5.14.

where S is the mean line of the boundaries. Equations (5.64) and (5.65) were first obtained by Bredt[1] and are known as Bredt's formulas.

If the cross section of the tubular member has more than two boundaries (Fig. 5.14), the portions of membrane inside the inner boundaries can be again replaced by weightless flat plates. Assuming that the thickness of the wall is small, we have

$$\tau_1 = \frac{Th_1}{Jt_1}$$

$$\tau_2 = \frac{Th_2}{Jt_2} \tag{5.66}$$

$$\tau_3 = \frac{T}{J}\frac{h_1 - h_2}{t_3} = \frac{\tau_1 t_1 - \tau_2 t_2}{t_3}$$

where h_1 and h_2 are the levels of the inner boundaries CC' and DD'. Equation (5.63) becomes

$$J = 2 \iint_R \psi \, dx \, dy + \sum_i 2h_i A_i' = 2h_1 A_1 + 2h_2 A_2$$

where A_i' is the area enclosed by the boundary S_i and A_1, A_2 are the areas enclosed by the mid-section curves S_1 and S_2. Therefore

$$T = 2\tau_1 t_1 A_1 + 2\tau_2 t_2 A_2 \tag{5.67}$$

Assume that the thicknesses t_1, t_2, t_3 are constant. Let s_1, s_2, and s_3 be the lengths of the mid-section curves. By applying Eq. (5.60) first over A_1 and then over A_2, we obtain

$$\tau_1 s_1 + \tau_3 s_3 = 2G\theta A_1 \qquad \tau_2 s_2 - \tau_3 s_3 = 2G\theta A_2 \tag{5.68}$$

[1] R. Bredt, Kritische Bemerkungen zur Drehungs-elastizität, Z. Ver. deut. Ing., Vol. 40, pp. 785–813, 1896.

τ_1, τ_2, τ_3, and θ can be calculated by solving Eqs. (5.67) and (5.68) simultaneously.

From Eq. (5.66), we note that, in a tubular branch of the cross section, τt is a constant. When several tubular members meet, as at point H, we have

$$\tau_1 t_1 = \tau_2 t_2 + \tau_3 t_3 \tag{5.69}$$

This suggests a hydrodynamical analogy, *viz.*, the quantity $q = \tau t$ is analogous to the quantity of ideal liquid circulating in a channel having the same shape as the tubular bar. Equation (5.69) then states that the amount of incoming liquid must be equal to the amount of liquid flowing out. The quantity q is therefore called *shear flow*.

For tubular sections with more than three boundaries, we shall illustrate the determination of the shearing stresses by the following numerical

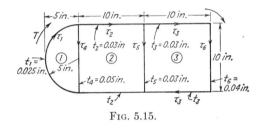

Fɪɢ. 5.15.

example: Figure 5.15 shows the cross section with the given dimensions. The applied torque is given as 100,000 in.-lb. From the given dimensions, we compute the areas as $A_1 = \pi(5)^2/2 = 39.3$ sq in., $A_2 = A_3 = 100$ sq in. Assume that the shearing stresses are positive in the direction shown. From the consideration of shear flow, we have

$$\tau_1 t_1 = \tau_2 t_2 + \tau_4 t_4 \qquad \tau_2 t_2 = \tau_3 t_3 + \tau_5 t_5 \qquad \tau_3 t_3 = \tau_6 t_6 \tag{5.70}$$

Since $T = 2\tau_1 t_1 A_1 + 2\tau_2 t_2 A_2 + 2\tau_3 t_3 A_3$, we have, by substituting the numerical values

$$100{,}000 = 2 \times 39.3 \times 0.025\tau_1 + 2 \times 100 \times 0.03\tau_2 + 2 \times 100 \times 0.03\tau_3$$
or $$1.965\tau_1 + 6\tau_2 + 6\tau_3 = 100{,}000 \tag{5.71}$$

From Eq. (5.60), we have

$$\tau_1 s_1 + \tau_4 s_4 = 2G\theta A_1 \qquad -\tau_4 s_4 + 2\tau_2 s_2 + \tau_5 s_5 = 2G\theta A_2$$
$$-\tau_5 s_5 + 2\tau_3 s_3 + \tau_6 s_6 = 2G\theta A_3 \tag{5.72}$$

Since $s_1 = 5\pi$, $s_2 = s_3 = s_4 = s_5 = s_6 = 10$, combining with Eqs. (5.70), we obtain

$$20.7\tau_1 - 6\tau_2 = 78.6G\theta \qquad -0.5\tau_1 + 3.6\tau_2 - \tau_3 = 20G\theta$$
$$-\tau_2 + 3.75\tau_3 = 20G\theta \tag{5.73}$$

Solving Eqs. (5.71) and (5.73) simultaneously, we find $\tau_1 = 5,740$ psi, $\tau_2 = 7,800$ psi, $\tau_3 = 6,940$ psi, $\tau_4 = -1,810$ psi, $\tau_5 = 960$ psi, and $\tau_6 = 5,200$ psi. The negative sign of τ_4 indicates that its direction is opposite to that assumed.

Problem 1. Given a circular steel tube with an outside diameter of 4 in., and a thickness of $\frac{5}{32}$ in. Compare the angle of twist and the maximum shearing stress of this tube with those of the same tube after it has been split by cutting along an element. Note that an open section bar is relatively weak in resisting torsion. In this problem, it will be found that the closed section is more than 400 times as stiff as the open section and more than 30 times as strong.

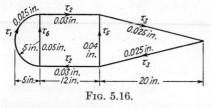

FIG. 5.16.

Problem 2. Given a thin tubular bar with the dimensions shown in Fig. 5.16. The bar is under the action of a torque of 100,000 in.-lb. Find the shearing stresses in the tube.

Ans. $\tau_1 = 6,360$ psi, $\tau_2 = 8,170$ psi, $\tau_3 = 5,720$ psi, $\tau_4 = 172$ psi, and $\tau_5 = -2,550$ psi

5.7. Torsion of Circular Shafts of Variable Diameter. Let us consider the twisting of a circular shaft of variable diameter by terminal couples (Fig. 5.17). In discussing bodies of revolution, it is convenient to make use of the cylindrical coordinates r, θ, z. We shall take the axis of

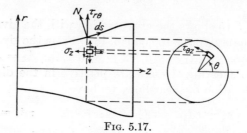

FIG. 5.17.

the shaft as the z axis. From Fig. 4.5, the equations of equilibrium of an element can be easily written down. Neglecting the body forces, we have

$$\frac{\partial \sigma_r}{\partial r} + \frac{1}{r}\frac{\partial \tau_{r\theta}}{\partial \theta} + \frac{\partial \tau_{rz}}{\partial z} + \frac{\sigma_r - \sigma_\theta}{r} = 0$$

$$\frac{\partial \tau_{rz}}{\partial r} + \frac{1}{r}\frac{\partial \tau_{\theta z}}{\partial \theta} + \frac{\partial \sigma_z}{\partial z} + \frac{\tau_{rz}}{r} = 0 \qquad (5.74)$$

$$\frac{\partial \tau_{r\theta}}{\partial r} + \frac{1}{r}\frac{\partial \sigma_\theta}{\partial \theta} + \frac{\partial \tau_{\theta z}}{\partial z} + \frac{2\tau_{r\theta}}{r} = 0$$

Denote the displacements in the r, θ, z directions by u, v, and w, respectively. The strain components ϵ_r, ϵ_θ, and $\gamma_{r\theta}$ can be derived in the same manner as in Sec. 4.3, while the strain components ϵ_z, $\gamma_{\theta z}$, and γ_{zr} can be easily written down from their standard formulas in the cartesian coordinates. Collecting these results, we have

$$\epsilon_r = \frac{\partial u}{\partial r} \qquad \epsilon_\theta = \frac{u}{r} + \frac{1}{r}\frac{\partial v}{\partial \theta}, \qquad \epsilon_z = \frac{\partial w}{\partial z}$$

$$\gamma_{r\theta} = \frac{1}{r}\frac{\partial u}{\partial \theta} + \frac{\partial v}{\partial r} - \frac{v}{r} \qquad \gamma_{\theta z} = \frac{1}{r}\frac{\partial w}{\partial \theta} + \frac{\partial v}{\partial z} \qquad (5.75)$$

$$\gamma_{zr} = \frac{\partial u}{\partial z} + \frac{\partial w}{\partial r}$$

In the case of a uniform circular shaft twisted by terminal couples, we found in Sec. 5.2 that there is no displacement in the direction of the axis of the shaft and the displacement of points in any cross section is in the tangential direction. We shall attempt to solve the present problem by assuming that in this case we also have

$$u = w = 0$$

We shall prove that the solution based on this assumption will satisfy the differential equations and the boundary conditions. From the uniqueness theorem, we can conclude that this is the correct solution. On account of rotational symmetry, v cannot depend on θ and will be a function of r and z only.

Thus, from (5.75), we find

$$\epsilon_r = \epsilon_\theta = \epsilon_z = \gamma_{zr} = 0 \qquad \gamma_{r\theta} = \frac{\partial v}{\partial r} - \frac{v}{r} \qquad \gamma_{\theta z} = \frac{\partial v}{\partial z} \qquad (5.76)$$

From Hooke's law, it follows readily that

$$\sigma_r = \sigma_\theta = \sigma_z = \tau_{zr} = 0 \qquad \tau_{r\theta} = G\left(\frac{\partial v}{\partial r} - \frac{v}{r}\right) \qquad \tau_{\theta z} = G\left(\frac{\partial v}{\partial z}\right) \quad (5.77)$$

Noting that the only nonvanishing stress components are $\tau_{r\theta}$ and $\tau_{\theta z}$, which are independent of θ, we find that the first two equations in (5.74) are identically satisfied and the third equation becomes

$$\frac{\partial \tau_{r\theta}}{\partial r} + \frac{\partial \tau_{\theta z}}{\partial z} + \frac{2\tau_{r\theta}}{r} = 0$$

This equation can be written as

$$\frac{\partial}{\partial r}(r^2\tau_{r\theta}) + \frac{\partial}{\partial z}(r^2\tau_{\theta z}) = 0 \qquad (5.78)$$

This equation is identically satisfied by introducing a stress function ψ such that

$$\frac{\partial \psi}{\partial r} = r^2\tau_{\theta z} \qquad \frac{\partial \psi}{\partial z} = -r^2\tau_{r\theta}$$

or

$$\tau_{r\theta} = -\frac{1}{r^2}\frac{\partial \psi}{\partial z} \qquad \tau_{\theta z} = \frac{1}{r^2}\frac{\partial \psi}{\partial r} \qquad (5.79)$$

To solve for the stress function, we must resort to the compatibility equation. Combining (5.77) and (5.79), we find that

$$\frac{\partial}{\partial r}\left(\frac{v}{r}\right) = -\frac{1}{r^3}\frac{\partial\psi}{\partial z} \qquad \frac{\partial}{\partial z}\left(\frac{v}{r}\right) = \frac{1}{r^3}\frac{\partial\psi}{\partial r}$$

Differentiating the first of these relations with respect to z and the second with respect to r and subtracting, we obtain the following compatibility equation:

$$\frac{\partial^2\psi}{\partial r^2} - \frac{3}{r}\frac{\partial\psi}{\partial r} + \frac{\partial^2\psi}{\partial z^2} = 0 \tag{5.80}$$

Let us now find the boundary conditions for ψ. Since the lateral surface of the shaft is free from external loads, it follows that the resultant shearing stress must be directed along the tangent to the boundary of the axial section, and its projection on the normal N to the boundary must be zero. Accordingly

$$\tau_{r\theta}\cos Nr + \tau_{\theta z}\cos Nz = 0$$

But $\cos Nr = dz/ds$, $\cos Nz = -dr/ds$, where ds is an element of the boundary. Substituting into this the expression (5.79), we obtain

$$\frac{\partial\psi}{\partial z}\frac{dz}{ds} + \frac{\partial\psi}{\partial r}\frac{dr}{ds} = 0$$

which gives

$$\frac{d\psi}{ds} = 0$$

or $\psi = $ constant on the boundary   (5.81)

The torsion problem of a circular shaft with variable diameter thus reduces to the solution of Eq. (5.80), together with the boundary condition (5.81).

The magnitude of the twisting moment can be easily computed by taking a cross section and calculating the moment by the shearing stress $\tau_{\theta z}$. Thus,

$$T = \int_0^a \tau_{\theta z} r(2\pi r)\ dr = 2\pi\int_0^a \frac{\partial\psi}{\partial r}\ dr = 2\pi[\psi(a,z) - \psi(0,z)] \tag{5.82}$$

If the shaft is conical (Fig. 5.18), we find that the ratio

$$\frac{z}{(r^2 + z^2)^{1/2}} = \cos\beta$$

on the boundary and is therefore a constant. Thus, any function of this ratio will satisfy the boundary condition (5.81). It is easy to verify that the function

$$\psi = C\left\{\frac{z}{(r^2 + z^2)^{1/2}} - \frac{1}{3}\left[\frac{z}{(r^2 + z^2)^{1/2}}\right]^3\right\}$$

where C is a constant, satisfies Eq. (5.80). Substituting this function into (5.82), the constant C can be determined, *viz.*,

$$C = -\frac{3T}{2\pi(2 - 3\cos\beta + \cos^3\beta)} \tag{5.83}$$

The shearing stresses $\tau_{r\theta}$ and $\tau_{\theta z}$ are thus

$$\tau_{r\theta} = -\frac{Cr^2}{(r^2 + z^2)^{5/2}} \qquad \tau_{\theta z} = -\frac{Crz}{(r^2 + z^2)^{5/2}} \tag{5.84}$$

where C is given by (5.83).

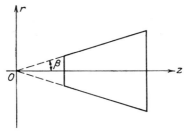

Fig. 5.18.

The problems encountered in practice are usually more complicated. In such cases, numerical methods of solution such as will be discussed in Chap. 6 can be used.[1]

---

[1] See, for example, R. V. Southwell, "Relaxation Methods in Theoretical Physics," Oxford University Press, New York, pp. 152–155, 1940; A. Thom and J. Orr, The Solution of the Torsion Problem for Circular Shafts of Varying Radius, *Proc. Roy. Soc.* (*London*), *A*, Vol. 131, pp. 30–37, 1931.

CHAPTER 6

FINITE-DIFFERENCE APPROXIMATIONS
AND THE RELAXATION METHOD

6.1. Finite Differences. Once an elasticity problem is formulated, our task becomes that of seeking the solution of the resulting differential equations together with the boundary conditions. In Chaps. 4 and 5, analytical methods are used in the solutions of a number of elasticity problems. In some problems, however, analytical solutions are not always possible, and we must resort to approximate numerical methods. One of these powerful methods is the *method of finite differences*. The idea behind this method is to replace the governing partial differential equations and the equations defining the boundary conditions by the corresponding *finite-difference equations*. This then reduces the problem to a set of simultaneous *algebraic* equations which can be solved without mathematical difficulty.

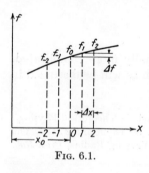

FIG. 6.1.

Before we proceed to convert the partial differential equations into finite-difference equations, some fundamental concepts about the finite-difference approximation should be mentioned. Let us assume that a function $f(x)$ of the variable x is known for equidistant values of x and that $f(x)$ is a continuous function. Figure 6.1 shows the curve $f = f(x)$. At some point 0 where $x = x_0$, by definition the derivative df/dx at the point 0 is

$$\left(\frac{df}{dx}\right)_0 = \lim_{\Delta x \to 0}\left(\frac{\Delta f}{\Delta x}\right)_0 = \lim_{\Delta x \to 0}\frac{f_1 - f_0}{x_1 - x_0} = \lim_{h \to 0}\frac{f_1 - f_0}{h} \qquad (6.1)$$

where $\Delta x = h$ is the interval, Δf is the difference between the values of f at points 1 and 0, and f_1, f_0 are the values of f at the points 1 and 0, respectively. The subscript 0 of df/dx indicates the point at which the derivative is taken. If h is small, the derivative df/dx is approximately equal to $\Delta f/\Delta x$. From Eq. (6.1), we have therefore, at point 0,

$$\left(\frac{df}{dx}\right)_0 \cong \frac{1}{h}\left(f_1 - f_0\right)$$

106

or, in general, at any point x,

$$\frac{df}{dx} \cong \frac{\Delta f}{h} = \frac{1}{h}[f(x+h) - f(x)] \tag{6.2}$$

where $\Delta f = f(x+h) - f(x)$ is called the *first difference* of the function f at x. In Eq. (6.2), the difference is given in terms of the values of the function at the point under consideration and at a point ahead of it. The difference in this form is called the *forward difference*. In a similar manner, the derivative can also be approximated by the *backward difference*, *viz.*, at point 0,

$$\left(\frac{df}{dx}\right)_0 \cong \frac{1}{h}(f_0 - f_{-1})$$

or in general, at any point x,

$$\frac{df}{dx} \cong \frac{1}{h}[f(x) - f(x-h)] \tag{6.3}$$

In terms of *central difference*, we have at the point 0

$$\left(\frac{df}{dx}\right)_0 \cong \frac{1}{2h}(f_1 - f_{-1})$$

or in general, at any point x,

$$\frac{df}{dx} \cong \frac{1}{2h}[f(x+h) - f(x-h)] \tag{6.4}$$

where in the above equation an interval of $\Delta x = 2h$ is considered.

We shall use the symbols $\bar{\Delta}$, Δ, $\underline{\Delta}$ to denote the *first forward, central,* and *backward differences,* respectively. Thus,

$$\bar{\Delta}f = f(x+h) - f(x) \qquad \Delta f = \frac{1}{2}[f(x+h) - f(x-h)]$$
$$\underline{\Delta}f = f(x) - f(x-h)$$

In a similar manner we may approximate the second derivative by the *second difference*. From the differential calculus,

$$\frac{d^2f}{dx^2} = \frac{d}{dx}\left(\frac{df}{dx}\right) \cong \frac{\Delta^2 f}{h^2} \tag{6.5}$$

where Δ^2 denotes second difference and we shall use the symbols $\bar{\Delta}^2$, Δ^2, $\underline{\Delta}^2$ to denote the *second forward, central,* and *backward differences,* respectively.

The second forward difference at point 0 (Fig. 6.1) can be obtained as follows:

$$(\bar{\Delta}^2 f)_0 = \bar{\Delta}(\bar{\Delta}f)_0 = \bar{\Delta}(f_1 - f_0) = \bar{\Delta}f_1 - \bar{\Delta}f_0 = (f_2 - f_1) - (f_1 - f_0)$$
$$= f_2 - 2f_1 + f_0$$

In the above calculation, it is seen that each $\bar{\Delta}$ can be used separately as an operator. Thus, $\bar{\Delta}^2$ is the same as the operator $\bar{\Delta}$ used twice; $(\bar{\Delta}f)_0 = \bar{\Delta}f_0$ and $\bar{\Delta}f_1$ are the same as the first forward differences at the points 0 and 1, respectively. At any point x, we have

$$\bar{\Delta}^2 f = f(x + 2h) - 2f(x + h) + f(x) \qquad (6.6)$$

In a like manner, the second backward difference at 0 is

$$(\underline{\Delta}^2 f)_0 = \underline{\Delta}(\underline{\Delta}f)_0 = \underline{\Delta}(f_0 - f_{-1}) = \underline{\Delta}f_0 - \underline{\Delta}f_{-1} = (f_0 - f_{-1}) - (f_{-1} - f_{-2})$$
$$= f_0 - 2f_{-1} + f_{-2}$$

or, at any point x,

$$\underline{\Delta}^2 f = f(x) - 2f(x - h) + f(x - 2h) \qquad (6.7)$$

Following the calculations in deriving (6.6) and (6.7), the second central difference at 0 would be

$$(\Delta^2 f)_0 = \Delta(\Delta f_0) = \frac{\Delta(f_1 - f_{-1})}{2} = \frac{f_2 - 2f_0 + f_{-2}}{4}$$

This formula gives the second central difference in terms of the values of the function at *two* intervals ahead of the point and *two* intervals behind it. A better approximation can be obtained if we can define the second central difference in terms of the values of the function at *one* interval ahead of and behind it. This can be accomplished by defining $\Delta^2 f$ as

$$(\Delta^2 f)_0 = \bar{\Delta}(\underline{\Delta}f)_0 \qquad \text{or} \qquad (\Delta^2 f)_0 = \underline{\Delta}(\bar{\Delta}f)_0$$

Thus, we have, for example, from the first formula

$$(\Delta^2 f)_0 = \bar{\Delta}(\underline{\Delta}f)_0 = \bar{\Delta}(f_0 - f_{-1}) = \bar{\Delta}f_0 - \bar{\Delta}f_{-1} = (f_1 - f_0) - (f_0 - f_{-1})$$
$$= f_1 - 2f_0 + f_{-1}$$

The same result is obtained by using the second formula. At any point x, we have therefore

$$\Delta^2 f = f(x + h) - 2f(x) + f(x - h) \qquad (6.8)$$

In general, the derivatives at any point can be better approximated by the corresponding central differences because these differences involve points on both sides of the point in question along the curve and therefore give better average values. Unless otherwise specified, we shall henceforth consider only the central differences.

Having demonstrated the method of deriving the first and second differences, the higher-order central differences can be easily found in a similar manner. For example, the third central difference at the point x is

$$\Delta^3 f = \Delta(\Delta^2 f) = \Delta[f(x + h) - 2f(x) + f(x - h)]$$
$$= \Delta f(x + h) - 2\Delta f(x) + \Delta f(x - h)$$
$$= \frac{f(x + 2h) - f(x)}{2} - 2\frac{f(x + h) - f(x - h)}{2} + \frac{f(x) - f(x - 2h)}{2}$$
$$= \frac{1}{2}[f(x + 2h) - 2f(x + h) + 2f(x - h) - f(x - 2h)] \qquad (6.9)$$

and the fourth central difference is

$$
\begin{aligned}
\Delta^4 f &= \Delta^2(\Delta^2 f) = \Delta^2[f(x+h) - 2f(x) + f(x-h)] \\
&= \Delta^2 f(x+h) - 2\,\Delta^2 f(x) + \Delta^2 f(x-h) \\
&= [f(x+2h) - 2f(x+h) + f(x)] - 2[f(x+h) - 2f(x) \\
&\qquad + f(x-h)] + [f(x) - 2f(x-h) + f(x-2h)] \\
&= f(x+2h) - 4f(x+h) + 6f(x) - 4f(x-h) + f(x-2h) \quad (6.10)
\end{aligned}
$$

Note that in the above derivations (Δ^2) is used as a unit operator which is defined by formula (6.8). From the above formulas, we see that the coefficients of the even-ordered differences are those of the binomial expansion of $(a - b)^n$. We can show that this is valid in the general case. Thus, for *even* differences, *i.e.*, for even n, the nth central difference is

$$
\begin{aligned}
\Delta^n f = f\left(x + \frac{n}{2}\,h\right) &- nf\left(x + \frac{n}{2}\,h - h\right) \\
&+ \frac{n(n-1)}{2} f\left(x + \frac{n}{2}\,h - 2h\right) - \cdots \\
+ (-1)^r \frac{n!}{r!(n-r)!} f\left(x + \frac{n}{2}\,h - rh\right) &+ \cdots + f\left(x - \frac{n}{2}\,h\right) \quad (6.11)
\end{aligned}
$$

where r is any integer equal to or less than n.

For *odd* differentials the corresponding differences may be obtained from the following formula,

$$
\frac{d^{n+1} f}{dx^{n+1}} \cong \frac{1}{2h} \left[\frac{\Delta^n f(x+h)}{h^n} - \frac{\Delta^n f(x-h)}{h^n} \right]
$$

or
$$
\Delta^{n+1} f = \Delta(\Delta^n f) = \tfrac{1}{2}[\Delta^n f(x+h) - \Delta^n f(x-h)] \quad (6.12)
$$

where n is an even number and $\Delta^n f(x+h)$ and $\Delta^n f(x-h)$ may be obtained from formula (6.11).

6.2. Finite-difference Equations. In the previous section, by assuming that f is a function of x only, we obtained the finite-difference approximations of the various derivatives. If f is a function of both x and y, we then have to deal with *partial derivatives*. Following the same reasoning as in the previous section, and taking $\Delta x = \Delta y = h$, we have, from the definition of partial derivatives,

$$
\frac{\partial f}{\partial x} \cong \frac{\Delta_x f}{2h} \qquad \frac{\partial f}{\partial y} \cong \frac{\Delta_y f}{2h}
$$
$$
\frac{\partial^2 f}{\partial x^2} \cong \frac{\Delta_x^2 f}{h^2} \qquad \frac{\partial^2 f}{\partial y^2} \cong \frac{\Delta_y^2 f}{h^2}
$$

where the subscripts of Δ_x and Δ_y denote the directions in which the differences are taken.

If we divide our domain into a square mesh as shown in Fig. 6.2 with $\Delta x = \Delta y = h$, at the point 0, we obtain, from Eqs. (6.4) and (6.8),

$$\frac{\partial f}{\partial x} \cong \frac{1}{2h} [f(x + h, y) - f(x - h, y)] = \frac{1}{2h} (f_1 - f_3)$$

$$\frac{\partial f}{\partial y} \cong \frac{1}{2h} [f(x, y + h) - f(x, y - h)] = \frac{1}{2h} (f_2 - f_4)$$

$$\frac{\partial^2 f}{\partial x^2} \cong \frac{1}{h^2} [f(x + h, y) - 2f(x,y) + f(x - h, y)]$$

$$= \frac{1}{h^2} (f_1 - 2f_0 + f_3)$$

$$\frac{\partial^2 f}{\partial y^2} \cong \frac{1}{h^2} [f(x, y + h) - 2f(x,y) + f(x, y - h)]$$

$$= \frac{1}{h^2} (f_2 - 2f_0 + f_4)$$

Now consider the Laplace operator

$$\nabla^2 f = \frac{\partial^2 f}{\partial x^2} + \frac{\partial^2 f}{\partial y^2}$$

From the above definitions, we obtain immediately

$$\nabla^2 f = \frac{1}{h^2} (f_1 + f_2 + f_3 + f_4 - 4f_0)$$

If our governing differential equation is a Laplace equation, $\nabla^2 f = 0$, the corresponding *finite-difference equation* at the point 0 is

$$f_1 + f_2 + f_3 + f_4 - 4f_0 = 0 \quad (6.13)$$

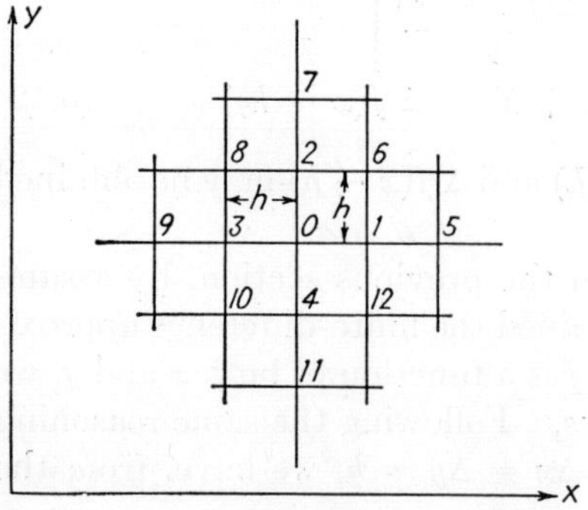

At every point in the domain, there is one finite-difference equation of the form (6.13).

If the domain is divided into a net with n inner points, n finite-difference equations are obtained. Together with the boundary conditions, we can solve for the values of the function at every point in the domain.

Fig. 6.2.

We note that the differential equation is now transformed into a system of algebraic equations which can be solved without any mathematical difficulty.

In a like manner, if the governing differential equation is of the Poisson's type, as Eq. (5.51),

$$\nabla^2 f = -2$$

the corresponding difference equation at 0 is

$$f_1 + f_2 + f_3 + f_4 - 4f_0 = -2h^2 \tag{6.14}$$

Next, let us consider the biharmonic equation

$$\nabla^4 f = \frac{\partial^4 f}{\partial x^4} + 2 \frac{\partial^4 f}{\partial x^2 \, \partial y^2} + \frac{\partial^4 f}{\partial y^4} = 0$$

Referring to Fig. 6.2 and using formulas (6.10) in the x and y directions, respectively, we have

$$\frac{\partial^4 f}{\partial x^4} \cong \frac{\Delta_x^4 f}{h^4} = \frac{1}{h^4} (f_5 - 4f_1 + 6f_0 - 4f_3 + f_9)$$

$$\frac{\partial^4 f}{\partial y^4} \cong \frac{\Delta_y^4 f}{h^4} = \frac{1}{h^4} (f_7 - 4f_2 + 6f_0 - 4f_4 + f_{11})$$

The finite-difference approximation of $\partial^4 f / (\partial x^2 \, \partial y^2)$ can be obtained as follows:

$$\frac{\partial^4 f}{\partial x^2 \, \partial y^2} = \frac{\partial^2}{\partial x^2} \left(\frac{\partial^2 f}{\partial y^2} \right) \cong \frac{\Delta_x^2 (\Delta_y^2 f)}{h^4}$$

$$= \frac{1}{h^4} \Delta_x^2 (f_2 - 2f_0 + f_4) = \frac{1}{h^4} (\Delta_x^2 f_2 - 2 \Delta_x^2 f_0 + \Delta_x^2 f_4)$$

$$= \frac{1}{h^4} (f_6 + f_8 + f_{10} + f_{12} - 2f_1 - 2f_2 - 2f_3 - 2f_4 + 4f_0)$$

Thus the finite-difference equation at 0 becomes

$$\frac{1}{h^4} [20f_0 - 8(f_1 + f_2 + f_3 + f_4) + 2(f_6 + f_8 + f_{10} + f_{12})$$

$$+ f_5 + f_7 + f_9 + f_{11}] = 0 \tag{6.15}$$

Problem. Transform the following differential equation into a finite-difference equation at 0:

$$\frac{\partial^2 f}{\partial r^2} - \frac{3}{r} \frac{\partial f}{\partial r} + \frac{\partial^2 f}{\partial z^2} = 0$$

Ans. In Fig. 6.2, let r, z be in the original x, y directions, respectively. The finite-difference equation at the point 0 is

$$f_1 \left(1 - \frac{3h}{2r_0} \right) + f_2 + f_3 \left(1 + \frac{3h}{2r_0} \right) + f_4 - 4f_0 = 0$$

6.3. Solution of the Finite-difference Equations. Let us take, as an example, the problem of a square bar under torsion. In terms of ψ, the governing differential equation is

$$\frac{\partial^2 \psi}{\partial x^2} + \frac{\partial^2 \psi}{\partial y^2} = -2 \qquad \text{in domain } R \tag{5.51}$$

and $\qquad\qquad \psi = 0 \qquad\qquad \text{on boundary } S \tag{5.52}$

Dividing the section into four square elements and numbering the nodal points of the network as shown in Fig. 6.3, we obtain the following difference equation corresponding to (5.51) at 0:

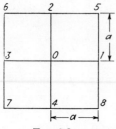

FIG. 6.3.

$$\psi_1 + \psi_2 + \psi_3 + \psi_4 - 4\psi_0 = -2h^2 \quad (6.16)$$

From the boundary conditions (5.51), we have

$$\psi_i = 0 \qquad i = 1, 2, \ldots, 8 \quad (6.17)$$

Substituting (6.17) into (6.16) and noting that $h = a$, we obtain

$$-4\psi_0 = -2a^2 \qquad \text{or} \qquad \psi_0 = 0.5a^2$$

The derivative $\partial\psi/\partial x$ at the nodal point 1 can be approximated by its first backward difference, *viz.*,

$$\left(\frac{\partial\psi}{\partial x}\right)_1 \cong \frac{1}{h}\left(\psi_1 - \psi_0\right) = -0.5a$$

From formula (5.53), the torsion constant is

$$J = 2 \iint_R \psi \, dx \, dy$$

where J is twice the volume under the ψ surface. By Simpson's rule [see Sec. 6.7, formula (6.47)], the volume can be easily computed, and we obtain

$$J \cong 2\left[\frac{h^2}{9}\left(16\psi_0\right)\right] = 1.778a^4$$

Substituting into formula (5.52), we find

$$\tau_{\max} = (\tau_{yz})_1 = -\frac{T}{J}\frac{\partial\psi}{\partial x} \cong -\frac{T}{1.778a^4}\left(-0.5a\right) = 0.281\frac{T}{a^3} \quad (6.18)$$

The analytical solution gives the value of $\tau_{\max}$ as $0.600T/a^3$. Our approximate solution here gives a value which is 53.2 per cent too low. With such a coarse mesh, a poor approximation is naturally to be expected.

In order to compare the approximate values of ψ, $\partial\psi/\partial x$, and J with the exact ones, we shall now find these values from the analytical solution. From the definition of ψ, Eqs. (5.49), we have

$$\frac{\partial\psi}{\partial x} = -\frac{\partial\phi}{\partial y} - x \qquad \frac{\partial\psi}{\partial y} = \frac{\partial\phi}{\partial x} - y$$

The partial derivatives $\partial\phi/\partial x$, $\partial\phi/\partial y$ can be easily calculated from Eq. (5.41). It then becomes a straightforward matter to compute the stress function ψ, which is

$$\psi = \frac{32a^2}{\pi^3} \sum_{n=0}^{\infty} \frac{(-1)^n}{(2n+1)^3} \left(1 - \frac{\cosh k_n y}{\cosh k_n b}\right) \cos k_n x \qquad (6.19)$$

In obtaining Eq. (6.19), the relation (5.40), *viz.*,

$$2x = \sum_{n=0}^{\infty} \frac{16(-1)^n a}{\pi^2(2n+1)} \sin k_n x$$

has been used.   Therefore

$$\frac{\partial \psi}{\partial x} = -\frac{16a}{\pi^2} \sum_{n=0}^{\infty} \frac{(-1)^n}{(2n+1)^2} \left(1 - \frac{\cosh k_n y}{\cosh k_n b}\right) \sin k_n x \qquad (6.20)$$

At $x = 0$, $y = 0$, we find from (6.19)

$$\psi_0 = 0.5894a^2$$

At $x = a$, $y = 0$, we find from (6.20)

$$\left(\frac{\partial \psi}{\partial x}\right)_1 = -1.350a$$

From formula (5.42), the exact value of J is

$$J = 2.250a^4$$

Comparing these values with the finite-difference solution, we see that ψ_0 is 17.9 per cent too low, $(\partial \psi/\partial x)_1$ is 63.0 per cent too low, and J is 21.0 per cent too low.

To improve the approximation, let us subdivide the domain into 16 square elements with $h = a/2$, and let us number the nodal points of the network as shown in Fig. 6.4.   Note that in numbering these points we have observed the symmetry of the solution and therefore the symmetrical points have the same number.   Writing down the finite-difference equations at the points 0, 1, 2, respectively, we have

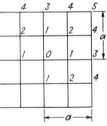

Fig. 6.4.

$$4\psi_1 - 4\psi_0 = -2\left(\frac{a}{2}\right)^2$$

$$\psi_0 + 2\psi_2 + \psi_3 - 4\psi_1 = -2\left(\frac{a}{2}\right)^2 \qquad (6.21)$$

$$2\psi_1 + 2\psi_4 - 4\psi_2 = -2\left(\frac{a}{2}\right)^2$$

On the boundary, we have

$$\psi_3 = \psi_4 = \psi_5 = 0 \tag{6.22}$$

Solving Eqs. (6.21) and (6.22) simultaneously, we obtain

$$\psi_0 = 0.5625a^2 \qquad \psi_1 = 0.4375a^2 \qquad \psi_2 = 0.3438a^2$$

From these values of ψ, we find,

$$\left(\frac{\partial \psi}{\partial x}\right)_3 \cong \frac{1}{h}(\psi_3 - \psi_1) = -0.8750a$$

$$J = 2 \iint_R \psi \, dx \, dy$$

$$\cong 2 \cdot \frac{h^2}{9} \cdot 4(\psi_5 + 4\psi_4 + \psi_3 + 4\psi_4 + 16\psi_2 + 4\psi_1 + \psi_3 + 4\psi_1 + \psi_0)$$

$$= 2.125a^4$$

and

$$\tau_{max} = -\frac{T}{J}\left(\frac{\partial \psi}{\partial x}\right)_3 \cong 0.412 \frac{T}{a^3}$$

Comparing with the exact values, we find that ψ_0 is 4.6 per cent too low, the numerical value of $(\partial \psi / \partial x)_3$ is 35.2 per cent too low, J is 5.6 per cent too low, and τ_{max} is 31.3 per cent too low.

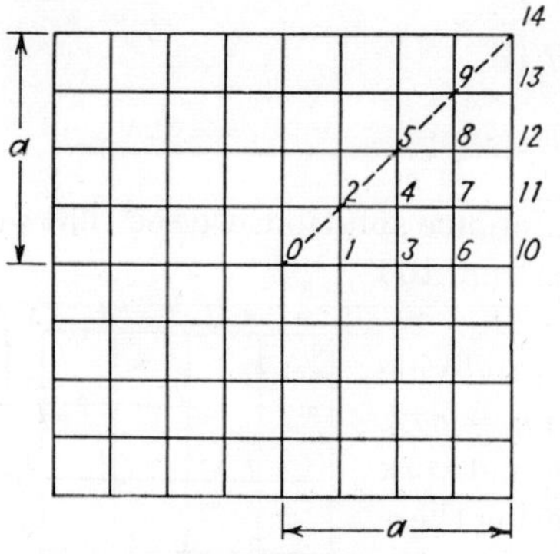

FIG. 6.5.

To reduce the size of the elements still further, let us subdivide the domain into 64 small squares each with $h = a/4$. Taking into account the symmetry of the solution, we shall number the nodal points as shown in Fig. 6.5. Writing down the finite difference equations at points 0 to 9 and noting that the values of ψ on the boundary are zero, we obtain 10 simultaneous equations for the 10 unknown ψ at the inner nodal points. Solving,[1] we find

$$\psi_0 = 0.5822a^2 \qquad \psi_1 = 0.5509a^2 \qquad \psi_2 = 0.5217a^2$$
$$\psi_3 = 0.4530a^2 \qquad \psi_4 = 0.4300a^2 \qquad \psi_5 = 0.3572a^2$$
$$\psi_6 = 0.2761a^2 \qquad \psi_7 = 0.2632a^2 \qquad \psi_8 = 0.2219a^2$$
$$\psi_9 = 0.1422a^2$$

---

[1] A large number of linear simultaneous equations can be solved by a short method proposed by Crout. See the paper by P. D. Crout, A Short Method for Evaluating Determinants and Solving Systems of Linear Equations with Real or Complex Coefficients, *Trans. AIEE*, Vol. 60, 1941.

From these values, we find

$$\left(\frac{\partial \psi}{\partial x}\right)_{10} \cong -1.1044a \qquad J \cong 2.2175a^4 \qquad \tau_{max} \cong 0.498\,\frac{T}{a^3}$$

Comparing with the analytical solutions, we find that ψ_0 is 1.2 per cent too low, the numerical value of $(\partial \psi / \partial x)_{10}$ is 22.7 per cent too low, J is 1.4 per cent too low, and τ_{max} is 17.0 per cent too low.

From the above comparison, we see that, with $h = a/4$, the errors in ψ_0 and J are already quite small. The large error in τ_{max} is due to the error in $(\partial \psi / \partial x)_{10}$. We shall discuss methods for improving the accuracy in Secs. 6.6 and 6.7.

6.4. Relaxation Method. From the examples worked out in the previous section, we observe that as h is made smaller and smaller the accuracy of the solution improves accordingly. However, as we decrease the interval h, the number of simultaneous equations increases so rapidly that the final solution of these simultaneous equations requires a prohibitive amount of labor. Instead of solving these equations by the conventional methods, many schemes have been proposed, among which is a method developed by Southwell known as the *relaxation method*. The time required to reach a solution of given accuracy is so much less for the relaxation method than for other methods that it will be discussed here in detail.

The relaxation method can be best described by working out a numerical example.[1] Let us consider here the problem of torsion of a square bar. To solve the problem, we first have the domain drawn and the net points chosen. By guess or whatever information is available from experiment, special solutions, prior work, etc., assume a set of values of ψ at each point. At any point 0 (Fig. 6.2) the finite-difference equation is

$$\psi_1 + \psi_2 + \psi_3 + \psi_4 - 4\psi_0 + 2h^2 = 0 \qquad (6.23)$$

If the assumed values of ψ are the correct ones, *i.e.*, these are the solutions of the finite-difference equations, upon substitution in equations such as (6.23), these equations become identically zero. In general, this is not so. Accordingly, we shall find

$$\psi_1 + \psi_2 + \psi_3 + \psi_4 - 4\psi_0 + 2h^2 = Q_0 \qquad (6.24)$$

---

[1] The relaxation method is discussed in detail in a book by R. V. Southwell, "Relaxation Methods in Theoretical Physics," Oxford University Press, New York, 1946. See also H. W. Emmons, The Numerical Solution of Partial Differential Equations, *Quart. Applied Math.*, Vol. 2, pp. 173–195, 1944; F. S. Shaw, Numerical Solutions of Boundary Value Problems by Relaxation Methods, "Numerical Methods of Analysis in Engineering," edited by L. E. Grinter, pp. 49–65, The Macmillan Company, New York, 1949.

where Q_0 is a numerical value which represents a measure of the error. Q_0 is called the *residual* at the nodal point 0. Similarly, the residuals at all the other inner points are computed and recorded at these points. For the correct values of ψ, the residuals Q will be zero everywhere. Our aim then is to reduce the residuals at all the nodal points to zero or very small values so that the last figure of the values of ψ will not be changed upon further reduction of Q.

Examine Eq. (6.24). If ψ_1 is altered by $+1$, Q_0 is altered by $+1$, and similarly for unit alterations to ψ_2, ψ_3, or ψ_4. If, however, ψ_0 is altered by $+1$, then Q_0 is altered by -4. The alteration of the residuals thus follows a definite pattern, and the residuals can be systematically reduced. The amount of work in calculating and changing the residuals can be reduced to some extent by the use of the so-called *relaxation operator*. The relaxation operator is actually a diagrammatical form of the finite-difference equation. For example, the relaxation operator of the present problem is that shown in Fig. 6.6. Remembering the relaxation operator, the residuals at each point can be computed with great ease. At the same time, the changing of the residuals is made easier because the operator indicates that a change of the value of ψ at the center point by $+1$ changes the residual at the center point by -4 and the residual at each of the surrounding four points by $+1$.

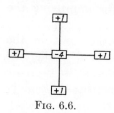

Fig. 6.6.

Now let us show the relaxation process by carrying out an example. Let us take $h = a/2$. The points are numbered as shown in Fig. 6.7. From the membrane analogy, we have certain ideas of how the values of ψ vary inside the domain at various points. From the simple case of $h = a$, we further know that ψ_{13} is approximately equal to $0.5a$. But let us deliberately make a bad first estimate and assume the values of ψ to be zero at all the points. From Eq. (6.24) and with the aid of the relaxation operator (Fig. 6.6), the residuals at all the inner points are calculated and recorded at the left lower corner of each point. The assumed values of ψ are recorded at the right lower corner of each point. This is shown as step 1 in Fig. 6.8. In order to avoid the writing of a^2 and the decimal points, the recorded values of Q and ψ are multiplied by the factor $1,000/a^2$.

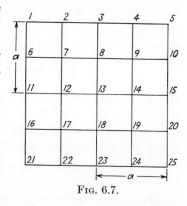

Fig. 6.7.

The second step is to pick the net point where the residual is the largest and start to reduce Q at this point. In the present case, Q is the same at

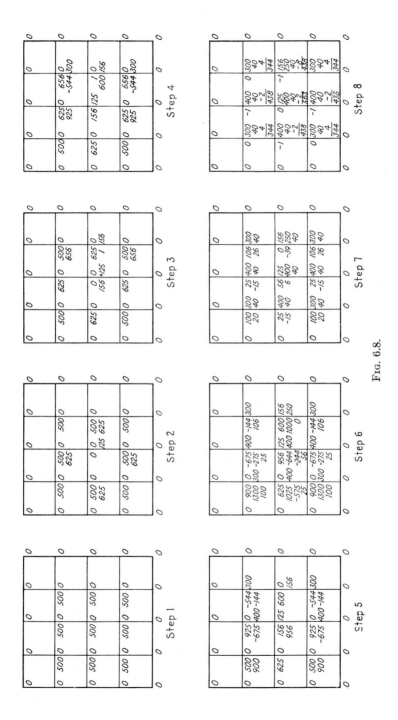

Fig. 6.8.

all points, and we may start at any point. Let us start at the center point and reduce the residual there to zero. Thus we have to add $+\frac{500}{4}$, or $+125$, at that point. With this alteration of ψ, the residuals at each of the surrounding four points are increased by an amount of $+125$. Record the *final values* of the residuals at the left lower corner of each point and the *change in ψ* at the right lower corner. This is shown as step 2 in Fig. 6.8.

Now let us reduce the residual at the point 14, which now becomes 625. To reduce it to a value near zero, we may add a value of $+\frac{625}{4}$, or 156, at this point. Thus the residual at 14 becomes $+1$, and the residuals at its surrounding points are shown as step 3 in Fig. 6.8. Point 15 is a boundary point, and the value of the function at this point is determined by the boundary condition. As the boundary condition is satisfied, the residual there is zero. We observe that, by reducing the residual at 14, the residual at point 13 is again increased. To reduce this additional residual, we must increase ψ_{13} again. This always happens when a point is surrounded by other points with residuals of the same sign. To make the convergence more rapid, instead of reducing Q_{13} in step 2 to zero we may increase ψ_{13} in step 2 so that Q_{13} becomes a negative value. This process is called *overshooting*. The amount of overshooting depends on the magnitudes of residuals at the surrounding points. By not overshooting enough or by overshooting too much we do no harm except that some time is lost.

Now both point 9 and point 19 have residuals of 656. To reduce them, let us overshoot the residuals by adding a value of 300 at both points. The changes in the residuals and the values of ψ are shown as step 4. Next we add 400 to the values of ψ at 8 and 18. The results are shown as step 5. We shall now add 400 at point 13, 400 at point 12, 300 each at points 7 and 17, and 250 at point 14. The final residuals are shown as step 6. The residuals have now been reduced to a maximum value of about 100. If we add 40 at all the inner points, we can reduce the residuals at all points to such an extent that the maximum value does not exceed 40. The final residuals are shown as step 7. After making some further change as shown in step 8, we have the residuals reduced to a maximum value of 1. Further change in the last figure of ψ cannot reduce the residuals any more, and therefore our solution is accurate to the third figure.

In the above example, we have deliberately lengthened the computation by starting with a bad first estimate and by ignoring the symmetrical property of the solution. For this particular problem, the solution of the finite-difference equations by the conventional method may even appear simpler. The real timesaving advantages of the relaxation method will show up only with more net points.

During the relaxation process, we should check our computation by evaluating from time to time the residuals at all the nodal points. If there are mistakes, the new residuals will not check with those which we have recorded. If this happens, it is not necessary to go back and change the previous computation but rather we may proceed with the correct values of residuals and try to reduce these values from there on. So far as the computation is concerned, no harm is done and only some time is wasted.

6.5. Block Relaxation and Lines of Symmetry. From the "operating instruction" in the preceding section, we found that the relaxation method is not an iteration method in the usual sense because its operation does not follow a rigid rule. The flexibility of the method, however, is actually the source of its great power because the computer may, without any effort, alter the procedure to attain a more rapid approach to the final answer (of no residuals). We shall now discuss a few short cuts in the relaxation technique which will serve to accelerate the elimination of residuals.

One of these relaxation techniques is the so-called *line* and *block relaxation*. In step 7 of the example considered in Sec. 6.4, we found that the residuals could be reduced by adding 40 to the values of ψ at all the net points. Altering simultaneously all the values of the function by the same amount at a group of points in a block of the domain is called block relaxation. Similarly, simultaneously altering the values of the function by the same amount at a group of points along a line in the domain is called line relaxation.

Consider the effect of the simultaneous changing of the function of two adjacent points by the same amount. Obviously this may be carried out by writing down separately the effects of each displacement and adding them together. In the case of the Laplace operator, by the use of unit operators, we can obtain the two-, three-, and four-point line-relaxation operators, as shown in Fig. 6.9, and the various block-relaxation operators as shown in Figs. 6.10 and 6.11. Inspecting the operators as shown in Figs. 6.9, 6.10, and 6.11 carefully, we find that it is possible to obtain a rule by which all such operators can be immediately written down by inspection. The rule for writing the line- and block-relaxation operators for Laplace or Poisson's equations is as follows: *By simultaneously altering the values of the function at a group of points in a region along a line or within a block by an amount of $+1$, the residuals at all points which, like a (Figs. 6.9 and 6.10), are directly connected with three points outside the line- or block-relaxation region are altered by an amount of -3. The residuals at all points which, like b, are connected with two outside points, are altered by an amount of -2. The residual at a point such as c is altered by an amount of -1 when the point is connected with one outside point. There*

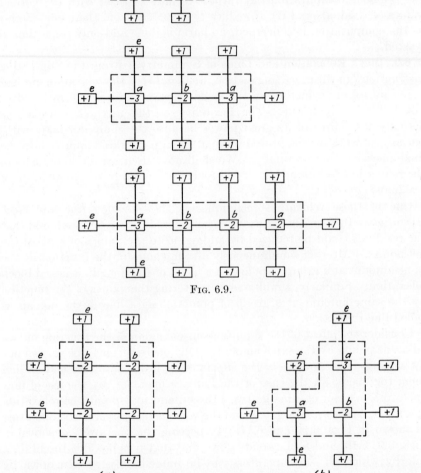

Fig. 6.9.

Fig. 6.10.

are no changes in the residuals at points such as d which are not directly connected with any outside points. The residuals at all points e, which are outside the line- or block-relaxation region but directly connected to one point within the region, are altered by +1. The residual at an outside point such as f which is directly connected to two inside points is altered by +2.

The advantage of the line and block relaxation can easily be seen from Fig. 6.11. For while the residuals at the points on the boundary of the block are altered, the residuals at points inside the block are not changed. Judicious use of block relaxation can prevent much of the "washing back" of residuals, thus saving much time in obtaining a solution.

Another useful relaxation technique is the observation of the lines of symmetry. In many problems the solution can easily be seen to be symmetrical with respect to one or more lines because of the symmetry of the domain and boundary conditions. In solving such problems, it is unnecessary to find the unknown function over the entire area. For example, in the case of the torsion of a square bar, there is an eightfold

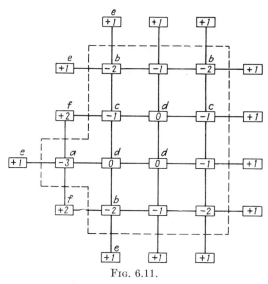

Fig. 6.11.

symmetry. Thus it is sufficient to find a solution in one-eighth of the entire domain, as shown in Fig. 6.12. There is no markedly new technique involved in solving such problems. It is merely necessary to remember that to preserve the symmetry *each time a point adjacent to a line of symmetry is altered the point which is symmetrical to this point is altered at the same time.* That is, such an operation is accompanied by an automatically equal change on the other side of the line of symmetry. As a result, a point on the line of symmetry will receive a change in its residual from both of the points being altered.

The technique concerning the lines of symmetry can be clearly illustrated by reworking the example in Sec. 6.4. Numbering these points as in Fig. 6.4, we have the center point as point 0, the side points as point 1, and the corner points as point 2. They are shown in the circles at the upper right corners of these points in Fig. 6.12. The relaxation method can be carried out in six steps.

Step 1. Assume $\psi = 0$ everywhere, so that the residuals are all 500.

Step 2. Add 125 at point 0. This results in a zero residual at 0.

Step 3. To attempt to reduce the residual at point 1 and not to alter the residual at point 0, we may perform the block relaxation by adding 100 to points 0 and 1. Note that when we add 100 to point 1 we actually add 100 to *all* the four symmetrical points. Point 0 is an "inner" point, and therefore its residual is not changed. Point 1 is connected with three outside points; its residual therefore alters by an amount of -3×100.

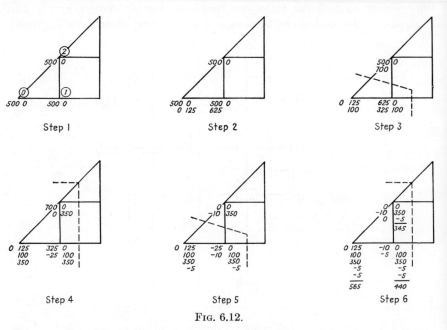

Fig. 6.12.

Point 2 is connected to point 1 and another symmetrical point to point 1, and its residual is thus altered by 2×100.

Step 4. A block relaxation of $+350$ on all points.

Step 5. A block relaxation of -5 on points 0 and 1.

Step 6. A block relaxation of -5 on all points. The final values of ψ at all the points are the algebraic sums of the values at the right lower corners of these points.

Problem. Find the maximum shearing stress in a rectangular bar under torsion with $b/a = 2$. Take (1) $h = a$, (2) $h = a/2$, (3) $h = a/4$.

6.6. Higher-order Finite-difference Approximations. One way to improve the accuracy of the finite-difference approximation is to take a finer mesh. Even with the use of relaxation methods the amount of labor required to solve a problem increases materially with the increase of the number of net points. To avoid this difficulty, Fox[1] proposed a method whereby the higher-order finite-difference approximation formulas are used instead of the standard first-order formulas given in Secs. 6.1 and 6.2. Although this approach has been criticized by Southwell,[2] it appears nevertheless that in most cases this method will indeed give a better approximation to the solution with a minimum increase of labor.

The higher-order finite-difference approximation formulas may be derived as follows: Any set of points can be connected by a curve which can be approximated by a power series. The greater the number of known points, the greater the number of terms in the power series that can be found and the better will be the approximation to the actual curve. If the values of f are known at $x = x_0, x_1, x_2 \ldots$, Newton's formula for fitting such a curve is

$$f = a_0 + a_1(x - x_0) + a_2(x - x_0)(x - x_1) + a_3(x - x_0)(x - x_1)(x - x_2)$$
$$+ a_4(x - x_0)(x - x_1)(x - x_2)(x - x_3) + \cdots \quad (6.25)$$

If the points are given for equally spaced values of x, with an interval of h, then $x_1 = x_0 + h$, $x_2 = x_0 + 2h$, etc. Now, if the successive values of the coordinates are substituted in Newton's formula, the coefficients a_0, a_1, a_2, etc., can be easily determined.

When $x = x_0$, $f = f_0$. Substituting in Eq. (6.25), it follows that $a_0 = f_0$, and Newton's formula becomes

$$f = f_0 + a_1(x - x_0) + a_2(x - x_0)(x - x_1)$$
$$+ a_3(x - x_0)(x - x_1)(x - x_2) + \cdots$$

When $x = x_1 = x_0 + h$, $f = f_1$, we have

$$f_1 = f_0 + a_1(x_0 + h - x_0)$$

from which

$$a_1 = \frac{f_1 - f_0}{h} = \frac{\bar{\Delta} f_0}{h}$$

where $\bar{\Delta} f_0$ is the first forward difference at $x = x_0$. We have thus

$$f = f_0 + \frac{\bar{\Delta} f_0}{h}(x - x_0) + a_2(x - x_0)(x - x_1)$$
$$+ a_3(x - x_0)(x - x_1)(x - x_2) + \cdots$$

[1] L. Fox, Some Improvements in the Use of Relaxation Methods for the Solution of Ordinary and Partial Differential Equations, *Proc. Roy. Soc.* (*London*), A, Vol. 190, pp. 31–59, 1947.

[2] R. V. Southwell, The Quest for Accuracy in Computations Using Finite Differences, "Numerical Methods of Analysis in Engineering," edited by L. E. Grinter, pp. 66–74, The Macmillan Company, New York, 1949.

If the process is continued, Newton's formula becomes

$$f = f_0 + \bar{\Delta}f_0\left(\frac{x - x_0}{h}\right) + \frac{1}{2!}\bar{\Delta}^2 f_0\left(\frac{x - x_0}{h}\right)\left(\frac{x - x_1}{h}\right)$$

$$+ \frac{1}{3!}\bar{\Delta}^3 f_0\left(\frac{x - x_0}{h}\right)\left(\frac{x - x_1}{h}\right)\left(\frac{x - x_2}{h}\right)$$

$$+ \frac{1}{4!}\bar{\Delta}^4 f_0\left(\frac{x - x_0}{h}\right)\left(\frac{x - x_1}{h}\right)\left(\frac{x - x_2}{h}\right)\left(\frac{x - x_3}{h}\right) + \cdots$$

If we let $(x - x_0)/h = u$, we have

$$\frac{(x - x_1)}{h} = \frac{[(x - x_0) - (x_1 - x_0)]}{h} = u - 1$$

Similarly we have $(x - x_2)/h = u - 2$, $(x - x_3)/h = u - 3$, etc. In terms of u, Newton's formula becomes

$$f = f_0 + u\,\bar{\Delta}f_0 + \frac{u(u - 1)}{2!}\bar{\Delta}^2 f_0 + \frac{u(u - 1)(u - 2)}{3!}\bar{\Delta}^3 f_0$$

$$+ \frac{u(u - 1)(u - 2)(u - 3)}{4!}\bar{\Delta}^4 f + \cdots \quad (6.26)$$

From Eq. (6.26), we see that the derivatives of f at the point $x = x_0$ can be expressed in terms of the finite differences at x_0 by a simple differentiation. Thus, noting that $u = (x - x_0)/h$ and $du/dx = 1/h$, we have

$$\left(\frac{df}{dx}\right)_0 = \left(\frac{df}{dx}\right)_{x=x_0} = \left(\frac{df}{du}\frac{du}{dx}\right)_{u=0}$$

$$= \frac{1}{h}\left(\bar{\Delta}f_0 + \frac{2u - 1}{2!}\bar{\Delta}^2 f_0 + \frac{3u^2 - 6u + 2}{3!}\bar{\Delta}^3 f_0\right.$$

$$\left.+ \frac{4u^3 - 18u^2 + 22u - 6}{4!}\bar{\Delta}^4 f_0 + \cdots\right)_{u=0}$$

$$= \frac{1}{h}\left(\bar{\Delta}f_0 - \frac{1}{2}\bar{\Delta}^2 f_0 + \frac{1}{3}\bar{\Delta}^3 f_0 - \frac{1}{4}\bar{\Delta}^4 f_0 + \cdots\right) \quad (6.27)$$

$$\left(\frac{d^2 f}{dx^2}\right)_0 = \frac{1}{h^2}\left(\bar{\Delta}^2 f_0 - \bar{\Delta}^3 f_0 + \frac{11}{12}\bar{\Delta}^4 f_0 - \cdots\right) \quad (6.28)$$

In a similar manner, it can be shown that the derivatives can be expressed in terms of the backward differences as follows:

$$\left(\frac{df}{dx}\right)_0 = \frac{1}{h}\left(\Delta f_0 + \frac{1}{2}\Delta^2 f_0 + \frac{1}{3}\Delta^3 f_0 + \frac{1}{4}\Delta^4 f_0 + \cdots\right) \quad (6.29)$$

$$\left(\frac{d^2 f}{dx^2}\right)_0 = \frac{1}{h^2}\left(\Delta^2 f_0 + \Delta^3 f_0 + \frac{11}{12}\Delta^4 f_0 + \cdots\right) \quad (6.30)$$

To express the derivatives in terms of the central differences, we must first transform the Newton's formula so that it is in terms of the central differences. By definition

$$\bar{\Delta} f_0 = f_1 - f_0$$
$$= \tfrac{1}{2}(f_1 - f_{-1}) + \tfrac{1}{2}(f_1 - 2f_0 + f_{-1})$$
$$= \Delta f_0 + \tfrac{1}{2}\,\Delta^2 f_0$$

where in the second step $f_{-1}/2$ is subtracted in the first parentheses and added in the second parentheses. In a similar manner, it can be shown that

$$\bar{\Delta}^2 f_0 = \Delta^2 f_0 + \Delta^3 f_0 + \tfrac{1}{2}\,\Delta^4 f_0$$
$$\bar{\Delta}^3 f_0 = \Delta^3 f_0 + \tfrac{3}{2}\,\Delta^4 f_0 + \Delta^5 f_0 + \tfrac{1}{2}\,\Delta^6 f_0$$
$$\bar{\Delta}^4 f_0 = \Delta^4 f_0 + 2\,\Delta^5 f_0 + 2\,\Delta^6 f_0 + \Delta^7 f_0 + \tfrac{1}{2}\,\Delta^8 f_0$$

and so forth. Substituting these relations into (6.26) and collecting terms, we obtain

$$f = f_0 + u\,\Delta f_0 + \frac{u^2}{2!}\,\Delta^2 f_0 + \frac{u(u^2 - 1^2)}{3!}\,\Delta^3 f_0 + \frac{u^2(u^2 - 1^2)}{4!}\,\Delta^4 f_0$$
$$+ \frac{u(u^2 - 1^2)(u^2 - 2^2)}{5!}\,\Delta^5 f_0 + \cdots \quad (6.31)$$

It is now possible to find the various derivatives of the curve in terms of the central differences. By differentiating Eq. (6.31), we find

$$\frac{df}{dx} = \frac{1}{h}\left(\Delta f_0 + u\,\Delta^2 f_0 + \frac{3u^2 - 1}{6}\,\Delta^3 f_0 + \frac{4u^3 - 2u}{24}\,\Delta^4 f_0 \right.$$
$$\left. + \frac{5u^4 - 15u^2 + 4}{120}\,\Delta^5 f_0 + \cdots \right)$$

At $x = x_0$, $u = 0$, the derivative df/dx at $x = x_0$ is therefore

$$\left(\frac{df}{dx}\right)_0 = \frac{1}{h}\left(\Delta f_0 - \frac{1}{6}\,\Delta^3 f_0 + \frac{1}{30}\,\Delta^5 f_0 - \cdots \right) \qquad (6.32)$$

and the second derivative is

$$\left(\frac{d^2 f}{dx^2}\right)_0 = \frac{1}{h^2}\left(\Delta^2 f_0 - \frac{1}{12}\,\Delta^4 f_0 + \frac{1}{90}\,\Delta^6 f_0 - \cdots \right) \qquad (6.33)$$

The higher derivatives can be found in a similar manner.

Formulas (6.27) to (6.30), (6.32), and (6.33) reduce to the standard finite-difference formulas if the higher-order differences in these formulas are neglected. Comparing (6.32) with (6.27) and (6.29), we see that, in reducing to the standard first-order formulas, the largest term neglected in (6.32) is $-\tfrac{1}{6}\,\Delta^3 f_0$, while those in (6.27) and (6.29) are $-\tfrac{1}{2}\,\bar{\Delta}^2 f_0$ and

$\frac{1}{2}\,\Delta^2 f_0$, respectively. In general, $-\frac{1}{6}\,\Delta^3 f_0$ will be smaller than $-\frac{1}{2}\,\bar{\Delta}^2 f_0$ and $\frac{1}{2}\,\Delta^2 f_0$. The central difference formula will, in general, therefore give a better approximation than the forward or backward difference formulas. Similar conclusions can be drawn in the approximation of higher derivatives by the various higher differences.

In the above derivation, f is assumed to be a function of x only. If f is a function of both x and y, the partial derivatives can be easily obtained by replacing the symbols $\bar{\Delta}$, Δ, or $\underset{\sim}{\Delta}$ by $\bar{\Delta}_x$, Δ_x, $\underset{\sim}{\Delta}_x$ or $\bar{\Delta}_y$, Δ_y, $\underset{\sim}{\Delta}_y$ respectively. Thus, in terms of central differences,

$$\begin{aligned}
\left(\frac{\partial^2 f}{\partial x^2}\right)_0 &= \frac{1}{h^2}\left(\Delta_x{}^2 f_0 - \frac{1}{12}\Delta_x{}^4 f_0 + \frac{1}{90}\Delta_x{}^6 f_0 - \cdots\right) \\
\left(\frac{\partial^2 f}{\partial y^2}\right)_0 &= \frac{1}{h^2}\left(\Delta_y{}^2 f_0 - \frac{1}{12}\Delta_y{}^4 f_0 + \frac{1}{90}\Delta_y{}^6 f_0 - \cdots\right)
\end{aligned} \tag{6.34}$$

Let us now return to the problem of torsion of a square bar. The differential equation

$$\frac{\partial^2 \psi}{\partial x^2} + \frac{\partial^2 \psi}{\partial y^2} = -2$$

can be transformed into finite-difference equations by means of the higher-order difference formulas (6.34). The higher-order finite-difference equation at 0 (Fig. 6.2) therefore becomes

$$\psi_1 + \psi_2 + \psi_3 + \psi_4 - 4\psi_0 + 2h^2 + \Omega = 0 \tag{6.35}$$

where $\quad \Omega = -\frac{1}{12}(\Delta_x{}^4\psi_0 + \Delta_y{}^4\psi_0) + \frac{1}{90}(\Delta_x{}^6\psi_0 + \Delta_y{}^6\psi_0) - \cdots$

Let the final solution of ψ be written in the form

$$\psi = \psi^{(0)} + \psi^{(1)} + \psi^{(2)} + \cdots \tag{6.36}$$

and let $\psi^{(0)}$, $\psi^{(1)}$, ... be the solutions of the following equations:

$$\begin{aligned}
\psi_1{}^{(0)} + \psi_2{}^{(0)} + \psi_3{}^{(0)} + \psi_4{}^{(0)} - 4\psi_0{}^{(0)} + 2h^2 &= 0 \quad &\text{in } R \\
\psi^{(0)} &= 0 \quad &\text{on } S
\end{aligned} \tag{6.37}$$

$$\psi_1{}^{(1)} + \psi_2{}^{(1)} + \psi_3{}^{(1)} + \psi_4{}^{(1)} - 4\psi_0{}^{(1)} + \Omega^{(0)} = 0$$

$$\Omega^{(0)} = -\frac{1}{12}(\Delta_x{}^4\psi_0{}^{(0)} + \Delta_y{}^4\psi_0{}^{(0)}) + \frac{1}{90}(\Delta_x{}^6\psi_0{}^{(0)} + \Delta_y{}^6\psi_0{}^{(0)}) - \cdots \tag{6.38}$$

$$\psi^{(1)} = 0 \quad \text{on } S$$

etc.

By adding (6.37), (6.38), and a series of similar equations the function ψ given by (6.36) satisfies Eq. (6.35) and the boundary condition

$$\psi = 0 \quad \text{on } S$$

The calculation can be carried out in the following manner: Note that $\psi^{(0)}$ is the solution which we have already computed in the previous sections. Take, for example, $h = a/4$. The values of $\psi^{(0)}$ at the points

$y/a = 0$ and $x/a = 1$, 0.75, 0.5, and 0 are shown in Table 6.1. The second central difference in the x direction at the point $x/a = 0.750$ is obtained from the formula

$$\Delta_x^2 \psi_{0.75} = \psi_{1.0} - 2\psi_{0.75} + \psi_{0.5} = (\psi_{1.0} - \psi_{0.75}) - (\psi_{0.75} - \psi_{0.5})$$

But $\psi_{1.0} - \psi_{0.75}$ and $\psi_{0.75} - \psi_{0.5}$ are the first central differences at the points $x = 0.875$ and $x = 0.625$, respectively. In order to facilitate the

TABLE 6.1. COMPUTATION OF THE FINITE DIFFERENCES AND Ω AT POINTS ON $y = 0$

x/a	$\psi^{(0)}$	$\Delta_x\psi^{(0)}$	$\Delta_x^2\psi^{(0)}$	$\Delta_x^3\psi^{(0)}$	$\Delta_x^4\psi^{(0)}$	$\Delta_x^5\psi^{(0)}$	$\Delta_x^6\psi^{(0)}$	$\Delta_y^4\psi^{(0)}$	$\Delta_y^6\psi^{(0)}$	$\Omega^{(0)}$
1.000	0									
0.875		$-2,761$								
0.750	2,761		-992		(-66)		(0)	-52	-44	9
0.625		$-1,769$		-202		$(+12)$				
0.500	4,530		-790		-78		(6)	-76	-26	13
0.375		$-$ 979		-124		6				
0.250	5,509		-666		-84		10	-82	$-$ 6	14
0.125		$-$ 313		$-$ 40		-4				
0.000	5,822		-626		-80		-8	-80	$-$ 8	13

TABLE 6.2. COMPUTATION OF THE FINITE DIFFERENCES AND Ω AT POINTS ON $y/a = 0.250$

x/a	$\psi^{(0)}$	$\Delta_x\psi^{(0)}$	$\Delta_x^2\psi^{(0)}$	$\Delta_x^3\psi^{(0)}$	$\Delta_x^4\psi^{(0)}$	$\Delta_x^5\psi^{(0)}$	$\Delta_x^6\psi^{(0)}$	$\Delta_y^4\psi^{(0)}$	$\Delta_y^6\psi^{(0)}$	$\Omega^{(0)}$
1.000	0									
0.875		$-2,632$								
0.750	2,632		-964		(-88)		(1)	-74	-45	13
0.625		$-1,668$		-213		(-1)				
0.500	4,300		-751		-87		(1)	-89	-12	15
0.375		$-$ 917		-126		-2				
0.250	5,217		-625		-85		1	-85	1	14
0.125		$-$ 292		$-$ 41		-3				
0.000	5,500		-584		-82		-6	-84	10	14

calculations, these odd central differences at points in between the required points are also recorded in the table. At the point $x = 0.750$, we note that $\Delta_x^4\psi^{(0)}$ cannot be calculated because its computation will involve points outside the domain. We could arbitrarily assign a value of zero for $\Delta_x^4\psi^{(0)}$ at this point. A better approximation will be obtained, however, if we extrapolate $\Delta_x^4\psi^{(0)}$ from the values at the other three points. This can be done graphically, and we find an extrapolated value of -66 at this point. These extrapolated values and values calculated from these extrapolated values are put in parentheses in the table. Similarly the values of $\psi^{(0)}$ and the difference $\Delta_x{}^n\psi^{(0)}$ at the net points with $y/a = 0.25, 0.5$, and 0.75 are shown in Tables 6.2, 6.3, 6.4, respectively. Because of symmetry, the values of $\Delta_y{}^n\psi^{(0)}$ at points $x/a = 0, 0.25, 0.50, 0.75$ and $y/a = 0$ have the same values as the values of $\Delta_x{}^n\psi(0)$ at $x/a = 0$ and $y/a = 0, 0.25, 0.50, 0.75$ which are computed in Tables 6.1, 6.2, 6.3, 6.4, respectively. Take these values from these tables, and record

TABLE 6.3. COMPUTATION OF THE FINITE DIFFERENCES AND Ω AT POINTS ON $y/a = 0.500$

x/a	$\psi^{(0)}$	$\Delta_x\psi^{(0)}$	$\Delta_x{}^2\psi^{(0)}$	$\Delta_x{}^3\psi^{(0)}$	$\Delta_x{}^4\psi^{(0)}$	$\Delta_x{}^5\psi^{(0)}$	$\Delta_x{}^6\psi^{(0)}$	$\Delta_y{}^4\psi^{(0)}$	$\Delta_y{}^6\psi^{(0)}$	$\Omega^{(0)}$
1.000	0									
0.875		$-2,219$								
0.750	2,219		-866		(-163)		(-60)	141	(-32)	24
0.625		$-1,353$		-241		(-49)				
0.500	3,572		-625		-114		(-24)	-114	(-24)	18
0.375		-728		-127		-25				
0.250	4,300		-498		-89		-12	-87	(1)	15
0.125		-230		-38		-13				
0.000	4,530		-460		-76		-26	-78	(6)	13

TABLE 6.4. COMPUTATION OF THE FINITE DIFFERENCES AND Ω AT POINTS ON $y/a = 0.750$

x/a	$\psi^{(0)}$	$\Delta_x\psi^{(0)}$	$\Delta_x{}^2\psi^{(0)}$	$\Delta_x{}^3\psi^{(0)}$	$\Delta_x{}^4\psi^{(0)}$	$\Delta_x{}^5\psi^{(0)}$	$\Delta_x{}^6\psi^{(0)}$	$\Delta_y{}^4\psi^{(0)}$	$\Delta_y{}^6\psi^{(0)}$	$\Omega^{(0)}$
1.000	0									
0.875		$-1,422$								
0.750	1,422		-625		(-240)		(-1)	(-240)	(-1)	40
0.625		-797		-241		(-99)				
0.500	2,219		-384		-141		(-32)	(-163)	(-60)	24
0.375		-413		-100		-67				
0.250	2,632		-284		-74		-45	(-88)	(1)	13
0.125		-129		-26		-22				
0.000	2,761		-258		-52		-44	(-66)	(0)	9

them in Table 6.1. The values of $\Omega^{(0)}$ can thus be calculated without any difficulty. With the values of $\Omega^{(0)}$ calculated, we may now find the values of $\psi^{(1)}$ by the standard relaxation method. These values are recorded in Fig. 6.13 together with the residuals at the various nodal points. The values of $\psi = \psi^{(0)} + \psi^{(1)}$ are shown in Fig. 6.14 together with analytical values which are recorded in upper right corners. The improvement is readily seen, the improved values of ψ all lying within 0.6 per cent of the analytical values. If further improvement is deemed desirable, we can also find $\psi^{(2)}, \psi^{(3)}$, etc., in a similar manner.

Let us now calculate the maximum shearing stress. In terms of the backward differences $\partial\psi/\partial x$ may be written as

$$\frac{\partial\psi}{\partial x} \cong \frac{1}{h}\left(\Delta\psi + \frac{1}{2}\Delta^2\psi + \frac{1}{3}\Delta^3\psi + \frac{1}{4}\Delta^4\psi + \cdots\right)$$

Thus, at the point (a,a),

$$\frac{\partial\psi}{\partial x} \cong \frac{4}{a}\bigg[(0 - 0.2793) + \frac{1}{2}(0 - 2 \times 0.2793 + 0.4584)$$

$$+ \frac{1}{3}(0 - 3 \times 0.2793 + 3 \times 0.4584 - 0.5574)$$

$$+ \frac{1}{4}(0 - 4 \times 0.2793 + 6 \times 0.4584 - 4 \times 0.5574 + 0.5890)\bigg]a^2$$

$$= -1.352a$$

By Simpson's rule,

$$J \cong 2.2460a^4$$

Thus

$$\tau_{\max} \cong \frac{0.602T}{a^3}$$

Comparing with the analytic values, we see that the error in $\partial\psi/\partial x$ is 0.15 per cent, the error in J is 0.17 per cent, and the error in $\tau_{\max}$ is only 0.33 per cent. The agreement with the analytic values is excellent.

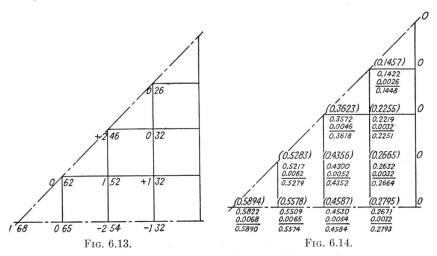

Fig. 6.13. Fig. 6.14.

It was pointed out in Sec. 6.3 that the large error in $\tau_{\max}$ obtained by the standard finite-difference approximation is due to the large error in $\partial\psi/\partial x$. In general, by using the standard first-order finite-difference formulas, the accuracy in the function obtained is always better than the derivatives of the function. If the derivatives are to be found, a much better approximation can be obtained by using the higher-order formulas to calculate these values, even if the function is obtained by the standard first-order finite-difference formulas.   For example, in Sec. 6.3, by taking $h = a/4$ the errors in ψ_0 and J were only 1.2 per cent and 1.4 per cent, respectively, but the error in $(\partial\psi/\partial x)_{10}$ was 22.7 per cent.   Without improving ψ, we may calculate $(\partial\psi/\partial x)_{10}$ by the higher-order finite-difference formula, which gives

$$\left(\frac{\partial\psi}{\partial x}\right)_{10} = \frac{4}{a}\left[(0 - 0.2761) + \frac{1}{2}(0 - 2 \times 0.2761 + 0.4530) \right.$$

$$+ \frac{1}{3}(0 - 3 \times 0.2761 + 3 \times 0.4530 - 0.5509)$$

$$\left. + \frac{1}{4}(0 - 4 \times 0.2761 + 6 \times 0.4530 - 4 \times 0.5509 + 0.5822) \right] a^2$$

$$= -1.3376a$$

and the error is only .91 per cent.   The improvement is obvious.

Problem.   Solve the torsion problem of the rectangular bar with $b/a = 2$ by using the higher-order finite-difference approximation formulas.

6.7. Method of Extrapolation.   If the function $f(x)$ has continuous derivatives in the interval $(x_0 - h) \leq x \leq (x_0 + h)$, then the functions $f(x_0 + h)$ and $f(x_0 - h)$ can be expanded into Taylor's series in powers of h as follows:

$$f(x_0 + h) = f_0 + hf_0' + \frac{h^2}{2!}f_0'' + \frac{h^3}{3!}f_0''' + \frac{h^4}{4!}f_0^{iv} + \cdots \quad (6.39)$$

$$f(x_0 - h) = f_0 - hf_0' + \frac{h^2}{2!}f_0'' - \frac{h^3}{3!}f_0''' + \frac{h^4}{4!}f_0^{iv} - \cdots \quad (6.40)$$

where $f_0', f_0'', \ldots, f_0^n$ are the first, second, $\ldots$, nth derivatives at $x = x_0$, respectively.

From (6.39) and (6.40), we find that the first central difference at $x = x_0$ is

$$\Delta f_0 = \frac{1}{2}[f(x_0 + h) - f(x_0 - h)] = hf_0' + \frac{h^3}{3!}f_0''' + \frac{h^5}{5!}f_0^v + \cdots$$

and the *error* e_1 in replacing the first derivative by the first central difference ratio becomes

$$e_1 = f_0' - \frac{\Delta f_0}{h} = -\frac{h^2}{3!}f_0''' - \frac{h^4}{5!}f_0^v - \cdots$$

Using (6.39) and (6.40), the second central difference at $x = x_0$ is

$$\Delta^2 f_0 = f(x_0 + h) - 2f(x_0) + f(x_0 - h) = h^2 f_0'' + \frac{h^4}{12}f_0^{iv} + \frac{h^6}{360}f_0^{vi} + \cdots$$

The *error* e_2 in replacing the second derivative by the second central difference ratio is therefore

$$e_2 = f_0'' - \frac{\Delta^2 f_0}{h^2} = -\frac{h^2}{12} f_0^{iv} - \frac{h^4}{360} f_0^{vi} - \cdots$$

In a similar manner, we can show that the error e_n in replacing the nth derivative by the nth central difference ratio is of the form

$$e_n = f_0{}^n - \frac{\Delta^n f_0}{h^n} = h^2 g_1(x_0) + h^4 g_2(x_0) + h^6 g_3(x_0) + \cdots \quad (6.41)$$

in which the functions $g_i(x_0)$ depend only on x_0 and are therefore independent of h. Equation (6.41) shows that the error depends on the even powers of h only, and the series converges rapidly if h is a small value. We shall call the error of this type the h^2 type. Equation (6.41) was first derived by Sheppard.[1]

We shall now proceed to prove that the error in the solution of a problem defined by a linear differential equation and linear boundary conditions, due to the substitution of finite-difference ratios for derivatives, is also of the h^2 type. The proof can be carried out in a general form. In order to simplify the discussion, however, we shall prove the theorem by considering a definite equation, say the Laplace equation

$$\frac{\partial^2 f}{\partial x^2} + \frac{\partial^2 f}{\partial y^2} = 0$$

Let f_1 and f_2 be the solutions of the differential equation and the corresponding finite-difference equation, respectively. Thus, we have

$$\frac{\partial^2 f_1}{\partial x^2} + \frac{\partial^2 f_1}{\partial y^2} = 0 \quad (6.42)$$

and

$$\frac{1}{h^2} (\Delta_x^2 f_2 + \Delta_y^2 f_2) = 0 \quad (6.43)$$

By extending Eq. (6.41) to the two-dimensional case, we readily obtain

$$\frac{\partial^2 f_2}{\partial x^2} - \frac{\Delta_x^2 f_2}{h^2} = h^2 g_1(x,y) + h^4 g_2(x,y) + \cdots$$

$$\frac{\partial^2 f_2}{\partial y^2} - \frac{\Delta_y^2 f_2}{h^2} = h^2 \bar{g}_1(x,y) + h^4 \bar{g}_2(x,y) + \cdots$$

or

$$\left(\frac{\partial^2 f_2}{\partial x^2} + \frac{\partial^2 f_2}{\partial y^2} \right) - \frac{1}{h^2} (\Delta_x^2 f_2 + \Delta_y^2 f_2) = h^2 \phi_1(x,y) + h^4 \phi_2(x,y) + \cdots$$

where g_i, $\bar{g}_i$, and ϕ_i are functions of x and y. Subtracting the above equation from (6.42) and noting that the second term on the left-hand side is

---

[1] W. F. Sheppard, Central Differences, *Proc. London Math. Soc.*, Vol. 31, 1899.

zero because of (6.43), we obtain

$$\left(\frac{\partial^2 f_1}{\partial x^2} + \frac{\partial^2 f_1}{\partial y^2}\right) - \left(\frac{\partial^2 f_2}{\partial x^2} + \frac{\partial^2 f_2}{\partial y^2}\right) = \left(\frac{\partial^2}{\partial x^2} + \frac{\partial^2}{\partial y^2}\right)e$$

$$= -h^2\phi_1(x,y) - h^4\phi_2(x,y) - \cdots$$

where $e = f_1 - f_2$ is the error in the solutions. Since the functions ϕ_i are independent of h and the differential operator $(\partial/\partial x^2) + (\partial/\partial y^2)$ is also independent of h, we may conclude that e must be of the form

$$e = h^2\bar{\phi}_1(x,y) + h^4\bar{\phi}_2(x,y) + \cdots \tag{6.44}$$

where $\bar{\phi}_i$ are functions of x and y and are independent of h. It is easily seen that this proof can be extended to other linear differential equations without any difficulty.[1]

With these results, we can now extrapolate new results from previous results calculated with several values of h. Take again the torsion problem as an example. In Sec. 6.3, we found that

$$\psi_0 = 0.5000a^2 \quad \text{when } h = a$$

$$\psi_0 = 0.5625a^2 \quad \text{when } h = \frac{a}{2} \tag{6.45}$$

$$\psi_0 = 0.5822a^2 \quad \text{when } h = \frac{a}{4}$$

Let $\bar{\psi}_0$ be the value of ψ at the center of the square as given by the solution of the differential equation. From Eq. (6.44), by neglecting terms containing h^6 and higher powers of h, we have

$$\bar{\psi}_0 - \psi_0 = h^2\bar{\phi}_1 + h^4\bar{\phi}_2$$

where $\bar{\phi}_1$ and $\bar{\phi}_2$ are now constants because we are referring to a definite point in this case. With the values of ψ_0 and h in (6.45), we obtain

$$\bar{\psi}_0 - 0.5000a^2 = a^2\bar{\phi}_1 + a^4\bar{\phi}_2$$

$$\bar{\psi}_0 - 0.5625a^2 = \left(\frac{a}{2}\right)^2\bar{\phi}_1 + \left(\frac{a}{2}\right)^4\bar{\phi}_2$$

$$\bar{\psi}_0 - 0.5822a^2 = \left(\frac{a}{4}\right)^2\bar{\phi}_1 + \left(\frac{a}{4}\right)^4\bar{\phi}_2$$

Solving, we obtain $\bar{\psi}_0 = 0.5891a^2$, which is only 0.05 per cent lower than the exact value. With the values of ψ_1 and ψ_2 (Fig. 6.4) calculated at $h = a/2$ and $h = a/4$, we can extrapolate these values by the formula

$$\bar{\psi} - \psi = h^2\bar{\phi}_1$$

[1] L. F. Richardson, The Approximate Arithmetical Solution by Finite Differences of Physical Problems Involving Differential Equations with an Application to the Stresses in a Masonry Dam, *Phil. Trans. Roy. Soc. London*, Vol. 210, 1911.

Carrying out the calculation, we find $\bar{\psi}_1 = 0.4582a^2$ and $\bar{\psi}_2 = 0.3617a^2$, which are 0.11 per cent and 0.16 per cent below their respective exact values. These somewhat larger errors are due to the fact that only the h^2 term is retained on the right-hand side of Eq. (6.44).

To find the values of $\partial\psi/\partial x$ at the point $x = a$, $y = 0$, we have to replace the derivative by backward difference ratios. To extrapolate these backward difference ratios, we shall find the error in such a replacement. From Eq. (6.40)

$$\underline{\Delta}_x\psi = \psi(x,y) - \psi(x - h, y) = h\frac{\partial\psi}{\partial x} - \frac{h^2}{2!}\frac{\partial^2\psi}{\partial x^2} + \frac{h^3}{3!}\frac{\partial^3\psi}{\partial x^2} - \cdots$$

The error is therefore

$$e = \frac{\partial\psi}{\partial x} - \frac{\underline{\Delta}_x\psi}{h} = h\alpha_1(x,y) + h^2\alpha_2(x,y) + \cdots \tag{6.46}$$

where α_i are functions of x, y.

Using the extrapolated values of ψ, we have at the point $x = a$, $y = 0$

$$\frac{\partial\psi}{\partial x} = \frac{0 - 0.5891a^2}{a} = -0.5891a \qquad \text{when } h = a$$

$$\frac{\partial\psi}{\partial x} = \frac{0 - 0.4582a^2}{0.5a} = -0.9164a \qquad \text{when } h = \frac{a}{2}$$

Therefore, if we denote by $\partial\bar{\psi}/\partial x$ the exact value, we have

$$\frac{\partial\bar{\psi}}{\partial x} + 0.5891a = a\alpha_1 \qquad \frac{\partial\bar{\psi}}{\partial x} + 0.9164a = \left(\frac{a}{2}\right)\alpha_1$$

Solving, we obtain $\partial\bar{\psi}/\partial x = -1.2437a$, the magnitude of which is 7.8 per cent below the analytic value.

To extrapolate the values of J, we must first investigate the form of the error in Simpson's rule. Let us start with Simpson's rule in the one-dimensional case. From Eq. (6.26), we have

$$f = f_0 + u\,\bar{\Delta}f_0 + \frac{u(u - 1)}{2!}\,\bar{\Delta}^2f_0 + \frac{u(u - 1)(u - 2)}{3!}\,\bar{\Delta}^3f_0 + \cdots$$

where $x = x_0 + hu$ and $dx = h\,du$. Let us now investigate Newton's formula over n equidistant intervals of width h. The limits of integration for x are x_0 and $x_0 + nh$. Hence the corresponding limits for u are 0 and n. We therefore have

$$I_1 = \int_{x_0}^{x_0+nh} f\,dx$$

$$= h\int_0^n \left[f_0 + u\,\bar{\Delta}f_0 + \frac{u(u - 1)}{2!}\,\bar{\Delta}^2f_0 + \cdots \right] du$$

$$= h\left[nf_0 + \frac{n^2}{2}\,\bar{\Delta}f_0 + \left(\frac{n^3}{3} - \frac{n^2}{2}\right)\frac{\bar{\Delta}^2f_0}{2} + \cdots \right]$$

Putting $n = 2$ and neglecting all differences above the second, we obtain

$$\int_{x_0}^{x_0+2h} f \, dx = h \left[2f_0 + 2 \bar{\Delta} f_0 + \left(\frac{8}{3} - 2 \right) \frac{\bar{\Delta}^2 f_0}{2} \right]$$
$$= h[2f_0 + 2f_1 - 2f_0 + \tfrac{1}{3}(f_2 - 2f_1 + f_0)]$$
$$= \frac{h}{3} (f_0 + 4f_1 + f_2)$$

For the next two intervals from x_0 to $x_0 + 2h$ we get in like manner

$$\int_{x_2}^{x_2+2h} f \, dx = \frac{h}{3} (f_2 + 4f_3 + f_4)$$

and so on. Adding all such expressions as these from x_0 to x_n, when n is even, we obtain

$$I_1 = \int_{x_0}^{x_0+nh} f \, dx = \frac{h}{3} (f_0 + 4f_1 + 2f_2 + 4f_3 + 2f_4 + \cdots$$
$$+ 2f_{n-2} + 4f_{n-1} + f_n) \quad (6.47)$$

This formula is known as Simpson's one-third rule or the one-dimensional Simpson's rule. The geometric significance of Simpson's one-third rule is that we replace the graph of the given function by $n/2$ arcs of second-degree parabola. In using this formula, it is important to note that the interval of integration must be divided into an even number of sub-intervals of width h.

Dividing the interval of integration into, say, six divisions, the exact value of the integral is

$$\bar{I}_1 = \int_{x_0-3h}^{x_0+3h} f(x) \, dx = \left[F(x) \right]_{x_0-3h}^{x_0+3h} = F(x_0 + 3h) - F(x_0 - 3h)$$

where $F(x) = \int f(x) \, dx$. If we expand the function $F(x_0 + 3h)$ and $F(x_0 - 3h)$ into Taylor series, similar to Eqs. (6.39) and (6.40), and remember that $F'(x) = f(x)$, $F''(x) = f'(x)$, etc., we have

$$F(x_0 + 3h) = F_0 + 3hf_0 + \frac{9h^2}{2!} f_0' + \frac{27h^3}{3!} f_0'' + \cdots$$

$$F(x_0 - 3h) = F_0 - 3hf_0 + \frac{9h^2}{2!} f_0' - \frac{27h^3}{3!} f_0'' + \cdots$$

Hence

$$\bar{I}_1 = 6hf_0 + 9h^3 f_0'' + 81\!\!\!\!\!/_{20} h^5 f_0^{iv} + 243\!\!\!\!\!/_{280} h^7 f_0^{vi} + \cdots$$

The value of this integral by Simpson's one-third rule is

$$I_1 = \frac{h}{3} \{ f(x_0 - 3h) + f(x_0 + 3h) + 4[f(x_0 - 2h) + f(x_0) + f(x_0 + 2h)]$$
$$+ 2[f(x_0 - h) + f(x_0 + h)] \}$$

Replacing the functions $f(x_0 - 3h)$, $f(x_0 + 3h)$, etc., by their Taylor expansions, we obtain

$$I_1 = 6hf_0 + 9h^3f_0'' + {}^{49}\!/_{12}h^5f_0^{iv} + {}^{329}\!/_{360}h^7f_0^{vi} + \cdots$$

The error in the one-dimensional Simpson's rule is therefore

$$e_{I_1} = \bar{I}_1 - I_1 = -\frac{h^5}{30}f_0^{iv} - \frac{29}{630}h^7f_0^{vi} - \cdots$$

$$= h^5\beta_1 + h^7\beta_2 + \cdots \qquad (6.48)$$

where the β_i are independent of h.

To derive the two-dimensional Simpson's rule, we have first to derive the two-dimensional Newton's formula. Carrying out calculations similar to the derivation of Eq. (6.26), and letting

$$u = \frac{x - x_0}{h} \qquad v = \frac{y - y_0}{h}$$

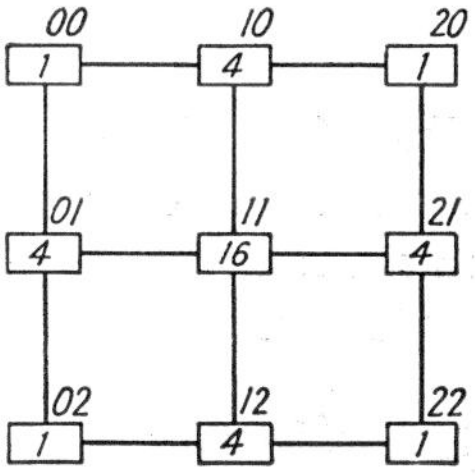

Fig. 6.15.

we have[1]

$$f(x,y) = f_0 + u\,\bar{\Delta}_x f_0 + v\,\bar{\Delta}_y f_0 + \frac{1}{2!}[u(u-1)\,\bar{\Delta}_x{}^2 f_0 + 2uv\,\bar{\Delta}_{xy}f_0$$

$$+ v(v-1)\,\bar{\Delta}_y{}^2 f_0] + \frac{1}{3!}[u(u-1)(u-2)\,\Delta_x{}^3 f_0 + 3uv(u-1)\,\bar{\Delta}_{xxy}f_0$$

$$+ 3uv(v-1)\,\bar{\Delta}_{xyy}f_0 + v(v-1)(v-2)\,\bar{\Delta}_y{}^3 f_0] + \cdots \qquad (6.49)$$

where $f_0 = f(x_0,y_0)$. Neglecting the third differences and remembering that $dx = h\,du$, $dy = h\,dv$, we have

$$I_2 = \int_{x_0}^{x_0+2h} \int_{y_0}^{y_0+2h} f(x,y)\,dx\,dy$$

$$= h^2 \int_0^2 \int_0^2 \left\{ f_0 + u\,\bar{\Delta}_x f_0 + v\,\bar{\Delta}_y f_0 + \frac{1}{2!}[u(u-1)\,\bar{\Delta}_x{}^2 f_0 + 2uv\,\bar{\Delta}_{xy}f_0 \right.$$

$$\left. + v(v-1)\,\bar{\Delta}_y{}^2 f_0] \right\} du\,dv$$

Performing the indicated integrations and expanding the differences in terms of the values of the function at various points (Fig. 6.15), we obtain

$$I_2 = \frac{h^2}{9}[16f_{11} + 4(f_{10} + f_{01} + f_{12} + f_{21}) + f_{00} + f_{02} + f_{22} + f_{20}] \qquad (6.50)$$

Formula (6.50) is represented diagrammatically in Fig. 6.15.

---

[1] The derivation can be found in "Mathematische Näherungsmethoden," by O. Biermann, pp. 138–144. See also J. B. Scarborough, "Numerical Mathematical Analysis," pp. 104–106, Johns Hopkins Press, Baltimore, 1930.

Formula (6.50) can be rewritten in either of the following forms:

$$I_2 = \frac{h}{3}\left[\frac{h}{3}(f_{00} + 4f_{01} + f_{02}) + 4\cdot\frac{h}{3}(f_{10} + 4f_{11} + f_{12})\right.$$
$$\left. + \frac{h}{3}(f_{20} + 4f_{21} + f_{22})\right]$$

or $\quad I_2 = \dfrac{h}{3}\left[\dfrac{h}{3}(f_{00} + 4f_{10} + f_{20}) + 4\cdot\dfrac{h}{3}(f_{01} + 4f_{11} + f_{21})\right.$
$$\left. + \frac{h}{3}(f_{02} + 4f_{12} + f_{22})\right]$$

These formulas show that formula (6.50) is equivalent to applying Simpson's rule to each vertical row in the diagram and then applying it again to the horizontal row thus obtained, or vice versa.

To find the error in formula (6.50), we first evaluate the integral

$$\bar{I}_2 = \int_{x_0-h}^{x_0+h}\int_{y_0-h}^{y_0+h} f(x,y)\,dx\,dy$$
$$= \int_{y_0-h}^{y_0+h}[F(x_0+h,\,y) - F(x_0-h,\,y)]\,dy = G(x_0+h,\,y_0+h)$$
$$- G(x_0+h,\,y_0-h) - G(x_0-h,\,y_0+h) + G(x_0-h,\,y_0-h) \quad (6.51)$$

in which $F(x,y) = \int f(x,y)\,dx$ and $G(x,y) = \int F(x,y)\,dy$. Expanding $G(x,y)$ into Taylor series and denoting $\partial^n/\partial x^n$ and $\partial^n/\partial y^n$ by $\partial_x{}^n$ and $\partial_y{}^n$, respectively, we obtain

$$G(x_0+h,\,y_0+h) = G_0 + h(\partial_x + \partial_y)G_0 + \frac{h^2}{2!}(\partial_x + \partial_y)^2 G_0$$
$$+ \frac{h^3}{3!}(\partial_x + \partial_y)^3 G_0 + \cdots$$

$$G(x_0+h,\,y_0-h) = G_0 + h(\partial_x - \partial_y)G_0 + \frac{h^2}{2!}(\partial_x - \partial_y)^2 G_0$$
$$+ \frac{h^3}{3!}(\partial_x - \partial_y)^3 G_0 + \cdots$$

$$G(x_0-h,\,y_0+h) = G_0 + h(-\partial_x + \partial_y)G_0 + \frac{h^2}{2!}(-\partial_x + \partial_y)^2 G_0$$
$$+ \frac{h^3}{3!}(-\partial_x + \partial_y)^3 G_0 + \cdots$$

$$G(x_0-h,\,y_0-h) = G_0 + h(-\partial_x - \partial_y)G_0 + \frac{h^2}{2!}(-\partial_x - \partial_y)^2 G_0$$
$$+ \frac{h^3}{3!}(-\partial_x - \partial_y)^3 G_0 + \cdots$$

where $G_0 = G(x_0, y_0)$.

Substituting these expressions into Eq. (6.51) and remembering that $\partial^2 G/\partial x\,\partial y = f(x,y)$, we obtain

$$\bar{I}_2 = 4h^2 f_0 + \frac{2h^4}{3}(\partial_x{}^2 + \partial_y{}^2)f_0 + \frac{h^6}{90}(3\partial_x{}^4 + 10\partial_x{}^2\partial_y{}^2 + 3\partial_y{}^4)f_0 + \cdots$$

From Simpson's rule (6.50), we have

$$I_2 = \frac{h^2}{9}\{16f(x_0,y_0) + 4[f(x_0,\, y_0 + h) + f(x_0 - h,\, y_0) + f(x_0,\, y_0 - h)$$
$$+ f(x_0 + h,\, y_0)] + f(x_0 - h,\, y_0 + h) + f(x_0 - h,\, y_0 - h)$$
$$+ f(x_0 + h,\, y_0 - h) + f(x_0 + h,\, y_0 + h)\}$$

Expanding these functions in Taylor series, we find

$$I_2 = \frac{h^2}{9}[36f_0 + 6h^2(\partial_x{}^2 + \partial_y{}^2)f_0 + h^4\left(\frac{\partial_x{}^4}{2} + \partial_x{}^2\partial_y{}^2 + \frac{\partial_y{}^4}{2}\right)f_0 + \cdots$$
$$= 4h^2 f_0 + \frac{2}{3}h^4(\partial_x{}^2 + \partial_y{}^2)f_0 + h^6\left(\frac{\partial_x{}^4}{18} + \frac{\partial_x{}^2\partial_y{}^2}{9} + \frac{\partial_y{}^4}{18}\right)f_0 + \cdots$$

The error is therefore

$$e_{I_2} = \bar{I}_2 - I_2 = -\frac{h^6}{45}(\partial_x{}^4 + \partial_y{}^4)f_0$$
$$+ h^8\left(-\frac{\partial_x{}^6}{945} + \frac{\partial_x{}^4\partial_y{}^2}{1,980} + \frac{\partial_x{}^2\partial_y{}^4}{1,980} - \frac{\partial_y{}^6}{945}\right)f_0 + \cdots$$
$$= h^6\bar{\beta}_1 + h^8\bar{\beta}_2 + \cdots \tag{6.52}$$

where the $\bar{\beta}_i$ are independent of h.

With the extrapolated values of ψ, we find by the two-dimensional Simpson's rule

$$J = 2.0946a^2 \qquad \text{when } h = a$$
$$J = 2.2316a^4 \qquad \text{when } h = \frac{a}{2}$$

Thus the extrapolated value of the torsional constant $\bar{J}$ can be found by solving the following equations:

$$\bar{J} - 2.0946a^4 = \beta_1 a^6 \qquad \bar{J} - 2.2316a^4 = \beta_1\left(\frac{a}{2}\right)^6$$

We obtain $\bar{J} = 2.2337a^4$, which is 0.5 per cent too low. The maximum shearing stress is thus

$$\tau_{\max} = \frac{T}{J}\frac{\partial\psi}{\partial x} = \frac{1.2437}{2.2337}\frac{T}{a^3} = 0.557\frac{T}{a^3}$$

which is 7.3 per cent too low in comparison with the analytic value.

From this example, we see that with very little increase in labor the error has been decreased to a value satisfactory for engineering purposes. It should be noted that in the process of extrapolation a large number of net points were sacrificed in order to obtain an accurate value of a few, and in the computation of the shear stress the spacing, h, is still relatively large. The method of extrapolation is particularly useful if we are interested only in the values of the function at certain points in the domain.

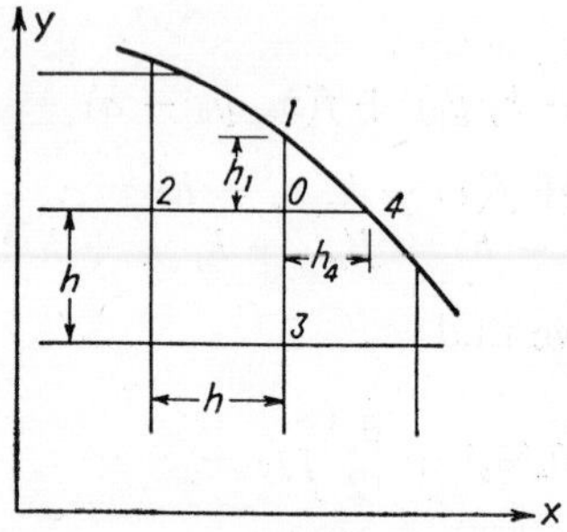

FIG. 6.16.

Problem. By the method of extrapolation, find the maximum shearing stress in the rectangular bar under torsion as assigned in Sec. 6.5.

6.8. Curved Boundaries and Change of Mesh Intervals. In many practical problems, the boundaries are curved. On dividing the region into a square mesh, points like that marked 0 (Fig. 6.16) occur, in which one or more of the associated "arms," 01, 02, 03, 04, are less than the standard interval h.

For such points the standard unit operators are incorrect, and it becomes necessary to develop special operators.

Let f_0, f_1, f_2, f_3, f_4 be the values of the function at points 0, 1, 2, 3, 4, respectively. Expand $f(x,y)$ into a power series in the neighborhood of the point $(0,0)$. Thus,

$$f(x,y) = f_0 + a_1x + a_2y + a_3x^2 + a_4y^2 + a_5xy + \cdots \qquad (6.53)$$

At $x = 0$, $y = h_1$, we have $f = f_1$, and at $x = 0$, $y = -h$, $f = f_3$. Therefore, from (6.53), it follows

$$f_1 = f_0 + a_2h_1 + a_4h_1{}^2 \qquad f_3 = f_0 - a_2h + a_4h^2$$

Solving, we find

$$a_2 = \frac{h^2(f_1 - f_0) + h_1{}^2(f_0 - f_3)}{hh_1(h + h_1)} \qquad a_4 = \frac{h(f_1 - f_0) - h_1(f_0 - f_3)}{hh_1(h + h_1)}$$

Similarly,

$$a_1 = \frac{h^2(f_4 - f_0) + h_4{}^2(f_0 - f_2)}{hh_4(h + h_4)} \qquad a_3 = \frac{h(f_4 - f_0) - h_4(f_0 - f_2)}{hh_4(h + h_4)}$$

At the point 0 $(x = 0$, $y = 0)$ we have

$$\left(\frac{\partial^2 f}{\partial x^2}\right)_0 = 2a_3 = 2\frac{h(f_4 - f_0) - h_4(f_0 - f_2)}{hh_4(h + h_4)}$$

$$\left(\frac{\partial^2 f}{\partial y^2}\right)_0 = 2a_4 = 2\frac{h(f_1 - f_0) - h_1(f_0 - f_3)}{hh_1(h + h_1)}$$

so that $(\nabla^2 f)_0$ may be written as

$$h^2\left(\frac{\partial^2 f}{\partial x^2} + \frac{\partial^2 f}{\partial y^2}\right)_0 \cong \frac{2}{\alpha_1(1 + \alpha_1)}f_1 + \frac{2}{1 + \alpha_4}f_2 + \frac{2}{1 + \alpha_1}f_3$$

$$+ \frac{2}{\alpha_4(1 + \alpha_4)}f_4 - \left(\frac{2}{\alpha_1} + \frac{2}{\alpha_4}\right)f_0$$

where $\alpha_1 = h_1/h$, $\alpha_4 = h_4/h$. When $0 < \alpha_1 < 1$ and $0 < \alpha_4 < 1$, we have

$$h^2(\nabla^2 f)_0 \cong Af_1 + Bf_2 + Cf_3 + Df_4 - (E + F)f_0 \qquad (6.54)$$

where the values of A, B, C, D, E, F can be found in tabulated form.[1]

The finite-difference approximation formulas for other differential equations near a curved boundary can be derived in a like manner.

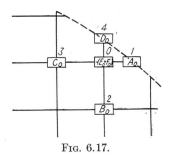

Fig. 6.17.

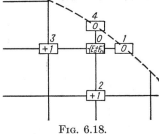

Fig. 6.18.

This finite-difference equivalent for the Laplace operator may then be used in precisely the same manner as the standard $(-4,1,1,1,1)$ operator. Diagrammatically, for an irregular star centered at point 0, the *residual operator*, *i.e.*, the operator from which the residual can be computed, is as in Fig. 6.17, where the numbers $A_0, \ldots,$ F_0 will all be known. The *relaxation operators*, however, are a little more tricky. Thus if the value of the function is altered by $+1$ at point 0, the residual there is altered by $-(E_0 + F_0)$. At the same time the stars centered at points 2 and 3 (Fig. 6.18), being regular stars, each receive an alteration to their residual of $+1$. No residuals are recorded at the boundary points 1 and 4. The relaxation operator for point 0 is, accordingly, as given in Fig. 6.18. Likewise, if we alter the value of the function at 2, the residual at 0 will change B_0 times the value altered at 2. The relaxation operator at point 2 is shown in Fig. 6.19.

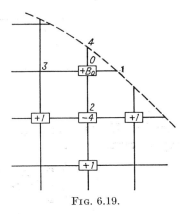

Fig. 6.19.

With all these "irregular stars" evaluated for a particular problem, the relaxation process may then be carried out in the manner already

[1] F. S. Shaw, The Torsion of Solid and Hollow Prisms in the Elastic and Plastic Range by Relaxation Methods, *Rept.* ACA-11, Australian Council for Aeronautics, November, 1944. See also F. S. Shaw, "Introduction to Relaxation Methods," Dover Publications, New York, 1953.

described. The presence of the irregular stars adds a little to the labor but nothing to the complexity of the method, and a little practice makes their use automatic.

The considerations of the preceding paragraphs enable us to find suitable improvement formulas for a region such as shown in Fig. 6.20, where the interval changes from the value h in one part of the mesh to double this value in another. Such a refinement of the mesh is sometimes desirable near a region of the boundary where the function curves vary

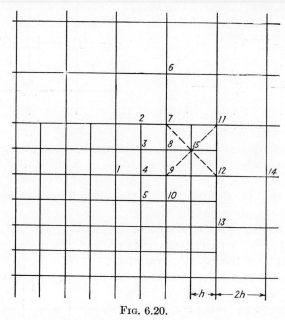

Fig. 6.20.

rapidly. If the governing differential equation is Laplace's equation, typical formulas are

$$f_4 = \tfrac{1}{4}(f_1 + f_3 + f_9 + f_5)$$
$$f_{12} = \tfrac{1}{4}(f_9 + f_{11} + f_{13} + f_{14})$$
$$f_7 = \tfrac{1}{6}(2f_2 + f_6 + f_{11} + 2f_8)$$
$$f_9 = \tfrac{1}{9}(2f_4 + 3f_8 + f_{12} + 3f_{10})$$
$$f_{15} = \tfrac{1}{4}(f_7 + f_9 + f_{11} + f_{12})$$
$$f_8 = \tfrac{1}{4}(f_3 + f_7 + f_9 + f_{15})$$
$$= \tfrac{1}{16}(4f_3 + 5f_7 + 5f_9 + f_{11} + f_{12})$$

The derivation is self-explanatory.

Problem. Solve, by the standard relaxation method, the torsion problem of an equilateral triangular bar by dividing the domain into square meshes. Find the maximum shearing stress.

6.9. Other Boundary Conditions.   In the example considered in the previous sections, the boundary condition assumes its simplest form, *viz.*, the function assumes a constant value of zero on the boundary. Many problems of practical importance have much more complicated boundary conditions, and the relaxation process becomes more complicated in these cases.   We shall now

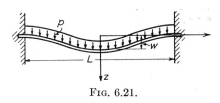

Fig. 6.21.

show how the relaxation process can be carried out in such a case by considering the bending of a beam with both ends built in under a uniformly distributed load p (Fig. 6.21).   The governing differential equation is

$$\frac{d^4w}{dx^4} = \frac{p}{EI} \tag{6.55}$$

where w is the lateral deflection, E is the Young's modulus, and I is the moment of inertia.   The boundary conditions are

$$w = 0, \frac{dw}{dx} = 0 \qquad \text{at } x = \pm \frac{L}{2}$$

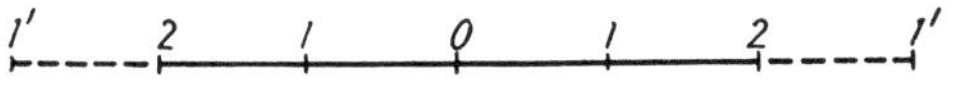

Fig. 6.22.

Taking $h = L/4$, the finite-difference equation at point 0 (Fig. 6.22) becomes

$$w_1 - 4w_2 + 6w_0 - 4w_2 + w_1 = \frac{ph^4}{EI} \tag{6.56}$$

where the symmetry of the deflection has been taken into account.   The relaxation operator is shown in Fig. 6.23. In order to write the boundary conditions in terms of central differences, let us introduce two imaginary points 1′ outside the beam.   Thus the boundary conditions become

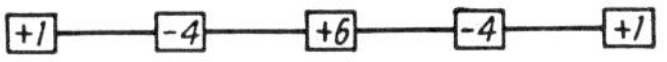

Fig. 6.23.

$$w_2 = 0 \qquad \text{and} \qquad w_{1'} - w_1 = 0 \tag{6.57}$$

The relaxation process can be carried out in the following steps (Fig. 6.24):

Step 1.   Assume $w = 0$ at all the points.   The residuals at all the points are

$$Q = \Delta_x{}^4w - \frac{ph^4}{EI} = -\frac{ph^4}{EI}$$

Instead of writing $-ph^4/EI$ as the residuals, let us multiply them by the factor $100EI/ph^4$ and record -100 at the lower left corners of points 0 and 1. Add $+40$ at point 0. The residual at 0 changes by the amount of 6×40 and becomes $+140$. The residual at 1 becomes

$$-100 - 4 \times 40 = -260$$

Step 2. Add 50 at point 1. From the boundary conditions, $w_{1'} = w_1$. Therefore when the deflection of the point is altered by an amount of $+50$,

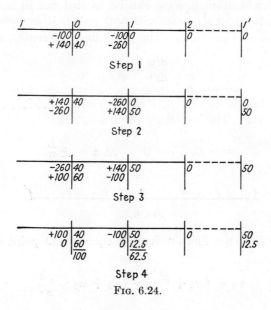

Fig. 6.24.

the same amount has to be added at the imaginary point $1'$. From the condition of symmetry, we have to add 50 at point 1 on the left of the line of symmetry. Thus, the residual at point 1 will be changed by 6×50 owing to the change at this point, 50 owing to the change at $1'$, and 50 owing to the symmetrical point at the left of point 0. Its final residual becomes $-260 + 8 \times 50 = +140$. The residual at point 0 is changed by an amount of 50×-4 on both sides of 0 and becomes

$$+140 - 8 \times 50 = -260$$

Step 3. Add 60 at point 0. The residuals at 0 and 1 become $+100$ and -100, respectively.

Step 4. Add 12.5 at point 1, and the residuals become zero both at 0 and 1.

The center deflection is thus

$$w_0 = 100 \times \frac{ph^4}{100EI} = \frac{ph^4}{EI} = \frac{p}{EI}\left(\frac{L}{4}\right)^4 = \frac{0.00391pL^4}{EI}$$

The exact value of w_0 is $0.002604pL^4/EI$.

Problem 1. Solve the above example by taking $h = L/6$, and then find the center deflection by the method of extrapolation.

Ans. $(w_0)_{h=L/6} = \dfrac{0.003183pL^4}{EI}$

$(w_0)_{\text{extrapolation}} = \dfrac{0.002604\ pL}{EI}$

Problem 2. Solve the above example by the higher-order finite-difference approximation formulas.

Problem 3. Find the maximum deflection of the beam if both ends are assumed to be hinged. *Hint:* Referring to Fig. 6.22, the boundary conditions are $w_2 = 0$ and $w_1 + w_{1'} = 0$, which follows from the condition that $M_2 = [EI(d^2w/dx^2)]_2 = 0$.

CHAPTER 7

ENERGY PRINCIPLES AND VARIATIONAL METHODS

7.1. Principle of Potential Energy. In the numerical solutions of elasticity problems, in addition to the methods of finite differences, there is another group of methods which are also powerful. These methods are based on the fact that the governing differential equations of an elasticity problem can be obtained as a direct consequence of the minimization of a certain energy expression. Instead of solving the differential equations, we may therefore seek a solution which will minimize the energy expression and may thereby avoid the mathematical difficulty in the solution of such differential equations. The technique of using these methods will be discussed in detail later in this chapter. In the development of these methods, we shall make use of a branch of higher mathematics called calculus of variations; for this reason, these methods are sometimes referred to as *variational methods*.

Before describing the variational methods, let us first derive the *principle of virtual work* enunciated by John Bernoulli in 1717. Consider a particle at point P (Fig. 7.1), and imagine that it is acted upon by certain forces. Let one of these be the force F. We shall suppose that we do not actually know how the particle moves under the action of the forces; but imagine that the particle undergoes a perfectly *arbitrary* small displacement denoted by δr. This displacement, it must be emphasized, need not be the one that actually takes place. It is sufficient that we can imagine its taking place. For this reason it will be called a *virtual displacement*, and the symbol δ is used here to denote a virtual infinitesimally small quantity. During this virtual displacement, it is clear that the work done is

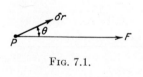

Fig. 7.1.

$$\delta W = F \, \delta r \cos \theta = F_r \, \delta r \tag{7.1}$$

where F_r is the component of F in the direction of δr. This work done during a virtual displacement is called the *virtual work*.

Now let us assume that the particle P is in equilibrium under the n forces $F_1, F_2, \ldots, F_n$. The principle of virtual displacement states that *if a particle is in equilibrium the total virtual work done by these n forces during any arbitrary virtual displacement of the particle is zero*. This can be easily verified as follows: Let the virtual displacement be δr. Then from (7.1) the virtual work done by any force $F_i(i = 1,2, \ldots ,n)$ is the product of the component of the force in the direction of the virtual displacement and the virtual displacement, *viz.*,

$$\delta W_i = F_{ir}\, \delta r$$

where the F_{ir} denote the component of the force F_i in the direction of r. The total virtual work is therefore

$$\delta W = \sum_{i=1}^{n} \delta W_i = F_{1r}\,\delta r + F_{2r}\,\delta r + \cdots + F_{nr}\,\delta r = \left(\sum_{i=1}^{n} F_{ir} \right) \delta r$$

But the equilibrium of these static forces requires that the summation of these forces in any direction be zero.   Hence

$$\sum_{i=1}^{n} F_{ir} = 0$$

It follows therefore that

$$\delta W = 0 \qquad\qquad (7.2)$$

That is, the total virtual work done during any virtual displacement is zero.

An elastic body may be considered as consisting of a system of particles. Thus an elastic body at rest, with its surface and body forces, constitutes a system of particles on each of which acts a set of forces in equilibrium. If there is any virtual displacement, from the above discussion we see that the virtual work done by the forces on any particle vanishes and therefore the total virtual work done by all the forces of the system vanishes.   The only difference between a particle in an elastic body and a free particle is that, in giving the virtual displacements in the former case, we must observe the condition of continuity of the material and the condition of consistency to the prescribed displacements on the boundary. The condition of continuity of the material is satisfied if the virtual displacements can be expressed in terms of continuous functions.   The condition of consistency to the prescribed boundary conditions can be best explained by considering an example, say the bending of a simply supported beam.   In this case, the boundary conditions require that the transverse or lateral displacements be zero at the two ends of the beam. Since the ends of the beam cannot move in the transverse directions, the virtual displacements in the transverse directions there must also be taken as zero.

Let u, v, w be, respectively, the x, y, z components of the actual displacement due to the external loads in an elastic body and δu, δv, δw the components of the virtual displacement.   These components of virtual displacement are assumed to be infinitesimally small quantities satisfying the conditions of continuity of an elastic deformation, *i.e.*, they are continuous functions of x, y, and z and are consistent with the prescribed boundary conditions. To simplify our discussion, let us consider an element of the elastic body $dx\ dy\ dz$ acted on by a one-dimensional stress system (Fig. 7.2). If we change the displacement u by the amount δu, the element is now displaced to the new position indicated by the dotted line in the figure. The total virtual work done against the mutual action between the particles is therefore

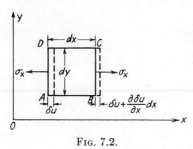

Fig. 7.2.

$$\sigma_x\left(\delta u + \frac{\partial \delta u}{\partial x}\,dx\right)dy\ dz - \sigma_x\,\delta u\ dy\ dz = \sigma_x\frac{\partial \delta u}{\partial x}\,dx\ dy\ dz \qquad (7.3)$$

Now, since the elastic body is continuous, owing to the virtual displacement δu, there will be also a change of strain. The x component of strain at A will now be

$$\epsilon_x + \delta\epsilon_x = \frac{\left(u + \dfrac{\partial u}{\partial x}\,dx + \delta u + \dfrac{\partial \delta u}{\partial x}\,dx\right) - (u + \delta u)}{dx} = \frac{\partial u}{\partial x} + \frac{\partial \delta u}{\partial x}$$

or $\delta\epsilon_x = \partial \delta u/\partial x$. But $\epsilon_x = \partial u/\partial x$; we have $\delta\epsilon_x = \delta(\partial u/\partial x)$. Hence

$$\delta\epsilon_x = \delta\left(\frac{\partial u}{\partial x}\right) = \frac{\partial \delta u}{\partial x} \qquad (7.4)$$

This means that if $f(x,y,z)$ is a continuous function of x, y, z and its derivatives exist, we may define

$$\delta df = d\delta f \qquad (7.5)$$

With (7.4), (7.3) can be written as

$$\sigma_x\,\delta\epsilon_x\,dx\ dy\ dz = E\epsilon_x\,\delta\epsilon_x\,dx\ dy\ dz \qquad (7.6)$$

Under this one-dimensional stress system, the strain energy stored in the element $dx\ dy\ dz$ is obtained in Sec. 3.5 as

$$dU = \frac{1}{2}\sigma_x\epsilon_x\,dx\ dy\ dz = \frac{E}{2}\,\epsilon_x{}^2\,dx\ dy\ dz \qquad (7.7)$$

Comparing (7.6) with (7.7), we find that the expression (7.6) is the same as δdU if we define the rules of operation for the operator δ to be the same as those for the differential operator d in the differential calculus. The only difference is that δ refers to a virtual change and d refers to an actual change. Analogous to the operator d, which is called the first differential, the operator δ is called the first *variation*.

In a manner similar to the derivation of strain energy in Sec. 3.5, we can show that the total work done against the mutual actions between the particles in an elastic body due to the virtual displacements δu, δv, δw is δU and therefore the total virtual work done by the mutual actions is $-\delta U$.

Now let us calculate the work done by the body forces and the forces applied at the boundary of the body. Let X, Y, Z be the x, y, z components of the body forces per unit volume and $\bar{X}$, $\bar{Y}$, $\bar{Z}$ be the x, y, z components of the boundary forces per unit area. The work done by the body forces is

$$\iiint\limits_{V} (X\,\delta u + Y\,\delta v + Z\,\delta w)\,dx\,dy\,dz \qquad (7.8)$$

and the work done by the boundary-surface forces is

$$\iint\limits_{A_1} (\bar{X}\,\delta u + \bar{Y}\,\delta v + \bar{Z}\,\delta w)\,dA \qquad (7.9)$$

where dA is the elementary area and the integration is taken over that part of the boundary surface of the body, A_1, on which the displacements are not described. This is because δu, δv, δw are zero over the part of the boundary surface where displacements are prescribed, and the integral (7.9) is not zero only on the part of the boundary surface where the surface forces are prescribed. To avoid confusion, it may be mentioned here that the part of the surface where forces are prescribed is the same as the part where displacements are not prescribed.

We have already concluded that the total work done during the virtual displacement vanishes. Therefore,

$$\iint\limits_{A_1} (\bar{X}\,\delta u + \bar{Y}\,\delta v + \bar{Z}\,\delta w)\,dA$$
$$+ \iiint\limits_{V} (X\,\delta u + Y\,\delta v + Z\,\delta w)\,dx\,dy\,dz - \delta U = 0$$

Since the external forces are taken as constant during the virtual displacement, we find that the operator δ in the above equation may be put before the integral signs. By changing the signs throughout, we have

$$\delta(U - W) = 0 \qquad (7.10)$$

where

$$W = \iint\limits_{A_1} (\bar{X}u + \bar{Y}v + \bar{Z}w)\,dA + \iiint\limits_{V} (Xu + Yv + Zw)\,dx\,dy\,dz \qquad (7.11)$$

The quantity $\Pi = U - W$ is called the *potential energy* of the system since U is the potential energy of deformation and $-W$ represents the potential energy of the external forces acting on the body if the potential energy of these forces for the unstressed condition ($u = v = w = 0$) is taken as zero.

Equation (7.10) states that, *in comparing various values of the dis-placements u, v, and w, the displacements which actually occur in an elastic system under the action of given external forces are those which lead to zero variation of the total energy of the system for any virtual displacement from the position of equilibrium.* Analogous to the expression

$$df = 0$$

in infinitesimal calculus, which means that f is an extremum (or a turning point), the expression

$$\delta\Pi = \delta(U - W) = 0$$

indicates that the potential energy of the system at the position of equilibrium is an extremum (or a turning point). For *stable* equilibrium, it can be shown that for any virtual displacement or variation of dis-placement the change in the total potential energy of the system is posi-tive and hence in this case the total potential energy of the system is a minimum. For elasticity problems with small displacements and strains, we find from the uniqueness theorem that there is only one equilibrium configuration. It can be shown, furthermore, that this equilibrium configuration is a stable one. Therefore we can conclude that, for an elastic body with small displacements and strains, the potential energy at equilibrium is a minimum. The *principle of potential energy* can be stated as follows:

Principle of Potential Energy. Of all displacements satisfying given boundary conditions, those which satisfy the equilibrium conditions make the potential energy Π assume a stationary value. For stable equilibrium, Π is a minimum.

7.2. Principle of Complementary Energy. Instead of varying the displacements from those at equilibrium, we may want to vary the stress components. Let us remember that when we are working with the displacements we have to concern ourselves only with the equilibrium equations, but if we are going to work with the stress components, in addition to the equilibrium equations, the compatibility equations must also be taken into account. In the following, we shall show that, of all the stresses satisfying the given boundary conditions and the condi-tions of equilibrium in the interior of the elastic body, the stresses which satisfy the compatibility equations will make some energy expression called the *complementary energy* assume a stationary value.

To simplify the derivation, let us consider the case of plane stress in an elastic plate. Let σ_x, σ_y, τ_{xy} be the actual stress components in the elastic body satisfying the conditions of equilibrium and compatibility as well as the given boundary conditions. Let $\delta\sigma_x$, $\delta\sigma_y$, $\delta\tau_{xy}$ be the small variations in the stress components such that the new stress components $\sigma_x + \delta\sigma_x$, $\sigma_y + \delta\sigma_y$, $\tau_{xy} + \delta\tau_{xy}$ satisfy the equilibrium equations but not the compatibility equation. On the part of the boundary where surface forces are prescribed, these new stress components must be such that these surface forces will not be changed; but on the other part of the boundary where displacements instead of surface forces are prescribed, there could be changes in the values of the surface forces.

Accordingly, we have

$$\frac{\partial(\sigma_x + \delta\sigma_x)}{\partial x} + \frac{\partial(\tau_{xy} + \delta\tau_{xy})}{\partial y} + X = 0$$

$$\frac{\partial(\tau_{xy} + \delta\tau_{xy})}{\partial x} + \frac{\partial(\sigma_y + \delta\sigma_y)}{\partial y} + Y = 0 \tag{7.12}$$

The body forces X and Y are given external forces and are therefore unchanged. By subtracting from (7.12) the equilibrium equations before the stress variations occur, we obtain

$$\frac{\partial\delta\sigma_x}{\partial x} + \frac{\partial\delta\tau_{xy}}{\partial y} = 0 \qquad \frac{\partial\delta\tau_{xy}}{\partial x} + \frac{\partial\delta\sigma_y}{\partial y} = 0 \tag{7.13}$$

On that part of the boundary A_2 where surface forces are not prescribed, corresponding to this variation of stress components, there will be some variation in the boundary surface forces. Let $\delta\bar{X}$ and $\delta\bar{Y}$ be these small changes in boundary forces. Then on A_2,

$$(\sigma_x + \delta\sigma_x)l + (\tau_{xy} + \delta\tau_{xy})m = \bar{X} + \delta\bar{X}$$
$$(\tau_{xy} + \delta\tau_{xy})l + (\sigma_y + \delta\sigma_y)m = \bar{Y} + \delta\bar{Y}$$

If we subtract from them the equations before the variation, we have

$$l\,\delta\sigma_x + m\,\delta\tau_{xy} = \delta\bar{X} \qquad l\,\delta\tau_{xy} + m\,\delta\sigma_y = \delta\bar{Y} \tag{7.14}$$

On that part of boundary surface A_1 where these forces are prescribed, we must have

$$l\,\delta\sigma_x + m\,\delta\tau_{xy} = 0 \qquad l\,\delta\tau_{xy} + m\,\delta\sigma_y = 0 \tag{7.15}$$

Owing to these changes in the stress components, from (3.51), we obtain the change in strain energy per unit thickness of the plate as

$$\delta U = U(\sigma_x + \delta\sigma_x, \sigma_y + \delta\sigma_y, \tau_{xy} + \delta\tau_{xy}) - U(\sigma_x,\sigma_y,\tau_{xy})$$

$$= \iint\limits_R \left[\frac{1}{E}(\sigma_x\,\delta\sigma_x + \sigma_y\,\delta\sigma_y - \nu\sigma_x\,\delta\sigma_y - \nu\sigma_y\,\delta\sigma_x) + \frac{1}{G}\tau_{xy}\,\delta\tau_{xy} \right] dx\,dy$$

where R is the area of the plate. By using Hooke's law, δU becomes

$$\delta U = \iint_R (\epsilon_x \, \delta\sigma_x + \epsilon_y \, \delta\sigma_y + \gamma_{xy} \, \delta\tau_{xy}) \, dx \, dy$$

Since σ_x, σ_y, τ_{xy} and consequently ϵ_x, ϵ_y, γ_{xy} satisfy the compatibility equation, we may write

$$\epsilon_x = \frac{\partial u}{\partial x} \qquad \epsilon_y = \frac{\partial v}{\partial y} \qquad \gamma_{xy} = \frac{\partial u}{\partial y} + \frac{\partial v}{\partial x}$$

and integrate the partial derivatives $\dfrac{\partial u}{\partial x}$, $\dfrac{\partial u}{\partial y}$, $\dfrac{\partial v}{\partial x}$, $\dfrac{\partial v}{\partial y}$ to obtain single-valued functions for u and v. Hence,

$$\frac{\partial u}{\partial x} \, \delta\sigma_x + \frac{\partial u}{\partial y} \, \delta\tau_{xy} = \frac{\partial(u \, \delta\sigma_x)}{\partial x} + \frac{\partial(u \, \delta\tau_{xy})}{\partial y} - u\left(\frac{\partial \delta\sigma_x}{\partial x} + \frac{\partial \delta\tau_{xy}}{\partial y}\right)$$

$$\frac{\partial v}{\partial x} \, \delta\tau_{xy} + \frac{\partial v}{\partial y} \, \delta\sigma_y = \frac{\partial(v \, \delta\tau_{xy})}{\partial x} + \frac{\partial(v \, \delta\sigma_y)}{\partial y} - v\left(\frac{\partial \delta\tau_{xy}}{\partial x} + \frac{\partial \delta\sigma_y}{\partial y}\right)$$

Substituting these relations into the expression for δU and using Green's theorem, which we derived in Chap. 5 as formulas (5.10) and (5.11), we obtain

$$\delta U = - \iint_R \left[u\left(\frac{\partial \delta\sigma_x}{\partial x} + \frac{\partial \delta\tau_{xy}}{\partial y}\right) + v\left(\frac{\partial \delta\tau_{xy}}{\partial x} + \frac{\partial \delta\sigma_y}{\partial y}\right) \right] dx \, dy$$

$$+ \int_S [u(\delta\sigma_x \, dy - \delta\tau_{xy} \, dx) + v(\delta\tau_{xy} \, dy - \delta\sigma_y \, dx)]$$

Using relations (5.13), we have

$$\delta\sigma_x \, dy - \delta\tau_{xy} \, dx = \left(\delta\sigma_x \frac{dy}{ds} - \delta\tau_{xy} \frac{dx}{ds}\right) ds = (l \, \delta\sigma_x + m \, \delta\tau_{xy}) \, ds$$

and

$$\delta\tau_{xy} \, dy - \delta\sigma_y \, dx = (l \, \delta\tau_{xy} + m \, \delta\sigma_y) \, ds$$

Thus we finally obtain

$$\delta U = - \iint_R \left[u\left(\frac{\partial \delta\sigma_x}{\partial x} + \frac{\partial \delta\tau_{xy}}{\partial y}\right) + v\left(\frac{\partial \delta\tau_{xy}}{\partial x} + \frac{\partial \delta\sigma_y}{\partial y}\right) \right] dx \, dy$$

$$+ \int_S [u(l \, \delta\sigma_x + m \, \delta\tau_{xy}) + v(l \, \delta\tau_{xy} + m \, \delta\sigma_y)] \, ds$$

where ds is an element of the boundary curve. Combining with Eqs. (7.13) to (7.15), we find

$$\delta U - \int_{S_1} (u \, \delta\bar{X} + v \, \delta\bar{Y}) \, ds = 0$$

where S_2 is that part of the boundary on which the surface forces are not prescribed. Since u and v are not varied on S_2 in this case, we may put the operator δ before the integral, *viz.*,

$$\delta \left[U - \int_{S_2} (u\bar{X} + v\bar{Y}) \, ds \right] = 0$$

In the general case of three-dimensional stress distribution, it can be shown in a similar manner that

$$\delta \Pi^* = \delta(U - W^*) = 0 \qquad (7.16)$$

where $\Pi^* = U - W^*$ is called the *complementary energy* of the system and

$$W^* = \iint\limits_{A_2} (u\bar{X} + v\bar{Y} + w\bar{Z}) \, dA \qquad (7.17)$$

where, as defined previously, A_2 is that part of the boundary on which the surface forces are not prescribed. Equation (7.16) proves the *principle of complementary energy*, which states that *for all stresses satisfying the equilibrium conditions in the interior and on that part of the boundary surface where the surface forces are prescribed, the actual state of stress, i.e., the stresses which satisfy the compatibility equations, is such that the complementary energy* Π^* *assumes a stationary value.* For problems with small strains and displacements, we can further show that Π^* is a minimum. It may be remarked that for nonlinear problems, the potential energy Π is still given by the formula $U - W$ but the complementary energy Π^* will not be equal to $U - W^*$ and the expression for Π^* must be derived separately in each particular case.[1]

7.3. The Principles of Potential and Complementary Energy Considered as Variational Principles. In the preceding sections we have stated that, for an elastic body in equilibrium, the displacements in the body will be such that the potential energy is a minimum and the stress components will be such that the complementary energy is a minimum. We shall now show that, by means of the methods in the calculus of variation, the governing differential equations can be derived as a consequence of these minimal principles.

Let us again consider the case of plane stress in an elastic plate. The governing differential equations in terms of displacements, in this case, can be written as

$$\frac{E}{1 - \nu^2} \left(\frac{\partial^2 u}{\partial x^2} + \frac{1 - \nu}{2} \frac{\partial^2 u}{\partial y^2} \right) + \frac{E}{2(1 - \nu)} \frac{\partial^2 v}{\partial x \, \partial y} + X = 0$$

$$\frac{E}{1 - \nu^2} \left(\frac{1 - \nu}{2} \frac{\partial^2 v}{\partial x^2} + \frac{\partial^2 v}{\partial y^2} \right) + \frac{E}{2(1 - \nu)} \frac{\partial^2 u}{\partial x \, \partial y} + Y = 0 \qquad (7.18)$$

---

[1] See, for example, Chi-Teh Wang, Principle and Application of Complementary Energy Method for Thin Homogeneous and Sandwich Plates and Shells with Finite Deflections, *NACA Tech. Note* 2620, February, 1952.

We shall show that these equations can be derived from the condition that the potential energy is a minimum. Our problem now is to determine the functions $u(x,y)$, $v(x,y)$ so that $\Pi = U - W$ is a minimum.

Let us assume that $u(x,y)$ and $v(x,y)$ are such functions and that δu, δv are arbitrary variations of u and v which satisfy the same conditions of continuity as do u and v. If we replace the functions u and v in Π by $u + \epsilon\,\delta u$ and $v + \epsilon\,\delta v$, where ϵ is an arbitrary small parameter, the potential energy Π becomes a function of the parameter ϵ and, according to the principle of potential energy, it becomes a minimum at $\epsilon = 0$. Hence

$$\frac{d\Pi(\epsilon)}{d\epsilon}\bigg|_{\epsilon=0} = 0 \tag{7.19}$$

But
$$\frac{d\Pi(\epsilon)}{d\epsilon} = \frac{dU(\epsilon)}{d\epsilon} - \frac{dW(\epsilon)}{d\epsilon}$$

From formula (3.53), we have

$$\frac{dU(\epsilon)}{d\epsilon} = \iint_R \left\{ \frac{E}{1-\nu^2}\left[\frac{\partial(u+\epsilon\,\delta u)}{\partial x}\frac{\partial\delta u}{\partial x} + \frac{\partial(v+\epsilon\,\delta v)}{\partial y}\frac{\partial\delta v}{\partial y} \right. \right.$$
$$+ \nu\frac{\partial(u+\epsilon\,\delta u)}{\partial x}\frac{\partial\delta v}{\partial y} + \nu\frac{\partial(v+\epsilon\,\delta v)}{\partial y}\frac{\partial\delta u}{\partial x} \bigg]$$
$$\left. + \frac{E}{2(1+\nu)}\left[\frac{\partial(u+\epsilon\,\delta u)}{\partial y} + \frac{\partial(v+\epsilon\,\delta v)}{\partial x} \right]\left[\frac{\partial\delta u}{\partial y} + \frac{\partial\delta v}{\partial x} \right] \right\}\, dx\,dy$$

and
$$\frac{dU}{d\epsilon}\bigg|_{\epsilon=0} = \iint_R \left\{ \frac{E}{1-\nu^2}\left[\left(\frac{\partial u}{\partial x} + \nu\frac{\partial v}{\partial y}\right)\frac{\partial\delta u}{\partial x} + \left(\frac{\partial v}{\partial y} + \nu\frac{\partial u}{\partial x}\right)\frac{\partial\delta v}{\partial y} \right] \right.$$
$$\left. + \frac{E}{2(1+\nu)}\left(\frac{\partial u}{\partial y} + \frac{\partial v}{\partial x}\right)\left(\frac{\partial\delta u}{\partial y} + \frac{\partial\delta v}{\partial x}\right) \right\}\, dx\,dy$$

Now
$$\frac{E}{1-\nu^2}\left(\frac{\partial u}{\partial x} + \nu\frac{\partial v}{\partial y}\right)\frac{\partial\delta u}{\partial x} + \frac{E}{2(1+\nu)}\left(\frac{\partial u}{\partial y} + \frac{\partial v}{\partial x}\right)\frac{\partial\delta u}{\partial y}$$
$$= \frac{\partial}{\partial x}(\sigma_x\,\delta u) + \frac{\partial}{\partial y}(\tau_{xy}\,\delta u)$$
$$- \left[\frac{E}{1-\nu^2}\frac{\partial}{\partial x}\left(\frac{\partial u}{\partial x} + \nu\frac{\partial v}{\partial y}\right) + \frac{E}{2(1+\nu)}\frac{\partial}{\partial y}\left(\frac{\partial u}{\partial y} + \frac{\partial v}{\partial x}\right) \right]\delta u$$
$$= \frac{\partial}{\partial x}(\sigma_x\,\delta u) + \frac{\partial}{\partial y}(\tau_{xy}\,\delta u)$$
$$- \left[\frac{E}{1-\nu^2}\left(\frac{\partial^2 u}{\partial x^2} + \frac{1-\nu}{2}\frac{\partial^2 u}{\partial y^2}\right) + \frac{E}{2(1-\nu)}\frac{\partial^2 v}{\partial x\,\partial y} \right]\delta u$$

$$\frac{E}{1-\nu^2}\left(\frac{\partial v}{\partial y} + \nu\frac{\partial u}{\partial x}\right)\frac{\partial\delta v}{\partial y} + \frac{E}{2(1+\nu)}\left(\frac{\partial u}{\partial y} + \frac{\partial v}{\partial x}\right)\frac{\partial\delta v}{\partial x}$$
$$= \frac{\partial}{\partial x}(\tau_{xy}\,\delta v) + \frac{\partial}{\partial y}(\sigma_y\,\delta v)$$
$$- \left[\frac{E}{1-\nu^2}\left(\frac{1-\nu}{2}\frac{\partial^2 v}{\partial x^2} + \frac{\partial^2 v}{\partial y^2}\right) + \frac{E}{2(1-\nu)}\frac{\partial^2 u}{\partial x\,\partial y} \right]\delta v$$

In the above calculation, Hooke's law has been used. From Green's theorem,

$$\iint_R \left[\frac{\partial}{\partial x} (\sigma_x \, \delta u) + \frac{\partial}{\partial y} (\tau_{xy} \, \delta u) \right] dx \, dy = \int_S (\sigma_x \, \delta u \, dy - \tau_{xy} \, \delta u \, dx)$$

where S is the boundary curve of the plate. Since

$$(\sigma_x \, dy - \tau_{xy} \, dx) = \left(\sigma_x \frac{dy}{ds} - \tau_{xy} \frac{dx}{ds} \right) ds$$
$$= (\sigma_x \cos Nx + \tau_{xy} \cos Ny) \, ds = \bar{X} \, ds$$

we have

$$\iint_R \left[\frac{\partial}{\partial x} (\sigma_x \, \delta u) + \frac{\partial}{\partial y} (\tau_{xy} \, \delta u) \right] dx \, dy = \int_S \bar{X} \, \delta u \, ds$$

Similarly,

$$\iint_R \left[\frac{\partial}{\partial x} (\tau_{xy} \, \delta v) + \frac{\partial}{\partial y} (\sigma_y \, \delta v) \right] dx \, dy = \int_S \bar{Y} \, \delta v \, ds$$

We obtain therefore

$$\frac{d\Pi(\epsilon)}{d\epsilon} \bigg|_{\epsilon=0} = - \iint_R \left\{ \left[\frac{E}{1 - \nu^2} \left(\frac{\partial^2 u}{\partial x^2} + \frac{1 - \nu}{2} \frac{\partial^2 u}{\partial y^2} \right) + \frac{E}{2(1 - \nu)} \frac{\partial^2 v}{\partial x \, \partial y} \right] \delta u \right.$$
$$+ \left[\frac{E}{1 - \nu^2} \left(\frac{1 - \nu}{2} \frac{\partial^2 v}{\partial x^2} + \frac{\partial^2 v}{\partial y^2} \right) + \frac{E}{2(1 - \nu)} \frac{\partial^2 u}{\partial x \, \partial y} \right] \delta v \left. \right\} dx \, dy$$
$$+ \int_{S_1} (\bar{X} \, \delta u + \bar{Y} \, \delta v) \, ds$$

Since the line integral vanishes on that part of the boundary where the displacement is prescribed, we may write S_1 instead of S in the last integral. From the definition of W, formula (7.11), we find that in the case of a plane-stress state,

$$\frac{dW(\epsilon)}{d\epsilon} \bigg|_{\epsilon=0} = \int_{S_1} (\bar{X} \, \delta u + \bar{Y} \, \delta v) \, ds + \iint_R (X \, \delta u + Y \, \delta v) \, dx \, dy$$

Hence the condition $\dfrac{d\Pi(\epsilon)}{d\epsilon} \bigg|_{\epsilon=0} = \dfrac{dU(\epsilon)}{d\epsilon} \bigg|_{\epsilon=0} - \dfrac{dW(\epsilon)}{d\epsilon} \bigg|_{\epsilon=0} = 0$ leads to

$$- \iint_R \left\{ \left[\frac{E}{1 - \nu^2} \left(\frac{\partial^2 u}{\partial x^2} + \frac{1 - \nu}{2} \frac{\partial^2 u}{\partial y^2} \right) + \frac{E}{2(1 - \nu)} \frac{\partial^2 v}{\partial x \, \partial y} + X \right] \delta u \right.$$
$$+ \left[\frac{E}{1 - \nu^2} \left(\frac{1 - \nu}{2} \frac{\partial^2 v}{\partial x^2} + \frac{\partial^2 v}{\partial y^2} \right) + \frac{E}{2(1 - \nu)} \frac{\partial^2 u}{\partial x \, \partial y} + Y \right] \delta v \left. \right\} dx \, dy = 0$$

$$(7.20)$$

Since the variations δu and δv are arbitrary functions, the only way for the integral (7.20) to be zero is that

$$\frac{E}{1 - \nu^2}\left(\frac{\partial^2 u}{\partial x^2} + \frac{1 - \nu}{2}\frac{\partial^2 u}{\partial y^2}\right) + \frac{E}{2(1 - \nu)}\frac{\partial^2 v}{\partial x\,\partial y} + X = 0$$

$$\frac{E}{1 - \nu^2}\left(\frac{1 - \nu}{2}\frac{\partial^2 v}{\partial x^2} + \frac{\partial^2 v}{\partial y^2}\right) + \frac{E}{2(1 - \nu)}\frac{\partial^2 u}{\partial x\,\partial y} + Y = 0$$

which are the governing differential equation (7.18).

In the above derivation, we have followed the method of the calculus of variation. The same results can be obtained if we interpret δ as an operator following the rules of operation of d. We shall demonstrate this by considering another example, *viz.*, a simply supported beam with constant cross section under uniformly distributed load (Fig. 7.3). The strain energy stored in a beam consists

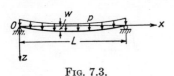

Fig. 7.3.

of two parts: the strain energy due to bending and that due to shear. Compared with the bending strain energy, the strain energy due to shear is usually negligible. The strain energy stored in the beam is then mainly that part due to bending, which is

$$U = \iiint_V \frac{\sigma_x^2}{2E}\,dx\,dy\,dz$$

From the analysis made in Secs. 4.2 and 9.1, we see that $\sigma_x = Mz/I$ and $M = EI\,(d^2w/dx^2)$, where I is the moment of inertia of the cross section with respect to the y axis and w is the lateral deflection. Let A be the cross-sectional area of the beam. Remembering that $\iint z^2\,dy\,dz = I$, the strain energy is then

$$U = \frac{1}{2}\int_0^L EI\left(\frac{d^2w}{dx^2}\right)^2 dx$$

For beams with constant cross section, EI is independent of x, and the bending strain energy is

$$U = \frac{EI}{2}\int_0^L \left(\frac{d^2w}{dx^2}\right)^2 dx \tag{7.21}$$

The potential energy due to the external load is

$$W = \int_0^L pw\,dx \tag{7.22}$$

where p is the intensity of the distributed load per unit length of the beam. The total potential energy of the system is

$$\Pi = U - W = \frac{EI}{2}\int_0^L \left(\frac{d^2w}{dx^2}\right)^2 dx - \int_0^L pw\,dx \tag{7.23}$$

Taking the first variation, we have

$$\delta\Pi = \frac{EI}{2}\int_0^L 2\frac{d^2w}{dx^2}\frac{d^2\delta w}{dx^2}\,dx - \int_0^L p\,\delta w\,dx$$

Integrating the first integral by parts,

$$\int_0^L 2\frac{d^2w}{dx^2}\frac{d^2\delta w}{dx^2}\,dx = \left[2\frac{d^2w}{dx^2}\frac{d\delta w}{dx}\right]_{x=0}^{x=L} - 2\int_0^L \frac{d^3w}{dx^3}\frac{d\delta w}{dx}\,dx$$

$$= \left[2\frac{d^2w}{dx^2}\frac{d\delta w}{dx} - 2\frac{d^3w}{dx^3}\delta w\right]_{x=0}^{x=L} + 2\int_0^L \frac{d^4w}{dx^4}\delta w\,dx$$

The condition $\delta\Pi = 0$ becomes

$$\int_0^L \left(EI\frac{d^4w}{dx^4} - p\right)\delta w\,dx + \left[EI\frac{d^2w}{dx^2}\frac{d\delta w}{dx} - EI\frac{d^3w}{dx^3}\delta w\right]_{x=0}^{x=L} = 0$$

Since $M = EI(d^2w/dx^2) = 0$ and $w = 0$ at $x = 0$ and $x = L$, $\delta w = 0$ at $x = 0$ and $x = L$ and the terms inside the brackets vanish on the boundary $x = 0$ and $x = L$. In the interior of the beam, δw is arbitrary, and the condition

$$\int_0^L \left(EI\frac{d^4w}{dx^4} - p\right)\delta w\,dx = 0$$

is possible only when

$$EI\frac{d^4w}{dx^4} - p = 0 \qquad (7.24)$$

which is the governing differential equation in this case.

Now let us consider the complementary energy. We shall take as an example the torsion of prismatical bars. We have already shown that there exists a stress function ψ such that

$$\tau_{yz} = -G\theta\frac{\partial\psi}{\partial x} \qquad \tau_{zx} = G\theta\frac{\partial\psi}{\partial y}$$

and the other stress components are zero. The variation of the stress function is equivalent to the variation of the stress components. In terms of the stress function, the strain energy stored in a bar of length L is

$$U = \frac{1}{2G}\iiint_V (\tau_{yz}^2 + \tau_{zx}^2)\,dx\,dy\,dz = \frac{G\theta^2 L}{2}\iint_R \left[\left(\frac{\partial\psi}{\partial x}\right)^2 + \left(\frac{\partial\psi}{\partial y}\right)^2\right]dx\,dy$$

where R, as before, denotes the cross-sectional area of the bar. W^* is zero over the lateral surfaces of the bar because the boundary force is prescribed there. On the two ends, we have

$$W^* = \left[\iint_R (\tau_{zx}u + \tau_{yz}v)\,dx\,dy\right]_{\substack{z=0 \\ z=L}}$$

As found in Chap. 5, the displacements u and v are $u = -\theta zy$ and $v = \theta zx$. At $z = 0$, $u = v = 0$. At $z = L$, $u = -\theta Ly$, $v = \theta Lx$. Hence

$$W^* = \theta L \iint_R (-y\tau_{zx} + x\tau_{yz})\, dx\, dy$$

$$= G\theta^2 L \iint_R \left(-y\frac{\partial\psi}{\partial y} - x\frac{\partial\psi}{\partial x}\right) dx\, dy$$

$$= 2G\theta^2 L \iint_R \psi\, dx\, dy - G\theta^2 L \oint_S (\psi x\, dy - \psi y\, dx)$$

in which the last step is obtained in exactly the same manner as the derivation of (5.53) in Chap. 5. The complementary energy of the system is therefore

$$\Pi^* = U - W^* = \frac{G\theta^2 L}{2} \iint_R \left[\left(\frac{\partial\psi}{\partial x}\right)^2 + \left(\frac{\partial\psi}{\partial y}\right)^2 - 4\psi\right] dx\, dy$$

$$- G\theta^2 L \oint_S (\psi x\, dy - \psi y\, dx) \quad (7.25)$$

and $\delta\Pi^* = \dfrac{G\theta^2 L}{2} \displaystyle\iint_R \left(2\frac{\partial\psi}{\partial x}\frac{\partial\delta\psi}{\partial x} + 2\frac{\partial\psi}{\partial y}\frac{\partial\delta\psi}{\partial y} - 4\delta\psi\right) dx\, dy$

$$- G\theta^2 L \oint_S \delta\psi(x\, dy - y\, dx)$$

Since

$$\frac{\partial\psi}{\partial x}\frac{\partial\delta\psi}{\partial x} + \frac{\partial\psi}{\partial y}\frac{\partial\delta\psi}{\partial y} = \frac{\partial}{\partial x}\left(\delta\psi\frac{\partial\psi}{\partial x}\right) + \frac{\partial}{\partial y}\left(\delta\psi\frac{\partial\psi}{\partial y}\right) - \left(\frac{\partial^2\psi}{\partial x^2} + \frac{\partial^2\psi}{\partial y^2}\right)\delta\psi$$

$$\delta\Pi^* = -G\theta^2 L \iint_R \left(\frac{\partial^2\psi}{\partial x^2} + \frac{\partial^2\psi}{\partial y^2} + 2\right)\delta\psi\, dx\, dy$$

$$+ G\theta^2 L \oint_S \left[\left(\frac{\partial\psi}{\partial x} - x\right) dy - \left(\frac{\partial\psi}{\partial y} - y\right) dx\right]\delta\psi$$

$$= -G\theta^2 L \iint_R \left(\frac{\partial\psi}{\partial x^2} + \frac{\partial^2\psi}{\partial y^2} + 2\right)\delta\psi\, dx\, d\xi$$

$$+ G\theta^2 L \oint_S \left[\left(\frac{\partial\psi}{\partial x} - x\right)\cos Nx + \left(\frac{\partial\psi}{\partial y} - y\right)\cos Ny\right]\delta\psi\, ds \quad (7.26)$$

On the boundary S, the surface forces are prescribed. In terms of ψ, the boundary condition is $\psi = $ constant. That means that

$$\delta\psi = 0 \qquad \text{on } S \quad (7.27)$$

The line integral in (7.26) therefore becomes zero. Since $\delta\psi$ is arbitrary in R, the only way that the surface integral in (7.26) will be zero is that

$$\frac{\partial^2\psi}{\partial x^2} + \frac{\partial^2\psi}{\partial y^2} + 2 = 0 \qquad \text{in } R \quad (7.28)$$

In Sec. 5.4, we have shown that the constant value of ψ on S may be taken as zero. With $\psi = 0$ on the boundary, the complementary energy becomes

$$\Pi^* = \frac{G\theta^2 L}{2} \iint\limits_{R} \left[\left(\frac{\partial\psi}{\partial x}\right)^2 + \left(\frac{\partial\psi}{\partial y}\right)^2 - 4\psi \right] dx\, dy \qquad (7.29)$$

7.4. Rayleigh-Ritz Method. By using the principles of minimum potential energy and complementary energy, we may find the solutions of the boundary-value problems in the theory of elasticity from another point of view. Instead of solving the governing differential equations together with the boundary conditions, a task often very difficult mathematically, we may interpret the problem as the one seeking the functions which satisfy the boundary conditions and minimize the potential energy Π or the complementary energy Π^*. For example, in the case of torsion of a prismatical bar, we may consider the problem as the one seeking the function ψ which will minimize the complementary energy

$$\Pi^* = \frac{G\theta^2 L}{2} \iint\limits_{R} \left[\left(\frac{\partial\psi}{\partial x}\right)^2 + \left(\frac{\partial\psi}{\partial y}\right)^2 - 4\psi \right] dx\, dy$$

and which satisfies the condition $\psi = 0$ on the boundary S. We note that, in the above process, we have replaced the differential equation by a minimization condition. A number of methods have been suggested for finding the approximate solutions of boundary-value problems according to such an approach.

One of the more important variational methods is the so-called Rayleigh-Ritz method.[1] The Rayleigh-Ritz method may be carried out as follows: First assume the solution in the form of a series which satisfies the boundary conditions but with undetermined parameters c_i. Second, insert these functions into the expression of the potential energy or the complementary energy, and carry out any required integration. The resulting expressions are functions of the undetermined parameters c_i, where $i = 1, 2, \ldots$. Since the potential energy or the complementary energy must be a minimum at equilibrium, these parameters can be determined from the minimizing conditions

$$\frac{\partial\Pi}{\partial c_1} = 0,\ \frac{\partial\Pi}{\partial c_2} = 0,\ \ldots \qquad \text{or} \qquad \frac{\partial\Pi^*}{\partial c_1} = 0,\ \frac{\partial\Pi^*}{\partial c_2} = 0,\ \ldots \qquad (7.30)$$

If n parameters are taken, Eq. (7.30) gives us n simultaneous equations from which these parameters may be solved. Substituting these values

---

[1] Lord Rayleigh, On the Calculation of Chladni's Figures for a Square Plate, *Phil. Mag.*, Vol. 22, pp. 225–229, 1911. W. Ritz, Über Eine Neue Methode zur Lösung Gewissen Variations-Problems der Mathematischen Physik, *J. f. Reine u. Angew. Math.*, Vol. 135, pp. 1–61, 1908.

of the parameters into the assumed form of the function, we have an approximate solution of the given problem. If the series which we assumed consists of a complete sequence,[1] it can be proved[2] that the solution so obtained is the exact solution of the boundary-value problem. In most problems, however, only a finite number of parameters can be taken, and therefore the solution obtained is only approximate.

Let us take as an example the torsion problem of a rectangular bar with sides $2a$ and $2b$ (Fig. 5.7). To satisfy the boundary condition $\psi = 0$ on sides $x = \pm a$ and $y = \pm b$, we may take the polynomial

$$\psi = (x^2 - a^2)(y^2 - b^2)(c_1 + c_2 x^2 + c_3 y^2 + c_4 x^2 y^2 + \cdots) \quad (7.31)$$

where $c_1, c_2, \ldots$, are undetermined parameters. Since we know that ψ is symmetrical with respect to the x and y axes, we have taken in (7.31) only terms with even power in x and y. Now, as a first approximation, let us take only one undetermined parameter in (7.31) and write

$$\psi = c_1(x^2 - a^2)(y^2 - b^2)$$

We obtain by substitution

$$\left(\frac{\partial \psi}{\partial x}\right)^2 + \left(\frac{\partial \psi}{\partial y}\right)^2 - 4\psi = 4c_1^2[x^2(y^2 - b^2)^2 + (x^2 - a^2)^2 y^2]$$
$$- 4c_1(x^2 - a^2)(y^2 - b^2)$$

Integrating, we find

$$\Pi^* = \frac{G\theta^2 L}{2} \int_{x=-a}^{x=a} \int_{y=-b}^{y=b} \left[\left(\frac{\partial \psi}{\partial x}\right)^2 + \left(\frac{\partial \psi}{\partial y}\right)^2 - 4\psi\right] dx\, dy$$
$$= \frac{G\theta^2 L}{2} \frac{64}{45} [2c_1^2 a^3 b^3(a^2 + b^2) - 5c_1 a^3 b^3]$$

From the minimizing condition $d\Pi^*/dc_1 = 0$, it follows that

$$c_1 = \frac{5}{4(a^2 + b^2)}$$

We obtain therefore the approximate solution

$$\psi = \frac{5}{4(a^2 + b^2)} (x^2 - a^2)(y^2 - b^2)$$

---

[1] An enumerable sequence contained in the class C is said to be complete if every function in C can be approximated by a finite linear combination of the functions with preassigned accuracy.

[2] See, for example, R. Courant and K. O. Friedrichs, "Methods of Mathematical Physics," Part II, p. 24, Institute of Mathematics and Mechanics, New York University, New York, 1943.

The torsional constant J is given by

$$J = 2 \iint_R \psi \, dx \, dy$$

$$= 2c_1 \int_{x=-a}^{x=a} \int_{y=-b}^{y=b} (x^2 - a^2)(y^2 - b^2) \, dx \, dy$$

$$= \frac{32}{9} a^3 b^3 c_1 = \frac{40}{9} \frac{(b/a)^3}{1 + (b/a)^2} a^4$$

The maximum shearing stress $\tau_{\max}$ occurs at the mid-points of the long sides, *i.e.*, at $x = \pm a$, $y = 0$. Thus,

$$\tau_{\max} = -\frac{T}{J}\left(\frac{\partial \psi}{\partial x}\right)_{\substack{x=a \\ y=0}} = \frac{T}{J} 2ab^2 c_1 = \frac{9}{16}\left(\frac{a}{b}\right)\frac{T}{a^3}$$

For $b/a = 1$ or a square bar, J given by the above approximate solution is $2.222a^4$ compared with the exact value of $2.250a^4$. The error is -1.2 per cent. The maximum shearing stress is $0.563t/a^3$ compared with the exact value of $0.600t/a^3$ with an error of -6.2 per cent. For $b/a = 10$, J given by the above approximate solution is $44.0a^4$ compared with the exact value of $49.92a^4$ with an error of -11.9 per cent. The maximum shearing stress is $0.0562T/a^3$ given by the approximate solution compared with the exact value of $0.0401T/a^3$ with an error of $+40.1$ per cent.

Now let us take three undetermined parameters c_1, c_2, and c_3. Thus

$$\psi = (x^2 - a^2)(y^2 - b^2)(c_1 + c_2 x^2 + c_3 y^2)$$

After integrations, we obtain

$$\Pi^* = \frac{G\theta^2 L}{2} \iint_R \left[\left(\frac{\partial \psi}{\partial x}\right)^2 + \left(\frac{\partial \psi}{\partial y}\right)^2 - 4\psi\right] dx \, dy$$

$$= \frac{G\theta^2 L}{2} \frac{64}{4,725} a^3 b^3 [210(a^2 + b^2)c_1^2 + a^4(66b^2 + 10a^2)c_2^2$$
$$+ b^4(66a^2 + 10b^2)c_3^2 + a^2(84b^2 + 60a^2)c_1 c_2$$
$$+ b^2(84a^2 + 60b^2)c_1 c_3 + 12a^2 b^2(a^2 + b^2)c_2 c_3$$
$$- 525c_1 - 105a^2 c_2 - 105b^2 c_3]$$

The conditions $\partial \Pi^*/\partial c_1 = 0$, $\partial \Pi^*/\partial c_2 = 0$, and $\partial \Pi^*/\partial c_3 = 0$ give, respectively,

$$140(a^2 + b^2)c_1 + a^2(28b^2 + 20a^2)c_2 + b^2(28a^2 + 20b^2)c_3 = 175$$
$$(84b^2 + 60a^2)c_1 + a^2(132b^2 + 20a^2)c_2 + 12b^2(a^2 + b^2)c_3 = 105$$
$$(84a^2 + 60b^2)c_1 + 12a^2(a^2 + b^2)c_2 + b^2(132a^2 + 20b^2)c_3 = 105$$

To simplify the solution of these equations, we may first substitute into them the numerical value of the ratio b/a. After the parameters c_1, c_2, and c_3 are determined, the torsional constant and the maximum shearing stress can be easily calculated and are

$$J = 2 \iint_R \psi \, dx \, dy = \frac{32}{9} a^3 b^3 \left(c_1 + \frac{a^2}{5} c_2 + \frac{b^2}{5} c_3 \right)$$

$$\tau_{\max} = - \left(\frac{T}{J} \frac{\partial \psi}{\partial x} \right)_{\substack{x=a \\ x=0}} = \frac{T}{J} 2ab^2(c_1 + c_2 a^2)$$

For $b/a = 1$, we find

$$c_1 = \frac{1{,}295}{2{,}216a^2} \qquad c_2 = c_3 = \frac{525}{4{,}432a^4}$$

which give the values of J and $\tau_{\max}$ as $2.246a^4$ and $0.626T/a^3$, respectively. The errors in J and $\tau_{\max}$ are thus -0.18 per cent and $+4.3$ per cent. For a rectangular bar of $b/a = 10$, we find

$$c_1 = \frac{0.008988}{a^2} \qquad c_2 = \frac{0.00002853}{a^4} \qquad c_3 = \frac{0.0002359}{a^4}$$

from which we obtain $J = 48.75a^4$ and $\tau_{\max} = 0.03699T/a^3$. The error in J is -2.3 per cent, and the error in $\tau_{\max}$ is -7.8 per cent.

Instead of taking polynomials to approximate the stress function, we may use the trigonometric series for that purpose. For example, we may assume

$$\psi = \sum_{m=0}^{\infty} \sum_{n=0}^{\infty} c_{mn} \cos (2m + 1) \frac{\pi x}{2a} \cos (2n + 1) \frac{\pi y}{2b} \qquad (7.32)$$

where c_{mn} are the undetermined parameters. Note that the assumed form of ψ satisfies the boundary condition. If we take the first term only and integrate, we obtain

$$\Pi^* = \frac{G\theta^2 L}{2} \iint_R \left[\left(\frac{\partial \psi}{\partial x} \right)^2 + \left(\frac{\partial \psi}{\partial y} \right)^2 - 4\psi \right] dx \, dy$$

$$= \frac{G\theta^2 L}{2} \left[\pi^2 c_{00}^2 \frac{ab}{4} \left(\frac{1}{a^2} + \frac{1}{b^2} \right) - 64 c_{00} \frac{ab}{\pi^2} \right]$$

The minimizing condition $d\Pi^*/dc_{00} = 0$ yields

$$c_{00} = \frac{128}{\pi^4} \frac{a^2 b^2}{a^2 + b^2}$$

from which we find

$$J = \frac{4{,}096}{\pi^6} \frac{(b/a)^2}{1 + (b/a)^2} a^3 b$$

and

$$\tau_{\max} = \frac{64}{\pi^3} \frac{(b/a)^2}{1 + (b/a)^2} \frac{Ta}{J}$$

For $b/a = 1$, the above formulas give us $J = 2.130a^4$ and

$$\tau_{max} = \frac{0.484T}{a^3}$$

The errors in J and τ_{max} are -5.3 per cent and -19.3 per cent, respectively. For $b/a = 10$, we find $J = 4.218a^3b$ and $\tau_{max} = 0.0484T/a^3$ with errors of -15.5 per cent and $+20.7$ per cent, respectively.

From the above example, we see that the accuracy of the solution improves when more undetermined parameters are taken. However, if we use two different series to approximate the function, we may find that by taking a few undetermined parameters in the first series the accuracy of the solution is much better than that obtained by taking many more parameters in the second series. The variational methods are useful only in cases where the exact solution is unknown. In such cases, it becomes very difficult to ascertain the accuracy of a solution. One way to get an idea of the probable accuracy of the solution is to solve the problem by successively taking more parameters and comparing the final results. If the results converge rapidly, we may conclude that the approximation is probably good.

We shall now take as a second example the deflection of the pin-ended beam under the action of uniform pressure p (Fig. 7.3). Let us assume the deflection curve in the form of a trigonometric series. The boundary conditions require that $w = d^2w/dx^2 = 0$ at $x = 0$ and L. To satisfy the boundary conditions, we may take

$$w = \sum_{n=1}^{\infty} c_n \sin \frac{n\pi x}{L}$$

in which c_1, c_2, . . . are the undetermined parameters. Substituting into (7.23) and integrating, we find the potential energy to be

$$\Pi = \frac{EI}{2} \int_0^L \left(\frac{d^2w}{dx^2}\right)^2 dx - \int_0^L pw\, dx = \frac{EI\pi^4}{4L^3} \sum_{n=1}^{\infty} n^4 c_n^2 - \frac{2pL}{\pi} \sum_{n=1,3,5} \frac{c_n}{n}$$

Minimizing Π with respect to c_n, we obtain

$$\frac{EI\pi^4}{4L^3} 2n^4 c_n - \frac{2pL}{\pi} \frac{1}{n} = 0 \qquad \text{for odd } n$$

and

$$\frac{EI\pi^4}{4L^3} 2n^4 c_n = 0 \qquad \text{if } n \text{ is even}$$

Hence

$$c_n = \frac{4pL^4}{EI\pi^5} \frac{1}{n^5} \qquad \text{for odd } n$$

and

$$c_n = 0 \qquad \text{for even } n$$

Thus, we find the deflection curve as

$$w = \frac{4pL^4}{EI\pi^5} \sum_{n=1,3,5}^{\infty} \frac{1}{n^5} \sin \frac{n\pi x}{L}$$

Since in the present case c_n is determined for all values of n, the above infinite series actually gives us the exact solution to the boundary-value problem. This series converges rapidly, and a few terms give a satisfactory approximation. The maximum deflection occurs at $x = L/2$ and is

$$w_{max} = \frac{4pL^4}{EI\pi^5} \left(1 - \frac{1}{3^5} + \frac{1}{5^5} - \cdots\right)$$

By taking only the first term of this series, we obtain

$$w_{max} = \frac{pL^4}{76.6EI}$$

The approximate solution gives us a factor of 76.6 in the denominator, while the exact value is 76.8, so that the error made in w_{max} by using only the first term of the series is only 0.26 per cent.

Problem 1. Assume $w = \sum_{n=1}^{\infty} c_n \sin (n\pi x/L)$. Determine c_n if the beam is under the action of a concentrated load P at $x = a$ instead of a uniformly distributed load p.
$Ans.$ $c_n = \frac{2PL^3}{EI\pi^4 n^4} \sin \frac{n\pi a}{L}$

Problem 2. In the problem of a cantilever beam bent by an end load P, assume the deflection curve to be $w = ax^2 + bx^3$, which satisfies the boundary conditions $w = dw/dx = 0$ at $x = 0$. Determine the parameters a and b.

Problem 3. Take three parameters c_{00}, c_{01}, c_{10} in (7.32), and find the torsional constants and maximum shearing stresses for a square bar and a rectangular bar with $b/a = 10$ under torsion.

7.5. Galerkin's Method. In Sec. 7.3 the condition that the potential energy or complementary energy be a minimum is shown to lead to

$$\iiint_V \left[\sum_i (DE)_i \delta f_i\right] dx\, dy\, dz = 0$$

where the $(DE)_i$ are the governing differential equations and the δf_i are the arbitrary variations of the various functions. For example, in the case of torsion of prismatical bars, the minimization of the complementary energy leads to

$$\iint_R (\nabla^2 \psi + 2)\, \delta\psi\, dx\, dy = 0 \tag{7.33}$$

if ψ satisfies the boundary conditions. If we assume ψ in terms of a series

$$\psi_n(x,y) = \sum_{i=1}^{n} c_i F_i(x,y) \tag{7.34}$$

in which the constants c_i are undetermined parameters and the functions F_i satisfy the boundary conditions, we find

$$\delta\psi_n = \frac{\partial\psi_n}{\partial c_1}\,\delta c_1 + \frac{\partial\psi_n}{\partial c_2}\,\delta c_2 + \cdots = F_1\,\delta c_1 + F_2\,\delta c_2 + \cdots \tag{7.35}$$

Substituting (7.34) and (7.35) into Eq. (7.33), we obtain

$$\iint_R (\nabla^2\psi_n + 2)(F_1\,\delta c_1 + F_2\,\delta c_2 + \cdots)\,dx\,dy = 0 \tag{7.36}$$

or $\displaystyle\iint_R (\nabla^2\psi_n + 2)F_1\,\delta c_1\,dx\,dy + \iint_R (\nabla^2\psi_n + 2)F_2\,\delta c_2\,dx\,dy + \cdots = 0$

Since δc_1, δc_2, . . . are arbitrary, the only way that the above equation can be identically zero is that each integral vanish individually. Thus, we have

$$\iint_R (\nabla^2\psi_n + 2)F_1\,\delta c_1\,dx\,dy = 0$$

$$\iint_R (\nabla^2\psi_n + 2)F_2\,\delta c_2\,dx\,dy = 0$$

. . . .

. . . .

Since δc_1, δc_2, etc., are independent of x and y, they may be taken outside the above integral and so we have

$$\iint_R (\nabla^2\psi_n + 2)F_1\,dx\,dy = 0$$

$$\iint_R (\nabla^2\psi_n + 2)F_2\,dx\,dy = 0 \tag{7.37}$$

. . . .

. . . .

If n parameters c_i are taken, there are n simultaneous equations in (7.37) from which these parameters can be determined. Unlike the Rayleigh-Ritz method, Galerkin's method does not require the formulation of an energy principle. This procedure was proposed by Galerkin[1] and is known as Galerkin's method.

Galerkin's method can be justified from another point of view as follows: Let us consider a two-dimensional case, and let $Q(x,y)$ represent the

[1] B. G. Galerkin, Series Solutions of Some Problems of Elastic Equilibrium of Rods and Plates, *Vestnik Inzhenerov*, Vol. 1, pp. 879–908, 1915.

governing differential equation. In the case of the torsion problem, we have

$$Q(x,y) = \nabla^2 \psi + 2$$

Then if
$$\iint\limits_R Q(x,y)\, dx\, dy = K < +\infty$$

and if the sequence F_i is complete in the sense that any function satisfying the boundary conditions can be approximated uniformly by the series $\sum\limits_i c_i F_i$ to any degree of accuracy by a proper choice of c_i, the condition

$$\iint\limits_R Q(x,y) F_i\, dx\, dy = 0 \qquad i = 1, 2, \ldots$$

implies that

$$Q(x,y) = 0 \qquad \text{in } R$$

To prove this, let us assume that $Q(x,y)$ is *not* identically zero in R. Then there exists a point (x_0,y_0) in R where $Q(x_0,y_0) \neq 0$. We assume that $Q(x_0,y_0) > 0$ at this point as well as in the region inside a small circle C of radius ϵ with its center at (x_0,y_0). This can determine a function $V(x,y)$ such that

$V(x,y) > 0$ in C' where C' denotes a small circle inside C, say with a radius $\epsilon/2$

$V(x,y) \geq 0$ inside the annular region between C' and C

$V(x,y) = 0$ outside C

Then
$$\iint\limits_R Q(x,y) V(x,y)\, dx\, dy = \iint\limits_C Q(x,y) V(x,y)\, dx\, dy$$
$$\geq \iint\limits_{C'} Q(x,y) V(x,y)\, dx\, dy = \eta > 0 \quad (7.38)$$

Now, since the sequence F_i is complete and since V satisfies the same boundary conditions as does ψ, we may expand V in a series of the functions $F_i \left(= \sum\limits_{i=1}^{N} d_i F_i \right)$ such that for N sufficiently large,

$$\left| V(x,y) - \sum_{i=1}^{N} d_i F_i \right| < \frac{\eta}{2K}$$

independent of x and y in R.

Then
$$\left| \iint\limits_R Q \left(V - \sum_{i=1}^{N} d_i F_i \right) dx\, dy \right| \leq \iint\limits_R |Q| \left| V - \sum_{i=1}^{N} d_i F_i \right| dx\, dy$$
$$\leq \frac{\eta}{2K} \iint |Q|\, dx\, dy = \frac{\eta}{2}$$

But $\iint\limits_{R} Q(x,y)F_i \, dx \, dy = 0$; we have therefore

$$\left| \iint\limits_{R} Q(x,y) V(x,y) \, dx \, dy \right| \leq \frac{\eta}{2} \tag{7.39}$$

Comparing with (7.38), we find that it is impossible to have $\eta \leq \eta/2$ unless $\eta = 0$. But $V(x,y)$ is not zero, and η can be zero only when

$$Q(x,y) \equiv 0 \qquad \text{in } R$$

which completes the proof.

We shall now illustrate the application of Galerkin's method by taking as an example the torsion problem for a rectangular bar. Assume, as in the previous section, that

$$\psi_1 = c_1(x^2 - a^2)(y^2 - b^2)$$

Substituting ψ_1 into the differential equation, we find

$$Q_1 = \nabla^2\psi_1 + 2 = 2c_1[(x^2 - a^2) + (y^2 - b^2)] + 2$$

Galerkin's method requires

$$\iint\limits_{R} Q_1 \frac{\partial\psi_1}{\partial c_1} \, dx \, dy = \iint\limits_{R} \{2c_1[(x^2 - a^2) + (y^2 - b^2)] + 2\}$$

$$(x^2 - a^2)(y^2 - b^2) \, dx \, dy = 0$$

from which it follows that

$$c_1 = \frac{5}{4} \frac{1}{a^2 + b^2}$$

This is the same as was found by the Rayleigh-Ritz method.

Problem 1. Assume ψ in the form of (7.32). Determine c_{00}, c_{01}, and c_{10} by Galerkin's method.

Problem 2. Solve the problems assigned in Sec. 7.5 by Galerkin's method.

7.6. Biezeno-Koch Method. From the previous derivation, we see that the vanishing of the first variation of the energy integral leads to

$$\iint\limits_{R} \left[\sum_i (DE)_i \, \delta f_i \right] dx \, dy = 0 \tag{7.40}$$

where we assume the problem to be two-dimensional. In the Rayleigh-Ritz method and Galerkin's method, we assume the functions in terms of series which satisfy the boundary conditions and take δf_i as the infinitesimal change in the assumed form of f_i. In the calculus of variation, δf_i may be chosen in any arbitrary manner. By the Biezeno-Koch method, if n undetermined parameters are taken, we shall divide the region R into n subregions R_i and take δf_i in the following manner:

$$\delta f(x,y) = \begin{cases} 1 & \text{in } R_i \\ 0 & \text{elsewhere in } R \end{cases} \tag{7.41}$$

In the case of the torsion problem, if we take $\delta\psi$ according to (7.41), (7.40) becomes

$$\iint\limits_{R_i} (\nabla^2\psi_n + 2) \, dx \, dy = 0 \tag{7.42}$$

Thus, we obtain n simultaneous equations corresponding to n parameters, and these parameters can be determined uniquely.

The Biezeno-Koch method was originally introduced[1] from a consideration of the error function, and the above interpretation was essentially that given by Courant.[2] Since $Q_n = \nabla^2\psi_n + 2$ represents an error function due to the approximation of ψ by ψ_n, one obvious way of requiring that the error function Q be small is to demand that it vanish at n points in the domain of the problem. In this procedure, known as the *collocation method*, the error is collocated, or assigned, at n points, and the n equations are obtained for determination of the parameters c_i. The Biezeno-Koch method can be interpreted as a modified form of collocation method in that it demands the vanishing of the mean error over each of n subregions R_i of R.

Let us illustrate these two methods by applying them to the torsion problem of a square bar. Assume, as before,

$$\psi_1 = c_1(x^2 - a^2)(y^2 - a^2) \tag{7.43}$$

from which we find

$$Q_1 = \nabla^2\psi_1 + 2 = 2c_1[(x^2 - a^2) + (y^2 - a^2)] + 2 \tag{7.44}$$

By the collocation method, we may let $Q(x,y) = 0$ at the point $x = 0$, $y = 0$ and obtain

$$c_1 = \frac{1}{2a^2}$$

The approximate values of torsional constant and maximum shearing stress are $1.778a^4$ and $0.562T/a^3$, respectively, and the corresponding errors in these values are -21.0 per cent and -6.3 per cent.

As a second approximation, let us take

$$\psi_3 = (x^2 - a^2)(y^2 - a^2)[c_1 + c_2(x^2 + y^2) + c_3x^2y^2] \tag{7.45}$$

In order to determine these three parameters c_1, c_2, c_3, we have to require that the error function

$$Q_3 = 2c_1(x^2 + y^2 - 2a^2) + 2c_2[6(2x^2y^2 - a^2x^2 - a^2y^2) + (x^2 - a^2)^2 + (y^2 - a^2)^2]$$
$$+ 2c_3[x^2(x^2 - a^2)(6y^2 - a^2) + y^2(y^2 - a^2)(6x^2 - a^2)] + 2$$

vanish at three points, say $(0,0)$, $(a/2, 0)$ and $(a/2, a/2)$. Thus we obtain

$$2a^2c_1 - 2a^4c_2 - 1 = 0$$
$$28a^2c_1 - a^4c_2 - 3a^6c_3 - 16 = 0$$
$$24a^2c_1 - 12a^4c_2 + 3a^6c_3 - 16 = 0$$

[1] C. B. Biezeno and J. J. Koch, Over een nieuwe Methode ter Berekening van vlakke Platen met Toepassing op Enkele voor de techniek belangrijke Belastingsgevallen, *Ingenieur*, Vol. 38, pp. 25–36, 1923. C. B. Biezeno, Graphical and Numerical Methods for Solving Stress Problems, *Proc. First Intern. Congr. Applied Mech.*, Delft, 1924, pp. 3–17.

[2] In the discussion of Biezeno's paper.

Solving, we have

$$c_1 = \frac{17}{26a^2} \qquad c_2 = \frac{2}{13a^4} \qquad c_3 = \frac{28}{39a^6}$$

With the expression of ψ as assumed in (7.45), the torsional constant is

$$J = 2\int\int\psi_3 \, dx \, dy = {}^{32}\!\!/_9 a^6(c_1 + \tfrac{2}{5}a^2c_2 + \tfrac{1}{25}a^4c_3)$$

and the maximum shearing stress is

$$\tau_{max} = -\frac{T}{J}\left(\frac{\partial\psi_3}{\partial x}\right)_{\substack{x=a \\ y=0}} = \frac{T}{J} 2a^3(c_1 + c_2a^2)$$

With the values of c_1, c_2, c_3 we just obtained, the approximate values of J and τ_{max} are $2.646a^4$ and $0.610T/a^3$, respectively, and the corresponding errors are then $+17.6$ per cent and $+1.7$ per cent.

Now let us determine these parameters by the Biezeno-Koch method. Assume ψ again in the form of (7.43), and take the region R_1 to be the entire region R of the square section. Equation (7.42) becomes

$$\int_{-a}^{a}\int_{-a}^{a}\{2c_1[(x^2 - a^2) + (y^2 - a^2)] + 2\} \, dx \, dy = 0$$

from which it follows that

$$c_1 = \frac{3}{4a^2} \qquad J = 2.667a^4 \qquad \tau_{max} = \frac{0.562T}{a^3}$$

and the errors in J and τ_{max} are $+18.5$ per cent and -6.3 per cent, respectively.

As a second approximation, let us take ψ_3 as given by (7.45). Now we have to subdivide the cross section into three regions. From the consideration of symmetry, we may take the three regions in the following manner:

$$R_1: \quad 0 \leq x \leq \frac{a}{2} \qquad 0 \leq y \leq \frac{a}{2}$$

$$R_2: \quad \frac{a}{2} \leq x \leq a \qquad 0 \leq y \leq \frac{a}{2}$$

$$R_3: \quad \frac{a}{2} \leq x \leq a \qquad \frac{a}{2} \leq y \leq a$$

Substituting (7.45) into Eq. (7.42) and integrating over the above regions, we obtain the following equation:

$$440a^2c_1 - 186a^4c_2 - 17a^6c_3 = 240$$
$$320a^2c_1 + 564a^4c_2 + 19a^6c_3 = 240$$
$$200a^2c_1 + 594a^4c_2 + 235a^6c_3 = 240$$

Solving, we have

$$c_1 = \frac{149}{252a^2} \qquad c_2 = \frac{5}{63a^4} \qquad c_3 = \frac{20}{63a^6}$$

The torsional constant $J = 2.260a^4$, which is 0.46 per cent greater than the exact value. The maximum shearing stress is $\frac{0.593T}{a^3}$, which is 1.2 per cent less than the exact value.

Problem 1. Assume ψ in the form of (7.32). Determine c by the Biezeno-Koch method.

Problem 2. Solve Prob. 2, Sec. 7.4, by the Biezeno-Koch method.

7.7. Reciprocal Theorem and Castigliano's Theorems. The reciprocal theorem and Castigliano's theorems have been used extensively in the elementary treatments of structures. We shall now show that these theorems are also valid in the general case of elastic bodies. We shall carry out the proofs in the case of plane stress of an elastic plate. The extension of the proofs to the three-dimensional case can easily be worked out.

Consider two equilibrium states of an elastic plate: one with displacements u, v, due to the body forces X, Y, and boundary surface forces $\bar{X}$, $\bar{Y}$; and the other with displacements u', v', due to body forces X', Y', and surface forces $\bar{X}'$, $\bar{Y}'$. The work per unit thickness of the plate that would be done by the unprimed forces if they acted through the primed displacements is

$$\iint_R (Xu' + Yv')\, dx\, dy + \int_S (\bar{X}u' + \bar{Y}v')\, ds$$

From the equilibrium equations, we have

$$\iint_R (Xu' + Yv')\, dx\, dy$$

$$= -\iint_R \left[\left(\frac{\partial \sigma_x}{\partial x} + \frac{\partial \tau_{xy}}{\partial y} \right) u' + \left(\frac{\partial \tau_{xy}}{\partial x} + \frac{\partial \sigma_y}{\partial y} \right) v' \right] dx\, dy$$

Noting that

$$\frac{\partial \sigma_x}{\partial x} u' + \frac{\partial \tau_{xy}}{\partial y} u' = \frac{\partial}{\partial x}(\sigma_x u') + \frac{\partial}{\partial y}(\tau_{xy} u') - \left(\sigma_x \frac{\partial u'}{\partial x} + \tau_{xy} \frac{\partial u'}{\partial y} \right)$$

$$\frac{\partial \tau_{xy}}{\partial x} v' + \frac{\partial \sigma_y}{\partial y} v' = \frac{\partial}{\partial x}(\tau_{xy} v') + \frac{\partial}{\partial y}(\sigma_y v') - \left(\tau_{xy} \frac{\partial v'}{\partial x} + \sigma_y \frac{\partial v'}{\partial y} \right)$$

and using Green's theorem as in Sec. 7.3, we obtain

$$\iint_R (Xu' + Yv')\, dx\, dy$$

$$= \iint_R \left[\left(\sigma_x \frac{\partial u'}{\partial x} + \tau_{xy} \frac{\partial u'}{\partial y} \right) + \left(\tau_{xy} \frac{\partial v'}{\partial x} + \sigma_y \frac{\partial v'}{\partial y} \right) \right] dx\, dy$$

$$- \int_S (\bar{X}u' + \bar{Y}v')\, ds$$

or $$\iint_R (Xu' + Yv')\, dx\, dy + \int_S (\bar{X}u' + \bar{Y}v')\, ds$$

$$= \iint_R \left[\left(\sigma_x \frac{\partial u'}{\partial x} + \tau_{xy} \frac{\partial u'}{\partial y} \right) + \left(\tau_{xy} \frac{\partial v'}{\partial x} + \sigma_y \frac{\partial v'}{\partial y} \right) \right] dx\, dy$$

Now from Hooke's law and the definitions of strain components,

$$\sigma_x = \frac{E}{1 - \nu^2}\left(\frac{\partial u}{\partial x} + \nu\,\frac{\partial v}{\partial y}\right) \qquad \sigma_y = \frac{E}{1 - \nu^2}\left(\frac{\partial v}{\partial y} + \nu\,\frac{\partial u}{\partial x}\right)$$

$$\tau_{xy} = G\left(\frac{\partial u}{\partial y} + \frac{\partial v}{\partial x}\right)$$

Substitution of these expressions into the last integral results in

$$\iint_R \left\{\frac{E}{1 - \nu^2}\left[\left(\frac{\partial u}{\partial x} + \nu\,\frac{\partial v}{\partial y}\right)\frac{\partial u'}{\partial x} + \left(\frac{\partial v}{\partial y} + \nu\,\frac{\partial u}{\partial x}\right)\frac{\partial v'}{\partial y}\right]\right.$$

$$\left. + G\left(\frac{\partial u}{\partial y} + \frac{\partial v}{\partial x}\right)\left(\frac{\partial u'}{\partial y} + \frac{\partial v'}{\partial x}\right)\right\}\,dx\,dy = \iint_R \left\{\frac{E}{1 - \nu^2}\left[\left(\frac{\partial u'}{\partial x} + \nu\,\frac{\partial v'}{\partial y}\right)\frac{\partial u}{\partial x}\right.\right.$$

$$\left.\left. + \left(\frac{\partial v'}{\partial y} + \nu\,\frac{\partial u'}{\partial x}\right)\frac{\partial v}{\partial y}\right] + G\left(\frac{\partial u'}{\partial y} + \frac{\partial v'}{\partial x}\right)\left(\frac{\partial u}{\partial y} + \frac{\partial v}{\partial x}\right)\right\}\,dx\,dy$$

Since

$$\sigma_x' = \frac{E}{1 - \nu^2}\left(\frac{\partial u'}{\partial x} + \nu\,\frac{\partial v'}{\partial y}\right) \qquad \sigma_y' = \frac{E}{1 - \nu^2}\left(\frac{\partial v'}{\partial y} + \nu\,\frac{\partial u'}{\partial x}\right)$$

$$\tau_{xy}' = G\left(\frac{\partial u'}{\partial y} + \frac{\partial v'}{\partial x}\right)$$

by an application of Green's theorem, we have

$$\iint_R (Xu' + Yv')\,dx\,dy + \int_S (\bar{X}u' + \bar{Y}v')\,ds$$

$$= \iint_R (X'u + Y'v)\,dx\,dy + \int_S (\bar{X}'u + \bar{Y}'v)\,ds \quad (7.46)$$

Thus, we obtain the *reciprocal theorem of Betti and Rayleigh: If an elastic body is subjected to two systems of body and surface forces, then the work that would be done by the first system of external forces in acting through the displacements due to the second system of forces is equal to the work that would be done by the second system of forces in acting through the displacements due to the first system of forces.*

From the principle of complementary energy, we have shown that

$$\delta(U - W^*) = 0$$

or

$$\delta U = \iint_{A_2} (u\,\delta\bar{X} + v\,\delta\bar{Y} + w\,\delta\bar{Z})\,dA \quad (7.47)$$

where A_2 is that part of the boundary on which the surface forces are not prescribed. Let us consider the case where the surface forces are concentrated loads instead of continuously distributed forces. Under these concentrated loads $P_1, P_2, \ldots$, the displacements at the points of application of the loads in the direction of the loads are $d_1, d_2, \ldots$. We may interpret the problem as the one in which the displacements $d_1, d_2, \ldots$ are prescribed at the boundary, while $P_1, P_2, \ldots$ are independent unknowns. The strain energy U can then be expressed in terms of the loads $P_1, P_2, \ldots$. The change of the strain energy due to the changes in the forces is then

$$\delta U = \frac{\partial U}{\partial P_1}\, \delta P_1 + \frac{\partial U}{\partial P_2}\, \delta P_2 + \cdots$$

and

$$\iint\limits_{A_2} (u\, \delta \bar{X} + v\, \delta \bar{Y} + w\, \delta \bar{Z})\, dA = d_1\, \delta P_1 + d_2\, \delta P_2 + \cdots$$

Equation (7.47) becomes therefore

$$\frac{\partial U}{\partial P_1}\, \delta P_1 + \frac{\partial U}{\partial P_2}\, \delta P_2 + \cdots = d_1\, \delta P_1 + d_2\, \delta P_2 + \cdots$$

or

$$\left(\frac{\partial U}{\partial P_1} - d_1 \right) \delta P_1 + \left(\frac{\partial U}{\partial P_2} - d_2 \right) \delta P_2 + \cdots = 0$$

Since the forces $P_1, P_2, \ldots$ are statically independent, the changes or variations $\delta P_1, \delta P_2, \ldots$ are completely arbitrary and we can take all but one of them equal to zero. Thus, we obtain

$$\frac{\partial U}{\partial P_1} - d_1 = 0 \qquad \frac{\partial U}{\partial P_2} - d_2 = 0 \qquad \cdots$$

or

$$\frac{\partial U}{\partial P_1} = d_1 \qquad \frac{\partial U}{\partial P_2} = d_2 \qquad \cdots$$

Therefore, if the strain energy U of an elastic system is written as a function of statically independent external forces $P_1, P_2, \ldots$, the partial derivatives of the strain energy with respect to any of these forces give the actual displacement of the point of application of the force in the direction of the force. This is the so-called *Castigliano's first theorem.*

If the boundary conditions of an elastic body are given in terms of prescribed surface forces, the surface integral on the right-hand side of Eq. (7.47) vanishes. Equation (7.47) becomes

$$\delta U = 0$$

This means that if we have an elastic system with given forces acting on the boundary, and if we consider such changes of stress components as satisfy the equations of equilibrium and the boundary conditions, the true stress components are those such that the strain energy is a minimum. This is the so-called *Castigliano's second theorem,* or the *theorem of least work.*

CHAPTER 8

SOLUTION BY MEANS OF COMPLEX VARIABLES

8.1. Complex Variables and Complex Functions. Many problems in the theory of elasticity can be solved with great mathematical simplicity by using *complex variables*. A complex variable z is formed by two real variables x and y so that

$$z = x + iy$$

where i represents $\sqrt{-1}$ and is called the *imaginary unit*. We shall call x the real part of the complex variable z, and y, the coefficient of i, the imaginary part. Since i does not belong to the real-number system, the meaning of equality, addition, subtraction, multiplication, and division must be defined. For instance, when we say two complex numbers are equal to each other, we mean that the real and imaginary parts of the two numbers must be identically equal. Thus,

$$x_1 + iy_1 = x_2 + iy_2$$

means $x_1 = x_2$ and $y_1 = y_2$. Similarly, in adding or subtracting two complex numbers, the real part of one complex number must be added to or subtracted from the real part of the other complex number, and the imaginary part must be added to or subtracted from the imaginary part. In multiplication and division, remembering that $i^2 = -1$, the operations are defined just as for real numbers. For example,

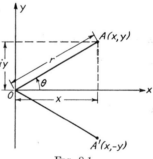

FIG. 8.1.

$$z^2 = (x + iy)^2 = x^2 + 2ixy + (iy)^2 = x^2 - y^2 + i2xy \qquad (8.1)$$

From these rules of operation, we see that a complex variable $z = x + iy$ may be represented geometrically by the point $A(x,y)$ in the xy plane (Fig. 8.1). The x axis in this case is called the real axis, and the y axis is called the imaginary axis. Converting to polar coordinates, we have

$$z = x + iy = r(\cos \theta + i \sin \theta) = re^{i\theta}$$

It can be seen from Fig. 8.1 that z may be interpreted as representing the vector OA. The complex variable representing the vector OA' is given by

$$\bar{z} = x - iy = r(\cos \theta - i \sin \theta) = re^{-i\theta}$$

171

$\bar{z}$ is called the *conjugate* of the complex variable z.   From these definitions, we find

$$z\bar{z} = r^2 \tag{8.2}$$

where $r = \sqrt{x^2 + y^2}$ is called the *absolute value,* or *modulus,* of the complex number z, and θ, its *argument.*

A function of the complex variable z is called a complex function.   As in the case of a complex variable, a complex function can also be split up into a real and an imaginary part, *viz.,*

$$f(z) = f(x + iy) = \phi(x,y) + i\psi(x,y)$$

where ϕ and ψ are functions of x and y.   For instance, as was shown in Eq. (8.1), the real and imaginary parts of the complex function $f(z) = z^2$ are

$$\phi = x^2 - y^2 \qquad \psi = 2xy$$

The function ψ is sometimes called the conjugate of the function ϕ, and vice versa.   Analogous to the case of a complex variable, the *conjugate function* of the complex function $f(z)$ is defined as

$$\bar{f}(\bar{z}) = \phi(x,y) - i\psi(x,y)$$

where the symbol $\bar{f}(\bar{z})$ denotes the conjugate function of $f(z)$.   If $f(z)$ is given in the form of a complex power series

$$f(z) = A_0 + A_1 z + A_2 z^2 + \cdots$$

where $A_0, A_1, A_2, \ldots$ are complex constants, it can be proved that

$$\bar{f}(\bar{z}) = \bar{A}_0 + \bar{A}_1 \bar{z} + \bar{A}_2 \bar{z}^2 + \cdots \tag{8.3}$$

where $\bar{A}_0, \bar{A}_1, \bar{A}_2$, etc., denote the conjugate complex numbers of A_0, A_1, A_2, etc., respectively.   The notation $\bar{f}(z)$ is sometimes used to denote the function

$$\bar{f}(z) = \bar{A}_0 + \bar{A}_1 z + \bar{A}_2 z^2 + \cdots \tag{8.4}$$

and it should not be confused with the conjugate function $\bar{f}(\bar{z})$.

Let us now examine the rules of differentiation for a complex function. A complex function $f(z)$ is called *analytic,* or *regular,* in a region R if it possesses a unique derivative at every point of the region R.   Points at which the function $f(z)$ ceases to have a derivative are called *singular points* of the analytic function.   Let $f(z)$ be an analytic function, and let us find the partial derivatives of $f(z)$ with respect to x and y.   Since

$$z = x + iy$$

we have

$$\frac{\partial z}{\partial x} = 1 \qquad \frac{\partial z}{\partial y} = i$$

and

$$\frac{\partial f}{\partial x} = \frac{df}{dz}\frac{\partial z}{\partial x} = \frac{df}{dz} \qquad \frac{\partial f}{\partial y} = \frac{df}{dz}\frac{\partial z}{\partial y} = i\frac{df}{dz}$$

If df/dz is to be unique, we must have

$$\frac{\partial f}{\partial y} = i\frac{\partial f}{\partial x}$$

But

$$\frac{\partial f}{\partial x} = \frac{\partial \phi}{\partial x} + i\frac{\partial \psi}{\partial x} \qquad \frac{\partial f}{\partial y} = \frac{\partial \phi}{\partial y} + i\frac{\partial \psi}{\partial y}$$

Therefore

$$\frac{\partial \phi}{\partial y} + i\frac{\partial \psi}{\partial y} = i\frac{\partial \phi}{\partial x} - \frac{\partial \psi}{\partial x}$$

Separating real and imaginary parts gives

$$\frac{\partial \phi}{\partial x} = \frac{\partial \psi}{\partial y} \qquad \frac{\partial \phi}{\partial y} = -\frac{\partial \psi}{\partial x} \tag{8.5}$$

These equations are the so-called "Cauchy-Riemann" conditions, and they are the necessary and sufficient conditions that $f(z)$ be analytic. It can be shown that if $f(z)$ is analytic in the region R, then not only do the first derivatives of ϕ and ψ exist in R, but also those of all higher orders.

Eliminating ψ in (8.5) by differentiating the first equation with respect to x and the second with respect to y and adding, we obtain

$$\frac{\partial^2 \phi}{\partial x^2} + \frac{\partial^2 \phi}{\partial y^2} = 0 \tag{8.6}$$

Similarly, we eliminate ϕ from these equations, and we find

$$\frac{\partial^2 \psi}{\partial x^2} + \frac{\partial^2 \psi}{\partial y^2} = 0 \tag{8.7}$$

Equations (8.6) and (8.7) show that the *real and imaginary parts of any analytic function of a complex variable* are solutions of the *Laplace equation*. Therefore, if the differential equation to be solved is a Laplace equation, our problem is to find the analytic function having a real or an imaginary part satisfying the boundary conditions. Since a Laplace equation is also called a harmonic equation, the functions ϕ and ψ, which satisfy the harmonic equation, are sometimes called *harmonic functions*.

8.2. Some Fundamental Relations of the Theory of Complex Variables. In the subsequent discussions, many fundamental relations in the theory of complex variables will be used. We shall now give a summary of these relations.

1. *Cauchy-Goursat Theorem.* *If a function $f(z)$ is single-valued and analytic within and on a closed curve S, then*

$$\oint_S f(z)\, dz = 0 \qquad (8.8)$$

Proof. Since $f(z) = \phi + i\psi$ and $dz = dx + i\, dy$, we have

$$\oint_S f(z)\, dz = \oint_S [(\phi\, dx - \psi\, dy) + i(\phi\, dy + \psi\, dx)]$$

From Green's theorem, we find

$$\oint_S (\phi\, dx - \psi\, dy) = -\iint_R \left(\frac{\partial \phi}{\partial y} + \frac{\partial \psi}{\partial x}\right) dx\, dy$$

$$\oint_S (\phi\, dy + \psi\, dx) = \iint_R \left(\frac{\partial \phi}{\partial x} - \frac{\partial \psi}{\partial y}\right) dx\, dy$$

where R is the region bounded by the curve S. In view of Cauchy-Riemann's conditions, Eqs. (8.5), the integrands of the two double integrals vanish throughout the region R. It follows therefore that

$$\oint_S f(z)\, dz = 0$$

A region R is said to be *simply connected* if every simple closed curve within it encloses only points of R. The annular region between two concentric circles, for example, is not simply connected. Such a region is called *multiply connected.* A multiply connected region can be made simply connected by introducing lines joining the inner curves to the outer curve, as shown in Fig. 8.2. By taking S in the direction as indicated by the arrows in Fig. 8.2, since $f(z)$ is analytic within and on the boundary of R, we have from formula (8.8), where the boldface integrals indicate that the integrations are taken in the clockwise direction while the other integrals indicate that the integrations are taken in the counterclockwise direction,

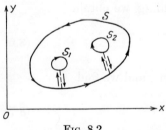

Fig. 8.2.

$$\oint_S f(z)\, dz + \boldsymbol{\oint}_{S_1} f(z)\, dz + \boldsymbol{\oint}_{S_2} f(z)\, dz = 0$$

or

$$\oint_S f(z)\, dz = \oint_{S_1} f(z)\, dz + \oint_{S_2} f(z)\, dz \qquad (8.9)$$

That is, when the integration over all the contours is performed in the same direction, then the integral $f(z)$ over the exterior contour S is equal to the sum of the integrals over the interior contours.

2. *The Cauchy Integral Formula.* Let $f(z)$ be single-valued and analytic within and on a closed curve S. If ζ is any point interior to S, then

$$f(\zeta) = \frac{1}{2\pi i} \oint_S \frac{f(z)}{z - \zeta} \, dz \qquad (8.10)$$

Proof. Let S_1 be a circle about ζ so that

$$|z - \zeta| = r_1$$

is small enough to make S_1 interior to S (Fig. 8.3). According to (8.9), we have

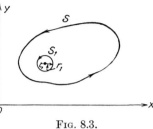

FIG. 8.3.

$$\oint_S \frac{f(z)}{z - \zeta} \, dz = \oint_{S_1} \frac{f(z)}{z - \zeta} \, dz = f(\zeta) \oint_{S_1} \frac{dz}{z - \zeta} + \oint_{S_1} \frac{f(z) - f(\zeta)}{z - \zeta} \, dz \quad (8.11)$$

But $z - \zeta = r_1 e^{i\theta}$ on S_1, and $dz = i r_1 e^{i\theta} \, d\theta$, so we have

$$\oint_{S_1} \frac{dz}{z - \zeta} = i \int_0^{2\pi} d\theta = 2\pi i \qquad (8.12)$$

for every positive r_1. Also $f(z)$ is continuous at $z = \zeta$ since regularity implies continuity. Hence, if we select any positive number ϵ, a positive number δ exists such that

$$|f(z) - f(\zeta)| < \epsilon \qquad \text{when } |z - \zeta| \leq \delta$$

If we take $r_1 = \delta$, then

$$\left| \oint_{S_1} \frac{f(z) - f(\zeta)}{z - \zeta} \, dz \right| \leq \oint_{S_1} \frac{|f(z) - f(\zeta)|}{|z - \zeta|} \, |dz| < \frac{\epsilon}{\delta} (2\pi\delta) = 2\pi\epsilon$$

By taking r_1 sufficiently small, we can make the absolute value of the above integral arbitrarily small. Since the other two integrals in (8.11) are independent of r_1, this integral must be also independent of r_1 and must be equal to zero. We have therefore

$$\oint_S \frac{f(z)}{z - \zeta} \, dz = 2\pi i f(\zeta)$$

which proves the theorem.

A formula for the derivative $f'(\zeta)$ can be obtained by differentiating the integral in Cauchy's integral formula with respect to ζ inside the integral sign. Thus

$$f'(\zeta) = \frac{1}{2\pi i} \oint_S \frac{f(z) \, dz}{(z - \zeta)^2}$$

and, in general,

$$f^{(n)}(\zeta) = \frac{n!}{2\pi i} \oint_S \frac{f(z) \, dz}{(z - \zeta)^{n+1}} \qquad (8.13)$$

3. *Power Series.* If $f(z)$ is analytic at all points within a circle S with center at a, then at each point z inside S

$$f(z) = f(a) + f'(a)(z - a) + \cdots + \frac{f^{(n)}(a)}{n!}(z - a)^n + \cdots \quad (8.14)$$

That is, the infinite series here converges to $f(z)$. This is the expansion of the function $f(z)$ by *Taylor's series* about the point $z = a$. When $a = 0$, this reduces to *Maclaurin's series*,

$$f(z) = f(0) + \sum_{n=1}^{\infty} \frac{f^{(n)}(0)}{n!} z^n \quad (8.15)$$

If $f(z)$ is analytic and single-valued on two concentric circles S_1 and S_2 and throughout the region between those two circles, then $f(z)$ may be represented at each point z between them by a convergent series of positive and negative powers of $z - a$, namely,

$$f(z) = \sum_{n=0}^{\infty} A_n(z - a)^n + \sum_{n=1}^{\infty} \frac{B_n}{(z - a)^n} \quad (8.16)$$

where
$$A_n = \frac{1}{2\pi i} \oint_{S_1} \frac{f(z)\, dz}{(z - a)^{n+1}} \qquad n = 0, 1, 2, \ldots$$

$$B_n = \frac{1}{2\pi i} \oint_{S_2} \frac{f(z)\, dz}{(z - a)^{-n+1}} \qquad n = 1, 2, \ldots$$

The series (8.13) is called *Laurent's series*.

4. *The Residue Theorem.* We have observed that a function $f(z)$ can always be represented by its Laurent series in a neighborhood of a singular point z_1. Let us now integrate the Laurent series around a curve S_1 enclosing $z = z_1$ and no other singularity of $f(z)$. If n is positive, we find from Eq. (8.8)

$$\oint_{S_1} (z - z_1)^n \, dz = 0$$

If $n = -1$, then from (8.12) we have

$$\oint_{S_1} \frac{dz}{z - z_1} = 2\pi i$$

To integrate $\oint_{S_1} dz/(z - z_1)^n$, $n > 1$, let us construct a small circle S_1' inside S_1 with radius r and with its center at $z = z_1$. Since $1/(z - z_1)^n$ is analytic within the region between S_1' and S_1 and on S_1 and S_1', we have

$$\oint_{S_1} \frac{dz}{(z - z_1)^n} = \oint_{S_1'} \frac{dz}{(z - z_1)^n} = \oint_{S_1'} \frac{i r e^{i\theta}\, d\theta}{r^n e^{in\theta}} = 0 \qquad \text{if } n > 1$$

Hence
$$\oint_{S_1} f(z)\, dz = \oint_{S_1} \left[\frac{B_1}{z - z_1} + \frac{B_2}{(z - z_1)^2} + \cdots + A_1(z - z_1) \right. $$
$$\left. + A_2(z - z_1)^2 + \cdots \right] dz = 2\pi i B_1$$

The coefficient of $1/(z - z_1)$ of B_1 is called the *residue* of $f(z)$ at the singular point $z = z_1$ and is denoted by K_1.

If the region R has n isolated singular points at $z_1, z_2, \ldots, z_n$, we can construct n small circles S_j so that each point is enclosed in a circle and the curve S and the n circles are all separated. These circles together with curve S form the boundary of a multiply connected domain in which $f(z)$ is analytic. From formula (8.9)

$$\oint_S f(z)\, dz = \oint_{S_1} f(z)\, dz + \oint_{S_2} f(z)\, dz + \cdots + \oint_{S_n} f(z)\, dz$$

This reduces to formula (8.17), because

$$\oint_{S_j} f(z)\, dz = 2\pi i K_j \qquad j = 1, 2, \ldots, n$$

and so the following theorem is proved:

Let S be a closed curve within and on which $f(z)$ is analytic except for a finite number of singular points $z_1, z_2, \ldots, z_n$, inside of S. If K_1, $K_2, \ldots, K_n$ denote the residues of $f(z)$ at these points, then

$$\oint_S f(z)\, dz = 2\pi i(K_1 + K_2 + \cdots + K_n) \tag{8.17}$$

5. *Conformal Mapping.* A real function of a real variable, say $y = f(x)$, can be represented graphically by plotting corresponding values of x and y as rectangular coordinates of points in the xy plane. We may say that the function $f(x)$ maps each point on the x axis into a point in the plane at a directed distance y above or below that point. The result of mapping all points of the x axis is a curve, the graph of the function. When the variables are complex, the graphical representation of functions is more complicated. If we have $z = f(\zeta)$, where $\zeta = \xi + i\eta$, then corresponding to each point (ξ, η) in the ζ plane for which $f(\xi + i\eta)$ is defined, there will be a point (x, y) in the z plane. The correspondence between points in the two planes is called a *mapping* of points in the ζ plane into points in the z plane by the *mapping function* $f(\zeta)$.

If S is a curve in the ζ plane and the point is allowed to move along S, then the corresponding point z will trace a curve S' in the z plane. The curve S' is called the *map* of S. If $f(\zeta)$ is analytic and $f'(\zeta) \neq 0$, it can be shown that, in such a mapping, if S_1 and S_2 are two curves in the ζ plane that intersect at an angle α, the corresponding curves S_1' and S_2' in the z plane also intersect at the angle α. The mapping performed by an analytic function $z = f(\zeta)$ when $f'(\zeta) \neq 0$ always preserves the angles and is called *conformal*. Henceforth the term *conformal mapping* will be used to signify transformation by means of analytic functions under the condition $f'(\zeta) \neq 0$.

We note that, by means of a conformal mapping function $z = f(\zeta)$, an analytic function of the complex variable z becomes another analytic function of the complex variable ζ, and its real and imaginary parts will again satisfy the Laplace equation. However, the boundary curve of the domain R in the z plane, which may not be convenient to work with, may be mapped into one in the ζ plane which will allow the boundary condition to be satisfied more easily.

8.3. Torsion of Prismatic Bars. The differential equation to be solved in the case of torsion of prismatic bars is a Laplace equation. If complex variables are used and if ϕ denotes the warping function, the problem may be reduced to the determination of an analytic function $F(z) = \phi + i\psi$, the real part of which satisfies the boundary condition (5.7). This boundary condition, however, is not convenient to work with. Let us therefore study the boundary condition which the function ψ must satisfy.

The real and the imaginary parts of an analytic function are related to each other by the Cauchy-Riemann equations, which in our case are

$$\frac{\partial \psi}{\partial x} = -\frac{\partial \phi}{\partial y} \qquad \frac{\partial \psi}{\partial y} = \frac{\partial \phi}{\partial x}$$

Substituting these relations into the boundary condition (5.7), we obtain

$$\left(\frac{\partial \psi}{\partial y} - y\right) l + \left(-\frac{\partial \psi}{\partial x} + x\right) m = 0 \qquad \text{on } S$$

Since $l = dy/ds$ and $m = -dx/ds$, we find after rearranging terms that

$$\frac{\partial \psi}{\partial y}\frac{dy}{ds} + \frac{\partial \psi}{\partial x}\frac{dx}{ds} = y\frac{dy}{ds} + x\frac{dx}{ds}$$

or

$$\frac{d\psi}{ds} = \frac{d}{ds}\frac{x^2 + y^2}{2}$$

Integration gives

$$\psi = \tfrac{1}{2}(x^2 + y^2) + C \qquad \text{on } S$$

Since the constant C in the above formula will not influence the magnitude of the stresses, we may therefore leave C undetermined. But

$$x^2 + y^2 = r^2 = z\bar{z}$$

in terms of the complex variable z, and the above boundary condition can be rewritten as

$$\psi = \tfrac{1}{2}z\bar{z} + C \qquad \text{on } S \tag{8.18}$$

Thus the torsion problem is solved if we succeed in determining the imaginary part of an analytic function $F(z)$ such that it assumes the value $\tfrac{1}{2}z\bar{z}$ on S.

To accomplish this, let us map the cross section of the bar, which is in the z plane, conformally onto a unit circle in the ζ plane by the mapping function

$$z = f(\zeta) \tag{8.19}$$

In terms of the complex variable ζ, the function $F(z)$ becomes

$$F(z) = \phi + i\psi = F[f(\zeta)] = F_1(\zeta) \tag{8.20}$$

and the boundary condition (8.18) becomes

$$\psi = \tfrac{1}{2} f(\zeta)\bar{f}(\bar{\zeta}) + C \qquad \text{on } S_1$$

where S_1 indicates the unit circle $|\zeta| = 1$. From the definition of conjugate functions, we have

$$\bar{F}_1(\bar{\zeta}) = \phi - i\psi$$

Thus
$$2i\psi = F_1(\zeta) - \bar{F}_1(\bar{\zeta})$$

and the above boundary condition becomes

$$F_1(\zeta) - \bar{F}_1(\bar{\zeta}) = if(\zeta)\bar{f}(\bar{\zeta}) + C' \qquad \text{on } S_1 \tag{8.21}$$

Assume that the mapping function $f(\zeta)$ is given. On the unit circle, it becomes a function of θ only and can be expanded into a complex Fourier series

$$f(t) = f(e^{i\theta}) = \sum_{-\infty}^{\infty} A_n e^{in\theta} \tag{8.22}$$

where the Fourier coefficients are given by the formula

$$A_n = \frac{1}{2\pi} \int_0^{2\pi} f(t)e^{-in\theta}\, d\theta \tag{8.23}$$

In the above formulas, $t = e^{i\theta}$ denotes points on the unit circle.

Since $F_1(\zeta)$ is analytic in the interior of the circle S_1, it can be expanded into the following power series:

$$F_1(\zeta) = \sum_{n=0}^{\infty} B_n \zeta^n \tag{8.24}$$

On the unit circle, we have

$$F_1(t) = \sum_{n=0}^{\infty} B_n e^{in\theta} \qquad \text{and} \qquad \bar{F}_1(\bar{t}) = \sum_{n=0}^{\infty} \bar{B}_n e^{-in\theta}$$

where the $\bar{B}_n$ are the conjugates of B_n. Substituting these series into Eq. (8.21), we find

$$\sum_0^{\infty} B_n e^{in\theta} - \sum_0^{\infty} \bar{B}_n e^{-in\theta} = i\left(\sum_{-\infty}^{\infty} A_n e^{in\theta}\right)\left(\sum_{-\infty}^{\infty} \bar{A}_n e^{-in\theta}\right) + C'$$

$$= i \sum_{-\infty}^{\infty} C_n e^{in\theta} + C''$$

where $C_n = \sum\limits_{m=-\infty}^{\infty} A_{n+m}\bar{A}_m$, $C_{-n} = \bar{C}_n$, $n = 0, 1, 2, \ldots, \infty$. Since the constant terms in $F_1(\zeta)$ are irrelevant to the torsion problem, we may leave them undetermined. Equating the coefficients of $e^{in\theta}$ on both sides of the equation except $n = 0$, we find

$$B_n = iC_n \qquad \bar{B}_n = -i\bar{C}_n$$

and
$$F_1(\zeta) = i \sum_{n=1}^{\infty} C_n\zeta^n + \text{constant} \tag{8.25}$$

Separating the real and imaginary parts, the above formula gives us at once the warping function ϕ and its conjugate ψ.

To express J in terms of $F_1(\zeta)$ and $f(\zeta)$, we may proceed as follows: From formula (5.15), we have

$$
J = \iint\limits_{R} (x^2 + y^2)\, dx\, dy + \iint\limits_{R} \left(x\,\frac{\partial \phi}{\partial y} - y\,\frac{\partial \phi}{\partial x} \right) dx\, dy
$$

$$
= \iint\limits_{R} \left[\frac{\partial}{\partial y}(x^2 y) + \frac{\partial}{\partial x}(xy^2) \right] dx\, dy + \iint\limits_{R} \left[\frac{\partial}{\partial y}(x\phi) - \frac{\partial}{\partial x}(y\phi) \right] dx\, dy
$$

$$
= -\oint_S xy(x\, dx - y\, dy) - \oint_S \phi(x\, dx + y\, dy)
$$

where the last step is obtained with the aid of Green's theorem. Since

$$x = \frac{z + \bar{z}}{2} \qquad y = \frac{z - \bar{z}}{2i}$$

we find

$$
\oint_S xy(x\, dx - y\, dy) = \frac{1}{8i} \oint_S (z^2 - \bar{z}^2)(z\, dz + \bar{z}\, d\bar{z})
$$

$$
= \frac{1}{8i} \oint_S (z^3\, dz + z^2\bar{z}\, d\bar{z} - \bar{z}^2 z\, dz - \bar{z}^3\, d\bar{z})
$$

But the Cauchy-Goursat theorem indicates that

$$\oint_S z^3\, dz = 0 \qquad \oint_S \bar{z}^3\, d\bar{z} = 0$$

Integrating the other terms in the integral by parts, and remembering that $(z\bar{z})^2$ is single-valued, we find

$$
\oint_S z^2\bar{z}\, d\bar{z} = \oint_S z^2\, d\left(\frac{\bar{z}^2}{2} \right) = -\oint_S \bar{z}^2 z\, dz
$$

Therefore,
$$J = \frac{1}{4i} \oint_S \bar{z}^2 z\, dz - \oint_S \phi\, d(z\bar{z}/2)$$

Now, $\phi = \frac{1}{2}[F_1(\zeta) + \bar{F}_1(\bar{\zeta})]$. The above formula can then be rewritten in the following form:

$$J = \frac{1}{4i} \oint_{S_1} [\bar{f}(\bar{\zeta})]^2 f(\zeta) \frac{df(\zeta)}{d\zeta}\, d\zeta$$

$$- \frac{1}{4} \oint_{S_1} [F_1(\zeta) + \bar{F}_1(\bar{\zeta})][f(\zeta)\, d\bar{f}(\bar{\zeta}) + \bar{f}(\bar{\zeta})\, df(\zeta)] \quad (8.26)$$

From formulas (5.5) and (5.16), we have

$$\tau_{zx} - i\tau_{yz} = \frac{T}{J}\left(\frac{\partial\phi}{\partial x} - i\frac{\partial\phi}{\partial y} - y - ix\right) = \frac{T}{J}\left[\frac{\partial\phi}{\partial x} + i\frac{\partial\psi}{\partial x} - i(x - iy)\right]$$

But, $\dfrac{\partial\phi}{\partial x} + i\dfrac{\partial\psi}{\partial x} = \dfrac{dF_1(\zeta)}{d\zeta}\dfrac{d\zeta}{dz} = \dfrac{F'_1(\zeta)}{f'(\zeta)}$, where $F'_1(\zeta)$ denotes $dF_1(\zeta)/d\zeta$ and $f'(\zeta)$ denotes $dz/d\zeta$ or $df(\zeta)/d\zeta$. Hence,

$$\tau_{zx} - i\tau_{yz} = \frac{T}{J}\left[\frac{F'_1(\zeta)}{f'(\zeta)} - i\bar{f}(\bar{\zeta})\right] \quad (8.27)$$

Thus, a complete solution of the torsion problem is obtained when the interior of the cross section of the bar can be mapped conformally into the interior of the unit circle.

Let us now take as an example the torsion of a bar with cardioid cross section. The equation of a cardioid in polar coordinates is

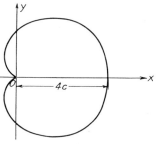

$$r = 2c(1 + \cos\theta)$$

where c is a constant. The torsion of a bar with cardioidal section is of some practical interest because it indicates the effect of the

Fig. 8.4.

presence of a keyway in a circular shaft. The cardioid section in the z plane (Fig. 8.4) can be mapped onto a unit circle in the ζ plane by the mapping function

$$z = f(\zeta) = c(1 - \zeta)^2 \quad (8.28)$$

On the unit circle, $\zeta = e^{i\theta}$, we have

$$f(t) = c(1 - 2e^{i\theta} + e^{2i\theta}) \quad\text{and}\quad \bar{f}(\bar{t}) = c(1 - 2e^{-i\theta} + e^{-2i\theta})$$

Hence $\qquad f(t)\bar{f}(\bar{t}) = c^2(e^{2i\theta} - 4e^{i\theta} - 4e^{-i\theta} + e^{-2i\theta} + 6)$

from which we find

$$C_2 = c^2 \qquad C_1 = -4c^2$$

Accordingly $\qquad F_1(\zeta) = ic^2(\zeta^2 - 4\zeta) + \text{constant}$

The torsional constant J can now be computed from formula (8.25). Noting that on $|\zeta| = 1$, $\bar{t} = 1/t$, we then have

$$J = \frac{c^4}{4i} \oint_{S_1} \left(1 - \frac{2}{t} + \frac{1}{t^2} \right)^2 (1 - 2t + t^2)(-2 + 2t)\, dt$$

$$- \frac{c^4}{4} \oint_{S_1} \left[i(t^2 - 4t) - i\left(\frac{1}{t^2} - \frac{4}{t} \right) \right] \left(2t - 4 + \frac{4}{t^2} - \frac{2}{t^3} \right) dt$$

$$= \frac{c^4}{2i} \oint_{S_1} \left(t^3 - 7t^2 + 21t - 35 + \frac{35}{t} - \frac{21}{t^2} + \frac{7}{t^3} - \frac{1}{t^4} \right) dt$$

$$- \frac{c^4 i}{2} \oint_{S_1} \left(t^3 - 6t^2 + 8t + 6 - \frac{18}{t} + \frac{6}{t^2} + \frac{8}{t^3} - \frac{6}{t^4} + \frac{1}{t^5} \right) dt$$

From the theorem of residues,

$$J = 2\pi i \left[\frac{c^4}{2i} \times 35 - \frac{c^4 i}{2} \times (-18) \right] = 17\pi c^4$$

Observe that, in the above integration, the undetermined constant in $F_1(\zeta)$ does not affect the value of J, which is as it should be.

The shearing stresses can be computed from formula (8.27) and are

$$\tau_{zx} - i\tau_{yz} = \frac{T}{J} \left[\frac{c^2 i(2\zeta - 4)}{-2c(1 - \zeta)} - i(1 - \bar{\zeta})^2 \right] = \frac{Ti}{17\pi c^4} \left[\frac{c(2 - \zeta)}{1 - \zeta} - (1 - \bar{\zeta})^2 \right]$$

For various values of $\zeta = \xi + i\eta$, the shearing stresses can be computed from the above formula. The coordinates of the corresponding point in the x plane can be found from the mapping function (8.28).

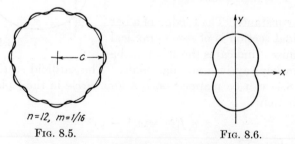

n=12, m=1/16

FIG. 8.5.   FIG. 8.6.

Problem 1. A grooved cross section in the z plane such as shown in Fig. 8.5 can be mapped onto a unit circle in the ζ plane by the mapping function.

$$z = f(\zeta) = c\zeta(1 + m\zeta^n)$$

where c, m, and n are positive real constants. Find the function ψ, the torsional constant J, and the stresses if a bar with such a cross section is under torsion.[1]

[1] See A. C. Stevenson, The Torsion of a Fluted Column. *Phil. Mag.*, Ser. 7, Vol. 34, pp. 115–120, 1943.

Problem 2. A prismatic bar with cross section the inverse of an ellipse with respect to its center is under torsion (Fig. 8.6).[1] The boundary of the cross section S is given by the parametric equations

$$\frac{x}{x^2 + y^2} = \frac{1}{c} \cosh k \cos u \qquad \frac{y}{x^2 + y^2} = \frac{1}{c} \sinh k \sin u$$

where u is the parameter, $c = 1/\sqrt{a^2 + b^2}$, and $\tanh k = b/a$. These parametric equations may be rewritten as

$$z = c \sec (w + ik), \qquad v = 0$$

where $w = u + iv$.

This cross section can be mapped conformally on a unit circle $|\zeta| = 1$ by the mapping function

$$z = \frac{2ce^k \zeta}{\zeta^2 + e^{2k}} = \sum_{n=0}^{\infty} a_n e^{inw}$$

where
$$a_n = \begin{cases} 0 & \text{if } n = 0, 2, 4, \ldots \\ 2c(-1)^{(n-1)/2} e^{-nk} & \text{if } n = 1, 3, 5, \ldots \end{cases}$$

Find the torsional constant and the shearing stresses.

Ans. $J = \pi c^4 (2 \operatorname{csch}^2 2k + \operatorname{csch}^4 2k)$

$$\tau_{zx} = -\frac{T}{J} 2c \sin u \left[\frac{\operatorname{csch} 2k \cosh (v + k)}{\cos 2u - \cosh 2(v + k)} + \frac{\sinh (v + k)}{\cos 2u + \cosh 2(v + k)} \right]$$

$$\tau_{yz} = -\frac{T}{J} 2c \cos u \left[\frac{\csc 2k \sinh (v + k)}{\cos 2u - \cosh 2(v + k)} - \frac{\cosh (v + k)}{\cos 2u + \cosh 2(v + k)} \right]$$

8.4. Torsion of Elliptical Bar. In the previous section, a complete solution of the torsion problem is obtained if the interior of the cross section of the bar can be mapped conformally into the interior of a unit circle. By mapping conformally, we mean that there will be no singular points of transformation at which $dz/d\zeta = 0$. There are, however, certain simple cross sections which cannot be simply expressed in this way. A familiar example is the elliptical cylinder, where the mapping function that transforms the interior of the ellipse into the interior of the unit circle is so complicated that the problem presents formidable difficulties. The problem, however, can be easily solved by introducing a cut in the ellipse along a line joining its foci and by mapping the ellipse with the cut on a circular ring. The mapping function in this case is a simple one, and in order to obtain the solution for the solid elliptical section, it is necessary merely to satisfy the condition of continuity of the function $F(z)$ as we approach the cut from either side.

Consider the mapping function

$$z = f(\zeta) = \frac{c}{2} \left(\zeta + \frac{1}{\zeta} \right) \tag{8.29}$$

where c is a real, positive constant. If we solve for ζ, we obtain

$$\zeta c = z \pm \sqrt{z^2 - c^2} = z \pm \sqrt{(z - c)(z + c)}$$

Let us consider the function

$$\zeta_1 = \pm \sqrt{(z - c)(z + c)}$$

[1] See T. J. Higgins, The Torsion of a Prism with Cross Section the Inverse of an Ellipse, *J. Applied Phys.*, Vol. 13, pp. 457–459, 1942. Also I. S. Sokolnikoff and R. D. Specht, "Mathematical Theory of Elasticity," 1st ed., pp. 183–185, McGraw-Hill Book Company, Inc., New York, 1946.

If we let

$$z - c = r_1 e^{i\theta_1} \qquad z + c = r_2 e^{i\theta_2}$$

then

$$\zeta_1 = \sqrt{r_1 r_2}\, e^{i(\theta_1 + \theta_2)/2}$$

Without imposing any restrictions, ζ_1 may take on two values for each z, one the negative of the other depending on the choice of θ_1 and θ_2. To show this, let z traverse a curve enclosing the point $z = c$ but not $z = -c$ (Fig. 8.7a). If the starting point is at $\theta_1 = \theta_1^*$, $\theta_2 = \theta_2^*$, then when the complete circuit is traversed, $\theta_1 = \theta_1^* + 2\pi$, $\theta_2 = \theta_2^*$, and the argument of ζ_1 will increase by the amount π. This means that, as z returns to its starting value, ζ_1 will not return to its original value at the same time. The same is true if z traverses a curve enclosing the point $z = -c$ but not $z = c$. But if the curve encloses both of these points (Fig. 8.7b), as z traverses it, θ_1 increases from θ_1^* to $\theta_1^* + 2\pi$ and θ_2 increases from θ_2^* to $\theta_2^* + 2\pi$; therefore ζ_1 returns to its original value. The points $A(z = c)$ and $B(z = -c)$ are called *branch points*. In order that ζ_1 be single-valued, we must exclude the possibility that z traverses a curve enclosing only one of the branch points. To do this, we may introduce an arbitrary

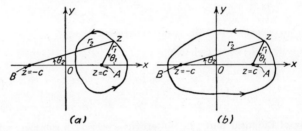

(a)   (b)

Fig. 8.7.

cut linking AB, called a *branch cut*. Thus ζ_1 is single-valued in the slit plane. The branch cut may be conveniently taken along the segment AB on the real axis.

Let us now return to the mapping function defined by (8.27). We observe that the boundary S_1 of the unit circle $|\zeta| = 1$ corresponds to the segment AB in the z axis. That is, the branch cut in the z plane is mapped onto a unit circle in the ζ plane. When the point $\zeta = t = e^{i\theta}$ describes the circle $|\zeta| = 1$, the corresponding point z describes the segment AB twice in accordance with the relation

$$z = x = c \cos \theta = \frac{c}{2}\left(t + \frac{1}{t}\right)$$

so that the points $t = e^{i\theta}$ and $\bar{t} = e^{-i\theta}$ in the ζ plane correspond to one and the same point of the segment AB. The circle S' of the radius ρ_1 in the ζ plane corresponds to the ellipse in the z plane whose semiaxes are

$$a = \frac{c}{2}\left(\rho_1 + \frac{1}{\rho_1}\right) \qquad b = \frac{c}{2}\left(\rho_1 - \frac{1}{\rho_1}\right)$$

Or, in terms of a and b,

$$\rho_1{}^2 = \frac{a + b}{a - b} \qquad \text{and} \qquad c^2 = a^2 - b^2 \tag{8.30}$$

Hence, the points $A(-c,0)$ and $B(c,0)$ are the foci of the ellipse.

In the ζ plane, it is evident that the boundary condition (8.21) must be satisfied on the circle S' or $|\zeta| = \rho_1$. On the unit circle S_1, the condition $F_1(t) = F_1(\bar{t})$ must be satisfied since the points $t = e^{i\theta}$ and $\bar{t} = e^{-i\theta}$ correspond to the same point of the segment AB in the z plane, and the function $F(z)$ will assume the same value as z is made to approach the cut AB from either side. Accordingly the function $F(z)$ will be analytic in the uncut circle.

The function $F_1(\zeta)$ must be single-valued and analytic in the ring between S_1 and S'. Hence, it can be expanded into the Laurent series

$$F_1(\zeta) = \sum_{n=-\infty}^{\infty} B_n \zeta^n \qquad (8.31)$$

which converges when $1 \le |\zeta| \le \rho_1$. On the unit circle, we must have

$$F_1(t) = F_1(\bar{t}) \qquad \text{or} \qquad \sum_{-\infty}^{\infty} B_n e^{in\theta} = \sum_{-\infty}^{\infty} B_n e^{-in\theta}$$

which requires

$$B_n = B_{-n}$$

It may be pointed out that although the above relation was obtained by taking the cut along the segment AB on the real axis, the same relation can be shown valid if the cut is taken along any other arbitrary curve joining AB. On the circle S', $\zeta = \rho_1 e^{i\theta}$, the condition (8.21) must be satisfied. Hence,

$$\sum_{-\infty}^{\infty} B_n \rho_1^n e^{in\theta} - \sum_{-\infty}^{\infty} \bar{B}_n \rho_1^n e^{-in\theta} = i \frac{c^2}{4} \left(\rho_1 e^{i\theta} + \frac{1}{\rho_1} e^{-i\theta} \right) \left(\rho_1 e^{-i\theta} + \frac{1}{\rho_1} e^{i\theta} \right) + C'$$

$$= i \frac{c^2}{4} \left[e^{i2\theta} + \left(\rho_1^2 + \frac{1}{\rho_1^2} \right) + e^{-i2\theta} \right] + C'$$

Equating the coefficient of $e^{in\theta}$ on both sides of the equation, we find

$$B_2 \rho_1^2 - \bar{B}_{-2} \rho_1^{-2} = \frac{ic^2}{4} \qquad B_{-2} \rho_1^{-2} - \bar{B}_2 \rho_1^2 = \frac{ic^2}{4}$$

But $\qquad\qquad B_n = B_{-n} \qquad \text{or} \qquad \bar{B}_n = \bar{B}_{-n}$

Then $\qquad\qquad B_2 \rho_1^2 - \bar{B}_2 \rho_1^{-2} = \frac{ic^2}{4} \qquad B_2 \rho_1^{-2} - \bar{B}_2 \rho_1^2 = \frac{ic^2}{4}$

Solving, we obtain

$$B_2 = B_{-2} = \frac{ic^2}{4} \frac{\rho_1^2}{\rho_1^4 + 1}$$

and all other B_n are zero. Accordingly,

$$F_1(\zeta) = \frac{ic^2}{4} \frac{\rho_1^2}{\rho_1^4 + 1} \left(\zeta^2 + \frac{1}{\zeta^2} \right) + \text{constant}$$

and since

$$z^2 = \frac{c^2}{4} \left(\zeta^2 + \frac{1}{\zeta^2} + 2 \right)$$

we obtain

$$F(z) = \frac{i\rho_1^2}{\rho_1^4 + 1} z^2 + \text{constant}$$

If we substitute into the above equation the expression of ρ_1 in terms of the major and minor semiaxes a and b, we get

$$F(z) = \frac{i}{2}\frac{a^2 - b^2}{a^2 + b^2} z^2 + \text{constant}$$

from which it follows that

$$\phi = -\frac{a^2 - b^2}{a^2 + b^2} xy + \text{constant}$$

This is precisely the expression we obtained in Sec. 5.2.

To compute J, let us substitute $\zeta = \rho_1 e^{i\theta}$ and $\bar{\zeta} = \rho_1 e^{-i\theta}$ into formula (8.26). Since on the circle S',

$$f(\zeta) = \frac{c}{2}\left(\rho_1 e^{i\theta} + \frac{1}{\rho_1}e^{-i\theta}\right) \qquad \bar{f}(\bar{\zeta}) = \frac{c}{2}\left(\rho_1 e^{-i\theta} + \frac{1}{\rho_1}e^{i\theta}\right)$$

we have

$$df(\zeta) = \frac{ic}{2}\left(\rho_1 e^{i\theta} - \frac{1}{\rho_1}e^{-i\theta}\right)d\theta$$

$$d\bar{f}(\bar{\zeta}) = \frac{ic}{2}\left(-\rho_1 e^{-i\theta} + \frac{1}{\rho_1}e^{i\theta}\right)d\theta$$

and
$$J = \frac{1}{4i}\int_0^{2\pi}\left[\frac{c}{2}\left(\rho_1 e^{-i\theta} + \frac{1}{\rho_1}e^{i\theta}\right)\right]^2\left[\frac{c}{2}\left(\rho_1 e^{i\theta} + \frac{1}{\rho_1}e^{-i\theta}\right)\right]\left[\frac{ic}{2}\left(\rho_1 e^{i\theta} - \frac{1}{\rho_1}e^{-i\theta}\right)\right]d\theta$$
$$-\frac{1}{4}\int_0^{2\pi}\left[\frac{ic^2}{4}\frac{\rho_1{}^2}{\rho_1{}^4 + 1}\left(\rho_1{}^2 e^{2i\theta} + \frac{1}{\rho_1{}^2}e^{-2i\theta}\right) - \frac{ic^2}{4}\frac{\rho_1{}^2}{\rho_1{}^4 + 1}\right.$$
$$\left(\rho_1{}^2 e^{-2i\theta} + \frac{1}{\rho_1{}^2}e^{2i\theta}\right)\left]\left[\frac{c}{2}\left(\rho_1 e^{-i\theta} + \frac{1}{\rho_1}e^{i\theta}\right)\frac{ic}{2}\right.$$
$$\left(\rho_1 e^{i\theta} - \frac{1}{\rho_1}e^{-i\theta}\right)d\theta + \frac{c}{2}\left(\rho_1 e^{i\theta} + \frac{1}{\rho_1}e^{-i\theta}\right)\frac{ic}{2}\left(-\rho_1 e^{-i\theta} + \frac{1}{\rho_1}e^{i\theta}\right)d\theta\right]$$

A straightforward integration gives

$$J = \frac{\pi c^4}{32}\left(\rho_1{}^4 - \frac{1}{\rho_1{}^4}\right) - \frac{\pi c^4}{8}\frac{\rho_1{}^4 - 1}{\rho_1{}^4 + 1}$$
$$= \frac{\pi}{4}ab(a^2 + b^2) - \frac{\pi}{4}ab\frac{(a^2 - b^2)^2}{a^2 + b^2}$$
$$= \frac{\pi a^3 b^3}{a^2 + b^2}$$

The shearing stresses can be computed from formula (8.27).

8.5. Plane-stress and Plane-strain Problems.

In Sec. 4.1, it was shown that the solution of a plane-stress or a plane-strain problem with gravitational body forces can be reduced to the determination of the stress function ψ which satisfies the biharmonic equation

$$\nabla^4 \psi = 0$$

We shall now carry out the solution of the biharmonic equation by means of complex variables.

Rewrite the biharmonic equation in the following form:

$$\nabla^2(\nabla^2 \psi) = 0$$

It follows then that the function

$$p = \nabla^2 \psi$$

satisfies the Laplace equation $\nabla^2 p = 0$. If we denote the conjugate of p by q, then

$$f_1(z) = p + iq$$

is an analytic function, and the integral of this function with respect to z is another analytic function. Let

$$F(z) = P + iQ = \tfrac{1}{4} \! \int \! f_1(z) \, dz \tag{8.32}$$

Then $\quad F'(z) = \dfrac{\partial P}{\partial x} + i \dfrac{\partial Q}{\partial x} = \dfrac{\partial Q}{\partial y} - i \dfrac{\partial P}{\partial y} = \dfrac{1}{4} f_1(z) = \dfrac{1}{4}(p + iq)$

Hence $\qquad\qquad \dfrac{\partial Q}{\partial y} = \dfrac{\partial P}{\partial x} = \dfrac{1}{4} p$

From these definitions we find

$$\nabla^2(xP + yQ) = 2 \frac{\partial P}{\partial x} + 2 \frac{\partial Q}{\partial y} = p$$

But $\nabla^2 \psi = p$. Therefore,

$$\nabla^2(\psi - xP - yQ) = 0$$

That is, the function $(\psi - xP - yQ)$ is a harmonic function, say P_1, and the stress function can be written as

$$\psi = xP + yQ + P_1 \tag{8.33}$$

The stress function ψ given by Eq. (8.33) can be written in several different forms. Let us construct the function

$$\chi(z) = P_1 + iQ_1$$

where Q_1 is the conjugate function of P_1. Noting that

$$\bar{z}F(z) = (x - iy)(P + iQ) = (xP + yQ) + i(xQ - yP)$$

we can write

$$\psi = \operatorname{Re}\left[\bar{z}F(z) + \chi(z)\right] \tag{8.34}$$

where the symbol Re denotes the real part of the function following it. If we denote the conjugate functions of $F(z)$ and $\chi(z)$ by $\bar{F}(\bar{z})$ and $\bar{\chi}(\bar{z})$, respectively, so that

$$\bar{F}(\bar{z}) = P - iQ \qquad \bar{\chi}(\bar{z}) = P_1 - iQ_1$$

then formula (8.34) can be written as

$$\psi = \tfrac{1}{2}[\bar{z}F(z) + z\bar{F}(\bar{z}) + \chi(z) + \bar{\chi}(\bar{z})] \tag{8.35}$$

Equations (8.34) and (8.35) show that any stress function can be expressed in terms of suitably chosen analytic functions.

Let us now express the displacements and the stresses in terms of these analytic functions. From Eqs. (3.27) and (4.4), we find that, in the case of plane stress where there is no body force, we have

$$\frac{\partial u}{\partial x} = \frac{1}{E}(\sigma_x - \nu\sigma_y) = \frac{1}{E}\left(\frac{\partial^2\psi}{\partial y^2} - \nu\frac{\partial^2\psi}{\partial x^2}\right)$$

$$\frac{\partial v}{\partial y} = \frac{1}{E}(\sigma_y - \nu\sigma_x) = \frac{1}{E}\left(\frac{\partial^2\psi}{\partial x^2} - \nu\frac{\partial^2\psi}{\partial y^2}\right) \qquad (8.36)$$

$$\frac{\partial v}{\partial x} + \frac{\partial u}{\partial y} = \frac{2(1+\nu)}{E}\tau_{xy} = -\frac{2(1+\nu)}{E}\frac{\partial^2\psi}{\partial x\,\partial y}$$

Recalling that

$$p = \nabla^2\psi = \frac{\partial^2\psi}{\partial x^2} + \frac{\partial^2\psi}{\partial y^2} \qquad \text{and} \qquad \frac{\partial Q}{\partial y} = \frac{\partial P}{\partial x} = \frac{1}{4}p$$

we obtain from the first two equations

$$\frac{\partial u}{\partial x} = \frac{1}{E}\left[\left(p - \frac{\partial^2\psi}{\partial x^2}\right) - \nu\frac{\partial^2\psi}{\partial x^2}\right]$$

$$= \frac{1}{E}\left[p - (1+\nu)\frac{\partial^2\psi}{\partial x^2}\right]$$

$$= \frac{1}{E}\left[4\frac{\partial P}{\partial x} - (1+\nu)\frac{\partial^2\psi}{\partial x^2}\right]$$

and
$$\frac{\partial v}{\partial y} = \frac{1}{E}\left[4\frac{\partial Q}{\partial y} - (1+\nu)\frac{\partial^2\psi}{\partial y^2}\right]$$

Integrating, we find

$$u = \frac{1}{E}\left[4P - (1+\nu)\frac{\partial\psi}{\partial x} + g_1(y)\right] \qquad v = \frac{1}{E}\left[4Q - (1+\nu)\frac{\partial\psi}{\partial y} + g_2(x)\right]$$

where $g_1(y)$ and $g_2(x)$ are arbitrary functions of y and x, respectively. Substituting these expressions into the third equation in (8.33) and canceling the common factor $1/E$, we obtain

$$4\left(\frac{\partial P}{\partial y} + \frac{\partial Q}{\partial x}\right) - 2(1+\nu)\frac{\partial^2\psi}{\partial x\,\partial y} + \frac{dg_1}{dy} + \frac{dg_2}{dx} = -2(1+\nu)\frac{\partial^2\psi}{\partial x\,\partial y}$$

But
$$\frac{\partial P}{\partial y} = -\frac{\partial Q}{\partial x}$$

Then
$$\frac{dg_1}{dy} + \frac{dg_2}{dx} = 0$$

which implies

$$\frac{dg_1}{dy} = -\frac{dg_2}{dx} = C$$

where C is a constant. Therefore

$$g_1 = Cy + C_1 \qquad g_2 = -Cx + C_2$$

From the definitions of the strain components, we find that these displacement components will not induce any strain and represent the rigid-body displacements. Discarding these terms, we obtain finally

$$u = \frac{1}{E}\left[4P - (1 + \nu)\frac{\partial \psi}{\partial x}\right] \qquad v = \frac{1}{E}\left[4Q - (1 + \nu)\frac{\partial \psi}{\partial y}\right]$$

or $$u + iv = \frac{1}{E}\left[4(P + iQ) - (1 + \nu)\left(\frac{\partial \psi}{\partial x} + i\frac{\partial \psi}{\partial y}\right)\right] \qquad (8.37)$$

Noting that

$$\frac{\partial z}{\partial x} = \frac{\partial \bar{z}}{\partial x} = 1 \qquad \frac{\partial z}{\partial y} = i \qquad \frac{\partial \bar{z}}{\partial y} = -i$$

from Eq. (8.35), we find that

$$\frac{\partial \psi}{\partial x} = \frac{1}{2}[\bar{z}F'(z) + F(z) + z\bar{F}'(\bar{z}) + \bar{F}(\bar{z}) + \chi'(z) + \bar{\chi}'(\bar{z})]$$

$$\frac{\partial \psi}{\partial y} = \frac{i}{2}[\bar{z}F'(z) - F(z) - z\bar{F}'(\bar{z}) + \bar{F}(\bar{z}) + \chi'(z) - \bar{\chi}'(\bar{z})]$$

Hence, $$\frac{\partial \psi}{\partial x} + i\frac{\partial \psi}{\partial y} = F(z) + z\bar{F}'(\bar{z}) + \bar{\chi}'(\bar{z}) \qquad (8.38)$$

Recalling that $P + iQ = F(z)$, we have

$$u + iv = \frac{3 - \nu}{E}F(z) - \frac{1 + \nu}{E}[z\bar{F}'(\bar{z}) + \bar{\chi}'(\bar{z})] \qquad (8.39)$$

This formula permits us to calculate the components of displacement for plane-stress problems whenever the functions $F(z)$ and $\chi(z)$ are known. A similar formula can be easily derived for plane-strain problems.

Now, let us examine the stress components. Differentiating Eq. (8.38) with respect to x and y, we find that

$$\frac{\partial^2 \psi}{\partial x^2} + i\frac{\partial^2 \psi}{\partial x\,\partial y} = F'(z) + z\bar{F}''(\bar{z}) + \bar{F}'(\bar{z}) + \bar{\chi}''(\bar{z})$$

$$\frac{\partial^2 \psi}{\partial x\,\partial y} + i\frac{\partial^2 \psi}{\partial y^2} = i[F'(z) - z\bar{F}''(\bar{z}) + \bar{F}'(\bar{z}) - \bar{\chi}''(\bar{z})]$$

Multiplying the second equation by i and subtracting and adding the resulting equation from and to the first equation, we obtain

$$\sigma_x + \sigma_y = 2F'(z) + 2\bar{F}'(\bar{z}) = 4\,\mathrm{Re}\,F'(z) \qquad (8.40)$$

$$\sigma_y - \sigma_x - 2i\tau_{xy} = 2[z\bar{F}''(\bar{z}) + \bar{\chi}''(\bar{z})] \qquad (8.41)$$

A more convenient form of (8.41) can be obtained if we change i to $-i$ on both sides of that equation. Then

$$\sigma_y - \sigma_x + 2i\tau_{xy} = 2[\bar{z}F''(z) + \chi''(z)] \qquad (8.42)$$

Formulas (8.40) and (8.42) give us the stress components if $F(z)$ and $\chi(z)$ are known.

Let us now calculate the resultant force acting on an arc AB drawn on the plate. Let $\bar{X}\,ds$ and $\bar{Y}\,ds$ repre-

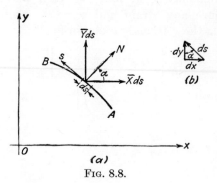

FIG. 8.8.

sent the x and y components of the force acting on the element of arc ds of AB from the positive side of the normal N. Then

$$\bar{X} = \sigma_x \cos \alpha + \tau_{xy} \sin \alpha$$
$$\bar{Y} = \sigma_y \sin \alpha + \tau_{xy} \cos \alpha$$

where α is the angle between the positive direction of the normal and the x axis. To ds correspond a dx and a dy as shown in Fig. 8.8b. If we let the positive direction of the arc ds be from A to B, then x decreases as s increases and a positive ds will correspond to a negative dx. Thus

$$\cos \alpha = \frac{dy}{ds} \qquad \text{and} \qquad \sin \alpha = -\frac{dx}{ds}$$

With these relations, together with

$$\sigma_x = \frac{\partial^2 \psi}{\partial y^2} \qquad \sigma_y = \frac{\partial^2 \psi}{\partial x^2} \qquad \tau_{xy} = -\frac{\partial^2 \psi}{\partial x \, \partial y}$$

we find that

$$\bar{X} = \frac{\partial^2 \psi}{\partial y^2}\frac{dy}{ds} + \frac{\partial^2 \psi}{\partial x \, \partial y}\frac{dx}{ds} = \frac{\partial}{\partial y}\left(\frac{\partial \psi}{\partial y}\right)\frac{dy}{ds} + \frac{\partial}{\partial x}\left(\frac{\partial \psi}{\partial y}\right)\frac{dx}{ds} = \frac{d}{ds}\left(\frac{\partial \psi}{\partial y}\right)$$

$$\bar{Y} = -\frac{\partial^2 \psi}{\partial x^2}\frac{dx}{ds} - \frac{\partial^2 \psi}{\partial x \, \partial y}\frac{dy}{ds} = -\frac{d}{ds}\left(\frac{\partial \psi}{\partial x}\right)$$

The components of the resultant force acting on AB are therefore

$$F_x = \int_A^B \bar{X}\,ds = \int_A^B \frac{d}{ds}\left(\frac{\partial \psi}{\partial y}\right)ds = \left[\frac{\partial \psi}{\partial y}\right]_A^B$$
$$F_y = \int_A^B \bar{Y}\,ds = -\int_A^B \frac{d}{ds}\left(\frac{\partial \psi}{\partial x}\right)ds = -\left[\frac{\partial \psi}{\partial x}\right]_A^B \tag{8.43}$$

where the symbol $\left[\;\;\right]_A^B$ represents the difference of the values of the quantity at B and at A.

The moment of the force on AB about the origin 0 is

$$M = \int_A^B (x\bar{Y} - y\bar{X})\,ds = -\int_A^B \left[x\,d\left(\frac{\partial \psi}{\partial x}\right) + y\,d\left(\frac{\partial \psi}{\partial y}\right)\right]$$

Integrating by parts, we obtain

$$M = - \left[x \frac{\partial \psi}{\partial x} + y \frac{\partial \psi}{\partial y} \right]_A^B + \left[\psi \right]_A^B \tag{8.44}$$

8.6. Solution of Plane-stress and Plane-strain Problems in Polar Coordinates. Let us now find the general solution of plane-stress and plane-strain problems in polar coordinates. Referring to Fig. 8.9, if we denote by v_r and v_θ the components of displacement at the point P in the directions of the polar coordinates r and θ, we have

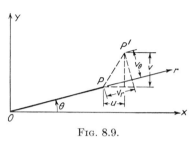

FIG. 8.9.

$$u = v_r \cos \theta - v_\theta \sin \theta \qquad v = v_r \sin \theta + v_\theta \cos \theta$$

Noting that $-1 = i^2$, we obtain

$$u + iv = v_r(\cos \theta + i \sin \theta) + iv_\theta(\cos \theta + i \sin \theta)$$
$$= (v_r + iv_\theta)e^{i\theta}$$

Hence
$$v_r + iv_\theta = e^{-i\theta}(u + iv)$$

$$= e^{-i\theta} \left\{ \frac{3 - \nu}{E} F(z) - \frac{1 + \nu}{E} [z\bar{F}'(\bar{z}) + \bar{\chi}'(\bar{z})] \right\} \tag{8.45}$$

for plane-stress problems. If we substitute $z = re^{i\theta}$ and $\bar{z} = re^{-i\theta}$ in the terms at the right-hand side of Eq. (8.45) and separate the real and imaginary parts, we obtain the displacements v_r and v_θ in polar coordinates.

In order to get expressions for the components of stress in polar coordinates, let us temporarily denote the coordinate axes r and θ by x' and y', respectively. Then

$$\sigma_r = \sigma_{x'} \qquad \sigma_\theta = \sigma_{y'} \qquad \tau_{r\theta} = \tau_{x'y'}$$

Noting that $l_1 = \cos \theta$, $m_1 = \sin \theta$, $l_2 = -\sin \theta$, $m_2 = \cos \theta$, we find from formulas (1.15)

$$\sigma_r = \sigma_x \cos^2 \theta + \sigma_y \sin^2 \theta + 2\tau_{xy} \sin \theta \cos \theta$$
$$\sigma_\theta = \sigma_x \sin^2 \theta + \sigma_y \cos^2 \theta - 2\tau_{xy} \sin \theta \cos \theta$$
$$\tau_{r\theta} = (-\sigma_x + \sigma_y) \sin \theta \cos \theta + \tau_{xy}(\cos^2 \theta - \sin^2 \theta)$$

It follows directly from these formulas that

$$\sigma_r + \sigma_\theta = \sigma_x + \sigma_y$$
$$\sigma_\theta - \sigma_r + 2i\tau_{r\theta} = (\sigma_y - \sigma_x + 2i\tau_{xy})e^{2i\theta}$$

From formulas (8.40) and (8.42), we have

$$\sigma_r + \sigma_\theta = 4 \operatorname{Re} F'(z) = 2[F'(z) + \bar{F}'(\bar{z})] \tag{8.46}$$
$$\sigma_\theta - \sigma_r + 2i\tau_{r\theta} = 2[\bar{z}F''(z) + \chi''(z)]e^{2i\theta} \tag{8.47}$$

If we subtract (8.47) from (8.46), we get

$$\sigma_r - i\tau_{r\theta} = F'(z) + \bar{F}'(\bar{z}) - [\bar{z}F''(z) + \chi''(z)]e^{2i\theta} \qquad (8.48)$$

8.7. General Solution for an Infinite Plate with a Circular Hole. Let us choose the origin of coordinates at the center of the circular hole. If the boundary conditions are given in terms of prescribed stresses over the boundary of the hole, then σ_r and $\tau_{r\theta}$ are known at $z = ae^{i\theta}$, where a is the radius of the hole.

The analytic functions $F'(z)$ and $\chi''(z)$ can be expanded into power series. Since the stresses must remain finite when $r \to \infty$, we find from formulas (8.46) and (8.48) that these functions must also remain finite at $r = \infty$. Therefore, these functions must have the form

$$F'(z) = \sum_{n=0}^{\infty} A_n z^{-n} \qquad \chi''(z) = \sum_{n=0}^{\infty} B_n z^{-n} \qquad (8.49)$$

where A_n, B_n are complex constants. From formulas (8.46) and (8.48), we observe that the stresses at infinity are given by the real part of the constant A_0 and the constant B_0. The imaginary part of the complex constant A_0 does not affect the state of stress.

Integrating (8.49) with respect to z, we find

$$F(z) = A_0 z + A_1 \log z - \sum_{n=2}^{\infty} \frac{A_n z^{-n+1}}{n-1} + c_1$$

$$\chi'(z) = B_0 z + B_1 \log z - \sum_{n=2}^{\infty} \frac{B_n z^{-n+1}}{n-1} + c_2$$

where c_1 and c_2 are complex constants. Noting that

$$\bar{F}'(\bar{z}) = \sum_{n=0}^{\infty} \bar{A}_n \bar{z}^{-n}$$

$$\bar{\chi}'(\bar{z}) = \bar{B}_0 \bar{z} + \bar{B}_1 \log \bar{z} - \sum_{n=2}^{\infty} \frac{\bar{B}_n \bar{z}^{-n+1}}{n-1} + \bar{c}_2$$

we have from (8.45)

$$\begin{aligned}
v_r + iv_\theta = e^{-i\theta} \Bigg[&\frac{3-\nu}{E} \left(A_0 z + A_1 \log z - \sum_{n=2}^{\infty} \frac{A_n z^{-n+1}}{n-1} + c_1 \right) \\
&- \frac{1+\nu}{E} \left(\bar{A}_0 z + r^2 \sum_{n=1}^{\infty} \bar{A}_n \bar{z}^{-(n+1)} \right) \\
&- \frac{1+\nu}{E} \left(\bar{B}_0 \bar{z} + \bar{B}_1 \log \bar{z} - \sum_{n=2}^{\infty} \frac{\bar{B}_n \bar{z}^{-n+1}}{n-1} + \bar{c}_2 \right) \Bigg] \qquad (8.50)
\end{aligned}$$

Let us examine the function log z. If we write $z = re^{i\theta}$, then

$$\log z = \log r + i\theta$$

We observe that this function is not single-valued because if we trace a path around the hole the value of θ increases from some value θ_1 to $\theta_1 + 2\pi$. The increment of $v_r + iv_\theta$ in going around the hole is therefore

$$2\pi i e^{-i\theta} \left(\frac{3 - \nu}{E} A_1 + \frac{1 + \nu}{E} \bar{B}_1 \right)$$

In order that $v_r + iv_\theta$ be single-valued, we must require that

$$(3 - \nu)A_1 + (1 + \nu)\bar{B}_1 = 0$$

or

$$A_1 = -\frac{1 + \nu}{3 - \nu} \bar{B}_1 \tag{8.51}$$

Since the stresses σ_r and $\tau_{r\theta}$ are given at $r = a$, we can expand $(\sigma_r - i\tau_{r\theta})_{r=a}$ in a complex Fourier series; then

$$(\sigma_r - i\tau_{r\theta})_{r=a} = \sum_{n=-\infty}^{\infty} C_n e^{in\theta} \tag{8.52}$$

where the coefficients C_n are given by the formula

$$C_n = \frac{1}{2\pi} \int_0^{2\pi} [\sigma_r(\theta) - \tau_{r\theta}(\theta)]_{r=a} \, e^{-in\theta} \, d\theta \qquad n = 0, 1, -1, -2, \ldots \tag{8.53}$$

From formula (8.48), we have

$$\sigma_r - i\tau_{r\theta} = F'(z) + \bar{F}'(\bar{z}) - [\bar{z}F''(z) + \chi''(z)]e^{2i\theta}$$

Substituting into the above expression the series (8.49) and (8.52) and noting that on the boundary of the circular hole $r = a$, we find that

$$\sum_{n=-\infty}^{\infty} C_n e^{in\theta} = \sum_{n=0}^{\infty} \frac{A_n}{a^n} e^{-in\theta} + \sum_{n=0}^{\infty} \frac{\bar{A}_n}{a^n} e^{in\theta} + \sum_{n=0}^{\infty} \frac{nA_n}{a^n} e^{-in\theta} - \sum_{n=0}^{\infty} \frac{B_n}{a^n} e^{-i(n-2)\theta}$$

$$= \sum_{n=0}^{\infty} \left[(1 + n)A_n - \frac{B_{n+2}}{a^2} \right] \frac{e^{-in\theta}}{a^n} - \frac{B_1}{a} e^{i\theta} - B_0 e^{i2\theta} + \sum_{n=0}^{\infty} \frac{\bar{A}_n}{a^n} e^{in\theta}$$

Comparing the coefficients of $e^{in\theta}$ on both sides of the above equation, we get

$$A_0 + \bar{A}_0 - \frac{B_2}{a^2} = C_0 \tag{8.54}$$

$$\frac{\bar{A}_1}{a} - \frac{B_1}{a} = C_1 \tag{8.55}$$

$$\frac{\bar{A}_2}{a^2} - B_0 = C_2 \tag{8.56}$$

$$\frac{\bar{A}_n}{a^n} = C_n \quad \text{if } n \geq 3 \qquad (8.57)$$

$$\frac{1+n}{a^n} A_n - \frac{B_{n+2}}{a^{n+2}} = C_{-n} \quad \text{if } n \geq 1 \qquad (8.58)$$

Since $A_0 + \bar{A}_0$ and B_0 describe the behavior of stresses at infinity, they are assumed to be known. We have pointed out before that the stresses do not depend on the magnitude of the imaginary part of the constant A_0. If we examine formula (8.50), we find that the imaginary part of A_0 will produce a rigid-body motion so far as the displacements are concerned. Therefore, the magnitude of the imaginary part of the constant A_0 is irrelevant to our problem, and we may arbitrarily assign its value to be zero. Then A_0 becomes real and $A_0 + \bar{A}_0 = 2A_0$.

From (8.51), we find that

$$\bar{A}_1 = -\frac{1+\nu}{3-\nu} B_1$$

Substituting into Eq. (8.55) and solving, we get

$$B_1 = -\frac{(3-\nu)C_1 a}{4} \qquad (8.59)$$

and it follows from (8.51) that

$$A_1 = \frac{(1+\nu)\bar{C}_1 a}{4} \qquad (8.60)$$

From Eq. (8.56), we obtain

$$A_2 = \bar{B}_0 a^2 + \bar{C}_2 a^2 \qquad (8.61)$$

Remembering that A_0 is now real, we find from Eq. (8.54)

$$B_2 = 2A_0 a^2 - C_0 a^2 \qquad (8.62)$$

Equations (8.57) and (8.58) give

$$A_n = \bar{C}_n a^n \quad \text{for } n \geq 3 \qquad (8.63)$$

and $$B_n = (n-1)a^2 A_{n-2} - a^n C_{-n+2} \quad \text{for } n \geq 3 \qquad (8.64)$$

Thus the coefficients are explicitly determined. Therefore the problem is completely solved if the stress distributions are given on the circular boundaries of the plate.

Take, as an example, the problem of a large plate containing a small circular hole of radius a in the middle and which is subjected to a uniform tension in the x direction. This problem was solved in Sec. 4.5 by another method. In this case the boundary conditions are that, at $r = \infty$,

$$\sigma_x = S \qquad \sigma_y = \tau_{xy} = 0$$

and, at $r = a$,

$$\sigma_r = \tau_{r\theta} = 0 \qquad (8.65)$$

From formulas (8.40) and (8.41), we find, at $r = \infty$,

$$S = 4A_0 \qquad -S = 2\bar{B}_0$$

Hence
$$A_0 = \frac{S}{4} \qquad B_0 = -\frac{S}{2}$$

Furthermore, from (8.52) and (8.65), we find that all Fourier coefficients C_n vanish. Formulas (8.59) to (8.64) give in this case

$$A_1 = 0 \qquad B_1 = 0$$
$$A_2 = -\frac{Sa^2}{2} \qquad B_2 = \frac{Sa^2}{2}$$
$$A_n = 0 \qquad \text{if } n \geq 3$$
$$B_3 = 0 \qquad B_4 = -\frac{3Sa^4}{2}$$
$$B_n = 0 \qquad \text{if } n \geq 5$$

Accordingly, the functions $F'(z)$ and $\chi''(z)$ are

$$F'(z) = \frac{S}{4}\left(1 - \frac{2a^2}{z^2}\right) \qquad \chi''(z) = -\frac{S}{2}\left(1 - \frac{a^2}{z^2} + \frac{3a^4}{z^4}\right)$$

Substituting these expressions into formulas (8.46) and (8.47), we find that

$$\sigma_r + \sigma_\theta = S\left(1 - 2\frac{a^2}{r^2}\cos 2\theta\right)$$

$$\sigma_\theta - \sigma_r + 2i\tau_{r\theta} = S\left(2\frac{a^2}{r^2}e^{-i2\theta} - e^{i2\theta} + \frac{a^2}{r^2} - 3\frac{a^4}{r^4}e^{-i2\theta}\right)$$

Hence
$$\sigma_r = \frac{S}{2}\left(1 - \frac{a^2}{r^2}\right) + \frac{S}{2}\left(1 + 3\frac{a^4}{r^4} - 4\frac{a^2}{r^2}\right)\cos 2\theta$$

$$\sigma_\theta = \frac{S}{2}\left(1 + \frac{a^2}{r^2}\right) - \frac{S}{2}\left(1 + 3\frac{a^4}{r^4}\right)\cos 2\theta$$

$$\tau_{r\theta} = -\frac{S}{2}\left(1 + 2\frac{a^2}{r^2} - 3\frac{a^4}{r^4}\right)\sin 2\theta$$

These are precisely the stresses we obtained in Sec. 4.5.

Dropping the nonessential constants of integration c_1 and c_2 in formula (8.50) and separating the real and imaginary parts, we get

$$v_r = \frac{S(1+\nu)}{2Er}\left[\frac{1-\nu}{1+\nu}r^2 + a^2 + \left(\frac{4a^2}{1+\nu} + r^2 - \frac{a^4}{r^2}\right)\cos 2\theta\right]$$

$$v_\theta = -\frac{S(1+\nu)}{2Er}\left(\frac{1-\nu}{1+\nu}2a^2 + r^2 + \frac{a^4}{r^2}\right)\sin 2\theta$$

Problem 1. Using the method of this section, determine the stress distribution in a uniformly stressed infinite plane with a small circular hole in the middle. The boundary conditions in this case are

$$\sigma_x = \sigma_y = S \qquad \tau_{xy} = 0$$

at infinity and $\sigma_r = \tau_{r\theta} = 0$ at $r = a$.

Ans. $F'(z) = \dfrac{S}{2}$, $\chi''(z) = \dfrac{Sa^2}{2}$

$$\sigma_r = S\left(1 - \frac{a^2}{r^2}\right),\ \sigma_\theta = S\left(1 + \frac{a^2}{r^2}\right),\ \tau_{r\theta} = 0$$

$$v_r = \frac{S(1 + \nu)}{Er}\left(\frac{1 - \nu}{1 + \nu}r^2 + a^2\right),\ v_\theta = 0$$

Problem 2. Find the stress distribution in an infinite plate with a circular hole if there is a uniform normal pressure of magnitude p applied along the edge of the hole. The stresses at infinity are assumed to be zero. The boundary conditions are

$$\begin{aligned}\sigma_x = \sigma_y = \tau_{xy} = 0 &\qquad \text{at } r = \infty \\ \sigma_r = -p \qquad \tau_{r\theta} = 0 &\qquad \text{at } r = a\end{aligned}$$

Ans. $F'(z) = 0$, $\chi''(z) = \dfrac{pa^2}{z^2}$

$$\sigma_r = -\frac{pa^2}{r^2},\ \sigma_\theta = \frac{pa^2}{r^2},\ \tau_{r\theta} = 0$$

$$v_r = \frac{pa^2(1 + \nu)}{Er},\ v_\theta = 0$$

Problem 3. Find the stress distribution in an infinite plate with a circular hole if the pressure p applied along the hole varies according to the formula

$$\sigma_r = p_0 \cos \theta \qquad \text{for } -\alpha \leq \theta \leq \alpha$$

and

$$\sigma_r = p_0 \cos (\pi - \theta) \qquad \text{for } \pi - \alpha \leq \theta \leq \pi + \alpha$$

and the stresses at infinity are assumed to be zero.

8.8. An Infinite Plate under the Action of Concentrated Forces and Moments. The method described in the preceding section can also be used to determine the stress distribution in an infinite plate under concentrated forces and moments. We begin by considering the case of an infinite plate of thickness h with a circular hole of radius a. Assume that the distribution of stress over the boundary of the hole is given by

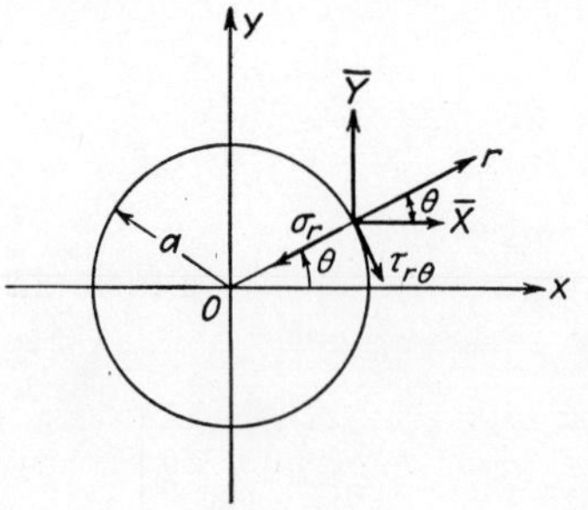

Fig. 8.10.

$$\bar{X} = \frac{P_x}{2\pi ah} \qquad \bar{Y} = \frac{P_y}{2\pi ah}$$

and the stresses at infinity are zero. P_x and P_y in the above expressions are constants and are the components of the resultant of external forces acting on the boundary of the hole. Observing that the positive normal N makes an angle $\theta + \pi$ with the positive direction of the x axis (Fig. 8.10), we have

$$(\sigma_r)_{r=a} = -\frac{1}{2\pi a h}(P_x \cos\theta + P_y \sin\theta)$$

$$(\tau_{r\theta})_{r=a} = -\frac{1}{2\pi a h}(-P_x \sin\theta + P_y \cos\theta)$$

Hence $$\sigma_r - i\tau_{r\theta} = -\frac{1}{2\pi a h}(P_x - iP_y)e^{i\theta}$$

on the circle. It follows from this equation that the nonvanishing coefficient in the expansion (8.53) is

$$C_1 = -\frac{1}{2\pi a h}(P_x - iP_y)$$

Let us assume that the stresses at infinity vanish. Then, we have

$$A_0 = B_0 = 0$$

From formulas (8.59) to (8.64), we find that

$$A_1 = -\frac{(1+\nu)(P_x + iP_y)}{8\pi h} \qquad A_n = 0 \text{ if } n \geq 2$$

$$B_1 = \frac{(3-\nu)(P_x - iP_y)}{8\pi h} \qquad B_2 = 0$$

$$B_3 = -a^2\frac{(1+\nu)(P_x + iP_y)}{4\pi h} \qquad B_n = 0 \text{ if } n \geq 4$$

Thus $$F'(z) = -\frac{(1+\nu)(P_x + iP_y)}{8\pi h}\frac{1}{z}$$

$$\chi''(z) = \frac{(3-\nu)(P_x - iP_y)}{8\pi h}\frac{1}{z} - \frac{(1+\nu)(P_x + iP_y)}{4\pi h}\frac{a^2}{z^3}$$

We now let the radius a of the hole tend to zero, at the same time allowing the components $\bar{X}$ and $\bar{Y}$ of the surface force to increase in such a way that the resultant force has always the same magnitude and direction. As a approaches zero, we find that the second term in $\chi''(z)$ approaches zero. Then

$$\chi''(z) = \frac{(3-\nu)(P_x - iP_y)}{8\pi h}\frac{1}{z}$$

Substituting these expressions of $F'(z)$ and $\chi''(z)$ into formulas (8.46) and (8.47), we have

$$\sigma_r + \sigma_\theta = -\frac{(1+\nu)(P_x \cos\theta + P_y \sin\theta)}{2\pi hr}$$

$$\sigma_\theta - \sigma_r + 2i\tau_{r\theta} = \frac{P_x \cos\theta + P_y \sin\theta}{\pi hr} + i\frac{(1-\nu)(P_x \sin\theta - P_y \cos\theta)}{2\pi hr}$$

Accordingly $$\sigma_r = -\frac{3+\nu}{4\pi h}\frac{P_x \cos\theta + P_y \sin\theta}{r}$$

$$\sigma_\theta = \frac{1-\nu}{4\pi h}\frac{P_x \cos\theta + P_y \sin\theta}{r} \qquad (8.66)$$

$$\tau_{r\theta} = \frac{1-\nu}{4\pi h}\frac{P_x \sin\theta - P_y \cos\theta}{r}$$

Formulas (8.66) give the distribution of stress due to a concentrated force applied at the origin of coordinates of an infinite plate.

Now let us find the stress distribution in an infinite plate due to a moment applied at the origin of the coordinates. In this case, we first consider the case of uniform tangential stress of magnitude T applied along the edge of a circular hole of radius a. Then at $r = a$

$$\sigma_r = 0 \qquad \tau_{r\theta} = T$$

We shall again assume that the stresses at infinity vanish, and therefore $A_0 = B_0 = 0$. Since

$$(\sigma_r - i\tau_{i\theta})_{r=a} = -iT$$

the coefficients in the Fourier expansion (8.52) all vanish except the constant term

$$C_0 = -iT$$

From formulas (8.59) to (8.64), we find

$$A_n = 0 \qquad \text{for all values of } n$$
$$B_n = 0 \qquad \text{for all values of } n \text{ except } n = 2$$
$$B_2 = -C_0a^2 = iTa^2$$

Now the moment of the external forces applied to the boundary of the hole is

$$M = -2\pi a^2 h T$$

Hence $\qquad B_2 = -\dfrac{iM}{2\pi h} \qquad$ and $\qquad F'(z) = 0, \; \chi''(z) = -\dfrac{iM}{2\pi h}\dfrac{1}{z^2}$

A simple calculation leads to

$$\sigma_r = \sigma_\theta = 0 \qquad \tau_{r\theta} = -\frac{M}{2\pi h r^2} \tag{8.67}$$

which gives the stress distribution in an infinite plate due to a couple of moment M acting uniformly about a hole of radius a. We observe that these formulas remain unchanged if we let the radius of the hole go to zero and increase T in such a way that the moment M remains constant. In this limiting case, the formulas (8.67) give the stress distribution in an infinite plate due to a concentrated couple of moment M acting at the origin of coordinates.

8.9. Circular Plate under Arbitrary Edge Thrust. General series solutions for circular boundary problems are very easily constructed. Since the stresses are finite and single-valued, the functions $F'(z)$ and $\chi''(z)$ are analytic and single-valued in the region $r \leq a$, where a is the radius of the circular plate. Thus we can write

$$F'(z) = \sum_{n=0}^{\infty} A_n z^n \qquad \chi''(z) = \sum_{n=0}^{\infty} B_n z^n \tag{8.68}$$

Suppose the circular plate is in equilibrium under the given edge loading

$$(\sigma_r - i\tau_{r\theta})_{r=a} = f(\theta) = \sum_{n=-\infty}^{\infty} C_n' e^{in\theta} \qquad (8.69)$$

where the complex Fourier coefficients C_n are given by the formula

$$C_n = \frac{1}{2\pi} \int_0^{2\pi} f(\theta) e^{-in\theta} \, d\theta \qquad (8.70)$$

Since the circular plate is in equilibrium, the stress resultants $F_x + iF_y$ and M around the boundary must vanish, and since

$$F_x + iF_y = \int_0^{2\pi} (\sigma_r + i\tau_{r\theta})_{r=a} e^{i\theta} a \, d\theta$$

$$M = \int_0^{2\pi} (\tau_{r\theta})_{r=a} a^2 \, d\theta$$

we have

$$C_{-1} = 0 \qquad \text{and} \qquad C_0 = \bar{C}_0$$

or C_0 is real.

Now changing the sign of i throughout the formula (8.69), substituting the resulting series and series (8.68) into Eq. (8.48), and noting that $z = ae^{i\theta}$ at $r = a$, we have

$$\sum_{-\infty}^{\infty} \bar{C}_n e^{-in\theta} = A_0 + \bar{A}_0 + \sum_{n=1}^{\infty} \bar{A}_n a^n e^{-in\theta} - \sum_{n=1}^{\infty} (n-1) A_n a^n e^{in\theta}$$

$$- \sum_{n=0}^{\infty} B_n a^n e^{i(n+2)\theta}$$

Comparing the coefficients of $e^{in\theta}$ on both sides of the above equation, we find that

$$\begin{aligned} A_0 + \bar{A}_0 &= C_0 \\ A_n &= C_n a^{-n} \qquad n = 1, 2, 3 \ldots \\ B_n &= -a^{-n}[(n+1)C_{n+2} + \bar{C}_{-(n+2)}] \qquad n = 0, 1, 2, 3 \ldots \end{aligned} \qquad (8.71)$$

As an example, let us consider a circular plate under edge pressure over equal and opposite arcs. In this case, we have

$$\sigma_r = -p \qquad \text{for } -\alpha \le \theta \le \alpha \text{ and } \pi - \alpha \le \theta \le \pi + \alpha$$

$$\tau_{r\theta} = 0 \qquad \text{for all values of } \theta$$

Then, from (8.70),

$$C_n = \frac{1}{2\pi} \left(\int_{-\alpha}^{\alpha} -pe^{-in\theta} \, d\theta + \int_{\pi-\alpha}^{\pi+\alpha} -pe^{-in\theta} \, d\theta \right)$$

or
$$C_0 = -\frac{2p\alpha}{\pi} \qquad C_{2n} = -\frac{p}{n\pi} \sin 2n\alpha \qquad C_{2n+1} = 0$$

Hence, we find from (8.71)

$$A_0 + \bar{A}_0 = -\frac{2p\alpha}{\pi}$$

$$A_{2n+1} = 0 \qquad B_{2n+1} = 0$$

$$A_{2n} = -\frac{p \sin 2n\alpha}{n\pi a^{2n}}$$

$$B_{2n} = \frac{2p \sin 2(n+1)\alpha}{\pi a^{2n}}$$

Since the imaginary part of A_0 does not affect the stresses, we may arbitrarily assign it the value zero. Then

$$F'(z) = -\frac{p}{\pi}\left(\alpha + \sum_{n=1}^{\infty} \frac{\sin 2n\alpha}{na^{2n}} z^{2n}\right) \qquad \chi''(z) = \frac{2p}{\pi}\sum_{n=0}^{\infty} \frac{\sin 2(n+1)\alpha}{a^{2n}} z^{2n}$$

Substituting these expressions into formulas (8.46) and (8.47), we obtain

$$\sigma_r + \sigma_\theta = -\frac{4p}{\pi}\left[\alpha + \sum_{n=1}^{\infty} \frac{\sin 2n\alpha}{n}\left(\frac{r}{a}\right)^{2n} \cos 2n\theta\right]$$

$$\sigma_\theta - \sigma_r + 2i\tau_{r\theta} = \frac{4p}{\pi}\sum_{n=0}^{\infty} \sin 2(n+1)\alpha \left(\frac{r}{a}\right)^{2n}\left(1 - \frac{r^2}{a^2}\right) e^{i2(n+1)\theta}$$

from which we find

$$\sigma_r = -\frac{2p}{\pi}\left[\alpha + \sum_{n=0}^{\infty}\left(\frac{r}{a}\right)^{2n}\left(1 - \frac{n}{n+1}\frac{r^2}{a^2}\right) \sin 2(n+1)\alpha \cos 2(n+1)\theta\right]$$

$$\sigma_\theta = -\frac{2p}{\pi}\left[\alpha + \sum_{n=0}^{\infty}\left(\frac{r}{a}\right)^{2n}\left(1 + \frac{n+2}{n+1}\frac{r^2}{a^2}\right) \sin 2(n+1)\alpha \cos 2(n+1)\theta\right]$$

$$\tau_{r\theta} = \frac{2p}{\pi}\sum_{n=0}^{\infty}\left(\frac{r}{a}\right)^{2n}\left(1 - \frac{r^2}{a^2}\right) \sin 2(n+1)\alpha \sin 2(n+1)\theta$$

8.10. Plates Bounded by Two Concentric Circles. Let us now consider a plate bounded by two concentric circles of outer radius b and inner radius a. We choose the origin of coordinates in the center of the circles and assume that the external forces are applied on the boundaries of the plate. The boundary conditions are then

$$(\sigma_r - i\tau_{r\theta})_{r=a} = f_1(\theta) = \sum_{n=-\infty}^{\infty} C_n e^{in\theta}$$

$$(\sigma_r - i\tau_{r\theta})_{r=b} = f_2(\theta) = \sum_{n=-\infty}^{\infty} C'_n e^{in\theta}$$

(8.72)

where the coefficients of the Fourier's series C_n and C'_n are given by the formulas

$$C_n = \frac{1}{2\pi} \int_0^{2\pi} f_1(\theta)e^{-in\theta} \, d\theta$$

$$C'_n = \frac{1}{2\pi} \int_0^{2\pi} f_2(\theta)e^{-in\theta} \, d\theta \qquad (8.73)$$

From formula (8.40), we find that the condition of single-valued stresses requires that the real part of $F'(z)$ be single-valued. Expressed in terms of complex series, $F'(z)$ must be of the following form:

$$F'(z) = A' \log z + \sum_{n=-\infty}^{\infty} A_n z^n \qquad (8.74)$$

From (8.41), we observe that the stresses are single-valued if $\chi''(z)$ is single-valued. Therefore, $\chi''(z)$ can be written in the form

$$\chi''(z) = \sum_{n=-\infty}^{\infty} B_n z^n \qquad (8.75)$$

If we integrate $F'(z)$ and $\chi''(z)$ as given by (8.74) and (8.75) and substitute the resulting expressions into (8.39), the condition that the components of displacement must be single-valued requires that

$$A' = 0 \qquad \text{and} \qquad (3 - \nu)A_{-1} + (1 - \nu)\bar{B}_{-1} = 0 \qquad (8.76)$$

Substituting the series (8.74) and (8.75) into formula (8.48), we obtain

$$\sum_{-\infty}^{\infty} [(1 - n)A_n - B_{n-2}a^{-2}]a^n e^{in\theta} + \sum_{-\infty}^{\infty} \bar{A}_n a^n e^{-in\theta} = \sum_{-\infty}^{\infty} C_n e^{-in\theta}$$

$$\sum_{-\infty}^{\infty} [(1 - n)A_n - B_{n-2}b^{-2}]b^n e^{in\theta} + \sum_{-\infty}^{\infty} \bar{A}_n b^n e^{-in\theta} = \sum_{-\infty}^{\infty} C'_n e^{in\theta}$$

where the condition $A' = 0$ has been used. Equating the coefficients of like powers of $e^{i\theta}$ on both sides of the above equations, we find that

$$\begin{aligned}
(A_0 + \bar{A}_0) - B_{-2}a^{-2} &= C_0 \\
(A_0 + \bar{A}_0) - B_{-2}b^{-2} &= C'_0 \\
(1 - n)A_n a^n - B_{n-2}a^{n-2} + \bar{A}_{-n}a^{-n} &= C_n \qquad n = \pm 1, \pm 2, \ldots \\
(1 - n)A_n b^n - B_{n-2}b^{n-2} + \bar{A}_{-n}b^{-n} &= C'_n \qquad n = \pm 1, \pm 2, \ldots
\end{aligned} \qquad (8.77)$$

Solving the first two of these equations, we get

$$A_0 + \bar{A}_0 = \frac{C'_0 b^2 - C_0 a^2}{b^2 - a^2} \qquad B_{-2} = \frac{(C'_0 - C_0)a^2 b^2}{b^2 - a^2} \qquad (8.78)$$

Since $A_0 + \bar{A}_0$ is real, $C_0' b^2 - C_0 a^2$ must also be real. This is true because a simple calculation shows that this requirement is equivalent to the condition that the resultant moment of all external forces vanishes. Since the addition of an imaginary constant to $F'(z)$ cannot affect the state of stress, we can assume that A_0 is real so that $A_0 = \bar{A}_0$.

If we let $n = 1$ in the third equation of (8.77), we obtain

$$\bar{A}_{-1} - B_{-1} = C_1 a$$

Forming the conjugate and solving it simultaneously with the second equation of (8.76), we get

$$A_{-1} = \frac{1 - \nu}{2 - \nu} \frac{\bar{C}_1 a}{2} \qquad B_{-1} = -\frac{3 - \nu}{2 - \nu} \frac{C_1 a}{2} \tag{8.79}$$

If we divide the third equation of (8.77) by $-a^{n-2}$ and the fourth by b^{n-2} and add, we obtain

$$(1 - n)(b^2 - a^2)A_n + [b^{-2(n-1)} - a^{-2(n-1)}]\bar{A}_{-n} = C_n' b^{-n+2} - C_n a^{-n+2} \tag{8.80}$$

Replacing n by $-n$ in (8.80) and forming the conjugate of the resulting expression, we obtain

$$(b^{2n+2} - a^{2n+2})A_n + (1 + n)(b^2 - a^2)\bar{A}_{-n} = \bar{C}_{-n}' b^{n+2} - \bar{C}_{-n} a^{n+2} \tag{8.81}$$

We can easily verify that the condition of the vanishing of the resultant of all forces applied to boundaries leads to

$$C_1' b - C_1 a = 0$$

For $n = 1$, we find that Eq. (8.80) is identically satisfied. Equation (8.81) gives

$$(b^4 - a^4)A_1 + 2(b^2 - a^2)\bar{A}_{-1} = \bar{C}_{-1}' b^3 - \bar{C}_{-1} a^3$$

Solving, we find that

$$A_1 = \frac{\bar{C}_{-1}' b^3 - \bar{C}_{-1} a^3}{b^4 - a^4} - \frac{1 - \nu}{2 - \nu} \frac{\bar{C}_1 a}{b^2 + a^2} \tag{8.82}$$

The remaining coefficients $A_n(n = \pm 2, \pm 3, \ldots)$ can be determined by solving the system of Eqs. (8.80) and (8.81). Hence

$$A_n = [(1 + n)(b^2 - a^2)(C_n' b^{-n+2} - C_n a^{-n+2})$$
$$- (b^{-2n+2} - a^{-2n+2})(\bar{C}_{-n}' b^{n+2} - \bar{C}_{-n} a^{n+2})]$$
$$/[(1 - n^2)(b^2 - a^2)^2 - (b^{2n+2} - a^{2n+2})(b^{-2n+2} - a^{-2n+2})] \tag{8.83}$$

The remaining coefficients B_n can now be determined from the third equation of (8.77). Thus

$$B_{n-2} = (1 - n)A_n a^2 + \bar{A}_{-n} a^{-2n+2} - C_n a^{-n+2} \tag{8.84}$$

As an example, let us consider the case of a thick cylinder subjected to uniform internal pressure p_i and external pressure p_o. In this case, we have

$$\sigma_r = -p_i \qquad \text{on } r = a$$
$$\sigma_r = -p_o \qquad \text{on } r = b$$
$$\tau_{r\theta} = 0 \qquad \text{on } r = a \text{ and } b$$

All coefficients in the Fourier's expansions (8.72) vanish except C_0 and C'_0, which are

$$C_0 = -p_i \qquad C'_0 = -p_o$$

The formulas (8.75) give

$$A_0 = -\frac{p_o b^2 - p_i a^2}{2(b^2 - a^2)} \qquad B_{-2} = \frac{(p_i - p_o)a^2 b^2}{b^2 - a^2}$$

and all remaining coefficients in (8.71) and (8.72) vanish. Hence

$$F'(z) = -\frac{p_o b^2 - p_i a^2}{2(b^2 - a^2)} \qquad \chi''(z) = \frac{(p_i - p_o)a^2 b^2}{b^2 - a^2} \frac{1}{z^2}$$

from which it follows that

$$\sigma_r = -\frac{p_o b^2 - p_i a^2}{b^2 - a^2} + \frac{(p_o - p_i)a^2 b^2}{b^2 - a^2} \frac{1}{r^2}$$
$$\sigma_\theta = -\frac{p_o b^2 - p_i a^2}{b^2 - a^2} - \frac{(p_o - p_i)a^2 b^2}{b^2 - a^2} \frac{1}{r^2}$$
$$\tau_{r\theta} = 0$$

The formulas check exactly with the ones we obtained in Sec. 4.4.

Problem 1. Verify that the conditions of vanishing resultant forces and moments on the boundaries are equivalent to

$$C'_1 b - C_1 a = 0 \qquad \text{and} \qquad C'_0 b^2 - C_0 a^2 = \text{real}$$

Problem 2. If the circular plate is subjected to a uniform edge pressure over equal and opposite arcs on the external boundary and zero pressure on the internal boundary, find the stress distribution in the plate. The boundary conditions in this case are

$$\sigma_r = -p \qquad \text{at } r = b \text{ and } -\alpha \le \theta \le \alpha \text{ and } \pi - \alpha \le \theta \le \pi + \alpha$$
$$\sigma_r = 0 \qquad \text{at } r = a$$
$$\tau_{r\theta} = 0 \qquad \text{at } r = a \text{ and } b$$

8.11. Elliptic Hole in a Plate under Simple Tension. Method of Conformal Transformation. In the preceding sections, a number of important problems were solved where the regions under consideration were bounded by circles. If the boundaries are not circular, the methods used in the preceding sections must be modified by the use of conformal transformation. Let us consider, as an example, the case of an elliptic hole in an infinite plate. The region outside the elliptic hole in the complex z plane can be mapped onto the region outside the unit circle in the complex ζ plane by the mapping function

$$z = f(\zeta) = c\left(\zeta + \frac{m}{\zeta}\right) \tag{8.85}$$

where $0 \leq m \leq 1$. It is easily checked that the boundary of the unit circle $|\zeta| = 1$ corresponds to the ellipse with center at the origin of the z plane and with semiaxes

$$a = c(1 + m) \qquad b = c(1 - m) \tag{8.86}$$

In terms of the major and minor axes, we have

$$c = \frac{a + b}{2} \qquad m = \frac{a - b}{a + b} \tag{8.87}$$

Let the major axis of the elliptic hole lie on the x axis and the uniform tensile stress S be inclined to the x axis by an angle β (Fig. 8.11). Let

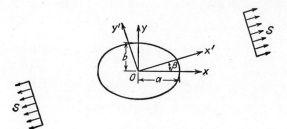

Fig. 8.11.

Ox', Oy' be cartesian axes obtained by rotating Ox through the angle β so as to bring it parallel to the direction of S. Then by Eqs. (1.15) and (1.17), we can easily verify that

$$\sigma_{x'} + \sigma_{y'} = \sigma_x + \sigma_y \qquad \sigma_{y'} - \sigma_{x'} + 2i\tau_{x'y'} = e^{2i\beta}(\sigma_y - \sigma_x + 2i\tau_{xy})$$

Since at infinity $\sigma_{x'} = S$, $\sigma_{y'} = \tau_{x'y'} = 0$, we have

$$\sigma_x + \sigma_y = S \qquad \sigma_y - \sigma_x + 2i\tau_{xy} = -Se^{-2i\beta} \qquad \text{at infinity}$$

and so, from formulas (8.40) and (8.42),

$$4\,\mathrm{Re}\,F'(z) = S \qquad 2[\bar{z}F''(z) + \chi''(z)] = -Se^{-2i\beta} \qquad \text{at infinity} \tag{8.88}$$

Since there is no external load applied at the boundary of the hole, the stress resultant acting at any point of the boundary must be zero. Therefore, on the elliptic hole, we have

$$F_x + iF_y = 0$$

or

$$F(z) + z\bar{F}'(\bar{z}) + \bar{\chi}'(\bar{z}) = 0 \tag{8.89}$$

With the aid of the mapping function $z = f(\zeta)$, we may express the functions $F(z)$ and $\chi(z)$ in terms of the variable ζ as follows:

$$F(z) = F[f(\zeta)] = F_1(\zeta) \qquad \chi(z) = \chi[f(\zeta)] = \chi_1(\zeta) \qquad (8.90)$$

Then
$$F'(z) = \frac{dF}{dz} = \frac{dF_1}{d\zeta}\frac{d\zeta}{dz} = \frac{F_1'(\zeta)}{f'(\zeta)}$$

$$\chi'(z) = \frac{d\chi}{dz} = \frac{d\chi_1}{d\zeta}\frac{d\zeta}{dz} = \frac{\chi_1'(\zeta)}{f'(\zeta)}$$

$$F''(z) = \frac{d}{d\zeta}\left[\frac{F_1'(\zeta)}{f'(\zeta)}\right]\frac{d\zeta}{dz} = \frac{F_1''(\zeta)f'(\zeta) - F_1'(\zeta)f''(\zeta)}{[f'(\zeta)]^3} \qquad (8.91)$$

$$\chi''(z) = \frac{d}{d\zeta}\left[\frac{\chi_1'(\zeta)}{f'(\zeta)}\right]\frac{d\zeta}{dz} = \frac{\chi_1''(\zeta)f'(\zeta) - \chi_1'(\zeta)f''(\zeta)}{[f'(\zeta)]^3}$$

Inserting these expressions in formulas (8.39), (8.40), (8.42), (8.43), and (8.44), we get

$$u + iv = \frac{3 - \nu}{E} F_1(\zeta) - \frac{1 + \nu}{E}\left[\frac{f(\zeta)}{f'(\zeta)}\bar{F}'(\bar{\zeta}) + \bar{\chi}'(\bar{\zeta})\right] \qquad (8.92)$$

$$\sigma_x + \sigma_y = 4\,\mathrm{Re}\,\frac{F_1'(\zeta)}{f'(\zeta)} \qquad (8.93)$$

$$\sigma_y - \sigma_x + 2i\tau_{xy} = \frac{2}{[f'(\zeta)]^3}[\bar{f}(\bar{\zeta})F_1''(\zeta)f'(\zeta) - \bar{f}(\bar{\zeta})F_1'(\zeta)f''(\zeta)$$
$$+ \chi_1''(\zeta)f'(\zeta) - \chi_1'(\zeta)f''(\zeta)] \qquad (8.94)$$

$$F_x + iF_y = -i\left[F_1(\zeta) + \frac{f(\zeta)}{\bar{f}'(\bar{\zeta})}\bar{F}_1'(\bar{\zeta}) + \frac{\bar{\chi}_1'(\bar{\zeta})}{\bar{f}'(\bar{\zeta})}\right]_A^B \qquad (8.95)$$

$$M = \mathrm{Re}\left[\chi_1(\zeta) - \frac{f(\zeta)}{f'(\zeta)}\chi_1'(\zeta) - \frac{f(\zeta)\bar{f}(\bar{\zeta})}{f'(\zeta)}F_1'(\zeta)\right]_A^B \qquad (8.96)$$

In order that the stresses be single-valued, the functions $F'(\zeta)$ and $\chi''(\zeta)$ must be of the form

$$F_1'(\zeta) = \sum_{n=0}^{\infty} A_n\zeta^{-n} \qquad \chi_1''(\zeta) = \sum_{n=0}^{\infty} B_n\zeta^{-n} \qquad (8.97)$$

From (8.89) and (8.95), we see that, on the circle $|\zeta| = 1$, we must have

$$\bar{f}'(\bar{\zeta})F_1(\zeta) + f(\zeta)\bar{F}_1'(\bar{\zeta}) + \bar{\chi}_1'(\bar{\zeta}) = 0$$

or, forming the conjugate,

$$f'(\zeta)\bar{F}_1(\bar{\zeta}) + \bar{f}(\bar{\zeta})F'(\zeta) + \chi_1'(\zeta) = 0 \qquad \text{at } |\zeta| = 1 \qquad (8.98)$$

Integrating (8.97), we obtain

$$F_1(\zeta) = A_0\zeta + A_1 \log \zeta + \sum_{n=2}^{\infty} \frac{A_n\zeta^{-n+1}}{-n+1} + A$$

$$\chi_1'(\zeta) = B_0\zeta + B_1 \log \zeta + \sum_{n=2}^{\infty} \frac{B_n\zeta^{-n+1}}{-n+1} + B \qquad (8.99)$$

where A and B are complex constants of integration. Substituting (8.99) in (8.92), we find that the components of displacement will be single-valued if

$$(3 - \nu)A_1 + (1 + \nu)\bar{B}_1 = 0 \tag{8.100}$$

The constants A, B and the real part of A_0 will give only rigid-body displacements, and they may be taken as zero. For $|\zeta| = 1$, we have

$$f'(\zeta) = c\left(1 - \frac{m}{\zeta^2}\right) = c(1 - me^{-i2\theta})$$

$$\bar{f}(\bar{\zeta}) = c\left(\bar{\zeta} + \frac{m}{\bar{\zeta}}\right) = c(e^{-i\theta} + me^{i\theta})$$

$$\bar{F}_1(\bar{\zeta}) = \bar{A}_0\bar{\zeta} + \bar{A}_1 \log \bar{\zeta} + \sum_{n=2}^{\infty} \frac{\bar{A}_n \bar{\zeta}^{-n+1}}{-n+1}$$

$$= \bar{A}_0 e^{-i\theta} - i\bar{A}_1\theta - \sum_{n=2}^{\infty} \frac{\bar{A}_n e^{i(n-1)\theta}}{n-1} \tag{8.101}$$

$$F_1'(\zeta) = \sum_{n=0}^{\infty} A_n e^{-in\theta}$$

$$\chi_1'(\zeta) = B_0 e^{i\theta} + iB_1\theta - \sum_{n=2}^{\infty} \frac{B_n e^{-i(n-1)\theta}}{n-1}$$

Substituting these expressions into (8.98), we obtain

$$c(1 - me^{-i2\theta})\left[\bar{A}_0 e^{-i\theta} - i\bar{A}_1\theta - \sum_{n=2}^{\infty} \frac{\bar{A}_n e^{i(n-1)\theta}}{n-1}\right]$$

$$+ c(e^{-i\theta} + me^{i\theta})\left(\sum_{n=0}^{\infty} A_n e^{-in\theta}\right) + B_0 e^{i\theta} + iB_1\theta - \sum_{n=2}^{\infty} \frac{B_n e^{-i(n-1)}}{n-1} = 0$$

Equating the coefficients of θ and $e^{in\theta}$ in the above equation, we get

$$c\bar{A}_1 + B_1 = 0$$

$$A_n = 0 \qquad \text{if } n \geq 3$$

$$-c\bar{A}_2 + \frac{cm}{3}\bar{A}_4 + cmA_0 + B_0 = 0$$

$$c\bar{A}_0 + cm\bar{A}_2 + cA_0 + mA_2 - B_2 = 0 \tag{8.102}$$

$$cA_1 + cmA_3 - \frac{B_3}{2} = 0$$

$$-cm\bar{A}_0 + cA_2 + cmA_4 - \frac{B_4}{3} = 0$$

$$B_n = 0 \qquad \text{if } n \geq 5$$

From the boundary conditions at infinity we find that

$$A_0 = \frac{cS}{4} \qquad B_0 = -\frac{c^2 S e^{-2i\beta}}{2}$$

Solving the first equation of (8.102) simultaneously with Eq. (8.100), we get

$$A_1 = B_1 = 0$$

The solution of the remaining equations in (8.102) gives

$$A_2 = \frac{cS}{4}(m - 2e^{2i\beta}) \qquad B_2 = \frac{c^2 S}{2}(1 + m^2 - 2m \cos 2\beta)$$

$$B_3 = 0 \qquad B_4 = -\frac{3cS}{2} e^{2i\beta}$$

Accordingly,

$$F'(\zeta) = \frac{cS}{4} + \frac{cS}{4}(m - 2e^{2i\beta})\zeta^{-2}$$

$$\chi''(\zeta) = -\frac{c^2 S}{2} e^{-2i\beta} + \frac{c^2 S}{2}(1 - m^2 - 2m \cos 2\beta)\zeta^{-2} - \frac{3cS}{2} e^{2i\beta}\zeta^{-4}$$

from which it follows that

$$
\begin{aligned}
\sigma_x + \sigma_y &= 4 \operatorname{Re} \frac{F'(\zeta)}{f'(\zeta)} \\
&= S[1 - m^2 - 2 \cos 2(\beta - \theta) + 2m \cos 2\theta \cos 2(\beta - \theta) \\
&\quad - 2m \sin 2\theta \sin 2(\beta - \theta)]/(1 + m^2 - 2m \cos 2\theta) \quad (8.103)
\end{aligned}
$$

The maximum stress occurs at the end of major axis ($\theta = 0$) when $\beta = \pi/2$. Since at that point $\sigma_x = 0$, we have

$$\sigma_{\max} = S \frac{1 - m^2 + 2 - 2m}{1 + m^2 - 2m} = S \frac{3 + m}{1 - m}$$

From (8.87) we have $m = (a - b)/(a + b)$. Hence

$$\sigma_{\max} = S\left(1 + 2\frac{a}{b}\right)$$

which becomes larger and larger as the ellipse is made more and more slender.

Problem 1. Determine the functions $F'(\zeta)$ and $\chi''(\zeta)$ when the infinite plate with elliptic hole is subjected to uniform tension. Verify that in this case the maximum stress, which occurs at the end of the major axis, is

$$\sigma_{\max} = \frac{2Sa}{b}$$

Problem 2. Instead of using formula (8.48), determine the functions $F'(z)$ and $\chi''(z)$ in the case of an infinite plate with circular hole subjected to simple tension at infinity by using formula (8.43) as was carried out in this section.

Problem 3. An infinite plate subjected to simple tension inclined to the x axis by an angle β at infinity is weakened by a curvilinear polygonal hole. The curvilinear polygonal hole in the z plane can be mapped onto a unit circle in the ζ plane by the mapping function

$$z = c(1 + m\zeta^{-n})$$

where c, m are real positive constants and $0 \leq m(n - 1) \leq 1$. Find the stress distribution in the plate.

CHAPTER 9

BENDING AND COMPRESSION OF BARS. ELASTIC STABILITY

9.1. Simple Bending of Prismatic Bars. When a bar is bent by two equal and opposite couples M (Fig. 9.1), the bar is said to be under *simple bending*. From experimental evidence, it is known that the only non-

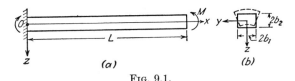

FIG. 9.1.

vanishing stress component in this case is σ_x and all the other stresses are zero. As a trial, let us assume therefore

$$\sigma_x = \sigma_x(x,y,z) \qquad \sigma_y = \sigma_z = \tau_{xy} = \tau_{yz} = \tau_{zx} = 0 \qquad (9.1)$$

where $\sigma_x(x,y,z)$ is an unknown function of x, y, and z. From Hooke's law, the strain components are then

$$\epsilon_x = \frac{\sigma_x}{E} \qquad \epsilon_y = \epsilon_z = -\frac{\nu\sigma_x}{E} \qquad \gamma_{xy} = \gamma_{yz} = \gamma_{zx} = 0$$

With these relations, we find that the equilibrium equations are identically satisfied if

$$\frac{\partial \sigma_x}{\partial x} = 0 \qquad (9.2)$$

This means that σ_x must be independent of x and is a function of y and z only. With (9.2), the compatibility equations reduce to

$$\frac{\partial^2 \sigma_x}{\partial y^2} = 0 \qquad (9.3)$$

$$\frac{\partial^2 \sigma_x}{\partial z^2} = 0 \qquad (9.4)$$

$$\frac{\partial^2 \sigma_x}{\partial y \, \partial z} = 0 \qquad (9.5)$$

Integrating Eq. (9.3), we obtain

$$\sigma_x = yf_1(z) + f_2(z) \qquad (9.6)$$

where $f_1(z)$ and $f_2(z)$ are unknown functions of z only. Substituting (9.6) into (9.5), we find that

$$\frac{df_1}{dz} = 0 \qquad \text{or} \qquad f_1(z) = C_1$$

where C_1 is a constant. Substitution of (9.6) into (9.4) results in

$$\frac{d^2f_2}{dz^2} = 0$$

which, upon integration, gives

$$f_2(z) = C_2 z + C_3$$

where C_2 and C_3 are constants. Hence

$$\sigma_x = C_1 y + C_2 z + C_3 \tag{9.7}$$

Let us take the origin of the coordinate system at the centroid of the cross section and the xz plane in the plane of the bending moment. Then, on any plane parallel to the yz plane, we must have

$$F_x = \iint\limits_A \sigma_x \, dA = 0 \quad M_y = \iint\limits_A \sigma_x z \, dA = M \quad M_z = \iint\limits_A \sigma_x y \, dA = 0 \tag{9.8}$$

where the integration is to be extended over the whole cross-sectional area A. Substituting (9.7) into (9.8) and integrating, the first condition requires that

$$C_3 = 0$$

and the last condition gives

$$C_1 I_z + C_2 I_{yz} = 0$$

where I_{yz} is the product of inertia and I_z is the moment of inertia of the cross section of the bar about the z axis. For symmetrical sections, $I_{yz} = 0$, and consequently $C_1 = 0$. From the second equation in (9.8), we find that

$$C_2 I_y = M \qquad \text{or} \qquad C_2 = \frac{M}{I_y}$$

Hence
$$\sigma_x = \frac{Mz}{I_y} \tag{9.9}$$

where I_y is the moment of inertia of the cross section of the bar about the y axis. This agrees with the simple bending formula derived in the strength of materials.

Let us now consider the displacements due to simple bending. From Eqs. (9.1) and (9.9) and the use of Hooke's law, we have

$$\frac{\partial u}{\partial x} = \frac{M}{EI_y} z \qquad (9.10)$$

$$\frac{\partial v}{\partial y} = -\frac{\nu M}{EI_y} z \qquad (9.11)$$

$$\frac{\partial w}{\partial z} = -\frac{\nu M}{EI_y} z \qquad (9.12)$$

$$\frac{\partial u}{\partial y} + \frac{\partial v}{\partial x} = \frac{\partial u}{\partial z} + \frac{\partial w}{\partial x} = \frac{\partial v}{\partial z} + \frac{\partial w}{\partial y} = 0 \qquad (9.13)$$

From Eq. (9.10), we obtain by a simple integration

$$u = \frac{M}{EI_y} xz + u_0(y,z)$$

where $u_0(y,z)$ is an unknown function of y and z. The first and second equations of (9.13) give

$$\frac{\partial v}{\partial x} = -\frac{\partial u}{\partial y} = -\frac{\partial u_0}{\partial y} \qquad \frac{\partial w}{\partial x} = -\frac{\partial u}{\partial z} = -\frac{M}{EI_y} x - \frac{\partial u_0}{\partial z}$$

from which
$$v = -\frac{\partial u_0}{\partial y} x + v_0(y,z)$$

$$w = -\frac{M}{EI_y} \frac{x^2}{2} - \frac{\partial u_0}{\partial z} x + w_0(y,z)$$

where $v_0(y,z)$ and $w_0(y,z)$ are unknown functions of y and z. Substituting these expressions into (9.11) and (9.12) and rearranging terms, we find

$$\frac{\partial^2 u_0}{\partial y^2} x = \frac{\partial v_0}{\partial y} + \frac{\nu M}{EI_y} z \qquad \frac{\partial^2 u_0}{\partial z^2} x = \frac{\partial w_0}{\partial z} + \frac{\nu M}{EI_y} z$$

Since the terms on the right-hand side of these equations are independent of x, we must have

$$\frac{\partial^2 u_0}{\partial y^2} = 0 \qquad \frac{\partial^2 u_0}{\partial z^2} = 0$$

and
$$\frac{\partial v_0}{\partial y} + \frac{\nu M}{EI_y} z = 0 \qquad \frac{\partial w_0}{\partial z} + \frac{\nu M}{EI_y} z = 0$$

Hence,
$$v_0 = -\frac{\nu M}{EI_y} yz + g_1(z) \qquad w_0 = -\frac{\nu M}{EI_y} \frac{z^2}{2} + g_2(y)$$

where $g_1(z)$ and $g_2(y)$ are functions of z and y, respectively. Thus, we obtain

$$v = -\frac{\partial u_0}{\partial y} x - \frac{\nu M}{EI_y} yz + g_1(z)$$

$$w = -\frac{M}{EI_y} \frac{x^2}{2} - \frac{\partial u_0}{\partial z} x - \frac{\nu M}{EI_y} \frac{z^2}{2} + g_2(y)$$

Substituting these expressions into the third equation of (9.13), *viz.*,

$$\frac{\partial v}{\partial z} + \frac{\partial w}{\partial y} = 0$$

we find

$$-2 \frac{\partial^2 u_0}{\partial y\, \partial z} x + \frac{dg_1(z)}{dz} + \frac{dg_2(y)}{dy} - \frac{\nu M}{EI_y} y = 0$$

Since the last three terms are independent of x, it follows that

$$\frac{\partial^2 u_0}{\partial y\, \partial z} = 0 \quad \text{and} \quad \frac{dg_2}{dy} - \frac{\nu M}{EI_y} y = - \frac{dg_1}{dz}$$

In this last equation, we observe that the terms on the left side are functions of y only and the term on the right side is a function of z only. A function of y can be equal to a function of z for all values of y and z only when both are equal to a constant, say a_1. The functions g_1, g_2, and u_0 are therefore to be determined from the equations

$$\frac{dg_1}{dz} = -a_1 \qquad \frac{dg_2}{dy} - \frac{\nu M}{EI_y} y = a_1$$

and

$$\frac{\partial^2 u_0}{\partial y^2} = 0 \qquad \frac{\partial^2 u_0}{\partial z^2} = 0 \qquad \frac{\partial^2 u_0}{\partial y\, \partial z} = 0$$

Comparing these with Eqs. (9.3) to (9.5), we find that

$$u_0 = a_2 y + a_3 z + a_4$$

By direct integration,

$$g_1 = -a_1 z + a_5 \qquad g_2 = \frac{\nu M}{EI_y} \frac{y^2}{2} + a_1 y + a_6$$

where a_2, a_3, a_4, a_5, and a_6 are constants of integration. The expressions for the displacements now become

$$u = \frac{M}{EI_y} xz + a_2 y + a_3 z + a_4$$

$$v = - \frac{\nu M}{EI_y} yz - a_2 x - a_1 z + a_5$$

$$w = - \frac{M}{2EI_y} (x^2 - \nu y^2 + \nu z^2) - a_3 x + a_1 y + a_6$$

To determine the constants of integration, let us assume that the centroid of the bar together with an element of the x axis and an element of the xz plane are fixed at the origin. Then at $x = y = z = 0$,

$$u = v = w = \frac{\partial v}{\partial x} = \frac{\partial v}{\partial z} = \frac{\partial w}{\partial x} = 0$$

from which we find that

$$a_1 = a_2 = a_3 = a_4 = a_5 = a_6 = 0$$

The displacements are therefore

$$u = \frac{M}{EI_y} xz \qquad v = - \frac{\nu M}{EI_y} yz \qquad w = - \frac{M}{2EI_y} (x^2 - \nu y^2 + \nu z^2) \quad (9.14)$$

In the plane $z = 0$, we find from (9.14) that $u = 0$ and $v = 0$. The plane $z = 0$ is therefore the neutral plane of the bar under bending. To find the deflection curve of the axis of the bar, let us consider a point on the axis, say $(x,0,0)$ before deformation. After bending, this point is displaced to (x',y',z'), where

$$x' = x + u = x \qquad y' = 0 + v = 0 \qquad z' = 0 + w = - \frac{M}{2EI_y} x^2$$

or

$$z' = - \frac{M}{2EI_y} x'^2$$

The deflection curve of the axis is thus a parabola with a radius of curvature R given by

$$\frac{1}{R} = \frac{d^2z'/dx'^2}{[1 + (dz'/dx')^2]^{3/2}} = - \frac{M/EI_y}{(1 + M^2x'^2/E^2I_y^2)^{3/2}} \cong - \frac{M}{EI_y} \quad (9.15)$$

if ML/EI_y is a small quantity. We once again obtain the Bernoulli-Euler's formula of the elementary theory of bending.

Consider a plane cross section of the bar before bending given by $x = C$. After deformation, points on this cross section will have the following new coordinates:

$$x' = C + u = C + \frac{M}{EI_y} zC = C \left(1 + \frac{M}{EI_y} z \right)$$

$$z' = z + w = z - \frac{M}{2EI_y} (C^2 - \nu y^2 + \nu z^2)$$

Combining these relations and neglecting terms containing higher degrees of M/EI_y, we obtain

$$x' \cong C \left(1 + \frac{M}{EI_y} z' \right)$$

That is, in pure bending, a plane cross section remains plane as assumed in the elementary theory. To examine the deformation of the cross section in its plane, consider the sides $y = \pm b_1$ (Fig. 9.1b). After bending, we have

$$y' = \pm b_1 + v = \pm b_1 \left(1 - \frac{\nu M}{EI_y} z\right) \cong \pm b_1 \left(1 - \frac{\nu M}{EI_y} z'\right)$$

The two sides remain straight but inclined to their original positions as shown in Fig. 9.1 by dotted lines. The other two sides $z \pm b_2$ of the cross section become after bending

$$z' = \pm b_2 + w = \pm b_2 - \frac{M}{2EI_y}[C^2 + \nu(b_2{}^2 - \nu y^2)]$$

$$\cong \pm b_2 - \frac{M}{2EI_y}[C^2 + \nu(b_2{}^2 - \nu y'^2)]$$

These sides are therefore bent into parabolic curves as shown in the figure.

Problem. Determine C_1, C_2, C_3 in Eq. (9.7) if the bending moment is applied in an oblique plane and the cross section of the bar is not symmetrical.

Ans. $\sigma_x = \dfrac{M_y I_z - M_z I_{zy}}{I_z I_y - I_{zy}{}^2} z + \dfrac{M_z I_y - M_y I_{zy}}{I_z I_y - I_{zy}{}^2} y$

9.2. Combined Bending and Compression of Prismatical Bars. Consider the case of a single lateral load acting on a compressed bar with simply supported, or hinged, ends (Fig. 9.2). By simply supported, or hinged, ends, we mean that these ends are so held that they are free to rotate but are unable to move in the z direction. Let us use the usual sign convention for the bending moment as given in strength of materials, *viz.*, a bending moment is positive if it produces a compressive stress in the top fiber of the beam. Thus, on the left of the load Q, the bending moment is

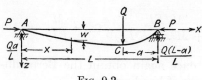

Fig. 9.2.

$$M = Pw + \frac{Qax}{L}$$

and, on the right side of the load Q,

$$M = Pw + \frac{Q(L - a)(L - x)}{L}$$

where L is the length of the bar, a is the distance of the load Q from the right support B, and w is the lateral deflection.

It can be shown that the Bernoulli-Euler formula

$$M = -\frac{EI}{R}$$

which we have shown to be valid in Secs. 4.2 and 9.1, is also valid in the present case.[1] In the above formula, I is the moment of inertia about the y axis. For small deflections, we have

$$\frac{1}{R} \cong \frac{d^2w}{dx^2} \quad \text{and} \quad M \cong -EI \frac{d^2w}{dx^2}$$

Therefore

$$EI \frac{d^2w}{dx^2} = -Pw - \frac{Qax}{L} \qquad \text{when } x \leq L - a \quad (9.16)$$

$$EI \frac{d^2w}{dx^2} = -Pw - \frac{Q(L-a)(L-x)}{L} \qquad \text{when } x \geq L - a \quad (9.17)$$

Introduce the notation

$$\frac{P}{EI} = k^2$$

Equation (9.16) becomes

$$\frac{d^2w}{dx^2} + k^2w = -\frac{Qa}{EIL} x$$

and the general solution is

$$w = C_1 \cos kx + C_2 \sin kx - \frac{Qa}{PL} x \qquad (9.18)$$

Similarly, the general solution of Eq. (9.17) is

$$w = C_3 \cos kx + C_4 \sin kx - \frac{Q(L-a)(L-x)}{PL} \qquad (9.19)$$

where C_1, C_2, C_3, C_4 are constants of integration to be determined by the boundary conditions.

At $x = 0$ and L, $w = 0$. We have, therefore,

$$C_1 = 0 \qquad \text{and} \qquad C_3 = -C_4 \tan kL$$

[1] The plus or minus used in the Bernoulli-Euler formula depends on the sign convention of M and the coordinate axes used. One way to establish the correct sign convention will be as follows: Assume that the beam is under positive bending moments. Draw the deflection curve due to these positive bending moments. If the curvature of the deflection curve is negative, the negative sign must be used in the Bernoulli-Euler formula. If the curvature is positive, the positive sign should be used. For example, in the present case, under the positive bending moments as defined, the deflection curve of the beam will be that shown in Fig. 9.2. For this deflection curve, we find the slope decreases as x increases and therefore the curvature is negative. Thus we must use the negative sign in the Bernoulli-Euler formula. On the other hand, if we choose the upward z axis as positive and use the same sign convention for M, we find the downward w becomes negative in this case and the slope becomes less negative or increases as x increases. $1/R$ is therefore positive, and the positive sign should be used in the Bernoulli-Euler formula.

At the point of application of the load Q, $x = L - a$, the two portions of the deflection curve, as given by Eqs. (9.18) and (9.19), must have the same deflection and slope. Then

$$C_2 \sin k(L - a) - \frac{Qa}{PL} (L - a) = C_4[\sin k(L - a)$$
$$- \tan kL \cos k(L - a)] - \frac{Qa}{PL} (L - a)$$

and

$$C_2 k \cos k(L - a) - \frac{Qa}{PL} = C_4 k[\cos k(L - a) + \tan kL \sin k(L - a)]$$
$$+ \frac{Q(L - a)}{PL}$$

Solving, we obtain

$$C_2 = \frac{Q \sin ka}{Pk \sin kL} \qquad C_4 = - \frac{Q \sin k(L - a)}{Pk \tan kL}$$

With these constants, the two portions of the deflection curve are

$$w = \frac{Q \sin ka}{Pk \sin kL} \sin kx - \frac{Qa}{PL} x \qquad \text{when } x \leq L - a$$
$$w = \frac{Q \sin k(L - a)}{Pk \sin kL} \sin k(L - x) - \frac{Q(L - a)(L - x)}{PL} \qquad \text{when } x \geq L - a$$

In the particular case of a load applied at the middle of the bar, the deflection curve is symmetrical, and the maximum deflection occurs at $x = L/2$. Substituting $x = L/2$ and $a = L/2$ into either of the above formulas, we find

$$w_{max} = \frac{Q \tan (kL/2)}{2Pk} - \frac{QL}{4P}$$

Since $P = k^2 EI$, the above expression can be written in the following form:

$$w_{max} = \frac{QL^3}{48EI} \frac{3[\tan (kL/2) - (kL/2)]}{(kL/2)^3} \tag{9.20}$$

With an increase of the axial load P, k increases. When $kL/2$ approaches the value of $\pi/2$, $\tan (kL/2)$ approaches infinity. That is, at $kL/2 = \pi/2$ or

$$P = \frac{\pi^2 EI}{L^2} \tag{9.21}$$

the deflection of the bar becomes infinite even though the lateral load Q is very small. The infinite deflection is due to the fact that an approximate formula for the curvature has been used. This formula is valid only when the deflection is small. However, the calculation does indicate that if a bar is under the action of a compressive load equal to that given by (9.21), no matter how small the lateral load is, the bar will have large deflections and will fail because of excessive bending. This limiting compressive load is called the *critical load*, or the *buckling load*. Since the buckling of columns was first discussed by Euler, buckling load is also called *Euler's load*. We shall discuss the significance of this load further in the next section.

9.3. Prismatic Bars under Axial Compression. Elastic Stability. When a perfectly straight bar is under the action of axial compression only, the bar is called a *column*. Let us consider a column which is hinged at both ends and is under a compressive load P passing through the centroid of the cross section. We shall now proceed to show that if the load P is less than the critical value, the column remains straight and undergoes only axial compression. This straight form of elastic equilibrium is *stable*, *i.e.*, if the column is displaced from this equilibrium form by an infinitesimal disturbance, say a small lateral force, the column will tend to come back to the straight form when the disturbance is removed. But if the load P is greater than the critical load, *two* equilibrium forms are possible.[1] The column may remain straight or may assume a bent form. We shall show that the straight form of equilibrium is *unstable* and the bent form of equilibrium becomes *stable*. At the critical load, the equilibrium is *neutral*. A body is said to be in unstable equilibrium if, when it is displaced from its equilibrium position by a small load, it will tend to displace still further when the load is removed. If the body will remain at the displaced position

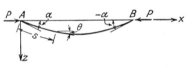

Fig. 9.3.

after the small load is removed, this body is said to be in neutral equilibrium.

Assume that the column is bent by a small disturbance. Taking the coordinate axes as shown in Fig. 9.3, the bending moment at any cross section mn is Pw and the differential equation of the deflection curve is

$$\frac{EI}{R} = -Pw$$

The exact expression of the curvature is

$$\frac{1}{R} = \frac{d\theta}{ds}$$

where s is the length of curve measured from the end A of the bent column and θ is the angle between the tangent to the curve and the x axis

---

[1] The uniqueness theorem as proved in Sec. 3.6 fails because the strain-displacement relation now becomes nonlinear. See Sec. 10.6.

as shown in Fig. 9.3. We have therefore

$$EI \frac{d\theta}{ds} + Pw = 0 \tag{9.22}$$

Differentiating Eq. (9.22) with respect to s and noting that

$$\frac{dw}{ds} = \sin \theta$$

we obtain

$$EI \frac{d^2\theta}{ds^2} + P \sin \theta = 0 \tag{9.23}$$

Multiplying both terms by $d\theta$ and noting that

$$\frac{d^2\theta}{ds^2} d\theta = \frac{d(d\theta/ds)}{ds} d\theta = d\left(\frac{d\theta}{ds}\right) \frac{d\theta}{ds}$$

Eq. (9.23) becomes, upon integration,

$$EI \int \frac{d\theta}{ds} d\left(\frac{d\theta}{ds}\right) + P \int \sin \theta \, d\theta = C$$

where C is a constant of integration. Then,

$$\frac{EI}{2} \left(\frac{d\theta}{ds}\right)^2 - P \cos \theta = C$$

At the end A, $\theta = \alpha$, and $M = EI(d\theta/ds) = 0$. C is therefore equal to $-P \cos \alpha$. Let $k^2 = P/EI$; then we have

$$\frac{1}{\sqrt{2}} \frac{d\theta}{ds} = \pm k \sqrt{\cos \theta - \cos \alpha}$$

Now as s increases, θ decreases. $d\theta/ds$ is therefore negative, and the minus sign should be chosen for the above radical. Then,

$$ds = - \frac{d\theta}{k \sqrt{2} \sqrt{\cos \theta - \cos \alpha}}$$

The total length of the column is given by the integration of ds.

$$L = \int ds = - \int_{\alpha}^{-\alpha} \frac{d\theta}{k \sqrt{2} \sqrt{\cos \theta - \cos \alpha}}$$

$$= \int_{-\alpha}^{\alpha} \frac{d\theta}{k \sqrt{2} \sqrt{\cos \theta - \cos \alpha}}$$

$$= \frac{1}{2k} \int_{-\alpha}^{\alpha} \frac{d\theta}{\sqrt{\sin^2 (\alpha/2) - \sin^2 (\theta/2)}}$$

Denoting sin $(\alpha/2)$ by p and introducing a new variable ϕ such that

$$\sin \frac{\theta}{2} = p \sin \phi$$

as θ varies from $-\alpha$ to $+\alpha$, $\sin \phi$ varies from -1 to $+1$ and ϕ from $-\pi/2$ to $\pi/2$. In terms of ϕ,

$$d\theta = \frac{2p \cos \phi\, d\phi}{\sqrt{1 - p^2 \sin^2 \phi}}$$

and

$$L = \frac{2}{k} \int_0^{\pi/2} \frac{d\phi}{\sqrt{1 - p^2 \sin^2 \phi}} = \frac{2K}{k} \qquad (9.24)$$

where $K = \int_0^{\pi/2} d\theta / \sqrt{1 - p^2 \sin^2 \phi}$ is called the complete elliptic integral of the first kind. For various values of p, K can be found in tabulated form.[1]

When the deflection is very small, α and therefore p are small and $p^2 \sin^2 \phi$ can be neglected in comparison with 1 in the above expression. In such a case,

$$L = \frac{2}{k} \int_0^{\pi/2} d\phi = \frac{\pi}{k} = \pi \sqrt{\frac{EI}{P}}$$

and we obtain

$$P = \frac{\pi^2 EI}{L^2}$$

which is the critical load for the column.

Let us now calculate the deflection at the mid-length of the column (*i.e.*, at $\theta = 0$). Since $dw = ds \sin \theta$, we have

$$\delta = \frac{1}{2k} \int_0^\alpha \frac{\sin \theta\, d\theta}{\sqrt{\sin^2 (\alpha/2) - \sin^2 (\theta/2)}}$$

In terms of ϕ, we find that

$$\delta = \frac{2p}{k} \int_0^{\pi/2} \sin \phi\, d\phi = \frac{2p}{k} \qquad (9.25)$$

For various values of α or p, we find from the table of elliptical integrals the values of K. From Eq. (9.24)

$$\frac{P}{P_{cr}} = \frac{PL^2}{\pi^2 EI} = \frac{4K^2}{\pi^2}$$

[1] Condensed tables of K can be found in "A Short Table of Integrals" by B. O. Peirce, p. 121, Ginn & Company, Boston, 1929.

and from (9.25) the maximum deflection δ/L is

$$\frac{\delta}{L} = \frac{2p}{\pi \sqrt{P/P_{cr}}}$$

The coordinate x_B can be calculated as follows:

$$x_B = \int dx = \int \cos\theta \, ds$$

$$= \frac{1}{2k} \int_{-\alpha}^{\alpha} \frac{\cos\theta \, d\theta}{\sqrt{\sin^2(\alpha/2) - \sin^2(\theta/2)}}$$

$$= \frac{2}{k} \int_0^{\pi/2} \frac{(1 - 2p^2 \sin^2\phi) \, d\phi}{\sqrt{1 - p^2 \sin^2\phi}}$$

Since $1 - 2p^2 \sin^2\phi = 2(1 - p^2 \sin^2\phi) - 1$, we find that

$$x_B = \frac{4}{k} \int_0^{\pi/2} \sqrt{1 - p^2 \sin^2\phi} \, d\phi - \frac{2}{k} \int_0^{\pi/2} \frac{d\phi}{\sqrt{1 - p^2 \sin^2\phi}}$$

$$= \frac{2(2\bar{E} - K)}{k}$$

or

$$\frac{x_B}{L} = 2\frac{\bar{E}}{K} - 1$$

where $\bar{E}$ is called the complete elliptic integral of the second kind.

For various values of α, the corresponding values of P/P_{cr}, x_B/L, and δ/L are computed in Table 9.1.

TABLE 9.1

α	20°	40°	60°	80°	100°	120°	140°	160°	176°
P/P_{cr}	1.015	1.063	1.152	1.293	1.518	1.884	2.541	4.029	9.116
x_B/L	0.970	0.881	0.741	0.560	0.349	0.123	−0.107	−0.340	−0.577
δ/L	0.110	0.211	0.296	0.359	0.396	0.402	0.375	0.313	0.211
M	0.112	0.224	0.341	0.464	0.601	0.757	0.953	1.261	1.923

Now let us examine the stability of the various equilibrium forms. The bending moment at the middle point of the column required for the column to be in equilibrium is $P\delta$. In nondimensional form, we have

$$M = \frac{P}{P_{cr}} \frac{\delta}{L} = \frac{4Kp}{\pi^2}$$

For various values of α, the nondimensional moment M can be computed and is given in Table 9.1. M is plotted vs. δ/L in Fig. 9.4. Assume that a compressive load P' is acting on the column and the column has a certain maximum deflection δ, where P' and δ may not be the corresponding equilibrium load and deflection. The nondimensional maximum bending moment in this case is then

$$M' = \frac{P'}{P_{cr}} \frac{\delta}{L}$$

Since P' does not depend on δ, the M' vs. δ/L curves are straight lines. The column is in equilibrium if

$$M = M'$$

i.e., when the M vs. δ/L curve intersects with the M' vs. δ/L curve. We see from Fig. 9.4 that when $P' < P_{cr}$, these curves intersect only at one point, viz., at the origin. The column therefore has only one possible

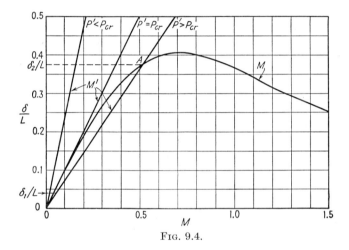

FIG. 9.4.

equilibrium form, i.e., the equilibrium form in which $\delta/L = 0$, or the straight form. When $P' > P_{cr}$, there are two points of intersection; one point corresponds to $\delta/L = 0$ and the other point with δ/L equal to some value different from zero. The column thus has two possible equilibrium forms, one straight form and one bent form.

Now at $\delta = 0$, let us assume that the column is displaced from the equilibrium form by a small disturbance and has now a deflection δ_1. If $P' < P_{cr}$, we see immediately from the curve that $M > M'$. This indicates that the bending moment due to P' is insufficient to maintain the column in this bent form and the column will return to its original straight form when the disturbance is removed. When $P' < P_{cr}$, the straight form of equilibrium is therefore stable. If $P' > P_{cr}$, then $M < M'$. Thus M' will bend the column still further and cause a larger deflection. This indicates that if $P' > P_{cr}$, the straight form of equilibrium is unstable. The column, after being displaced from the straight form, will continue to bend until δ/L reaches the value where M and M' intersect again. At this point (point A in Fig. 9.4) if the column is displaced from the equilibrium position so that its maximum deflection will have a value greater than δ_2/L, we see that $M > M'$ and the column will come back to the equilibrium position denoted by A. Or if the column is disturbed so that its maximum deflection is less than δ_2/L, M then becomes less than M' and the column will bend still further and come back to its equilibrium position A. This bent form of equilibrium is therefore stable. At $P' = P_{cr}$, the M' vs. δ/L curve is tangent to the M vs. δ/L curve at the origin. Therefore, if the disturbance is infinitesimally small, the column will remain in equilibrium at the displaced position. The column is therefore in *neutral equilibrium*.[1]

The load-deflection curve of the column is plotted in Fig. 9.5 from the values in Table 9.1. It is clearly seen that at a given load P the column

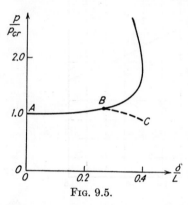

FIG. 9.5.

has one equilibrium form ($\delta/L = 0$) when $P/P_{cr} < 1$ and two equilibrium forms when $P/P_{cr} > 1$. If we assume the deflection to be very small, we obtain the same critical load which gives the bifurcation point of the P/P_{cr} vs. δ/L curve. It is to be noted that, in the previous discussion, we have assumed that the material remains elastic as the load increases. At some point B in Fig. 9.5, the combined compressive and bending stress reaches the elastic limit at the extreme fiber. Beyond this point, the resistance of the column decreases rapidly and the load-deflection curve will now follow the dotted line BC. Thus the maximum compressive load an ideal column will sustain is the load corresponding to that at point B and is slightly higher than the buckling, or critical, load P_{cr}. We shall show later that the maximum compressive load an actual column can carry is also approximately equal to P_{cr}. The actual determination of this maximum load requires tedious computation, while the calculation of the buckling load can be made relatively simple. Thus, in designing a column, we shall take the buckling load as the maximum load a column can carry.

9.4. Buckling Loads for Columns with Constant Cross Sections. In the previous section it was shown that if only the buckling load is to be determined, the calculation can be greatly simplified by assuming the deflection to be small and using the approximate formula for curvature.

---

[1] See F. L. Ryder, A Rational Explanation of Column Behavior, *Trans. ASCE*, Vol. 113, pp. 40–78, 1948.

We shall now make use of simplification and calculate the buckling loads of columns with constant cross section under various end conditions. Using the approximate formula for the curvature,

$$\frac{1}{R} = \frac{d^2w}{dx^2}$$

Eq. (9.22) becomes

$$EI \frac{d^2w}{dx^2} + Pw = 0 \tag{9.26}$$

for a column with both ends hinged. This equation follows from the condition that the sum of the bending moments at any section is zero. It assumes this simple form because there happen to be in this case no moments and shearing forces acting at the end supports. For other end conditions, there will be in general an unknown shear and bending moment acting at the end support, and the equilibrium equation will be of the following form,

$$EI \frac{d^2w}{dx^2} + Pw = Qx + M_0 \tag{9.27}$$

where Q is the shear force and M_0 is the bending moment at the end of the column. Differentiating Eq. (9.27) with respect to x, we obtain

$$\frac{d}{dx}\left(EI \frac{d^2w}{dx^2}\right) + P\frac{dw}{dx} = Q$$

Upon further differentiation, we have

$$\frac{d^2}{dx^2}\left(EI \frac{d^2w}{dx^2}\right) + P\frac{d^2w}{dx^2} = 0 \tag{9.28}$$

which is the differential equation of equilibrium for a column with any boundary conditions. Equation (9.28) expresses the condition that the sum of shear forces on an element of the column is zero.

For columns with constant cross sections made of homogeneous material, EI is independent of x and Eq. (9.28) reduces to

$$\frac{d^4w}{dx^4} + k^2 \frac{d^2w}{dx^2} = 0 \tag{9.29}$$

where, as defined before, $k^2 = P/EI$. Equation (9.29) is an ordinary differential equation with constant coefficients, and its solution is well known. The general solution is

$$w = C_1 \sin kx + C_2 \cos kx + C_3 x + C_4 \tag{9.30}$$

where C_1, C_2, C_3, and C_4 are constants.

Let us now consider columns with various boundary conditions.

Case 1.   *Column with Both Ends Hinged.*   In the case of a column with both ends hinged (Fig. 9.6a), the boundary conditions are that the deflection and the bending moment are zero at both ends.   We have, therefore,

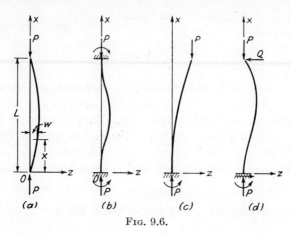

Fig. 9.6.

$w = 0$ and $d^2w/dx^2 = 0$ at $x = 0$ and $x = L$.   Thus, from (9.30), we find that

$$C_2 + C_4 = 0 \qquad C_1 \sin kL + C_2 \cos kL + C_3 L + C_4 = 0$$
$$C_2 = 0 \qquad -C_1 k^2 \sin kL - C_2 k^2 \cos kL = 0$$

Solving, we have

$$C_2 = 0 \qquad C_4 = 0 \qquad C_3 = 0 \qquad C_1 \sin kL = 0$$

The last condition requires that either $C_1 = 0$ or $\sin kL = 0$.   When $C_1 = 0$, w is identically zero.   This means that the unbent form of the column is a possible equilibrium form.   If C_1 is not zero, we must have

$$\sin kL = 0$$

from which $\qquad kL = n\pi \qquad n = 1, 2, 3, \ldots$

or $$P_n = \frac{n^2\pi^2 EI}{L^2} \qquad (9.31)$$

This means that if P_n is equal to the value given by (9.31), it is possible for the column to have an equilibrium form with deflection other than zero.   In other words, the bent form of equilibrium is possible only if P_n is equal to the value given by (9.31).   The smallest value of P_n occurs at $n = 1$; we have thus

$$P_{cr} = \frac{\pi^2 EI}{L^2}$$

The deflection curve is thus

$$w = C_1 \sin \frac{\pi x}{L}$$

The magnitude of the deflection depends on the value of C_1, which cannot be determined by the approximate theory and can be calculated only when the exact formula of curvature is used. The solution $C_n = 0$ $(n = 1,2,3,4)$ is called a *trivial solution*. The problem of determining the values of k leading to a nontrivial solution, *i.e.*, a solution where $C_n \neq 0$, is sometimes called an *eigenvalue problem*. Thus we see that, by using the approximate formula for the curvature, our problem reduces to the determination of the smallest load at which a bent form of equilibrium becomes possible.

Case 2. Column with Both Ends Built In. The boundary conditions for such a column (Fig. 9.6*b*) are $w = 0$ and $dw/dx = 0$ at $x = 0$ and L. Combining with (9.30), these conditions become

$$C_2 + C_4 = 0 \qquad C_1 \sin kL + C_2 \cos kL + C_3 L + C_4 = 0$$

$$kC_1 + C_3 = 0 \qquad kC_1 \cos kL - kC_2 \sin kL + C_3 = 0$$

Solving, we obtain

$$C_4 = -C_2 \qquad C_3 = -kC_1$$
$$C_1(\sin kL - kL) + C_2(\cos kL - 1) = 0$$
$$C_1(\cos kL - 1) - C_2 \sin kL = 0$$

Eliminating C_1 from the last two equations, we have

$$C_2[(\cos kL - 1)^2 + \sin kL(\sin kL - kL)] = 0$$

which, after simplification, gives

$$C_2 \sin \frac{kL}{2} \left(\sin \frac{kL}{2} - \frac{kL}{2} \cos \frac{kL}{2} \right) = 0$$

To find the nontrivial solution, we have either

$$\sin \frac{kL}{2} = 0 \qquad \text{or} \qquad \sin \frac{kL}{2} - \frac{kL}{2} \cos \frac{kL}{2} = 0$$

If $\sin (kL/2) = 0$, we have

$$\frac{kL}{2} = n\pi \qquad n = 1, 2, \ldots$$

and

$$P_n = \frac{4n^2\pi^2 EI}{L^2}$$

The smallest load is, when $n = 1$,

$$P_1 = \frac{4\pi^2 EI}{L^2}$$

Now, let us examine the equation

$$\sin \frac{kL}{2} - \frac{kL}{2} \cos \frac{kL}{2} = 0$$

which can be written as

$$\tan \phi - \phi = 0 \tag{9.32}$$

where $\phi = kL/2$. This equation can be solved by a graphical method as follows: First $\tan \phi$ is plotted vs. ϕ as shown in Fig. 9.7. The solutions of

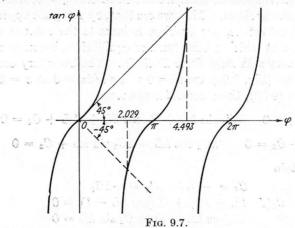

Fig. 9.7.

(9.32) will then lie on the 45° line where $\tan \phi = \phi$. The smallest root is found to be

$$\phi = \frac{kL}{2} = 4.493$$

which corresponds to

$$P = \frac{80.64EI}{L^2}$$

As this P is larger than P_1, we conclude that the critical load in this case is equal to P_1, that is,

$$P_{cr} = \frac{4\pi^2 EI}{L^2}$$

With $\sin (kL/2) = 0$, we find that $C_1 = 0$, and the deflection curve is therefore

$$w = C_2\left(1 - \cos \frac{2\pi x}{L}\right)$$

where C_2 is undetermined.

Case 3. *Columns with One End Built In and the Other End Free.* The boundary conditions in this case (Fig. 9.6c) are that, at the built-in end, $x = 0$, $w = 0$, and $dw/dx = 0$; and, at the free end, $x = L$, $d^2w/dx^2 = 0$, and $(d^3w/dx^3) + k^2(dw/dx) = 0$, where the last equation expresses the condition that the shear force at the free end is zero. Combining with (9.30), we have

$$C_2 + C_4 = 0 \qquad C_1k + C_3 = 0$$
$$C_1 \sin kL + C_2 \cos kL = 0 \qquad C_3 = 0$$

Solving, we find that

$$C_1 = C_3 = 0 \qquad C_4 = -C_2 \qquad C_2 \cos kL = 0$$

The last condition requires either $C_2 = 0$, which gives the trivial solution, or $\cos kL = 0$, which gives

$$kL = (2n + 1)\frac{\pi}{2} \qquad n = 0, 1, \ldots$$

or

$$P_n = \frac{(2n + 1)^2\pi^2EI}{4L^2}$$

The minimum P occurs at $n = 0$ and is

$$P_{cr} = \frac{\pi^2EI}{4L^2}$$

The deflection curve of the column is then

$$w = C_2\left(1 - \cos\frac{\pi x}{2L}\right)$$

Case 4. *Columns with One End Built In and the Other End Hinged.* The boundary conditions in this case (Fig. 9.6d) are that, at $x = 0$, $w = 0$ and $dw/dx = 0$; and, at $x = L$, $w = 0$ and $d^2w/dx^2 = 0$. Substituting (9.30) into these conditions, we obtain

$$C_2 + C_4 = 0 \qquad C_1k + C_3 = 0$$
$$C_1 \sin kL + C_2 \cos kL + C_3L + C_4 = 0 \qquad C_1 \sin kL + C_2 \cos kL = 0$$

Solving, we have

$$C_2 = -C_1kL \qquad C_3 = -C_1k$$
$$C_4 = C_1kL \qquad C_1(\sin kL - kL \cos kL) = 0$$

The last condition gives either the trivial solution $C_1 = 0$ or

$$\sin kL - kL \cos kL = 0$$

from which k is to be determined. This equation can again be written in the form of (9.32), viz.,

$$\tan \phi - \phi = 0$$

where $\phi = kL$. The smallest root is

$$kL = 4.493$$

which gives

$$P_{cr} = \frac{20.16EI}{L^2}$$

The deflection curve is then

$$w = C_1[\sin kx - kL \cos kx + k(L - x)]$$

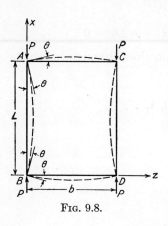

FIG. 9.8.

9.5. Buckling of Frames. Columns with Both Ends Elastically Supported. Consider the buckling of a symmetrical frame as shown in Fig. 9.8. Let us assume that the joints are rigid, *i.e.*, they are capable of resisting bending moments and will preserve the angles between various members. Let us also assume that the joints are not to move laterally. The boundary conditions for the column AB are then, at $x = 0$, $w = 0$ and $dw/dx = \theta$; and, at $x = L$, $w = 0$ and $dw/dx = -\theta$. We have therefore, from (9.30),

$$C_2 + C_4 = 0 \qquad C_1k + C_3 = \theta$$
$$C_1 \sin kL + C_2 \cos kL + C_3L + C_4 = 0$$
$$C_1k \cos kL - C_2k \sin kL + C_3 = -\theta$$

Solving, we find that

$$C_2 = \frac{1 + \cos kL}{\sin kL} C_1 \qquad C_3 = 0$$

$$C_4 = -\frac{1 + \cos kL}{\sin kL} C_1 \qquad \theta = kC_1$$

Hence

$$w = C_1 \left[\sin kx + \frac{1 + \cos kL}{\sin kL} (\cos kx - 1) \right]$$

The moment acting on the end A of the member AB is then

$$M_1 = \left(-EI \frac{d^2w}{dx^2} \right)_{x=L} = EIk^2C_1 \left(\sin kL + \frac{1 + \cos kL}{\sin kL} \cos kL \right)$$

Let us now consider the deflection of the member AC under the end moments M_1. Referring to the coordinates as shown in Fig. 9.9, the equilibrium equation is

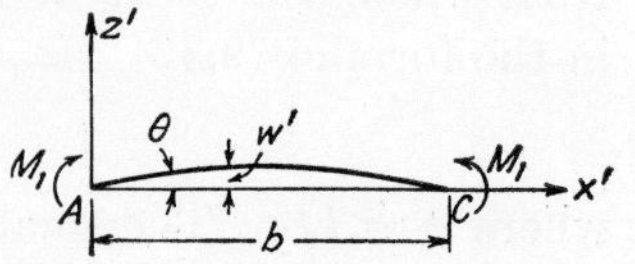

$$EI_1 \frac{d^2w'}{dx'^2} = M_1$$

FIG. 9.9.

which gives after integration

$$w' = \frac{M_1}{EI_1} \frac{x'^2}{2} + C_5 x' + C_6$$

From the boundary conditions that $w' = 0$, $dw'/dx' = \theta$ at $x' = 0$ and $w' = 0$, $dw'/dx' = -\theta$ at $x' = b$, we obtain

$$C_6 = 0 \qquad C_5 = \theta$$

$$\frac{M_1}{EI_1} \frac{b^2}{2} + C_5 b + C_6 = 0 \qquad \frac{M_1}{EI_1} b + C_5 = -\theta$$

Solving, we have

$$\theta = -\frac{M_1 b}{2EI_1}$$

Substituting the relations $\theta = kC_1$ and

$$M_1 = EIk^2 C_1 \left(\sin kL + \frac{1 + \cos kL}{\sin kL} \cos kL \right)$$

into the above equation and simplifying, we obtain

$$C_1 \left(\tan \frac{kL}{2} + \frac{Ib}{I_1 L} \frac{kL}{2} \right) = 0$$

To find the nontrivial solution, we let

$$\tan \frac{kL}{2} + \frac{Ib}{I_1 L} \frac{kL}{2} = 0$$

from which k and P_{cr} can be determined. In the case of a square frame with equal members, $b = L$ and $I = I_1$, we have

$$\tan \frac{kL}{2} + \frac{kL}{2} = 0 \tag{9.33}$$

This equation can be solved in a similar manner to Eq. (9.32). If we plot $\tan \phi$ vs. ϕ, the values of ϕ when $\tan \phi = -\phi$ are given by the points of intersection of the curve $\tan \phi$ and a $-45°$ line as shown by the dotted line in Fig. 9.7. The smallest root in this case is

$$\phi = \frac{kL}{2} = 2.029$$

which gives

$$P_{cr} = \frac{16.47 EI}{L^2}$$

9.6. Buckling of Columns with Variable Cross Sections. It can be shown that a column with constant cross section is not the most economical form of structure to carry compressive loads. To obtain a more efficient design, we must use columns with variable cross sections. In such cases, however, the solution of the differential equation often becomes very difficult. In this section we shall show how some of the problems can be solved.

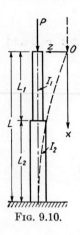

FIG. 9.10.

As a first example, let us consider the column as shown in Fig. 9.10. The column consists of two portions, each with a constant cross section. Let I_1 and I_2 be the moments of inertia of the cross sections for the thinner and thicker portions of the column, respectively. The column is assumed to be built in at one end and free at the other end. If we take the coordinate axes as shown in the figure, the equations of equilibrium are

$$EI_1 \frac{d^2w_1}{dx^2} + Pw_1 = 0 \qquad \text{when } 0 \leq x \leq L_1$$

$$EI_2 \frac{d^2w_2}{dx^2} + Pw_2 = 0 \qquad \text{when } L_1 \leq x \leq L$$

Let $k_1{}^2 = P/EI_1$ and $k_2{}^2 = P/EI_2$. The solutions of these equations are

$$w_1 = C_1 \sin k_1x + C_2 \cos k_1x \qquad \text{when } 0 \leq x \leq L_1$$
$$w_2 = C_3 \sin k_2x + C_4 \cos k_2x \qquad \text{when } L_1 \leq x \leq L$$

where C_1, C_2, C_3, C_4 are constants of integration. The boundary conditions are that $w_1 = 0$ at $x = 0$ and $dw_2/dx = 0$ at $x = L$. From these boundary conditions, we find that

$$C_2 = 0 \qquad C_3 = C_4 \tan k_2L$$

At $x = L_1$, we must have $w_1 = w_2$ and $dw_1/dx = dw_2/dx$. Thus

$$C_1 \sin k_1L_1 = C_4(\tan k_2L \sin k_2L_1 + \cos k_2L_1)$$
and $\qquad C_1k_1 \cos k_1L_1 = C_4k_2(\tan k_2L \cos k_2L_1 - \sin k_2L_1)$

Solving, we have

$$C_1 = C_4\left(\tan k_2L \frac{\sin k_2L_1}{\sin k_1L_1} + \frac{\cos k_2L_1}{\sin k_1L_1}\right)$$

and

$$C_4\left[(\tan k_2L \tan k_2L_1 + 1) - \frac{k_2}{k_1}\tan k_1L_1(\tan k_2L - \tan k_2L_1)\right] = 0$$

The last equation gives us the trivial solution $C_4 = 0$, or

$$(\tan k_2L \tan k_2L_1 + 1) - \frac{k_2}{k_1} \tan k_1L_1(\tan k_2L - \tan k_2L_1) = 0$$

Noting that

$$\tan k_2L_2 = \tan k_2(L - L_1) = \frac{\tan k_2L - \tan k_2L_1}{1 + \tan k_2L \tan k_2L_1}$$

the above equation may be rewritten in the following form,

$$\tan k_1L_1 \tan k_2L_2 = \frac{k_1}{k_2} \qquad (9.34)$$

from which P_{cr} can be determined. Equation (9.34) can be solved as follows. Write the critical load in the form

$$P_{cr} = \frac{m^2EI_2}{L^2}$$

where m^2 is a numerical factor depending on the ratios $\alpha_1 = L_1/L$ and $\alpha_2 = \sqrt{I_2/I_1}$. Substituting into Eq. (9.34), we find

$$\tan m\alpha_1\alpha_2 \tan m(1 - \alpha_1) = \alpha_2 \qquad (9.35)$$

With the values of α_1 and α_2 given, for several values of m, the corresponding values of $[\tan m\alpha_1\alpha_2 \tan m(1 - \alpha_1)]$ are computed. The smallest value of m which satisfies Eq. (9.35) can be determined by analytical or by graphical interpolation. For example, with $\alpha_1 = 0.4$ and $\alpha_2^2 = 2.5$, we find $m = 1.46$, which corresponds to the critical load

$$P_{cr} = \frac{2.12EI_2}{L^2}$$

As a second example, let us consider the buckling of a built-in column consisting of four angles connected by diagonals (Fig. 9.11). Let us again assume that the lower

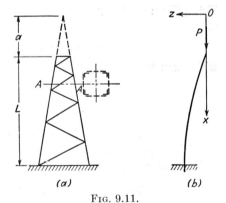

(a)   (b)

FIG. 9.11.

end of the column is built in and the upper end free. The moment of inertia of any cross section AA can be represented with sufficient accuracy by the formula

$$I_x = I_1\left(\frac{x}{a}\right)^2$$

where I_1 is the moment of inertia at the top of the column and x is the vertical distance down from the vertex of the extended column.

Taking the coordinate axes as shown in Fig. 9.11b, the differential equation of the deflection curve is

$$EI_1 \left(\frac{x}{a}\right)^2 \frac{d^2w}{dx^2} + Pw = 0 \qquad (9.36)$$

This is a homogeneous linear differential equation which, as shown in Sec. 4.4, can be reduced to a differential equation with constant coefficients by the substitution $\xi = \log x$. In terms of the variable ξ, Eq. (9.36) becomes

$$\frac{d^2w}{d\xi^2} - \frac{dw}{d\xi} + \frac{Pa^2}{EI_1} w = 0 \qquad (9.37)$$

The solution of Eq. (9.37) is of the form

$$w = e^{q\xi}$$

Substituting into (9.37) and dividing out the factor $e^{q\xi}$, the result is

$$q^2 - q + \frac{Pa^2}{EI_1} = 0$$

from which we obtain

$$q = \frac{1}{2} \pm i \sqrt{\frac{Pa^2}{EI_1} - \frac{1}{4}}$$

Using the notation $\beta = \sqrt{(Pa^2/EI_1) - \frac{1}{4}}$, the general solution of (9.37) is

$$w = C_1' e^{(\frac{1}{2} + i\beta)\xi} + C_2' e^{(\frac{1}{2} - i\beta)\xi}$$

which can be written in the following form:

$$w = \sqrt{x}\left[C_1 \sin\left(\beta \log \frac{x}{a}\right) + C_2 \cos\left(\beta \log \frac{x}{a}\right)\right]$$

where C_1', C_2', C_1, and C_2 are constants of integration. The boundary conditions are that $w = 0$ at $x = a$ and $dw/dx = 0$ at $x = a + L$. To satisfy these conditions, we find

$$C_2 = 0 \qquad \text{and} \qquad C_1[\tan(2\beta \log \alpha) - 2\beta] = 0$$

where $\alpha^2 = a/(a + L)$. The trivial solution is $C_1 = 0$. The buckling load can be determined from the equation

$$\tan (2\beta \log \alpha) = 2\beta \qquad (9.38)$$

With α given, the above equation is of the form

$$\tan K\phi = \phi$$

where K is equal to $\log \alpha$ and is a constant. The solution of this equation can be obtained in a similar manner to the case of Eqs. (9.32) and (9.33).

For $\alpha^4 = 0.5$, $\beta = 4.82$, and therefore

$$P_{cr} = \frac{4.046 EI_1}{L^2}$$

9.7. The Failure of Actual Columns. In the above discussion, we have assumed that the column is initially straight, centrally loaded, and made of material of homogeneous composition. An actual column is more or less imperfect since it may be initially bent and may not be completely homogeneous. It is obvious that the effect due to nonhomogeneity of the material cannot be taken into account in the general theoretical discussion and will not be considered here. Let us consider the deflection of a centrally loaded column which is initially bent. Assume that the column has constant cross sections. Let w_0 denote the initial deflection of the column axis from the line of thrust (Fig. 9.12). Then the change of curvature at any section is $(d^2w/dx^2) - (d^2w_0/dx^2)$, and the differential equation for the deflection becomes

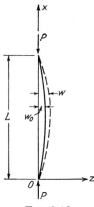

FIG. 9.12.

$$\frac{d^2w}{dx^2} - \frac{d^2w_0}{dx^2} + k^2w = 0 \qquad (9.39)$$

where, as before, $k^2 = P/EI$. The form of w will now depend upon the form of w_0. Let

$$w_0 = \sum_{n=1}^{\infty} \bar{\delta}_n \sin \frac{n\pi x}{L}$$

where $\bar{\delta}_n$ are given constants. The solution of Eq. (9.39) can be expressed in terms of a trigonometric series as follows:

$$w = \sum_{n=1}^{\infty} \delta_n \sin \frac{n\pi x}{L}$$

On substitution, we find

$$\delta_n = \frac{\bar{\delta}_n}{1 - (P/P_n)} \qquad (9.40)$$

where

$$P_n = \frac{n^2\pi^2 EI}{L^2}$$

The deflection of the column at its center can be obtained by substituting $x = L/2$ in the above equation, or

$$\delta' = \delta_{max} = \delta_1 - \delta_3 + \delta_5 - \cdots \qquad (9.41)$$

For an actual column corresponding to the ideal one discussed previously, the deflection vs. load curve is shown in Fig. 9.13. The loading of the column will follow the curve FG according to Eq. (9.40). However, when the deflection is large, the simplified form of curvature is no longer a good approximation. If the exact formula for the curvature is used, the loading of the column will follow the curve FIH. At some point I or I' on the curve, the maximum stress in the column reaches the elastic limit, and then the actual curve FIJ of $FI'J'$ will drop away from FH.

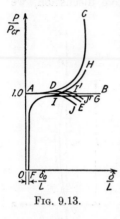

FIG. 9.13.

It is to be noted that, for an actual column, there is only one form of equilibrium, *i.e.*, the bent form, which is stable. Therefore, there is no equilibrium load at which an exchange of stabilities occurs. However, the curve FG does approach the line AB as an asymptote. But the loading curve will break away from the curve FG before the deflection becomes too large. The failing load which corresponds to the point I or I' in Fig. 9.13 can be either greater or smaller than the buckling load for the corresponding ideal column but is usually close to it if the buckling stress of the column is in the elastic range.

Referring to Eq. (9.40) since $P_n = n^2 P_{cr}$, we have

$$\delta_n = \frac{\bar{\delta}_n}{1 - (P/n^2 P_{cr})} \tag{9.42}$$

As P approaches P_{cr}, we see that

$$\frac{\delta_1}{\bar{\delta}_1} \to \infty \qquad \frac{\delta_2}{\bar{\delta}_2} \to \frac{4}{3} \qquad \frac{\delta_3}{\bar{\delta}_3} \to \frac{9}{8} \qquad \cdots$$

Therefore, $\delta_1 \gg \delta_2 > \delta_3 > \cdots$.

By substituting Eq. (9.42) into (9.41), it is evident that, if P is a fairly large fraction of P_{cr}, the center deflection δ' is approximately equal to δ_1, that is,

$$\delta' \cong \delta_1 = \frac{\bar{\delta}_1}{1 - (P/P_{cr})} \tag{9.43}$$

and Eq. (9.43) is a close approximation of Eq. (9.41). The P vs. δ' curve approximates a rectangular hyperbola having the horizontal line $P = P_{cr}$ as an asymptote.

Since the deflections measured in testing are usually referred to the initial position, they are $\delta' - \bar{\delta}$ rather than δ'. Also $\bar{\delta}_1$ is usually the dominating part of $\bar{\delta}$. If we write $\delta = \delta' - \bar{\delta}_1$, Eq. (9.43) can be written as

$$\delta = \delta_1 - \bar{\delta}_1 = \frac{\bar{\delta}_1}{(P_{cr}/P) - 1}$$

or $$P_{cr}\frac{\delta}{P} - \delta = \bar{\delta}_1 \qquad (9.44)$$

It is seen that if δ/P is plotted against δ, when P is near to P_{cr}, the test results will be approximately a straight line and the inverse of the slope of this line is a measure of the buckling load P_{cr}. Timoshenko[1] also shows that this relationship holds true when there is some eccentricity in applying the load. This is the well-known Southwell's method[2] and has been widely used for estimating the elastic buckling load from test results. However, because of the happy coincidence that the failing load of a column is close to its theoretical elastic buckling load, it is rather a common practice to regard the failing load as the buckling load and the importance of Southwell's method has not been properly emphasized. This is because, for imperfect columns, the buckling load is not defined, and all actual columns are more or less imperfect; thus, in the strict sense, actual testing of buckling is impossible. Southwell's method, however, provides a theoretically sound basis for analyzing the experimental data, *i.e.*, from the test results of an imperfect column the buckling load of the corresponding perfect column can be estimated.

9.8. Lateral Buckling of Beams with Narrow Cross Sections. A beam with a narrow rectangular section, when bent in its plane, may become unstable at some *critical* value of the load and buckle sidewise as shown in Figs. 9.14 and 9.15. Let us begin with the case of a simply supported beam bent by couples M at the ends. In calculating the critical value of M, we shall follow the same method of formulation as in the case of columns. We assume that, under the action of the couples M in the vertical plane, the beam is disturbed so as to have a small lateral deflection, and from the equilibrium equations we determine the smallest value of M at which such a lateral bent form is possible.

Figure 9.14 shows such a beam. We shall represent the moment M acting on a positive surface by a vector using the right-hand rule. At any section mn which is at a distance x from the origin, we see, from Fig. 9.14d and c,

$$M \cos \alpha \cos \beta = -EI_y \frac{d^2w}{dx^2} \qquad M \cos \alpha \sin \beta = -EI_z \frac{d^2v}{dx^2} \qquad M \sin \alpha = GJ \frac{d\beta}{dx}$$

where I_x and I_y are moments of inertia with respect to the x and y axes, respectively, and GJ is the torsional rigidity of the beam. For rectangular

[1] S. Timoshenko, "Theory of Elastic Stability," p. 178, McGraw-Hill Book Company, Inc., New York, 1936.
[2] R. V. Southwell, On the Analysis of Experimental Observations in Problems of Elastic Stability, *Proc. Roy. Soc. (London), A*, Vol. 135, pp. 601–616, April, 1932.

cross sections, we have

$$I_z = \frac{hb^3}{12} \qquad I_y = \frac{bh^3}{12} \qquad J = hb^3\kappa$$

where the value of κ is given in Table 5.1 for various b/h ratios.

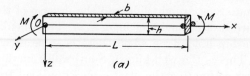

(a)

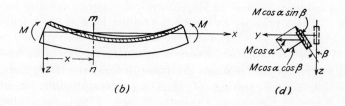

(b)   (d)

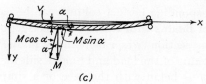

(c)

FIG. 9.14.

Since u, v, w, α, and β are small, we have

$$\sin \alpha \cong \alpha = \frac{dv}{dx} \qquad \cos \alpha \cong 1 \qquad \sin \beta \cong \beta \qquad \cos \beta \cong 1$$

With these approximate relations, the equilibrium equations become

$$EI_y \frac{d^2w}{dx^2} = -M \qquad EI_z \frac{d^2v}{dx^2} = -M\beta \qquad GJ \frac{d\beta}{dx} = M \frac{dv}{dx} \quad (9.45)$$

The first equation of (9.45) is of no interest because it gives the vertical deflection of a beam under end couples M. Differentiating the third equation with respect to x and eliminating d^2v/dx^2 by using the second equation, we obtain

$$GJ \frac{d^2\beta}{dx^2} + \frac{M^2}{EI_z}\beta = 0$$

or

$$\frac{d^2\beta}{dx^2} + k^2\beta = 0 \qquad\qquad (9.46)$$

where $k^2 = M^2/GJEI_z$. For beams with constant cross sections, k^2 is independent of x, and the general solution of Eq. (9.46) is

$$\beta = C_1 \sin kx + C_2 \cos kx$$

The boundary conditions are that $\beta = 0$ at $x = 0$ and $x = L$. We have therefore

$$C_2 = 0 \qquad \text{and} \qquad C_1 \sin kL = 0$$

If $C_1 = 0$, we have the trivial solution, which indicates the unbuckled form. The buckled form is possible only when

$$\sin kL = 0$$

or
$$M_{cr} = \frac{\pi \sqrt{GJEI_z}}{L} \tag{9.47}$$

Now let us consider the case of a cantilever beam bent by an end load P. The force P is assumed to be applied at the centroid of the cross

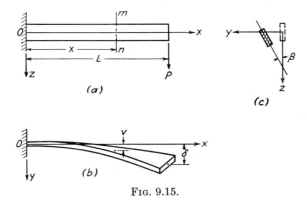

(a)

(b)

(c)

Fig. 9.15.

section and in the xz plane. Assume that the beam is bent laterally owing to a small disturbance (Fig. 9.15). At any cross section mn which is at a distance x from the origin, we have a bending moment of $P(L - x)$ and a torsional moment $P(\delta - v)$. Following the same reasoning as in the derivation of Eqs. (9.45), we find the equations of equilibrium in this case as follows:

$$EI_y \frac{d^2w}{dx^2} = P(L - x)$$

$$EI_z \frac{d^2v}{dx^2} = P(L - x)\beta \tag{9.48}$$

$$GJ \frac{d\beta}{dx} = -P(L - x)\frac{dv}{dx} + P(\delta - v)$$

Eliminating v from the second and third equations, we have

$$\frac{d^2\beta}{dx^2} + \frac{P^2L^2}{GJEI_z}\left(1 - \frac{x}{L}\right)^2 \beta = 0 \qquad (9.49)$$

Let $k_1^2 = P^2L^4/GJEI_z$ and $\xi = 1 - (x/L)$. Equation (9.49) becomes

$$\frac{d^2\beta}{d\xi^2} + k_1^2\xi^2\beta = 0 \qquad (9.50)$$

The solution of Eq. (9.50) can be expressed by a power series as follows:

$$\beta = a_1\xi^{m_1} + a_2\xi^{m_2} + a_3\xi^{m_3} + \cdots$$

Substituting this series into Eq. (9.50), we have

$$a_1m_1(m_1 - 1)\xi^{m_1-2} + a_2m_2(m_2 - 1)\xi^{m_2-2} + a_3m_3(m_3 - 1)\xi^{m_3-2}$$
$$+ \cdots + k_1^2a_1\xi^{m_1+2} + k_1^2a_2\xi^{m_2+2} + \cdots = 0$$

The above equation is satisfied if we let

$$
\begin{aligned}
m_1(m_1 - 1) &= 0 \qquad &(9.51)\\
a_2m_2(m_2 - 1) &= -k_1^2a_1 \qquad &m_2 - 2 = m_1 + 2\\
a_3m_3(m_3 - 1) &= -k_1^2a_2 \qquad &m_3 - 2 = m_2 + 2 \qquad \text{etc.}
\end{aligned}
$$

Or, in general,

$$\left.\begin{aligned} a_j &= -\frac{k_1^2a_{j-1}}{m_j(m_j - 1)}\\ m_j &= m_{j-1} + 4 \end{aligned}\right\} j = 2, 3, \ldots \qquad (9.52)$$

From (9.51), we find

$$m_1 = 0 \text{ or } +1$$

In accordance with these two solutions for m_1, we obtain two series satisfying Eq. (9.50) and find the general solution of this equation as

$$\beta = C_1\left(1 - \frac{k_1^2}{3\cdot 4}\xi^4 + \frac{k_1^4}{3\cdot 4\cdot 7\cdot 8}\xi^8 - \cdots\right)$$
$$+ C_2\left(\xi - \frac{k_1^2}{4\cdot 5}\xi^5 + \frac{k_1^4}{4\cdot 5\cdot 8\cdot 9}\xi^9 - \cdots\right) \qquad (9.53)$$

where C_1 and C_2 are constants.

At $x = 0$, $\beta = 0$. At $x = L$, the torsional moment is zero, and therefore $d\beta/dx = 0$. The boundary conditions are therefore that $\beta = 0$ for $\xi = 1$ and $d\beta/dx = 0$ for $\xi = 0$. This last condition requires that $C_2 = 0$. To obtain the nontrivial solution, we must solve the equation

$$1 - \frac{k_1^2}{3\cdot 4} + \frac{k_1^4}{3\cdot 4\cdot 7\cdot 8} - \frac{k_1^6}{3\cdot 4\cdot 7\cdot 8\cdot 11\cdot 12} + \cdots = 0 \qquad (9.54)$$

A table of numerical values of the left side of Eq. (9.54) as a function of k_1 has been calculated by Prandtl.[1]   The smallest root is

$$k_1 = 4.013$$

which gives the buckling load as

$$P_{cr} = \frac{4.013 \sqrt{GJEI_z}}{L^2} \tag{9.55}$$

[1] L. Prandtl, dissertation "Kipperscheinungen," Nuremberg, 1899.

CHAPTER 10

NUMERICAL METHODS IN THE DETERMINATION OF BUCKLING LOADS

10.1. Finite-difference Approximations. From the examples worked out in Chap. 9, it is seen that the determination of the buckling load by

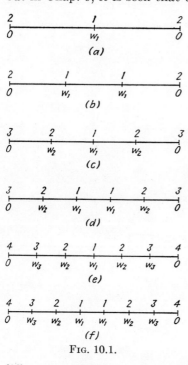

means of analytical methods can be quite tedious and difficult. In fact, in many cases where the cross section of the column is a variable, analytical solutions have not even been possible and numerical methods must be employed. The first method which we shall discuss is the method of finite differences.

The application of finite-difference approximations to the solutions of buckling problems can best be explained by working out several examples.

Example 1. Simply Supported Column with Constant Cross Section. The differential equation in this case is

$$\frac{d^2w}{dx^2} + k^2w = 0$$

FIG. 10.1.

with the boundary conditions that $w = 0$ at $x = 0$ and L. As defined previously, $k^2 = P/EI$. The finite-difference equation at any point x is then

$$\frac{w(x + h) - 2w(x) + w(x - h)}{h^2} + k^2w(x) = 0$$

or
$$w(x + h) + (k^2h^2 - 2)w(x) + w(x - h) = 0 \qquad (10.1)$$

where $h = L/n$, n being the number of intervals into which the column is divided. If we take $n = 2$ or $h = L/2$ (Fig. 10.1a), the finite-difference equation at the point $x = L/2$ is

$$0 + (k^2h^2 - 2)w_1 + 0 = 0 \qquad \text{or} \qquad \left(\frac{k^2L^2}{4} - 2\right)w_1 = 0$$

Solving, we have either the trivial solution

240

$$w_1 = 0 \quad \text{or} \quad k^2 = \frac{P}{EI} = \frac{8}{L^2}$$

which gives

$$P_{cr} = \frac{8EI}{L^2}$$

The exact analytical solution in this case gives $P_{cr} = \pi^2 EI/L^2$ or $9.86960EI/L^2$. The error in the finite-difference solution is thus -19 per cent.

For $n = 3$ or $h = L/3$, noting that the deflection curve is symmetrical with respect to the middle point of the curve (Fig. 10.1b), and applying Eq. (10.1) at $x = L/3$, we have

$$w_1 + (k^2 h^2 - 2)w_1 + 0 = 0 \quad \text{or} \quad \left(k^2 \frac{L^2}{9} - 1\right) w_1 = 0$$

which gives the trivial solution $w_1 = 0$ or

$$P_{cr} = \frac{9EI}{L^2} \quad \text{error, } -9\%$$

For $n = 4$ or $h = L/4$, the finite-difference equations at $x = L/4, L/2$ are

$$w_1 + (k^2 h^2 - 2)w_2 + 0 = 0 \qquad w_2 + (k^2 h^2 - 2)w_1 + w_2 = 0$$

or

$$w_1 + (k^2 h^2 - 2)w_2 = 0 \qquad (k^2 h^2 - 2)w_1 + 2w_2 = 0 \qquad (10.2)$$

From algebra, the solution of the system of simultaneous equations

$$a_{11}x_1 + a_{12}x_2 + \cdots + a_{1n}x_n = a_{10}$$
$$a_{21}x_1 + a_{22}x_2 + \cdots + a_{2n}x_n = a_{20}$$
$$\cdots \cdots \cdots \cdots \cdots$$
$$a_{n1}x_1 + a_{n2}x_2 + \cdots + a_{nn}x_n = a_{n0}$$

can be written as

$$x_1 = \frac{\begin{vmatrix} a_{10} & a_{12} & \cdots & a_{1n} \\ a_{20} & a_{22} & \cdots & a_{2n} \\ \cdots & \cdots & \cdots & \cdots \\ a_{n0} & a_{n2} & \cdots & a_{nn} \end{vmatrix}}{\begin{vmatrix} a_{11} & a_{12} & \cdots & a_{1n} \\ a_{21} & a_{22} & \cdots & a_{2n} \\ \cdots & \cdots & \cdots & \cdots \\ a_{n1} & a_{n2} & \cdots & a_{nn} \end{vmatrix}}$$

$$x_2 = \frac{\begin{vmatrix} a_{11} & a_{10} & \cdots & a_{1n} \\ a_{21} & a_{20} & \cdots & a_{2n} \\ \cdots & \cdots & \cdots & \cdots \\ a_{n1} & a_{n0} & \cdots & a_{nn} \end{vmatrix}}{\begin{vmatrix} a_{11} & a_{12} & \cdots & a_{1n} \\ a_{21} & a_{22} & \cdots & a_{2n} \\ \cdots & \cdots & \cdots & \cdots \\ a_{n1} & a_{n2} & \cdots & a_{nn} \end{vmatrix}}$$

etc. If $a_{10} = a_{20} = \cdots = a_{n0} = 0$, then we have from the above formulas the trivial solution $x_1 = x_2 = \cdots = x_n = 0$ unless the determinant in the denominator of these formulas is also zero, *viz.*,

$$\begin{vmatrix} a_{11} & a_{12} & \cdots & a_{1n} \\ a_{21} & a_{22} & \cdots & a_{2n} \\ \cdots & \cdots & \cdots & \cdots \\ a_{n1} & a_{n2} & \cdots & a_{nn} \end{vmatrix} = 0 \qquad (10.3)$$

Therefore Eqs. (10.2) will give us the nontrivial solution only when the determinant

$$\begin{vmatrix} 1 & (k^2h^2 - 2) \\ (k^2h^2 - 2) & 2 \end{vmatrix} = 0$$

or

$$(k^2h^2 - 2)^2 - 2 = 0$$

Solving, we have

$$k^2h^2 - 2 = \pm \sqrt{2}$$

The value of k^2 is smaller if we take the negative sign before the square root which gives

$$P_{cr} = \frac{9.3726EI}{L^2} \qquad \text{error, } -5\%$$

For $n = 5$ or $h = L/5$, Eq. (10.1) at the points $L/5$, $2L/5$ (Fig. 10.1d) becomes

$$w_1 + (k^2h^2 - 2)w_2 = 0 \qquad (k^2h^2 - 1)w_1 + w_2 = 0$$

To obtain the nontrivial solution, we must have

$$\begin{vmatrix} 1 & (k^2h^2 - 2) \\ (k^2h^2 - 1) & 1 \end{vmatrix} = 0$$

or

$$(k^2h^2 - 2)(k^2h^2 - 1) - 1 = 0$$

Solving, we find that the root which makes k^2 smaller is

$$k^2h^2 = 0.380$$

Hence

$$P_{cr} = \frac{9.549EI}{L^2} \qquad \text{error, } -3.2\%$$

For $n = 6$ or $h = L/6$, Eq. (10.1) at the points $x = L/6$, $L/3$, $L/2$ becomes

$$w_2 + (k^2h^2 - 2)w_3 = 0$$
$$w_1 + (k^2h^2 - 2)w_2 + w_3 = 0$$
$$(k^2h^2 - 2)w_1 + 2w_2 = 0$$

The corresponding determinantal equation is

$$\begin{vmatrix} 0 & 1 & (k^2h^2 - 2) \\ 1 & (k^2h^2 - 2) & 1 \\ (k^2h^2 - 2) & 2 & 0 \end{vmatrix} = 0$$

or

$$(k^2h^2 - 2)[(k^2h^2 - 2)^2 - 3] = 0$$

The root which corresponds to the smallest k^2 is $k^2h^2 = 0.27$, and therefore

$$P_{cr} = \frac{9.646EI}{L^2} \qquad \text{error, } -2.3\%$$

For $n = 7$ or $h = L/7$ (Fig. 10.1*f*), Eq. (10.1) at the points $x = L/7$, $2L/7$, $3L/7$ becomes

$$w_2 + (k^2h^2 - 2)w_3 = 0$$
$$w_1 + (k^2h^2 - 2)w_2 + w_3 = 0$$
$$(k^2h^2 - 1)w_1 + w_2 = 0$$

The condition for the nontrivial solution is

$$\begin{vmatrix} 0 & 1 & (k^2h^2 - 2) \\ 1 & (k^2h^2 - 2) & 1 \\ (k^2h^2 - 1) & 1 & 0 \end{vmatrix} = 0$$

or

$$(k^2h^2 - 2)^3 + (k^2h^2 - 2)^2 - 2(k^2h^2 - 2) - 1 = 0$$

Solving, we find the smallest k^2 occurs at

$$k^2h^2 - 2 = -1.80$$

which corresponds to

$$P_{cr} = \frac{9.705EI}{L^2} \qquad \text{error, } -1.7\%$$

In the above example, a large number of approximations has been computed. It should be noted that, since the approximations $n = 3, 5, 7$ involve determinants of the same order as the approximations $n = 2, 4, 6$, in practice only the odd approximations would be computed.

Example 2. Simply Supported Column with Variable Moment of Inertia. If in the previous example the moment of inertia I varies according to the law

$$I(x) = I_0\left(1 + \sin\frac{\pi x}{L}\right)$$

where I_0 is a constant, we find that the finite-difference equation at any point x is

$$EI_0\left(1 + \sin\frac{\pi x}{L}\right)\frac{w(x + h) - 2w(x) + w(x - h)}{h^2} + Pw(x) = 0$$

or

$$w(x + h) + \left[\frac{k^2h^2}{1 + \sin \pi x/L} - 2\right]w(x) + w(x - h) = 0 \quad (10.4)$$

where $k^2 = P/EI_0$. The boundary conditions are $w = 0$ at $x = 0$ and $x = L$.

If we take $n = 2$ or $h = L/2$ (Fig. 10.1a) at $x = L/2$, Eq. (10.4) becomes

$$0 + \left[\frac{k^2 L^2/4}{1 + \sin \pi/2} - 2 \right] w_1 + 0 = 0$$

We have therefore

$$\frac{k^2 L^2}{8} - 2 = 0 \qquad \text{or} \qquad P_{cr} = \frac{16 E I_0}{L^2}$$

We see from the above example that, with variable moment of inertia, there is no additional difficulty in solving the problem. The only difference between the present case and the previous one is that the coefficient of $w(x)$ in Eq. (10.4) is now a function of x, and proper values of x should be substituted when the equation is applied to various points. The solution for other values of n can be carried out in the same manner as in the previous example. The values of $P_{cr} L^2/EI_0$ for $n = 3$ and 4 are found to be 16.79 and 17.24, respectively. The exact solution is unknown in this case. By assuming a sinusoidal deflection curve, the energy method gives the buckling load as $18.05 EI_0/L^2$ (see Sec. 10.5). The probable errors in the buckling loads computed for $n = 2, 3, 4$ are -11.4 per cent, -7 per cent, and -4.5 per cent, respectively.

In the above two examples, we see that as n increases, the value of P_{cr} approaches the exact value given by the analytical solution. This is not always true when the moment of inertia is a variable. To show this, let us assume that the moment of inertia varies according to the following formula:

$$I(x) = \begin{cases} I_0 \left(1 + \dfrac{2x}{L} \right) & \text{when } 0 \leq x \leq \dfrac{L}{2} \\[2mm] I_0 \left(3 - \dfrac{2x}{L} \right) & \text{when } \dfrac{L}{2} \leq x \leq L \end{cases}$$

The finite-difference equation at any point x then becomes

$$w(x + h) + \left[\frac{k^2 h^2}{1 + (2x/L)} - 2 \right] w(x) + w(x - h) = 0$$

$$\text{when } 0 \leq x \leq \frac{L}{2} \quad (10.5)$$

Table 10.1 gives the results of the computations. The buckling load computed by the energy method with an assumed sinusoidal deflection curve is $16.53 EI_0/L^2$. Compared with this value the probable errors are computed and given in Table 10.1.

TABLE 10.1

n	$P_{cr}L^2/EI_0$	Probable error, per cent
2	16.000	-3.23
3	15.000	-9.27
4	16.000	-3.23
5	15.892	-3.83
6	16.253	-1.70
7	16.179	-2.15

Example 3. Lateral Buckling of a Cantilever Beam of Narrow Cross Section. The governing differential equation in this case was derived in Sec. 9.8 as

$$\frac{d^2\beta}{dx^2} + \frac{P^2L^2}{GJEI_z}\left(1 - \frac{x}{L}\right)^2 \beta = 0$$

and the boundary conditions are $\beta = 0$ at $x = 0$, $d\beta/dx = 0$ at $x = L$. The corresponding finite-difference equation at any section x is

$$\beta(x + h) + \left[k_1^2h^2\left(1 - \frac{x}{L}\right)^2 - 2\right]\beta(x) + \beta(x - h) = 0 \quad (10.6)$$

and
$$\beta(0) = 0 \qquad \beta_{m+1} = \beta_{m-1}$$

where $k_1^2 = P^2L^2/GJEI_z$ and m is the point at $x = L$. β_{m+1} is an imaginary point. Referring to Fig. 10.2a, we find the finite-difference equations at $x = L/2$ and L to be

$$\beta_2 + [k_1^2h^2(1 - \tfrac{1}{2})^2 - 2]\beta_1 = 0$$
$$[k_1^2h^2(1 - 1)^2 - 2]\beta_2 + 2\beta_1 = 0$$

The determinantal equation for computing the nontrivial solution is therefore

$$\begin{vmatrix} 1 & \left(\dfrac{k_1^2h^2}{4} - 2\right) \\ -2 & 2 \end{vmatrix} = 0$$

or
$$2\left(\frac{k_1^2h^2}{4} - 2\right) + 2 = 0$$

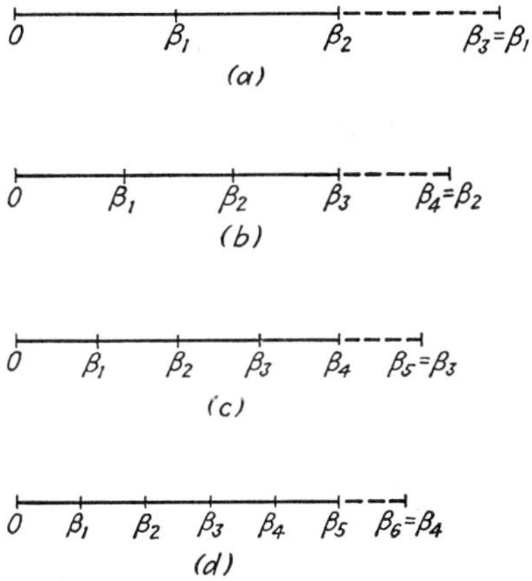

which gives

$$P_{cr} = \frac{4\sqrt{GJEI_z}}{L^2} \qquad \text{error, } -0.32\%$$

(a)

(b)

(c)

(d)

FIG. 10.2.

For $n = 3, 4, 5$, computations can be carried out in the same manner, and we find the values of $P_{cr}L^2/\sqrt{GJEI_z}$ to be 3.933, 3.959, and 3.976, respectively. The exact value is 4.013 [Eq. (9.55)], and the errors are therefore -1.9 per cent, -1.3 per cent, and -0.92 per cent, respectively.

10.2. Relaxation Method. As can be seen from the examples worked out in the previous section, by reducing the mesh size or h, the accuracy in the buckling load is usually improved. As the number of mesh points increases, two difficulties arise. First, the labor in expanding the determinant increases rapidly. Second, the degree of the resultant equation will be high, and the solution of this equation becomes difficult. In problems of elastic stability, only the root which corresponds to the lowest buckling load is of interest. Many relaxation procedures have been proposed,[1] and in what follows we shall describe a method which appears to be best adapted to elastic-stability problems.

We shall take as an example the buckling problem of a simply supported column with constant cross section. Let us consider the case with $n = 7$. The relaxation method can be carried out in the following steps:

Step 1. Assume $w_1 = 1$, $w_2 = 0.8$, and $w_3 = 0.4$. Note that in the buckling problems the exact value of the amplitude of the deflection curve cannot be determined and only the ratios of the deflections at various points along the column are of interest. For example, all the deflection curves obtained in Sec. 9.4 are determined except the maximum amplitude C_1. The values of the assumed w_1, w_2, w_3 are actually the relative ratios. These values are recorded in the first column at the right of nodal points.

Rewrite the finite-difference equation (10.1) in the following form:
$$w(x + h) - 2w(x) + w(x - h) = -k^2h^2w(x)$$
or
$$\Delta^2w(x) = -k^2h^2w(x) \qquad (10.7)$$

Compute, from the assumed values of the w, the values of Δ^2w at each nodal point, and record these values in the second column. For example, we have (Fig. 10.1f)

At point 1: $\Delta^2w_1 = w_1 - 2w_1 + w_2 = 1.0 - 2 \times 1.0 + 0.8 = -0.2$
At point 2: $\Delta^2w_2 = w_1 - 2w_2 + w_3 = -0.2$
At point 3: $\Delta^2w_3 = w_2 - 2w_3 + 0 = 0$

Next, we shall compute the values of k^2h^2 from the three difference equations at the three nodal points. That is,

At 1: $k^2h^2 = -\dfrac{\Delta^2w_1}{w_1} = \dfrac{0.2}{1.0} = 0.2$

At 2: $k^2h^2 = -\dfrac{\Delta^2w_2}{w_2} = \dfrac{0.2}{0.8} = 0.25$

At 3: $k^2h^2 = -\dfrac{\Delta^2w_3}{w_3} = \dfrac{0}{0.4} = 0$

---

[1] See, for example, R. V. Southwell, "Relaxation Methods in Engineering Science," Oxford University Press, New York, 1940; A. Vazsonyi, A Numerical Method in the Theory of Vibrating Bodies, *J. Applied Phys.*, Vol. 15, No. 8, pp. 598–606, August, 1944.

These values are recorded in the third column. The results are shown in Fig. 10.3 as step 1.

Step 2. If the ratios between w_1, w_2, w_3 are assumed correctly, the values of k^2h^2 computed by all these three equations will be the same. They are obviously not in our case. From the previous computations, say, with $n = 3$, we found $k^2L^2 = 9$. Therefore the lowest root in the

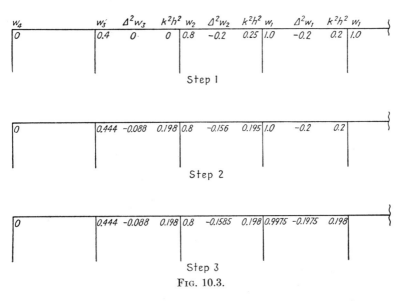

Fig. 10.3.

present case should give the value of k^2L^2 somewhere near the value of 9. The value of k^2h^2 will be approximately

$$k^2h^2 = \frac{k^2L^2}{n^2} = \frac{9}{49} = 0.18$$

With this in mind, let us change the values of w_1, w_2, w_3. We observe that the largest error in k^2h^2 is at point 3. Let us increase w_3 to 0.444 without changing the values of w_2 and w_1. We have thus

$$\Delta^2w_3 = -0.088 \qquad (k^2h^2)_3 = 0.198$$
and
$$\Delta^2w_2 = -0.156 \qquad (k^2h^2)_2 = 0.195$$

This is recorded as step 2 in Fig. 10.3.

Step 3. Now let us reduce w_1 to 0.9975 without changing w_2 and w_3. Then

$$\Delta^2w_1 = -0.1975 \qquad (k^2h^2)_1 = 0.198$$
$$\Delta^2w_2 = -0.1585 \qquad (k^2h^2)_2 = 0.198$$

These values are recorded as step 3 in Fig. 10.3.

Since the values of k^2h^2 at all the nodal points are the same now, we have found the correct solution. The critical load is therefore

$$P_{cr} = \frac{9.70EI}{L^2}$$

It may again be emphasized that the recorded values of w_1, w_2, w_3 are only relative ratios. There can be many sets of values w_1, w_2, w_3 which will satisfy these finite-difference equations. But if we divide them through by a common factor, we shall find that the relative ratios are the same and hence the buckling load is the same.

10.3. Higher-order Finite-difference Approximations. In solving the buckling problems, we can again improve our results by using higher-order finite-difference approximation formulas which we derived in Sec. 6.6. Let us illustrate this method by again taking as an example the buckling problem of a simply supported column with constant cross section. From formula (6.33), we have

$$\frac{d^2w}{dx^2} = \frac{1}{h^2}\left(\Delta^2 w - \frac{1}{12}\Delta^4 w + \frac{1}{90}\Delta^6 w - \cdots\right)$$

Using this formula, the finite-difference equation corresponding to the differential equation

$$\frac{d^2w}{dx^2} + k^2w = 0$$

is

$$\Delta^2 w - \tfrac{1}{12}\Delta^4 w + \tfrac{1}{90}\Delta^6 w - \cdots + k^2h^2w = 0 \qquad (10.8)$$

If we neglect the sixth- and higher-order differences, at any point x, Eq. (10.8) becomes

$$w(x + h) - 2w(x) + w(x - h) - \tfrac{1}{12}[w(x + 2h) - 4w(x + h)$$
$$+ 6w(x) - 4w(x - h) + w(x - 2h)] + k^2h^2w(x) = 0$$

or

$$-w(x + 2h) + 16w(x + h) + (12k^2h^2 - 30)w(x)$$
$$+ 16w(x - h) - w(x - 2h) = 0 \qquad (10.9)$$

Since this difference equation involves the values of w two points to the left and two points to the right of x, w_{m+1} must be used when the equation is applied to the points $m - 1$, where m denotes the boundary points. Introducing an imaginary mesh point outside each of the boundary points, and remembering that, for a simply supported end,

$$w = \frac{d^2w}{dx^2} = 0 \qquad \text{at the boundary}$$

then by expressing d^2w/dx^2 by first-order differences, we find

$$w_{m+1} - 2w_m + w_{m-1} = 0$$

or
$$w_{m+1} = -w_{m-1}$$

since w_m is zero.

Proceeding as in Sec. 10.1, the following results are obtained:

Approximation $n = 2$. By applying Eq. (10.9) at $x = L/2$ (Fig. 10.4a), we find

$$w_1 + 0 + \left(12k^2\frac{L^2}{4} - 30\right)$$

$$w_1 + 0 + w_1 = 0$$

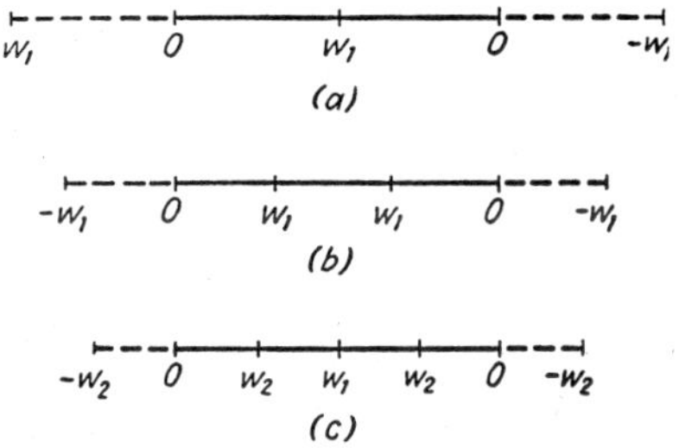

which gives

$$k^2L^2 = 9.33$$

or $P_{cr} = \dfrac{9.33EI}{L^2}$ error, -5.5%

FIG. 10.4.

Approximation $n = 3$. By applying Eq. (10.9) at $x = L/3$ (Fig. 10.4b), we find

$$w_1 + 0 + \left(12k^2\frac{L^2}{9} - 30\right)w_1 + 16w_1 + 0 = 0$$

and
$$P_{cr} = \frac{9.75EI}{L^2}$$ error, -1.21%

Approximation $n = 4$. By applying Eq. (10.9) at $x = L/4, L/2$ (Fig. 10.4c), we have

$$-w_2 + 0 + \left(12k^2\frac{L^2}{16} - 30\right)w_2 + 16w_1 - w_2 = 0$$

$$0 + 16w_2 + \left(12k^2\frac{L^2}{16} - 30\right)w_1 + 16w_2 + 0 = 0$$

from which we obtain the determinantal equation

$$\begin{vmatrix} (0.75k^2L^2 - 30) & 16 \\ 32 & (0.75k^2L^2 - 30) \end{vmatrix} = 0$$

Solving, we find

$$P_{cr} = \frac{9.83EI}{L^2}$$ error, -0.40%

The improvement in the solution is readily seen.

10.4. Methods of Extrapolation. In solving the buckling problem, only one quantity is to be determined, *viz.*, the buckling load. In such a case, the method of extrapolation[1] appears to be very useful. In order to

---

[1] M. G. Salvadori, Numerical Computation of Buckling Loads by Finite Differences, *Trans. ASCE*, Vol. 116, pp. 590–636, 1951.

apply the method of extrapolation, we shall first prove that the *error in the buckling load due to the finite-difference approximation is of the h^2 type if the governing differential equation is one with constant coefficients.*

Let $\bar{w}$ be the solution of the differential equation and w that of the corresponding finite-difference equation. Let $\bar{k}^2$ be the value obtained by solving the differential equation and k^2 the corresponding value given by the solution of the finite-difference equation. Consider the case of a simply supported column with constant cross section. The differential equation is

$$\frac{d^2\bar{w}}{dx^2} + \bar{k}^2\bar{w} = 0$$

for which the boundary conditions are $\bar{w} = 0$ at $x = 0$ and L. The corresponding difference equation is

$$w(x + h) - 2w(x) + w(x - h) + k^2h^2w(x) = 0 \qquad (10.10)$$

with the boundary conditions that $w = 0$ at $x = 0$ and $x = L$.

The finite-difference equation (10.10) may be solved by assuming the solution to be the form

$$w = ce^{mx} \qquad (10.11)$$

where c is a constant. Substituting in (10.10), we have

$$ce^{mx+mh} - 2ce^{mx} + ce^{mx-mh} + ck^2h^2e^{mx} = 0$$

or
$$[(e^{mh} + e^{-mh}) + (k^2h^2 - 2)]ce^{mx} = 0$$

which requires

$$(e^{mh} + e^{-mh}) + (k^2h^2 - 2) = 0$$

or
$$\cosh mh + \left(\frac{k^2h^2}{2} - 1\right) = 0 \qquad (10.12)$$

Three forms of the solution for m may be obtained according to whether $|(k^2h^2/2) - 1| > 1$, $|(k^2h^2/2) - 1| = 1$, or $|(k^2h^2/2) - 1| < 1$. In the first two cases, it can be shown that the resulting solution for w cannot satisfy the boundary conditions, and therefore these cases will not be considered. When $|(k^2h^2/2) - 1| < 1$, we have $\cosh mh < 1$, which is impossible unless m is a pure imaginary number. Writing $m = i\lambda$, Eq. (10.12) becomes

$$\cos \lambda h = 1 - \frac{k^2h^2}{2} \qquad (10.13)$$

which gives

$$\lambda = \pm \frac{1}{h} \cos^{-1}\left(1 - \frac{k^2h^2}{2}\right)$$

Substituting these values of λ in (10.11), the values of k^2 can then be determined from the boundary conditions. As this procedure proves rather laborious, we may carry out the solution by first determining the value of λ from the boundary conditions and then solving k^2 from Eq. (10.13). Since λ can be either positive or negative, the general solution of w is

$$w = c_1 \sin \lambda x + c_2 \cos \lambda x \tag{10.14}$$

To satisfy the boundary conditions, we must have

$$\lambda = \frac{n\pi}{L} \tag{10.15}$$

where n is any integer and $n = 1$ at buckling. Since $1 - \cos 2\theta = 2 \sin^2 \theta$, rewriting Eq. (10.14) and substituting the value of λ obtained from (10.15), we obtain

$$k^2 \left(\frac{h}{2}\right)^2 = \sin^2 \frac{\pi h}{L 2} \tag{10.16}$$

But $\sin \theta = \theta - (\theta^3/3!) + (\theta^5/5!) \cdots$. By expanding the sine function in (10.16), we find

$$k^2 \left(\frac{h}{2}\right)^2 = \left[\frac{\pi}{L}\frac{h}{2} - \frac{1}{3!}\left(\frac{\pi}{L}\frac{h}{2}\right)^3 + \cdots\right]^2 = \frac{\pi^2}{L^2}\left(\frac{h}{2}\right)^2 - \frac{2}{3!}\left(\frac{\pi}{L}\right)^4\left(\frac{h}{2}\right)^4 + \cdots$$

Dividing this through by $(h/2)^2$,

$$k^2 = \frac{\pi^2}{L^2} - \frac{2}{3!}\left(\frac{\pi}{L}\right)^4\left(\frac{h}{2}\right)^2 + \cdots = \bar{k}^2 - \alpha_1 h^2 - \alpha_2 h^4 + \cdots$$

where α_1, α_2 are independent of h. This results from the fact that $\bar{k}^2 = \pi^2/L^2$. Thus we have proved that in this case the error e is of the h^2 type, viz.,

$$e = \bar{k}^2 - k^2 = \alpha_1 h^2 + \alpha_2 h^4 + \cdots \tag{10.17}$$

If the column is not simply supported at both ends, we must use the differential equation (9.29) and, in a similar manner, we can again prove that the error is of the h^2 type.

If we neglect α_2, α_3, etc., in Eq. (10.17), we have

$$\bar{k}^2 - k^2 = \alpha_1 h^2$$

Let n_i and n_j represent the number of subintervals in which L is divided. Then for $h_i = L/n_i$ and $h_j = L/n_j$, we have

$$\bar{k}^2 - k_i^2 = \alpha_1 h_i^2 = \frac{\alpha_1 L^2}{n_i^2} \qquad \bar{k}^2 - k_j^2 = \alpha_1 h_j^2 = \frac{\alpha_1 L^2}{n_j^2} \tag{10.18}$$

where $k_i{}^2$ and $k_j{}^2$ are the values of k^2 obtained corresponding to $n = n_i$ and n_j, respectively. Eliminating $\alpha_1 L^2$ between these two equations, we find

$$\bar{k}_{i,j}{}^2 = \frac{n_j{}^2 k_j{}^2 - n_i{}^2 k_i{}^2}{n_j{}^2 - n_i{}^2} = a_{n_j} k_j{}^2 - a_{n_i} k_i{}^2 \qquad (10.19)$$

where $\bar{k}_{i,j}{}^2$ is the extrapolated value of k^2. Table 10.2 gives the coefficients a_{n_j}, a_{n_i} of the h^2 *extrapolation formula* (10.19) for the most commonly used values of n_i and n_j.

TABLE 10.2. h^2 EXTRAPOLATION

n_j/n_i	a_{n_j}	a_{n_i}
2/1	$\frac{4}{3} = 1.33333$	$\frac{1}{3} = 0.33333$
3/2	$\frac{9}{5} = 1.8$	$\frac{4}{5} = 0.8$
4/3	$\frac{16}{7} = 2.28571$	$\frac{9}{7} = 1.28571$
5/4	$\frac{25}{9} = 2.77778$	$\frac{16}{9} = 1.77778$
5/3	$\frac{25}{16} = 1.5625$	$\frac{9}{16} = 0.5625$
6/5	$\frac{36}{11} = 3.272727$	$\frac{25}{11} = 2.272727$
7/5	$\frac{49}{24} = 2.041667$	$\frac{25}{24} = 1.041667$
7/6	$\frac{49}{13} = 3.769234$	$\frac{36}{13} = 2.769234$

Since Eq. (10.19) is homogeneous in n, the h^2 extrapolation coefficients of Table 10.2 are only functions of the ratios n_j/n_i; for instance, the (2,1) extrapolation formula holds also for (4,2).

If in Eq. (10.17) we take into consideration the first two terms of the series and apply the formula to three approximations $k_i{}^2$, $k_j{}^2$, $k_k{}^2$, obtained by subdividing the characteristic length L into $n_i < n_j < n_k$ parts, we have

$$\bar{k}^2 - k_i{}^2 = \frac{\alpha_1 L^2}{n_i{}^2} + \frac{\alpha_2 L^4}{n_i{}^4}$$

$$\bar{k}^2 - k_j{}^2 = \frac{\alpha_1 L^2}{n_j{}^2} + \frac{\alpha_2 L^4}{n_j{}^4}$$

$$\bar{k}^2 - k_k{}^2 = \frac{\alpha_1 L^2}{n_k{}^2} + \frac{\alpha_2 L^4}{n_k{}^4}$$

By elimination of $\alpha_1 L^2$ and $\alpha_2 L^4$ between these three equations, we obtain the (h^2, h^4) *extrapolation formula:*

$$\bar{k}_{i,j,k}{}^2 = \frac{n_k{}^4(n_j{}^2 - n_i{}^2)k_k{}^2 - n_j{}^4(n_k{}^2 - n_i{}^2)k_j{}^2 + n_i{}^4(n_k{}^2 - n_j{}^2)k_i{}^2}{n_k{}^4(n_j{}^2 - n_i{}^2) - n_j{}^4(n_k{}^2 - n_i{}^2) + n_i{}^4(n_k{}^2 - n_j{}^2)}$$
$$= a_{n_k} k_k{}^2 - a_{n_j} k_j{}^2 + a_{n_i} k_i{}^2 \qquad (10.20)$$

where $\bar{k}_{i,j,k}{}^2$ is the extrapolated value of k^2.

T<small>ABLE</small> 10.3. (h^2, h^4) E<small>XTRAPOLATIONS</small>

$n_k/n_j/n_i$	a_{n_k}		a_{n_j}		a_{n_i}	
3/2/1	243/120	= 2.025	128/120	= 1.06667	5/120	= 0.04167
4/3/2	1,280/420	= 3.04762	972/420	= 2.31429	112/420	= 0.26667
5/4/3	4,375/1,008	= 4.34028	4,096/1,008	= 4.06349	729/1,008	= 0.72321
6/5/4	11,664/1,980	= 5.89091	12,500/1,980	= 6.31313	2,816/1,980	= 1.42222
7/6/5	26,411/3,432	= 7.69551	31,104/3,432	= 9.06294	8,125/3,432	= 2.36742
5/3/1	5,000/3,072	= 1.62760	1,944/3,072	= 0.63281	16/3,072	= 0.00521
7/5/3	38,416/15,360	= 2.50104	25,000/15,360	= 1.62760	1,944/15,360	= 0.12656

Table 10.3 gives the (h^2, h^4) extrapolation coefficients for the most commonly used values of n_i, n_j, n_k. Here again the values of n may be multiplied by a common factor without changing the formulas.

Let us now apply the method of extrapolation to the examples computed in Sec. 10.1. In the case of the first example, the h^2 extrapolation formula [Eq. (10.19) and Table 10.2] applied to the first few values of $k^2 L^2$ gives the following results with the errors indicated in parentheses:

$$\bar{k}_{2,3}{}^2 L^2 = 1.8 \times 9 - 0.8 \times 8 = 9.8 \qquad (-0.71\%)$$
$$\bar{k}_{3,4}{}^2 L^2 = 2.28571 \times 9.37264 - 1.2857 \times 9 = 9.852 \qquad (-0.18\%)$$
$$\bar{k}_{4,5}{}^2 L^2 = 2.77778 \times 9.549 - 1.77778 \times 9.373 = 9.862 \qquad (-0.08\%)$$

The (h^2, h^4) extrapolation [Eq. (10.20) and Table 10.3] gives

$$\bar{k}_{2,3,4}{}^2 L^2 = 3.04762 \times 9.37264 - 2.31429 \times 9 + 0.26667 \times 8 = 9.8690$$
$$(-0.006\%)$$
$$\bar{k}_{3,5,7}{}^2 L^2 = 2.50104 \times 9.7054 - 1.62760 \times 9.549 + 0.12656 \times 9 = 9.8696$$
$$(0\%)$$

It is seen that the extrapolated values are so near the true value that in practice two approximations and an h^2 extrapolation would give a result more than sufficiently accurate.

The proof of formula (10.17) cannot be extended to the cases where the governing differential equation has variable coefficients. However, by studying the results of many problems worked out, it appears that the method of extrapolation can still be used as an empirical method. We shall observe in these cases the following points:

1. The extrapolation formulas assume that the successive approximations k^2 approach $\bar{k}^2$ *from the same side*. When the approach to $\bar{k}^2$ is of the oscillating type, the formulas may be used separately in connection with the approximations from above or from below. The two extrapolated values thus obtained may be usefully compared. It is unsafe to use extrapolation without having at least three approximate values of k^2.

2. Even if the approximate values of k^2 approach the true value monotonically (either from above or from below), it is not known offhand whether the extrapolated value is above or below the true value.

3. It is true that, in general, the (h^2,h^4) extrapolation gives better results than the h^2 extrapolation, but it is impossible to determine offhand whether an h^2 extrapolation based on larger n_i will give better results than an (h^2,h^4) extrapolation based on smaller n_i or even on three n_i the largest of which is the same as the largest n_i of the h^2 extrapolation.

In the second example solved in Sec. 10.1, when $I(x) = I_0[1 + \sin (\pi x/L)]$, we observe that the approach of k^2 to $\bar{k}^2$ is monotonic.[1] The extrapolation method gives the following results, with errors in parentheses:

$$\bar{k}_{2,3}^2 L^2 = 1.8 \times 16.79 - 0.8 \times 16 = 17.42 \qquad (-3.5\%)$$
$$\bar{k}_{3,4}^2 L^2 = 2.286 \times 17.24 - 1.286 \times 16.79 = 17.81 \qquad (-1.3\%)$$
$$\bar{k}_{2,3,4}^2 L^2 = 3.0476 \times 17.24 - 2.3143 \times 16.79 + 0.2667 \times 16 = 17.95$$
$$(-0.55\%)$$

If $I(x) = I_0[1 + (2x/L)]$ when $0 \leq x \leq L/2$ and $I(x) = I_0[3 - (2x/L)]$ when $L/2 \leq x \leq L$, we see that the approach of k^2 to $\bar{k}^2$ is one-sided, but not monotonic, while the separate sequences of even and odd n_j are both monotonic. The extrapolations of Table 10.4 are obtained by using these sequences.

TABLE 10.4

n	$k^2 L^2$	Error, per cent	h^2 extrapolations			(h^2,h^4) extrapolations		
			n	$k^2 L^2$	Error, per cent	n	$k^2 L^2$	Error, per cent
2	16.0000	−3.23	2, 4	16.0000	−3.23	2, 4, 6	16.5114	−0.13
3	15.0000	−9.27	3, 5	16.3933	−0.85	3, 5, 7	16.4964	−0.22
4	16.0000	−3.23	4, 6	16.4546	−0.48			
5	15.8917	−3.83	5, 7	16.4774	−0.34			
6	16.2526	−1.70						
7	16.1786	−2.15						

In the case of the lateral buckling of a cantilever beam with narrow cross section, we observe that the convergence of k^2 to $\bar{k}^2$ is monotonic after $n = 3$. The h^2 extrapolation may be applied for $n = 3$, 4 and $n = 4$, 5, while the (h^2,h^4) extrapolation may be applied to any sequence, and in particular for $n = 2$, 3, 4 and $n = 3$, 4, 5. Table 10.5 gives the results of the computations.

[1] A monotonically increasing function is one in which for every sequence of increasing values of the argument the corresponding values of the function always increase; similarly, a function is monotonically decreasing if its values decrease as the argument increases.

TABLE 10.5

			h^2 extrapolations			(h^2, h^4) extrapolations		
n	k^2L^2	Error, per cent	n	k^2L^2	Error, per cent	n	k^2L^2	Error, per cent
2	4.000	−0.32	3, 4	3.992	−0.52	2, 3, 4	4.030	+0.42
3	3.933	−1.9	4, 5	4.006	−0.17	3, 4, 5	4.014	+0.025
4	3.959	−1.3						
5	3.976	−0.92						

10.5. Energy Method. Let us consider the equilibrium of a column when the compressive load on the column is *equal to* the buckling load. From our discussion in Sec. 9.3, we saw that there were two possible equilibrium forms: the straight form and the bent form. Assume that the column is now in the straight form, which, being unstable, will jump to the bent form because of any small disturbance. During this exchange of equilibrium forms, the strain energy in the column is increased, since to the energy of compression some energy of bending of the column will be added. At the same time the potential energy of the load diminishes, owing to the approach of its points of application. This decrease in potential energy is equal to the work done by the loads at the ends of the column. Since the straight and bent forms of the column are both possible equilibrium forms *under the same load*, there will be no energy lost or gained during this exchange of equilibrium forms. The additional amount of bending energy stored in the column must therefore be equal to the work done by the loads.

Fig. 10.5.

The bending energy stored in the column with deflection w is given in Sec. 7.3 as

$$U = \frac{1}{2} \int_0^L EI \left(\frac{d^2w}{dx^2}\right)^2 dx$$

The shortening of the column due to bending can be found as follows:

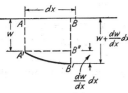

Fig. 10.6.

Consider an element AB of the axis of the column with length dx before bending (Fig. 10.6). We note that this element has already been under compression. After bending, AB will displace to the position $A'B'$. Since the compressive load is not changed, the column will be under the same axial stress as that before bending and there will be no change in the length along the neutral axis, $A'B'$, that is, the arc length of $A'B'$ is equal to dx.

The shortening of the element AB in the x direction is therefore

$$AB - A'B'' = dx - \left[dx^2 - \left(\frac{dw}{dx} \, dx \right)^2 \right]^{\frac{1}{2}}$$

$$= dx - dx \left[1 - \frac{1}{2} \left(\frac{dw}{dx} \right)^2 + \cdots \right]$$

$$\cong \frac{1}{2} \left(\frac{dw}{dx} \right)^2 dx$$

where in the last step the higher-order terms have been neglected. The approach of the ends of the column is therefore

$$u = \frac{1}{2} \int_0^L \left(\frac{dw}{dx} \right)^2 dx$$

As the ends of the column approach each other, P remains constant. The work done by the load P is consequently

$$Pu = \frac{P}{2} \int_0^L \left(\frac{dw}{dx} \right)^2 dx$$

The condition of conservation of energy requires

$$U = Pu$$

or
$$\frac{1}{2} \int_0^L EI \left(\frac{d^2w}{dx^2} \right)^2 dx = \frac{P}{2} \int_0^L \left(\frac{dw}{dx} \right)^2 dx \qquad (10.21)$$

from which
$$P = \frac{\int_0^L EI \, (d^2w/dx^2)^2 dx}{\int_0^L (dw/dx)^2 \, dx} \qquad (10.22)$$

This is the so-called *Rayleigh's formula*. To obtain the lowest value which is the buckling load, we have

$$P_{cr} = \min P = \left[\frac{\int_0^L EI (d^2w/dx^2)^2 \, dx}{\int_0^L (dw/dx)^2 \, dx} \right]_{\min} \qquad (10.23)$$

The notation min P in (10.23) really indicates the least value of a discrete sequence of eigenvalues. It can be shown, however, that of all the deflections w satisfying the boundary conditions the actual deflection corresponding to the first mode will make P a minimum in the sense of calculus of variation.

To show this, let

$$\bar{\Pi} = U - Pu$$

Carrying out the variation in w, we have

$$\delta\bar{\Pi} = \int_0^L EI \frac{d^2w}{dx^2} \frac{d^2\delta w}{dx^2}\, dx - P \int_0^L \frac{dw}{dx} \frac{d\delta w}{dx}\, dx$$

$$= \left\{ EI \frac{d^2w}{dx^2} \delta\left(\frac{dw}{dx}\right) - \left[\frac{d}{dx}\left(EI \frac{d^2w}{dx^2}\right) + P \frac{dw}{dx}\right] \delta w \right\}_0^L$$

$$+ \int_0^L \left[\frac{d^2}{dx^2}\left(EI \frac{d^2w}{dx^2}\right) + P \frac{d^2w}{dx^2}\right] \delta w\, dx$$

where the last step was obtained by integration by parts. On the boundary, $x = 0$ and L, the boundary conditions are combinations of the cases where $M = EI(d^2w/dx^2) = 0$,

$$Q = \text{shear} = \left(\frac{d}{dx}\right)\left[EI\left(\frac{d^2w}{dx^2}\right)\right] + P \frac{dw}{dx} = 0$$

dw/dx is given, and w is given. The terms in the brackets therefore become zero. In the interior of the column, the equilibrium condition is

$$\frac{d^2}{dx^2}\left(EI \frac{d^2w}{dx^2}\right) + P \frac{d^2w}{dx^2} = 0$$

Therefore $\qquad \delta\bar{\Pi} = 0 \qquad$ or $\qquad \delta U - P\,\delta u = 0$

Substituting into the above equation the identity

$$P = \frac{U}{u}$$

we find the condition $\delta\bar{\Pi} = 0$ leads to

$$u\,\delta U - U\,\delta u = 0$$

which is exactly the condition requiring that

$$\delta P = \frac{u\,\delta U - U\,\delta u}{u^2} = 0$$

This means that of all the deflections satisfying the boundary conditions, the actual deflection is the one which makes P a minimum.

Having established the above statement, we shall now show by the following examples the calculation of buckling loads by the Rayleigh-Ritz method.

Example 1. *Simply Supported Column with Constant Cross Section.* The boundary conditions in this case are $w = 0$ and $d^2w/dx^2 = 0$ at $x = 0$ and $x = L$. To satisfy these conditions, we may assume

$$w = \sum_{n=1}^{\infty} C_n \sin \frac{n\pi x}{L}$$

Integrating, we find

$$U = \frac{1}{2} \int_0^L EI \left(\frac{d^2w}{dx^2}\right)^2 dx = \frac{\pi^4 EI}{4L^3} \sum_{n=1}^{\infty} n^4 C_n{}^2$$

$$u = \frac{1}{2} \int_0^L \left(\frac{dw}{dx}\right)^2 dx = \frac{\pi^2}{4L} \sum_{n=1}^{\infty} n^2 C_n{}^2$$

and
$$P = \frac{U}{u} = \frac{\pi^2 EI}{L^2} \frac{\displaystyle\sum_{n=1}^{\infty} n^4 C_n{}^2}{\displaystyle\sum_{n=1}^{\infty} n^2 C_n{}^2}$$

$$= \frac{\pi^2 EI}{L^2} \frac{C_1{}^2 + 16C_2{}^2 + 81C_3{}^2 + \cdots}{C_1{}^2 + 4C_2{}^2 + 9C_3{}^2 + \cdots}$$

$$= \frac{\pi^2 EI}{L^2} \frac{1 + 16(C_2/C_1)^2 + 81(C_3/C_1)^2 + \cdots}{1 + 4(C_2/C_1)^2 + 9(C_3/C_1)^2 + \cdots}$$

To find the buckling load, we must adjust the parameters C_2/C_1, C_3/C_1, etc., in such a way that P is a minimum which can be obtained by letting $\partial P/\partial(C_2/C_1) = 0$, $\partial P/\partial(C_3/C_1) = 0$, etc. Carrying out the calculation, we find that these conditions require that $C_2/C_1 = C_3/C_1 = \cdots = 0$. Hence,

$$P_{cr} = \min P = \frac{\pi^2 EI}{L^2}$$

which is the value given by the exact solution. This result was obtained because the assumed form of the deflection curve happened to include the exact solution.

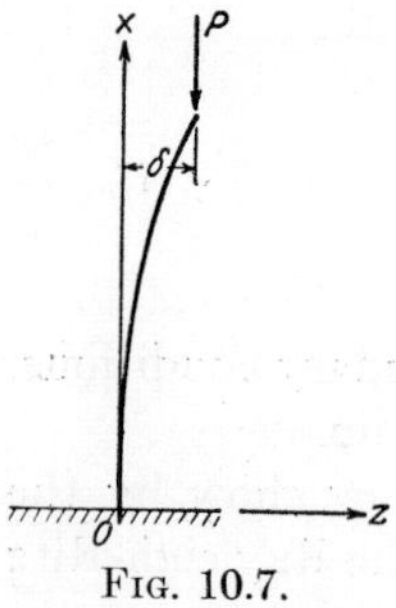

Example 2. Column with One End Built In and the Other End Free. The boundary conditions in this case are $w = 0$ and $dw/dx = 0$ at $x = 0$. To satisfy the boundary conditions, let us assume

$$w = \left(\frac{x}{L}\right)^2 \sum_{n=0}^{\infty} C_n \left(\frac{x}{L}\right)^n$$

Fig. 10.7.

Since this form of the deflection curve will not result in a general expression for all values of n after the integration, let us take only the first two terms in the series and write

$$w = C_0 \left(\frac{x}{L}\right)^2 + C_1 \left(\frac{x}{L}\right)^3$$

If the cross section of the column is constant, substituting the above expression for w into formula (10.22) and integrating, we have

$$P = \frac{4EI}{L^2} \frac{C_0{}^2 + 3C_0C_1 + 3C_1{}^2}{\frac{4}{3}C_0{}^2 + 3C_0C_1 + (9C_1{}^2/5)}$$

$$= \frac{4EI}{L^2} \frac{1 + 3(C_1/C_0) + 3(C_1/C_0)^2}{\frac{4}{3} + 3(C_1/C_0) + \frac{9}{5}(C_1C_0)^2} \tag{10.24}$$

If we take only one parameter in the series, $C_1 = 0$ and we have

$$P_{cr} = \frac{3EI}{L^2}$$

which is the minimum P. The error in this case is $+21.6$ per cent. With two parameters we can find the minimum value of P by differentiating (10.24) with respect to C_1/C_0 and setting the resulting expression level to zero. Then

$$\frac{dP}{d(C_1/C_0)} = 0$$

$$= \{[\tfrac{4}{3} + 3(C_1/C_0) + \tfrac{9}{5}(C_1/C_0)^2][3 + 6(C_1/C_0)]$$
$$- [1 + 3(C_1/C_0) + 3(C_1/C_0)^2][3 + \tfrac{18}{5}(C_1/C_0)]\}/[\tfrac{4}{3} + 3(C_1/C_0)$$
$$+ \tfrac{9}{5}(C_1/C_0)^2]^2$$

or

$$18\left(\frac{C_1}{C_0}\right)^2 + 22\frac{C_1}{C_0} + 5 = 0$$

which gives

$$\frac{C_1}{C_0} = -0.301 \text{ or } -0.92$$

Substituting these values into (10.24), we find that the root

$$\frac{C_1}{C_0} = -0.301$$

gives a smaller value of P and therefore

$$P_{cr} = \frac{2.49EI}{L^2}$$

The error becomes in this case $+0.92$ per cent.

Note that the magnitude of C_1 is again undetermined in the present case, as we have found previously. If more than two parameters are retained, the ratios of these parameters can be determined from the conditions

$$\frac{\partial P}{\partial(C_1/C_0)} = 0 \qquad \frac{\partial P}{\partial(C_2/C_0)} = 0 \qquad \text{etc.}$$

There is no mathematical difficulty in this case, but the calculation may become quite lengthy. An alternative method of calculation, which appears to be simpler, can be carried out as follows: We have proved that the condition

$$\delta P = 0$$

is equivalent to

$$\delta \bar{\bar{\Pi}} = 0$$

From Eq. (10.24), we find that

$$\bar{\Pi}' = (C_0{}^2 + 3C_0C_1 + 3C_1{}^2) - P'\left(\frac{4}{3} C_0{}^2 + 3C_0C_1 + \frac{9C_1{}^2}{5}\right)$$

where $\bar{\Pi}'$ is $\bar{\Pi}$ times a constant and $P' = PL^2/4EI$. The conditions $\partial\bar{\Pi}'/\partial C_0 = 0$ and $\partial\bar{\Pi}'\ \partial C_1 = 0$ become

$$2(1 - \tfrac{4}{3}P')C_0 + 3(1 - P')C_1 = 0$$
$$3(1 - P')C_0 + 2(3 - \tfrac{9}{5}P')C_1 = 0$$

The determinantal equation for the nontrivial solution is

$$\begin{vmatrix} 2(1 - \tfrac{4}{3}P') & 3(1 - P') \\ 3(1 - P') & 2(3 - \tfrac{9}{5}P') \end{vmatrix} = 0$$

from which we obtain

$$3P'^2 - 26P' + 15 = 0$$

or

$$P' = \frac{26 \pm \sqrt{(26)^2 - 3 \times 4 \times 15}}{6} = 0.6217 \text{ or } 8.045$$

Hence

$$P_{cr} = 4 \times 0.6217 \frac{EI}{L^2} = 2.487 \frac{EI}{L^2}$$

With P' determined, we may compute the ratio C_1/C_0 from the equation $\partial\bar{\Pi}'/\partial C_0 = 0$ if so desired.

Example 3. *Simply Supported Columns with Variable Cross Sections.* Let the moment of inertia of the cross-sectional area of the column vary according to the formula

$$I = I_0\left(1 + \sin\frac{\pi x}{L}\right)$$

Since the only conditions that the assumed expression for w has to satisfy are the boundary conditions, we may again take

$$w = \sum_{n=1}^{\infty} C_n \sin\frac{n\pi x}{L}$$

Since the deflection curve must be symmetrical with respect to the middle point of the column, all the even parameters must be zero. If we retain two parameters in the series, we have

$$w = C_1 \sin\frac{\pi x}{L} + C_3 \sin\frac{3\pi x}{L}$$

Integrating, we find that

$$
U = \frac{1}{2} \int_0^L EI \left(\frac{d^2w}{dx^2}\right)^2 dx
$$

$$
= \frac{1}{2} \int_0^L EI_0 \left(1 + \sin\frac{\pi x}{L}\right) \left[-C_1 \left(\frac{\pi}{L}\right)^2 \sin\frac{\pi x}{L} - C_3 \left(\frac{3\pi}{L}\right)^2 \sin\frac{3\pi x}{L} \right]^2 dx
$$

$$
= \frac{1}{2} EI_0 \left(\frac{\pi}{L}\right)^3 \left[\left(\frac{4}{3} + \frac{\pi}{2}\right) C_1{}^2 - \frac{24}{5} C_1 C_3 + \left(\frac{2{,}916}{35} + \frac{81\pi}{2}\right) C_3{}^2 \right]
$$

$$
u = \frac{1}{2} \int_0^L \left(\frac{dw}{dx}\right)^2 dx = \frac{1}{2}\left(\frac{\pi}{L}\right)^2 \left(\frac{L}{2} C_1{}^2 + \frac{L}{2} 9C_3{}^2\right)
$$

and
$$
P = \frac{EI_0 \pi}{L^2} \frac{(\tfrac{8}{3} + \pi)C_1{}^2 - \tfrac{48}{5}C_1 C_3 + [(5{,}832/35) + 81\pi]C_3{}^2}{C_1{}^2 + 9C_3{}^2}
$$

The conditions $\partial\overline{\Pi}'/\partial C_1 = 0$ and $\partial\overline{\Pi}'/\partial C_3 = 0$ are

$$
2[(\tfrac{8}{3} + \pi) - P']C_1 - \tfrac{48}{5}C_3 = 0
$$

$$
-\frac{48}{5} C_1 + 2\left[\left(\frac{5{,}832}{35} + 81\pi\right) - 9P'\right] C_3 = 0
$$

where $P' = PL^2/EI_0\pi$. The determinantal equation for the nontrivial solution gives

$$
9P'^2 - \left(\frac{5{,}832}{35} + 81\pi + 24 + 9\pi\right) P' + \left(\frac{8}{3} + \pi\right)\left(\frac{5{,}832}{35} + 81\pi\right)
$$

$$
- \left(\frac{24}{5}\right)^2 = 0
$$

Solving, we find that

$$
P' = 5.746 \qquad \text{or} \qquad P_{cr} = 18.05 \frac{EI_0}{L^2} \tag{10.25}
$$

The corresponding value of C_3/C_1 is 0.01297.

For columns with both ends simply supported and columns with one end built in and the other end free, if the origin of coordinate axis is taken at the free end in the latter case, the equilibrium equation may be written as

$$
EI \frac{d^2w}{dx^2} + Pw = 0 \tag{10.26}
$$

Timoshenko has observed that, if we substitute $-Pw/EI$ for d^2w/dx^2 in the expression for U, we have

$$
\frac{P^2}{2} \int_0^L \frac{w^2}{EI} dx - \frac{P}{2} \int_0^L \left(\frac{dw}{dx}\right)^2 dx = 0
$$

or
$$
P_{cr} = \min P = \left[\frac{\int_0^L (dw/dx)^2\, dx}{\int_0^L (w^2/EI)\, dx}\right]_{\min} \tag{10.27}
$$

This is called *Timoshenko's formula*, and it can be shown (Sec. 10.7) that the approximate buckling load calculated by using Timoshenko's formula is always closer to the exact value than that computed by using Rayleigh's formula.

As an example, we shall now recalculate the buckling load in Example 3 by using Timoshenko's formula. Let us take only one parameter C_1. In this case, we have

$$\int_0^L \left(\frac{dw}{dx}\right)^2 dx = \frac{C_1^2 L}{2}\left(\frac{\pi}{L}\right)^2$$

$$\int_0^L \frac{w^2}{EI}\, dx = \int_0^L \frac{C_1^2 \sin^2(\pi x/L)\, dx}{EI_0[1 + \sin(\pi x/L)]}\, dx$$

$$= \frac{C_1^2}{EI_0}\int_0^L \left(\sin\frac{\pi x}{L} - 1 + \frac{1}{1 + \sin(\pi x/L)}\right) dx$$

$$= \frac{C_1^2 L}{EI_0}\left(\frac{4}{\pi} - 1\right)$$

Therefore
$$P_{cr} = \frac{(C_1^2 L/2)(\pi/L)^2}{(C_1^2 L/EI_0)[(4/\pi) - 1]} = 18.06\,\frac{EI_0}{L^2}$$

which is only 0.05 per cent different from the value computed by taking two parameters in Example 3.

Since Eq. (10.26) is not a general differential equation for all boundary conditions, (10.27) is not a general formula. For example, in the case of a column with one end built in and one end free, if the coordinates are taken as shown in Fig. 10.7, the differential equation is

$$EI\,\frac{d^2w}{dx^2} - P(\delta - w) = 0$$

where δ is the deflection at the free end of the column. Timoshenko's formula in this case becomes

$$P_{cr} = \left[\frac{\displaystyle\int_0^L (dw/dx)^2\, dx}{\displaystyle\int_0^L [(\delta - w)^2/EI]\, dx}\right]_{\min} \tag{10.28}$$

Problem 1. The moment of inertia of a simply supported column varies according to the formula

$$I(x)\begin{cases} = I_0\left(1 + \dfrac{2x}{L}\right) & 0 \le x \le \dfrac{L}{2} \\[2mm] = I_0\left(3 - \dfrac{2x}{L}\right) & \dfrac{L}{2} \le x \le L \end{cases}$$

Assume $w = C_1 \sin(\pi x/L) + C_3 \sin(3\pi x/L)$. Find the buckling loads by Rayleigh's formula. Using one parameter, calculate the buckling load by Timoshenko's formula.

Problem 2. Recalculate the buckling load in Example 2 by using Timoshenko's formula (10.28).

Problem 3. The moment of inertia of a column with one end built in and the other end free varies according to the formula

$$I = I_0 \left(1 + \sin^2 \frac{\pi x}{2L}\right)$$

Assuming the deflection curve as $w = C_1 \sin (\pi x/2L)$, calculate the buckling loads by Rayleigh's formula and Timoshenko's formula.

Ans. Rayleigh's formula: $P_{cr} = \dfrac{4.32EI_0}{L^2}$

Timoshenko's formula: $P_{cr} = \dfrac{4.22EI_0}{L^2}$

10.6. Derivation of Rayleigh's Formula from Principle of Potential Energy.

In Sec. 3.5, we proved the uniqueness theorem of Kirchhoff which states: An elastic body can assume one and only one equilibrium configuration under a given external loading. From the energy point of view, this means that the potential energy Ⅱ of the internal and external forces (see Sec. 7.1) has one and only one extremal and the extremal is a minimum. The uniqueness theorem holds as long as the stress components are linear functions of the strain components and the strain components are linear functions of the displacements. Then the potential energy Ⅱ is of, at most, the second degree in the displacements, and geometrical considerations show directly that a "parabola" of the second degree can have one and only one minimum. The situation changes, however, when some of the displacements become large so that the linearized strain-displacement formulas can no longer be used with sufficient accuracy. This happens particularly to bodies for which one dimension is small compared with the others, structures in the form of columns, thin plates, and thin shells. For example, a column can, without exceeding the proportional limit, undergo bending deflections several times greater than its thickness, and under these circumstances the quadratic term of the transverse dis-

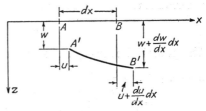

FIG. 10.8.

placements in the strain-displacement formula is no longer small compared with the linear term. The strain energy, and therefore the potential energy Ⅱ, contains terms of higher than the second degree in the displacements, and a parabola of higher order can naturally have several extremals and therefore several equilibrium positions.

Now let us find the relation between strain and displacement. Consider an element AB of the column before deformation. After deformation, AB is displaced to $A'B'$ (Fig. 10.8). Note that Fig. 10.8 is not the same as Fig. 10.6. In Fig. 10.6, the element AB is already under the compressive load P_{cr} and then bent, with P_{cr} remaining constant, while, in Fig. 10.8, AB is the element before the load is applied. Therefore

$$\epsilon_x = \frac{A'B' - AB}{AB} = \frac{\left[\left(dx + \frac{du}{dx}\,dx\right)^2 + \left(\frac{dw}{dx}\,dx\right)^2\right]^{\frac{1}{2}} - dx}{dx}$$

$$= \frac{du}{dx} + \frac{1}{2}\left(\frac{dw}{dx}\right)^2$$

where, as explained in the preceding paragraph, $(dw/dx)^2$ is now of the same magnitude as du/dx, while terms such as $(du/dx)^2$ and $(dw/dx)^3$ can still be neglected. From Hooke's law, the corresponding stress is

$$\sigma_x = E\epsilon_x = E\left[\frac{du}{dx} + \frac{1}{2}\left(\frac{dw}{dx}\right)^2\right]$$

and therefore the energy of compression is

$$U_1 = \frac{1}{2}\int_0^L EA\left[\frac{du}{dx} + \frac{1}{2}\left(\frac{dw}{dx}\right)^2\right]^2 dx$$

where A is the cross-sectional area of the column. The bending-strain energy is

$$U_2 = \frac{1}{2}\int_0^L EI\left(\frac{d^2w}{dx^2}\right)^2 dx$$

The approach of the ends of the column is given by $-[u(L) - u(0)]$, and the compressive load on the column is $P = -\sigma_x A$. The potential of the external forces W, from formula (7.11), is

$$W = -P[u(L) - u(0)]$$

The potential energy of the system is then

$$\Pi = U_1 + U_2 - W$$

$$= \frac{1}{2}\int_0^L EA\left[\frac{du}{dx} + \frac{1}{2}\left(\frac{dw}{dx}\right)^2\right]^2 dx + \frac{1}{2}\int_0^L EI\left(\frac{d^2w}{dx^2}\right)^2 dx$$
$$+ P[u(L) - u(0)] \quad (10.29)$$

Now let us calculate the variations.

$$\Pi(u + \delta u, w + \delta w) - \Pi(u,w) = \delta\Pi + \frac{1}{2}\delta^2\Pi + \cdots$$

$$= \frac{1}{2}\int_0^L EA\left[\frac{du}{dx} + \frac{d\delta u}{dx} + \frac{1}{2}\left(\frac{dw}{dx} + \frac{d\delta w}{dx}\right)^2\right]^2 dx$$

$$+ \frac{1}{2}\int_0^L EI\left(\frac{d^2w}{dx^2} + \frac{d^2\delta w}{dx^2}\right)^2 dx + P[u + \delta u]_0^L$$

$$- \frac{1}{2}\int_0^L EA\left[\frac{du}{dx} + \frac{1}{2}\left(\frac{dw}{dx}\right)^2\right]^2 dx - \frac{1}{2}\int_0^L EI\left(\frac{d^2w}{dx^2}\right)^2 dx - P[u]_0^L$$

$$= \int_0^L EA \left[\frac{du}{dx} + \frac{1}{2}\left(\frac{dw}{dx}\right)^2\right] \frac{d\delta u}{dx} \, dx$$

$$+ \int_0^L \left\{ EA \left[\frac{du}{dx} + \frac{1}{2}\left(\frac{dw}{dx}\right)^2\right] \frac{dw}{dx} \frac{d\delta w}{dx} + EI \frac{d^2w}{dx^2} \frac{d^2\delta w}{dx^2} \right\} \, dx$$

$$+ \frac{1}{2} \int_0^L EA \left(\frac{d\delta u}{dx}\right)^2 dx$$

$$+ \int_0^L EA \frac{dw}{dx} \frac{d\delta u}{dx} \frac{d\delta w}{dx} \, dx + \frac{1}{2} \int_0^L EA \left(\frac{dw}{dx}\right)^2 \left(\frac{d\delta w}{dx}\right)^2 dx$$

$$+ \frac{1}{2} \int_0^L \left\{ EA \left[\frac{du}{dx} + \frac{1}{2}\left(\frac{dw}{dx}\right)^2\right] \left(\frac{d\delta w}{dx}\right)^2 + EI \left(\frac{d^2\delta w}{dx^2}\right)^2 \right\} dx + P[\delta u]_0^L$$

From this we find that

$$\delta\Pi = \int_0^L EA \left[\frac{du}{dx} + \frac{1}{2}\left(\frac{dw}{dx}\right)^2\right] \frac{d\delta u}{dx} \, dx$$

$$+ \int_0^L \left\{ EA \left[\frac{du}{dx} + \frac{1}{2}\left(\frac{dw}{dx}\right)^2\right] \frac{dw}{dx} \frac{d\delta w}{dx} + EI \frac{d^2w}{dx^2} \frac{d^2\delta w}{dx^2} \right\} \, dx + P[\delta u]_0^L$$

$$(10.30)$$

$$\frac{1}{2} \delta^2\Pi = \frac{1}{2} \int_0^L EA \left(\frac{d\delta u}{dx}\right)^2 dx + \int_0^L EA \frac{dw}{dx} \frac{d\delta u}{dx} \frac{d\delta w}{dx} \, dx$$

$$+ \frac{1}{2} \int_0^L EA \left(\frac{dw}{dx}\right)^2 \left(\frac{d\delta w}{dx}\right)^2 dx$$

$$+ \frac{1}{2} \int_0^L \left\{ EA \left[\frac{du}{dx} + \frac{1}{2}\left(\frac{dw}{dx}\right)^2\right] \left(\frac{d\delta w}{dx}\right)^2 + EI \left(\frac{d^2\delta w}{dx^2}\right)^2 \right\} dx \quad (10.31)$$

Integrating by parts, the condition $\delta\Pi = 0$ yields

$$\left[\left\{ EA \left[\frac{du}{dx} + \frac{1}{2}\left(\frac{dw}{dx}\right)^2\right] + P \right\} \delta u \right]_0^L - \int_0^L \frac{d}{dx} \left\{ EA \left[\frac{du}{dx} + \frac{1}{2}\left(\frac{dw}{dx}\right)^2\right] \right\} \delta u \, dx$$

$$+ \left[\left\{ EA \left[\frac{du}{dx} + \frac{1}{2}\left(\frac{dw}{dx}\right)^2\right] \frac{dw}{dx} - \frac{d}{dx}\left(EI \frac{d^2w}{dx^2} \right) \right\} \delta w + EI \frac{d^2w}{dx^2} \delta\left(\frac{dw}{dx}\right) \right]_0^L$$

$$+ \int_0^L \left[\frac{d^2}{dx^2}\left(EI \frac{d^2w}{dx^2} \right) - \frac{d}{dx}\left\{ EA \left[\frac{du}{dx} + \frac{1}{2}\left(\frac{dw}{dx}\right)^2\right] \frac{dw}{dx} \right\} \right] \delta w \, dx = 0$$

Since on the boundary $EA[(du/dx) + \frac{1}{2}(dw/dx)^2] = \sigma_x A = -P$, and the boundary conditions require either

$$EA \left[\frac{du}{dx} + \frac{1}{2}\left(\frac{dw}{dx}\right)^2\right] \frac{dw}{dx} - \frac{d}{dx}\left(EI \frac{d^2w}{dx^2} \right) = 0$$

or $\delta w = 0$, and either $EI(d^2w/dx^2) = 0$ or $\delta(dw/dx) = 0$, the terms in the first brackets are zero on the boundary. Since δu and δw are arbitrary in the interior, the coefficients of δu and δw in the integrands must be zero. Thus

$$\frac{d}{dx}\left\{EA\left[\frac{du}{dx} + \frac{1}{2}\left(\frac{dw}{dx}\right)^2\right]\right\} = 0 \qquad (10.32)$$

$$\frac{d^2}{dx^2}\left(EI\frac{d^2w}{dx^2}\right) - \frac{d}{dx}\left\{EA\left[\frac{du}{dx} + \frac{1}{2}\left(\frac{dw}{dx}\right)^2\right]\frac{dw}{dx}\right\} = 0 \qquad (10.33)$$

From (10.32), we obtain

$$EA\left[\frac{du}{dx} + \frac{1}{2}\left(\frac{dw}{dx}\right)^2\right] = \text{constant}$$

and from the boundary conditions we find that this constant is equal to $-P$. Hence

$$EA\left[\frac{du}{dx} + \frac{1}{2}\left(\frac{dw}{dx}\right)^2\right] = -P \qquad (10.34)$$

With Eq. (10.34), (10.33) becomes

$$\frac{d^2}{dx^2}\left(EI\frac{d^2w}{dx^2}\right) + P\frac{d^2w}{dx^2} = 0 \qquad (10.35)$$

which is the governing differential equation of column buckling.

An elastic body is in equilibrium when the first variation of the potential energy is zero, or

$$\delta\Pi = 0$$

which indicates that Π is an extremum or a stationary point. In the determination of the stability of the equilibrium states, we must examine the second variation of the potential energy. It can be shown that an equilibrium state is stable if the potential energy of *every* neighboring state has a larger value. In other words, we have a stable equilibrium state if Π is a minimum, *i.e.*, if we have $\delta\Pi = 0$ and $\delta^2\Pi > 0$. Similarly, if Π is a maximum, that is $\delta\Pi = 0$ and $\delta^2\Pi < 0$, the equilibrium state is an unstable one. In the case of the buckling of a column, the straight form of equilibrium is stable when $P < P_{cr}$, unstable when $P > P_{cr}$, and in neutral equilibrium when $P = P_{cr}$. Therefore as P increases for some value less than P_{cr} to some value greater than P_{cr}, $\delta^2\Pi$ changes from a positive value to a negative value. At $P = P_{cr}$, we must have $\delta^2\Pi = 0$. Therefore the condition $\delta^2\Pi = 0$ determines the stability limit.

Now let us examine $\delta^2\Pi$ as given by Eq. (10.31). When $\delta\Pi = 0$, we have

$$EA\left[\frac{du}{dx} + \frac{1}{2}\left(\frac{dw}{dx}\right)^2\right] = -P$$

or

$$\frac{d\delta u}{dx} + \frac{dw}{dx}\frac{d\delta w}{dx} = 0 \qquad (10.36)$$

The first three integrals in (10.31) can be combined and written as

$$\frac{1}{2} \int_0^L \left[EA \left(\frac{d\delta u}{dx} + \frac{dw}{dx} \frac{d\delta w}{dx} \right) \frac{d\delta u}{dx} + EA \left(\frac{d\delta u}{dx} + \frac{dw}{dx} \frac{d\delta w}{dx} \right) \frac{dw}{dx} \frac{d\delta w}{dx} \right] dx$$

which vanishes because of Eq. (10.36). With (10.34), we have

$$\delta^2 \Pi = \int_0^L \left[-P \left(\frac{d\delta w}{dx} \right)^2 + EI \left(\frac{d^2 \delta w}{dx^2} \right)^2 \right] dx$$

and the condition $\delta^2 \Pi = 0$ becomes

$$-P \int_0^L \left(\frac{d\delta w}{dx} \right)^2 dx + \int_0^L EI \left(\frac{d^2 \delta w}{dx^2} \right)^2 dx = 0$$

or

$$P = \frac{\int_0^L EI (d^2 \delta w / dx^2)^2 \, dx}{\int_0^L (d\delta w / dx)^2 \, dx} \tag{10.37}$$

where δw is any small variation of w from the straight form of the column. Since for the straight form, $w = 0$, then δw represents the actual deflection of the buckled column. Formula (10.37) is therefore the same as Rayleigh's formula. The above derivation is essentially the one given by Marguerre.[1]

10.7. Errors in the Buckling Loads Calculated by the Energy Method. In Sec. 10.5, we have shown that approximate values of buckling loads can be calculated by the Rayleigh-Ritz method, from Rayleigh's or Timoshenko's formula. We shall now show that the buckling loads calculated in this way are always larger than the exact value, and the value calculated by Rayleigh's formula is always larger than that calculated by Timoshenko's formula.

The general differential equation is

$$\frac{d^2}{dx^2} \left(EI \frac{d^2 w}{dx^2} \right) + P \frac{d^2 w}{dx^2} = 0$$

where I may be a function of x. Let $w_1, w_2, \ldots, w_n$ be the deflection functions corresponding, respectively, to $P_1, P_2, \ldots,$ and P_n. That is, w_n satisfies the boundary conditions and the equation

$$\frac{d^2}{dx^2} \left(EI \frac{d^2 w_n}{dx^2} \right) + P_n \frac{d^2 w_n}{dx^2} = 0 \tag{10.38}$$

where P_n is the nth critical load as defined in Sec. 9.4. For example, for simply supported columns with constant cross section $P_n = n^2 \pi^2 EI / L^2$

[1] K. Marguerre, Über die Anwendung der Energetischen Methode auf Stablität-probleme, *Jahrb.* 1938 *DVL*, pp. 252–262. Also *NACA Tech. Mem.* 1138.

and $P_1 = P_{cr}$. Now suppose that we assume an approximate function for w. This assumed function w can be represented by the infinite series

$$w = C_1 w_1 + C_2 w_2 + \cdots = \sum_{n=1}^{\infty} C_n w_n$$

where $C_1, C_2 \ldots$ are constants so determined that $\sum_{n=1}^{\infty} C_n w_n$ will represent w to any degree of accuracy desired.

Let

$$I_n = C_n{}^2 \int_0^L \left(\frac{dw_n}{dx}\right)^2 dx$$

Then
$$\int_0^L \left(\frac{dw}{dx}\right)^2 dx = \int_0^L \left(C_1 \frac{dw_1}{dx} + C_2 \frac{dw_2}{dx} + \cdots\right)^2 dx$$

$$= \sum_{n=1}^{\infty} I_n + \int_0^L \left(\sum_{n=1}^{\infty} \sum_{m=1}^{\infty} C_n C_m \frac{dw_n}{dx}\frac{dw_m}{dx}\right) dx \tag{10.39}$$

where $m \neq n$. To prove that the cross product integrals in (10.39) vanish, let us multiply both terms in (10.38) by $w_m\, dx$ and integrate them by parts. We obtain

$$\left\{w_m\left[\frac{d}{dx}\left(EI \frac{d^2 w_n}{dx^2}\right) + P_n \frac{dw_n}{dx}\right] - \frac{dw_m}{dx} EI \frac{d^2 w_n}{dx^2}\right\}_0^L$$
$$+ \int_0^L EI \frac{d^2 w_n}{dx^2}\frac{d^2 w_m}{dx^2}\, dx - P_n \int_0^L \frac{dw_m}{dx}\frac{dw_n}{dx}\, dx = 0 \tag{10.40}$$

Now, let us examine the boundary conditions. If an end is simply supported, the boundary conditions are

$$w_n = 0 \quad\text{and}\quad EI \frac{d^2 w_n}{dx^2} = 0$$

If the end is built in, we have

$$w_n = 0 \quad\text{and}\quad \frac{dw_n}{dx} = 0$$

and if the end is free, then

$$EI \frac{d^2 w_n}{dx^2} = 0 \quad\text{and}\quad \frac{d}{dx}\left(EI \frac{d^2 w_n}{dx^2}\right) + P_n \frac{dw_n}{dx} = 0$$

Therefore, no matter whether the ends are simply supported, built in, or free, the boundary terms in (10.40) vanish and we have

$$\int_0^L EI \frac{d^2 w_n}{dx^2}\frac{d^2 w_m}{dx^2}\, dx - P_n \int_0^L \frac{dw_m}{dx}\frac{dw_n}{dx}\, dx = 0 \tag{10.41}$$

Similarly, if we multiply the equation

$$\frac{d^2}{dx^2}\left(EI \frac{d^2 w_m}{dx^2}\right) + P_m \frac{d^2 w_m}{dx^2} = 0$$

by $w_n\,dx$ and integrate, we obtain

$$\int_0^L EI\,\frac{d^2w_m}{dx^2}\frac{d^2w_n}{dx^2}\,dx - P_m \int_0^L \frac{dw_n}{dx}\frac{dw_m}{dx}\,dx = 0$$

Subtracting the above equation from (10.41), we find

$$(P_m - P_n)\int_0^L \frac{dw_n}{dx}\frac{dw_m}{dx}\,dx = 0$$

When $n \neq m$, $P_n \neq P_m$; therefore

$$\int_0^L \frac{dw_n}{dx}\frac{dw_m}{dx}\,dx = 0$$

$$\int_0^L EI\,\frac{d^2w_n}{dx^2}\frac{d^2w_m}{dx^2}\,dx = 0$$

if $n \neq m$. Hence

$$\int_0^L \left(\frac{dw}{dx}\right)^2 dx = \sum_{n=1}^{\infty} I_n$$

Now $\displaystyle\int_0^L EI\left(\frac{d^2w}{dx^2}\right)^2 dx = \int_0^L EI\left(\sum_{n=1}^{\infty} C_n\frac{d^2w_n}{dx^2}\right)^2 dx$

$$= \sum_{n=1}^{\infty} C_n^2 \int_0^L EI\left(\frac{d^2w_n}{dx^2}\right)^2 dx + \sum_{n=1}^{\infty}\sum_{m=1}^{\infty} C_n C_m \int_0^L EI\,\frac{d^2w_n}{dx^2}\frac{d^2w_m}{dx^2}\,dx$$

If we let $m = n$ in (10.41), we obtain

$$\int_0^L EI\left(\frac{d^2w_n}{dx^2}\right)^2 dx = P_n \int_0^L \left(\frac{dw_n}{dx}\right)^2 dx$$
$$= P_n I_n / C_n^2$$

Therefore $\displaystyle\int_0^L EI\left(\frac{d^2w}{dx^2}\right)^2 dx = \sum_{n=1}^{\infty} P_n I_n$

The approximate buckling load calculated by Rayleigh's formula, P_R, is

$$P_R = \frac{\displaystyle\sum_{n=1}^{\infty} P_n I_n}{\displaystyle\sum_{n=1}^{\infty} I_n} = P_1 \frac{I_1 + I_2(P_2/P_1) + I_3(P_3/P_1) + \cdots}{I_1 + I_2 + I_3 + \cdots}$$

Since $P_n/P_1 > 1$ when $n > 1$,

$$\frac{I_1 + I_2(P_2/P_1) + I_3(P_3/P_1) + \cdots}{I_1 + I_2 + I_3 + \cdots} \geq 1 \quad \text{or} \quad P_R \geq P_1$$

where P_1 is the exact critical load. $P_R = P_1$ when $I_2, I_3, \ldots$ are zero.

If the boundary conditions of the column are such that the differential equation is

$$EI \frac{d^2w}{dx^2} + Pw = 0 \tag{10.42}$$

from (10.27) we find that the buckling load calculated from Timoshenko's formula, P_T, is

$$P_T = \frac{\int_0^L (dw/dx)^2 \, dx}{\int_0^L (w^2/EI) \, dx}$$

Now

$$\int_0^L \frac{w^2}{EI} \, dx = \int_0^L \frac{1}{EI} \Big(\sum_{n=1}^{\infty} C_n w_n \Big)^2 dx$$

$$= \sum_{n=1}^{\infty} C_n^2 \int_0^L \frac{w_n^2}{EI} \, dx + \sum_{n=1}^{\infty} \sum_{m=1}^{\infty} C_m C_n \int_0^L \frac{w_n w_m}{EI} \, dx$$

where $n \neq m$. With (10.42), we have

$$\int_0^L \frac{w_n^2}{EI} \, dx = -\frac{1}{P_n} \int_0^L w_n \frac{d^2w_n}{dx^2} \, dx$$

$$= -\frac{1}{P_n} \Big[w_n \frac{dw_n}{dx} \Big]_0^L + \frac{1}{P_n} \int_0^L \Big(\frac{dw_n}{dx} \Big)^2 dx$$

$$= I_n/P_n C_n^2$$

$$\int_0^L \frac{w_n w_m}{EI} \, dx = -\frac{1}{P_m} \int_0^L w_n \frac{d^2w_m}{dx^2} \, dx = 0$$

because in this case the boundary conditions are that $w_n(dw_n/dx) = 0$ at $x = 0$ and $x = L$. Therefore

$$P_T = \frac{\displaystyle\sum_{n=1}^{\infty} I_n}{\displaystyle\sum_{n=1}^{\infty} (I_n/P_n)} = P_1 \frac{I_1 + I_2 + I_3 + \cdots}{I_1 + I_2(P_1/P_2) + I_3(P_1/P_3) + \cdots}$$

Since $(P_1/P_n) < 1$ for $n > 1$, we have

$$\frac{I_1 + I_2 + I_3 + \cdots}{I_1 + I_2(P_1/P_2) + I_3(P_1/P_3) + \cdots} \geq 1 \quad \text{or} \quad P_T \geq P_1$$

To prove $P_R \geq P_T$, we must show that

$$\frac{P_1 I_1 + P_2 I_2 + \cdots}{I_1 + I_2 + \cdots} \geq \frac{I_1 + I_2 + \cdots}{(I_1/P_1) + (I_2/P_2) + \cdots}$$

Or $(P_1 I_1 + P_2 I_2 + \cdots) \Big(\dfrac{I_1}{P_1} + \dfrac{I_2}{P_2} + \cdots \Big) \geq (I_1 + I_2 + \cdots)^2$

Carrying out the multiplication, we have now to show

$$\sum_{\substack{n \ m \\ (n>m)}}^{\infty} \sum^{\infty} I_m I_n \left(\frac{P_n}{P_m} + \frac{P_m}{P_n}\right) \geq \sum_{\substack{n \ m \\ (n>m)}}^{\infty} \sum^{\infty} 2I_n I_m \quad \text{or} \quad \frac{P_n}{P_m} + \frac{P_m}{P_n} \geq 2$$

But $\quad P_n^2 + P_m^2 \geq 2P_n P_m \quad$ or $\quad P_n^2 - 2P_n P_m + P_m^2 \geq 0$

since $(P_n - P_m)^2 \geq 0$. We have therefore proved that $P_R \geq P_T$.

10.8. Determination of Lower Bounds of the Buckling Loads for Columns with Variable Cross Section. In the previous section, we have proved that the energy methods always give a buckling load which is higher than or equal to the value given by the solution of the differential equation. We shall call this value an *upper bound* of the buckling load. Since the buckling load is to be taken as the allowable load in the design of columns, a higher value will lead to an unsafe design and it is important to ascertain the maximum possible error in such a case. This can be accomplished by formulating a method which will always give a *lower bound* of the buckling load.

Let us define

$$P_C = -\frac{\int_0^L [EI(d^2w/dx^2)](d^2/dx^2)[EI(d^2w/dx^2)]\,dx}{\int_0^L EI(d^2w/dx^2)^2\,dx} \tag{10.43}$$

As in the previous section, we shall let w be represented by the infinite series

$$w = \sum_{n=1}^{\infty} C_n w_n$$

where the functions w_n are as defined before. Thus

$$\int_0^L \frac{d^2}{dx^2}\left(EI\frac{d^2w}{dx^2}\right)\left(EI\frac{d^2w}{dx^2}\right)dx$$

$$= \int_0^L \left[\sum_{n=1}^{\infty}\frac{d^2}{dx^2}\left(EI\frac{d^2w_n}{dx^2}\right)\right]\left(\sum_{n=1}^{\infty} EI\frac{d^2w_n}{dx^2}\right)dx$$

$$= -\int_0^L \left(\sum_{n=1}^{\infty} P_n\frac{d^2w_n}{dx^2}\right)\left(\sum_{n=1}^{\infty} EI\frac{d^2w_n}{dx^2}\right)dx$$

$$= -\sum_{n=1}^{\infty} P_n \int_0^L EI\left(\frac{d^2w_n}{dx^2}\right)^2$$

$$\qquad - \sum_{n=1}^{\infty}\sum_{m=1}^{\infty} P_n \int_0^L EI\frac{d^2w_n}{dx^2}\frac{d^2w_m}{dx^2}\,dx$$

where $n \neq m$. From Sec. 10.7, we have

$$\int_0^L EI \left(\frac{d^2 w_n}{dx^2}\right)^2 dx = I_n P_n / C_n^2 \qquad \int_0^L EI \frac{d^2 w_n}{dx^2} \frac{d^2 w_m}{dx^2} dx = 0$$

Substitution of these relations into (10.43) results in

$$P_C = \frac{\displaystyle\sum_{n=1}^{\infty} I_n P_n^2}{\displaystyle\sum_{n=1}^{\infty} I_n P_n} = P_1 \frac{I_1 P_1 + I_2 P_2 (P_2/P_1) + \cdots}{I_1 P_1 + I_2 P_2 + \cdots} \geq P_1 \quad (10.44)$$

Now,

$$P_R - \frac{P_C - P_R}{(P_2/P_R) - 1} = P_R \frac{P_2 - P_C}{P_2 - P_R}$$

$$= \frac{\displaystyle\sum_{n=1}^{\infty} I_n P_n \left[P_2 - \left(\displaystyle\sum_{n=1}^{\infty} I_n P_n^2 \Big/ \displaystyle\sum_{n=1}^{\infty} I_n P_n\right)\right]}{\displaystyle\sum_{n=1}^{\infty} I_n \left[P_2 - \left(\displaystyle\sum_{n=1}^{\infty} I_n P_n \Big/ \displaystyle\sum_{n=1}^{\infty} I_n\right)\right]}$$

$$= \frac{P_2 \displaystyle\sum_{n=1}^{\infty} I_n P_n - \displaystyle\sum_{n=1}^{\infty} I_n P_n^2}{P_2 \displaystyle\sum_{n=1}^{\infty} I_n - \displaystyle\sum_{n=1}^{\infty} I_n P_n}$$

$$= P_1 \frac{I_1(P_2 - P_1) - I_3(P_3 - P_2)(P_3/P_1) - I_4(P_4 - P_2)(P_4/P_1) - \cdots}{I_1(P_2 - P_1) - I_3(P_3 - P_2) - I_4(P_4 - P_2) - \cdots}$$

$$\leq P_1$$

Thus, we arrive at a formula which gives the upper and lower bounds of the buckling load, *viz.*,

$$\left(P_R - \frac{P_C - P_R}{(P_2/P_R) - 1}\right) \leq P_{cr} \leq P_R$$

Since the exact value of P_2 for a column with a variable cross section is unknown, we shall use the value of P_2 for a column with the same boundary conditions but with constant cross section which is equal to the minimum cross section of the actual column. We see by such a substitution that the above inequality is still valid. Therefore[1] we obtain

[1] This formula was originally given, in a different form, for a special case by G. Temple and W. Bickley in "Rayleigh's Principle and Its Applications," p. 173, Oxford University Press, New York, 1933. The method was generalized in "Eigenwertprobleme und ihre numerische Behandlung" by L. Collatz, Akademische Ver-

$$P_R - \frac{P_c - P_R}{[(P_2)_{min}/P_R] - 1} \leq P_{cr} \leq P_R \qquad (10.45)$$

as long as $(P_2)_{min} > P_R$, where the values of $(P_2)_{min}$ for columns with various boundary conditions are as follows:

Both ends simply supported: $(P_2)_{min} = \dfrac{4\pi^2(EI)_{min}}{L^2}$

Both ends built in: $(P_2)_{min} = \dfrac{16\pi^2(EI)_{min}}{L^2}$

One end built in, other end free: $(P_2)_{min} = \dfrac{9\pi^2(EI)_{min}}{4L^2}$

One end built in, other end hinged: $(P_2)_{min} = \dfrac{59.68(EI)_{min}}{L^2}$

We shall now illustrate this method by working out a few examples.

Example 1. *Columns with Both Ends Hinged.* Assume that the moment of inertia of the cross section of the column varies according to the formula

$$I = I_0\left(1 + \sin\frac{\pi x}{L}\right)$$

If we assume, as in Sec. 10.5, that

$$w = C_1 \sin\frac{\pi x}{L}$$

and substitute this expression into (10.45) and integrate, we have

$$P_c = -\frac{\int_0^L [EI(d^2w/dx^2)](d^2/dx^2)[EI(d^2w/dx^2)]\, dx}{\int_0^L EI(d^2w/dx^2)^2\, dx}$$

$$= \frac{2\pi^2 EI_0}{L^2} = 19.74\,\frac{EI_0}{L^2}$$

As we have worked out in Sec. 10.5,

$$P_R = \frac{1.849\pi^2 EI_0}{L^2} = 18.25\,\frac{EI_0}{L^2}$$

Since $(EI)_{min}$ in this case is EI_0, we have

$$(P_2)_{min} = \frac{4\pi^2 EI_0}{L^2}$$

lagsgesellschaft, Becker and Erler Kom-Ges., Leipzig, 1945. See also C. C. Miesse, Determination of the Buckling Load for Columns of Variable Stiffness, *J. Applied Mech., Trans. ASME*, Vol. 71, pp. 406–410. The proof given here is much simpler than those given by the preceding references.

Substituting into formula (10.45), we find that

$$\frac{17.50 EI_0}{L^2} \leq P_{cr} \leq \frac{18.25 EI_0}{L^2}$$

This shows that P_R has a maximum error of $+4.5$ per cent. To get a better approximation, we may take

$$w = C_1 \sin \frac{\pi x}{L} + C_3 \sin \frac{3\pi x}{L}$$

where C_3 was determined in Sec. 10.5 to be $0.01297 C_1$. The computation can be carried out in the same manner, and we shall leave this as a problem for the reader.

Example 2. Column with One End Built In and the Other End Hinged. Let EI be given by the formula

$$EI = EI_0 \left[1 - \frac{1}{3} \left(\frac{x}{L} \right)^2 \right]$$

The boundary conditions in this case are $w = 0$ and $dw/dx = 0$ at $x = 0$, $w = 0$ and $d^2w/dx^2 = 0$ at $x = L$. To satisfy these conditions, we may assume

$$w = C \left(\frac{x}{L} \right)^2 \left[1 - \frac{1}{3} \left(\frac{x}{L} \right) - \frac{5}{3} \left(\frac{x}{L} \right)^2 + \left(\frac{x}{L} \right)^3 \right]$$

Substituting this expression into formula (10.44) and integrating, we find that

$$P_C = 17.98 \frac{EI_0}{L^2}$$

From formula (10.23), we find that

$$P_R = 17.88 \frac{EI_0}{L^2}$$

Now, $(EI)_{min} = \frac{2}{3} EI_0$. Hence

$$(P_2)_{min} = 39.79 \frac{EI_0}{L^2}$$

Substituting these values into formula (10.45), we find that

$$17.79 \frac{EI_0}{L^2} \leq P_{cr} \leq 17.88 \frac{EI_0}{L^2}$$

which gives P_{cr} to within 0.3 per cent.

If the boundary conditions of the column are such that the differential equation can be written in the form

$$EI \frac{d^2w}{dx^2} + Pw = 0$$

we can find the buckling load by Timoshenko's formula. In such cases, we may derive another formula which gives closer bounds than formula (10.45). By using the results obtained in Sec. 10.7, we obtain

$$P_T - \frac{P_R - P_T}{(P_2/P_T) - 1} = P_T \frac{P_2 - P_R}{P_2 - P_T}$$
$$= P_1 \frac{I_1[(P_2/P_1) - 1)] - I_3[1 - (P_2/P_3)](P_3/P_1) - \cdots}{I_1[(P_2/P_1) - 1] - I_3[1 - (P_2/P_3)] - \cdots}$$
$$\leq P_1$$

Therefore, we have

$$P_T - \frac{P_R - P_T}{[(P_2)_{\min}/P_T] - 1} \leq P_{cr} \leq P_T \tag{10.46}$$

as long as $(P_2)_{\min} > P_T$.

In Example 1, if we again assume that

$$w = C_1 \sin \frac{\pi x}{L}$$

we find that

$$P_T = 18.06 \frac{EI_0}{L^2}$$

Using (10.46), we obtain

$$17.90 \frac{EI_0}{L^2} \leq P_{cr} \leq 18.06 \frac{EI_0}{L^2}$$

Thus we have P_{cr} to within 0.5 per cent.

Problem 1. Assuming that

$$w = C_1 \left(\sin \frac{\pi x}{L} + 0.01297 \sin \frac{3\pi x}{L} \right)$$

find the upper and lower bounds of the buckling load of the column given in Example 1 by using formula (10.45).

Problem 2. Determine the buckling load for a column which is built in at one end and free at the other, with length L and stiffness

$$EI(x) = EI_0 \left(1 + \cos \frac{\pi x}{2L} \right)$$

CHAPTER 11

BENDING AND BUCKLING OF THIN PLATES

11.1. Differential Equation for the Bending of Thin Plates. When the thickness of an elastic body is small compared with the other dimensions, we call it a thin plate. Let h be the thickness of the plate. The plane parallel to the faces of the plate and bisecting the thickness of the plate, in the undeformed state, is called the middle plane of the plate. We choose the coordinate axes so that the x and y axes are in the middle plane of the plate and the z axis is perpendicular to the middle plane.

If a thin plate is bent with small deflection, *i.e.*, when the deflection of the middle plane is small compared with the thickness h, the following assumptions can be made.

1. The normals of the middle plane before bending are deformed into the normals of the middle plane after bending.

2. The stress σ_z is small compared with the other stress components and may be neglected in the stress-strain relations.

3. The middle plane remains unstrained after bending.

Consider a section of the plate parallel to the xz plane as shown in Fig.

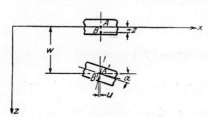

FIG. 11.1.

11.1. After bending, a point A on the middle plane is deflected to A' with a deflection w. According to the first assumption, a point on the normal to the undeformed middle plane, such as B, which is at a distance z from A, is now displaced to B', which is on the normal to the middle plane after bending. From Fig. 11.1, it is observed that the displacement of the point B' in the x direction is

$$u = -z\alpha$$

Since the deflection is small, $\alpha \cong \tan \alpha = \partial w/\partial x$ and

$$u = -z \frac{\partial w}{\partial x} \tag{11.1}$$

Similarly, the displacement of the point B' in the y direction is

$$v = -z \frac{\partial w}{\partial y} \tag{11.2}$$

276

The assumption that the normals of the middle plane before bending are deformed into the normals of the middle plane after bending is equivalent to assuming that the shearing strains γ_{xz} and γ_{yz} are zero. This follows directly from the definitions of the shearing strains. For example, consider the shearing strain γ_{xz}, which is defined as the change in the right angle subtended by the line elements parallel to the x and z axes during deformation. In the present case, the normal is in the z direction. The right angle between the normal and the x axis will, according to the assumption, remain a right angle after bending, and consequently $\gamma_{xz} = 0$. Following a similar reasoning, we find that γ_{yz} is also zero. The assumption of zero γ_{xz} and γ_{yz} will lead to several inconsistencies later in the development of the theory. Therefore, instead of assuming these shearing strains to be zero, we shall assume that they are not zero but are small enough to be neglected.

Instead of the geometrical considerations used in deriving Eqs. (11.1) and (11.2), these equations can also be obtained directly from the assumption that γ_{xz} and γ_{yz} are negligible. For example,

$$u = \int_0^z \frac{\partial u}{\partial z}\, dz$$

Since z is small, we may write

$$u = \left(\frac{\partial u}{\partial z}\right)_{z=0} z$$

But, at $z = 0$,

$$(\gamma_{xz})_{z=0} = \left(\frac{\partial u}{\partial z} + \frac{\partial w}{\partial x}\right)_{z=0} = 0$$

or

$$\left(\frac{\partial u}{\partial z}\right)_{z=0} = -\frac{\partial w}{\partial x}$$

where w is the deflection of the middle plane. Thus

$$u = -z\frac{\partial w}{\partial x}$$

Equation (11.2) can also be derived in a similar manner. This alternative method of derivation will be useful in deriving the strain components for thin shells.

From the definition of strain, we have

$$\epsilon_x = \frac{\partial u}{\partial x} \qquad \epsilon_y = \frac{\partial v}{\partial y} \qquad \gamma_{xy} = \frac{\partial u}{\partial y} + \frac{\partial v}{\partial x}$$

By making use of the relations (11.1) and (11.2) we obtain

$$\epsilon_x = -z\frac{\partial^2 w}{\partial x^2} \qquad \epsilon_y = -z\frac{\partial^2 w}{\partial y^2} \qquad \gamma_{xy} = -2z\frac{\partial^2 w}{\partial x\,\partial y} \qquad (11.3)$$

According to assumption 2, the stress-strain relations for a thin plate in bending are

$$\epsilon_x = \frac{1}{E}\left(\sigma_x - \nu\sigma_y\right) \qquad \epsilon_y = \frac{1}{E}\left(\sigma_y - \nu\sigma_x\right) \qquad \gamma_{xy} = \frac{1}{G}\tau_{xy} \qquad (11.4)$$

from which we obtain

$$\sigma_x = \frac{E}{1 - \nu^2}\,(\epsilon_x + \nu\epsilon_y)$$

$$\sigma_y = \frac{E}{1 - \nu^2}\,(\epsilon_y + \nu\epsilon_x) \tag{11.5}$$

$$\tau_{xy} = G\gamma_{xy} = \frac{E}{2(1 + \nu)}\,\gamma_{xy}$$

Substituting Eq. (11.3) into the above formulas, we find

$$\sigma_x = -\frac{Ez}{1 - \nu^2}\left(\frac{\partial^2 w}{\partial x^2} + \nu\frac{\partial^2 w}{\partial y^2}\right)$$

$$\sigma_y = -\frac{Ez}{1 - \nu^2}\left(\frac{\partial^2 w}{\partial y^2} + \nu\frac{\partial^2 w}{\partial x^2}\right) \tag{11.6}$$

$$\tau_{xy} = -\frac{Ez}{1 + \nu}\frac{\partial^2 w}{\partial x\,\partial y}$$

With these relations, the bending and twisting moments per unit length acting on any section of the plate parallel to the xz and yz planes (Fig.

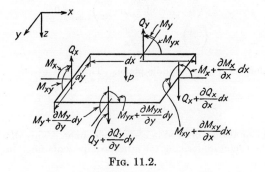

FIG. 11.2.

11.2) can be obtained by integration.   Thus

$$M_x = \int_{-h/2}^{h/2}\sigma_x z\,dz$$

$$= -\int_{-h/2}^{h/2}\frac{Ez}{1 - \nu^2}\left(\frac{\partial^2 w}{\partial x^2} + \nu\frac{\partial^2 w}{\partial y^2}\right)z\,dz$$

Since w is the deflection of the middle plane, it does not depend upon z. Hence

$$M_x = -\frac{E}{1 - \nu^2}\left(\frac{\partial^2 w}{\partial x^2} + \nu\frac{\partial^2 w}{\partial y^2}\right)\int_{-h/2}^{h/2}z^2\,dz$$

$$= -D\left(\frac{\partial^2 w}{\partial x^2} + \nu\frac{\partial^2 w}{\partial y^2}\right) \tag{11.7}$$

where D denotes $Eh^3/12(1 - \nu^2)$ and is called the *flexural rigidity of the plate*. Similarly, we have

$$M_y = \int_{-h/2}^{h/2} \sigma_y z \, dz = -D\left(\frac{\partial^2 w}{\partial y^2} + \nu \frac{\partial^2 w}{\partial x^2}\right)$$

$$M_{xy} = M_{yx} = -\int_{-h/2}^{h/2} \tau_{xy} z \, dz = D(1 - \nu)\frac{\partial^2 w}{\partial x \, \partial y}$$

(11.8)

where the negative sign before the integral for M_{xy} is due to the fact that, for positive τ_{xy} and positive z, dM_{xy} is negative.

Let us now consider the equilibrium of an element $dx \, dy$ of the plate as shown in Fig. 11.2. The plate is assumed to be under the action of a normal, distributed load with intensity p. In addition to the bending and twisting moments, there will be vertical shearing forces acting on the sides of the element due to the shearing stresses τ_{zx} and τ_{yz}. Let Q_x and Q_y be the shearing forces per unit length parallel to the y and x axes, respectively. Then

$$Q_x = \int_{-h/2}^{h/2} \tau_{zx} \, dz \qquad Q_y = \int_{-h/2}^{h/2} \tau_{yz} \, dz$$

(11.9)

Earlier in this section, we have pointed out that the assumption 1 is equivalent to assuming that $\gamma_{zx} = \tau_{zx}/G$ and $\gamma_{yz} = \tau_{yz}/G$ are negligible. Now, in the derivation of the equilibrium equations, we have to include the resultant forces due to these shearing-stress components. This can be explained as follows: We first observe that p is equal to σ_z at the outer surface of the plate and is therefore of the same order of magnitude as σ_z. According to assumption 2, σ_z is also negligible. The assumption here is that although the terms τ_{zx}/G and τ_{yz}/G are negligible in comparison with the other terms in the expressions

$$\frac{\partial u}{\partial z} = -\frac{\partial w}{\partial x} + \frac{\tau_{zx}}{G} \qquad \frac{\partial v}{\partial z} = -\frac{\partial w}{\partial y} + \frac{\tau_{yz}}{G}$$

the shearing forces Q_x and Q_y are of the same order of magnitude as the applied load p and the moments M_x, M_y, and M_{xy}.

The equilibrium of the element of the plate requires the summations of the forces in the x, y, and z directions as well as the moments about these axes to be zero. Since the stress components vary from point to point in the plate, the resulting moments and shearing forces must also be functions of x and y. Let us neglect the body forces, which are usually small compared with the lateral load p. Since the middle plane is assumed unstrained, the summations of forces in the x and y directions are identically zero. The condition that the sum of the z components of the forces be zero becomes

$$\frac{\partial Q_x}{\partial x} dx\, dy + \frac{\partial Q_y}{\partial y} dy\, dx + p\, dx\, dy = 0$$

or
$$\frac{\partial Q_x}{\partial x} + \frac{\partial Q_y}{\partial y} + p = 0 \qquad (11.10)$$

Taking moments of all the forces acting on the element with respect to the x axis and neglecting higher-order terms, we obtain the equation of equilibrium

$$\frac{\partial M_{xy}}{\partial x} dx\, dy - \frac{\partial M_y}{\partial y} dy\, dx + Q_y\, dx\, dy = 0$$

or
$$\frac{\partial M_{xy}}{\partial x} - \frac{\partial M_y}{\partial y} + Q_y = 0 \qquad (11.11)$$

Similarly, the equation of equilibrium for the moments with respect to the y axis gives

$$\frac{\partial M_{yx}}{\partial y} - \frac{\partial M_x}{\partial x} + Q_x = 0 \qquad (11.12)$$

From Eqs. (11.7), (11.8), (11.11), and (11.12), we find that

$$Q_x = \frac{\partial M_x}{\partial x} - \frac{\partial M_{yx}}{\partial y} = -\frac{\partial}{\partial x}\left[D\left(\frac{\partial^2 w}{\partial x^2} + \nu \frac{\partial^2 w}{\partial y^2}\right)\right] - \frac{\partial}{\partial y}\left[D(1 - \nu)\frac{\partial^2 w}{\partial x\, \partial y}\right]$$

$$Q_y = \frac{\partial M_y}{\partial y} - \frac{\partial M_{xy}}{\partial x} = -\frac{\partial}{\partial y}\left[D\left(\frac{\partial^2 w}{\partial y^2} + \nu \frac{\partial^2 w}{\partial x^2}\right)\right] - \frac{\partial}{\partial x}\left[D(1 - \nu)\frac{\partial^2 w}{\partial x\, \partial y}\right]$$

For a plate with constant thickness, D is a constant, and we have

$$Q_x = -D\frac{\partial}{\partial x}\left(\frac{\partial^2 w}{\partial x^2} + \frac{\partial^2 w}{\partial y^2}\right) \qquad Q_y = -D\frac{\partial}{\partial y}\left(\frac{\partial^2 w}{\partial x^2} + \frac{\partial^2 w}{\partial y^2}\right) \quad (11.13)$$

Substituting (11.13) into (11.10), we obtain the differential equation which governs the small deflection of a thin plate with constant thickness under bending, *viz.*,

$$\frac{\partial^4 w}{\partial x^4} + 2\frac{\partial^4 w}{\partial x^2\, \partial y^2} + \frac{\partial^4 w}{\partial y^4} = \frac{p}{D}$$

or
$$\nabla^4 w = \frac{p}{D} \qquad (11.14)$$

11.2. Boundary Conditions. We shall first formulate the boundary conditions for a rectangular plate with edges parallel to the x and y axes.

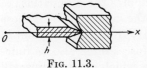

Simply Supported Edge. When a supported edge of a plate is free to rotate, it is called a simply supported edge (Fig. 11.3). Thus, if the edge $x = a$ is simply supported, the deflection as well as the bending moment along the edge must be zero. That is,

Fig. 11.3.

$$(w)_{x=a} = 0 \qquad (M_x)_{x=a} = -D\left(\frac{\partial^2 w}{\partial x^2} + \nu \frac{\partial^2 w}{\partial y^2}\right)_{x=a} = 0$$

But the condition $w = 0$ along the edge $x = a$ means also that

$$\frac{\partial w}{\partial y} = \frac{\partial^2 w}{\partial y^2} = 0$$

along this edge. The boundary conditions for a simply supported edge can therefore be written as

$$(w)_{x=a} = 0 \qquad \left(\frac{\partial^2 w}{\partial x^2}\right)_{x=a} = 0 \qquad (11.15)$$

Built-in or Clamped Edge. If the edge $x = a$ is built in or clamped, along this edge the deflection as well as the slope of the middle plane must be zero. That is,

$$(w)_{x=a} = 0 \qquad \left(\frac{\partial w}{\partial x}\right)_{x=a} = 0 \qquad (11.16)$$

Free Edge. If the edge $x = a$ is free, there must be no bending and twisting moments as well as no vertical shearing forces along the edge; viz.,

$$(M_x)_{x=a} = 0 \qquad (M_{xy})_{x=a} = 0 \qquad (Q_x)_{x=a} = 0$$

It was shown, however, by Kirchhoff[1] that only two boundary conditions are sufficient for the complete determination of the deflection w satisfying Eq. (11.14) and the three conditions derived from physical reasoning are too many. This inconsistency is due to the assumption that the normals of the middle plane before bending are deformed into the normals of the middle plane after bending. Without using such an assumption, a sixth-order differential equation can be obtained for which all the three boundary conditions can be satisfied.[2] It can be shown, however, that, except in the immediate region of the boundary, the stress distribution given by this new equation is substantially the same as that given by Eq. (11.14). If the plate is *thin*, the sixth-order terms can be neglected and this new equation reduces to Eq. (11.14). This justifies the use of Eq. (11.14) in the study of the bending of thin plates. In order to avoid the inconsistency in the boundary conditions, Kirchhoff pointed out that the two conditions prescribing M_{xy} and Q_x can be replaced by a single one. The reason is that the twisting moment acting on an element of the edge of the plate may be replaced by two statically equivalent vertical forces, which can then be combined with the vertical shearing forces. Owing to such a replacement, the stress distribution in the immediate neighborhood of the

[1] G. Kirchhoff, Über das Gleichgewicht und die Bewegung einer elastischen Scheibe, *J. reine u. angew. Math.*, Vol. 40, pp. 51–88, 1850.

[2] See E. Reissner, The Effect of Transverse Shear Deformation on the Bending of Elastic Plates, *J. Applied Mech.*, Vol. 67, pp. A69–77, 1945; K. O. Friedrichs, "The Edge Effect in the Bending of Plates," Reissner Anniversary Volume, pp. 197–210, Edwards Bros., Inc., Ann Arbor, Mich., 1949.

edge will naturally be affected, but the stress distribution in the rest of the plate will remain essentially the same.

Consider the edge $x = a$. On an element of length dy we have the twisting moment $M_{xy}\,dy$, which may be replaced by two vertical forces of the magnitude M_{xy} at a distance of dy apart, as shown by the solid arrows in Fig. 11.4. At the next element of length dy, the twisting moment will be of the magnitude $[M_{xy} + (\partial M_{xy}/\partial y)\,dy]\,dy$, which may be replaced by the vertical forces of magnitude $M_{xy} + (\partial M_{xy}/\partial y)\,dy$ as shown by the

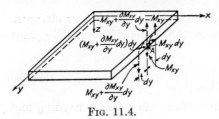

Fig. 11.4.

dotted lines in Fig. 11.4. At point A, because of the foregoing replacements of statically equivalent systems we find that there is a net vertical force of the magnitude $(\partial M_{xy}/\partial y)\,dy$ or a vertical force per unit length of the magnitude $\partial M_{xy}/\partial y$. For positive M_{xy}, the statically equivalent vertical forces are directed upward and are therefore negative according to our sign convention. Thus, for a free edge, instead of requiring both M_{xy} and Q_x to be zero along the edge, we may require that the statically equivalent vertical force be zero. That is

$$(V_x)_{x=a} = \left(Q_x - \frac{\partial M_{xy}}{\partial y} \right)_{x=a} = 0$$

Using (11.8) and (11.13), we may express this condition in terms of w as follows:

$$\left[\frac{\partial^3 w}{\partial x^3} + (2 - \nu)\frac{\partial^3 w}{\partial x\,\partial y^2} \right]_{x=a} = 0 \tag{11.17}$$

The condition that $M_x = 0$ requires that

$$\left(\frac{\partial^2 w}{\partial x^2} + \nu\frac{\partial^2 w}{\partial y^2} \right)_{x=a} = 0 \tag{11.18}$$

Equations (11.17) and (11.18) may be taken as the boundary conditions for a free edge.

11.3. Bending of Simply Supported Rectangular Plates. Consider a simply supported rectangular plate under a lateral loading given by the equation

$$p = p(x,y)$$

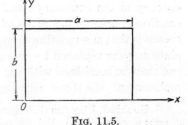

Fig. 11.5.

Let us take the coordinate axes as shown in Fig. 11.5. As we have shown in Sec. 11.1, the deflection of the plate must satisfy the differential equation

$$\frac{\partial^4 w}{\partial x^4} + 2 \frac{\partial^4 w}{\partial x^2 \, \partial y^2} + \frac{\partial^4 w}{\partial y^4} = \frac{p(x,y)}{D} \qquad (11.19)$$

with the boundary conditions

$$w = 0, \quad \frac{\partial^2 w}{\partial x^2} = 0 \qquad \text{at } x = 0 \text{ and } x = a$$

$$w = 0, \quad \frac{\partial^2 w}{\partial y^2} = 0 \qquad \text{at } y = 0 \text{ and } y = b \qquad (11.20)$$

We observe that the above boundary conditions are satisfied if the deflection is expressed by the following Fourier series,

$$w = \sum_{m=1}^{\infty} \sum_{n=1}^{\infty} A_{mn} \sin \frac{m\pi x}{a} \sin \frac{n\pi y}{b} \qquad (11.21)$$

where the A_{mn} are undetermined coefficients. These coefficients can be determined so that Eq. (11.19) is satisfied.

Let us first expand $p(x,y)$ in terms of a Fourier series, *viz.*,

$$p(x,y) = \sum_{m=1}^{\infty} \sum_{n=1}^{\infty} a_{mn} \sin \frac{m\pi x}{a} \sin \frac{n\pi y}{b} \qquad (11.22)$$

To calculate any particular Fourier coefficient $a_{m'n'}$, we multiply both sides of (11.22) by $\sin(m'\pi x/a) \sin(n'\pi y/b) \, dx \, dy$ and carry out the integration with respect to x from 0 to a and with respect to y from 0 to b. That is,

$$\int_0^a \int_0^b p(x,y) \sin \frac{m'\pi x}{a} \sin \frac{n'\pi y}{b} \, dx \, dy$$

$$= \sum_{m=1}^{\infty} \sum_{n=1}^{\infty} \int_0^a \int_0^b a_{mn} \sin \frac{m\pi x}{a} \sin \frac{m'\pi x}{a} \sin \frac{n\pi y}{b} \sin \frac{n'\pi y}{b} \, dx \, dy$$

Noting that

$$\int_0^a \sin \frac{m\pi x}{a} \sin \frac{m'\pi x}{a} \, dx = 0 \qquad \text{when } m \neq m'$$

$$= \frac{a}{2} \qquad \text{when } m = m'$$

and

$$\int_0^b \sin \frac{n\pi y}{b} \sin \frac{n'\pi y}{b} \, dy = 0 \qquad \text{when } n \neq n'$$

$$= \frac{b}{2} \qquad \text{when } n = n'$$

we find after integration

$$\sum_{m=1}^{\infty} \sum_{n=1}^{\infty} \int_0^a \int_0^b a_{mn} \sin \frac{m\pi x}{a} \sin \frac{m'\pi x}{a} \sin \frac{n\pi y}{b} \sin \frac{n'\pi y}{b} \, dx \, dy = \frac{ab}{4} a_{m'n'}$$

It follows therefore that

$$a_{m'n'} = \frac{4}{ab} \int_0^a \int_0^b p(x,y) \sin \frac{m'\pi x}{a} \sin \frac{n'\pi y}{b} \, dx \, dy \qquad (11.23)$$

To determine the coefficient A_{mn} in the expression for w, we substitute (11.21) and (11.22) into Eq. (11.19). This gives

$$\sum_{m=1}^{\infty} \sum_{n=1}^{\infty} \left\{ A_{mn} \left[\left(\frac{m\pi}{a} \right)^4 + 2 \left(\frac{m\pi}{a} \right)^2 \left(\frac{n\pi}{b} \right)^2 + \left(\frac{n\pi}{b} \right)^4 \right] \right.$$
$$\left. - \frac{a_{mn}}{D} \right\} \sin \frac{m\pi x}{a} \sin \frac{n\pi y}{b} = 0$$

Since the above equation must be valid for all values of x and y, it follows that

$$A_{mn}\pi^4 \left(\frac{m^2}{a^2} + \frac{n^2}{b^2} \right)^2 - \frac{a_{mn}}{D} = 0$$

or

$$A_{mn} = \frac{1}{\pi^4 D} \frac{a_{mn}}{[(m^2/a^2) + (n^2/b^2)]^2}$$

Hence

$$w = \frac{1}{\pi^4 D} \sum_{m=1}^{\infty} \sum_{n=1}^{\infty} \frac{a_{mn}}{[(m^2/a^2) + (n^2/b^2)]^2} \sin \frac{m\pi x}{a} \sin \frac{n\pi y}{b} \qquad (11.24)$$

where a_{mn} is given by formula (11.23). The expression w given by (11.24) is the general solution for a thin rectangular plate under the lateral loading $p(x,y)$.

In the particular case of a rectangular plate under a uniformly distributed load of intensity $p(x,y) = p_0$, we find, from formula (11.23), that

$$a_{mn} = \frac{4p_0}{ab} \int_0^a \int_0^b \sin \frac{m\pi x}{a} \sin \frac{n\pi y}{b} \, dx \, dy = \frac{16p_0}{\pi^2 mn}$$

where m and n are odd integers. $a_{mn} = 0$ if m or n is even. Hence

$$w = \frac{16p_0}{\pi^6 D} \sum_{m=1,3,5}^{\infty} \sum_{n=1,3,5}^{\infty} \frac{\sin(m\pi x/a) \sin(n\pi y/b)}{mn[(m^2/a^2) + (n^2/b^2)]^2} \qquad (11.25)$$

The vanishing of all terms with even m or n in series (11.25) may be observed from the following physical reasoning: Under a uniform load, the deflection surface of the plate must be symmetrical. With the coordinate axes shown in Fig. 11.5, the terms with even m or n give unsymmetrical deflections and naturally should be zero. The maximum deflection of the plate occurs at the center of the plate and is

$$(w)_{x=a/2,\,y=b/2} = \frac{16p_0}{\pi^6 D} \sum_{m=1,3,5}^{\infty} \sum_{n=1,3,5}^{\infty} \frac{(-1)^{\frac{m+n}{2}-1}}{mn\left(\dfrac{m^2}{a^2} + \dfrac{n^2}{b^2}\right)^2} \qquad (11.26)$$

This series converges very rapidly, and the first few terms will in general give a satisfactory answer. For example, in the case of a square plate, by taking $\nu = 0.3$, we find that the deflection given by the first four terms in the series is

$$(w)_{x=a/2,\,y=b/2} = 0.0443p_0 \frac{a^4}{Eh^3}$$

which is accurate to the third significant figure.

With the expression for the deflection of the plate determined, we can find the bending moments in the plate by substituting (11.25) into formulas (11.7) and (11.8). Hence

$$M_x = \frac{16p_0}{\pi^4} \sum_{m=1,3,5}^{\infty} \sum_{n=1,3,5}^{\infty} \frac{\left(\dfrac{m^2}{a^2} + \nu\dfrac{n^2}{b^2}\right)}{mn\left(\dfrac{m^2}{a^2} + \dfrac{n^2}{b^2}\right)^2} \sin\frac{m\pi x}{a} \sin\frac{n\pi y}{b}$$

$$(11.27)$$

$$M_y = \frac{16p_0}{\pi^4} \sum_{m=1,3,5}^{\infty} \sum_{n=1,3,5}^{\infty} \frac{\left(\nu\dfrac{m^2}{a^2} + \dfrac{n^2}{b^2}\right)}{mn\left(\dfrac{m^2}{a^2} + \dfrac{n^2}{b^2}\right)^2} \sin\frac{m\pi x}{a} \sin\frac{n\pi y}{b}$$

The maximum bending moments occur also at the center of the plate. For a square plate, $a = b$, we find that the first five terms of the series give

$$(M_x)_{x=a/2,\,y=b/2} - (M_y)_{x=a/2,\,y=b/2} = 0.0479p_0 a^2$$

Comparing formulas (11.6) with (11.7) and (11.8), we find that the bending stresses can be expressed in terms of the bending moments as follows:

$$\sigma_x = \frac{12M_x z}{h^3} \qquad \sigma_y = \frac{12M_y z}{h^3}$$

The maximum bending stresses occur at $z = \pm h/2$. For a uniformly loaded square plate, we have

$$\sigma_{\max} = 0.287p_0 \frac{a^2}{h^2}$$

Problem 1. A simply supported rectangular plate is under the action of hydrostatic pressure. In this case, the load is distributed according to the formula

$$p(x,y) = \frac{p_0 x}{a}$$

Find the deflection, moments, and stresses in the plate.

$$\textit{Ans. } w = \frac{8p_0}{\pi^6 D} \sum_{m=1}^{\infty} \sum_{n=1,3,5}^{\infty} \frac{(-1)^{m+1}}{mn \left(\frac{m^2}{a^2} + \frac{n^2}{b^2}\right)^2} \sin \frac{m\pi x}{a} \sin \frac{n\pi y}{b}$$

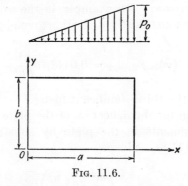

Fig. 11.6.

Problem 2. A simply supported square plate is under a uniformly distributed load. Find the maximum deflection by the finite-difference approximation and the relaxation method. *Hint:* For a simply supported plate, the boundary conditions can be written as $w = 0$ and $\nabla^2 w = \frac{\partial^2 w}{\partial x^2} + \frac{\partial^2 w}{\partial y^2} = 0$ along the edges. With the boundary conditions so written, the differential equation can be put into the following form:

$$\nabla^2 M = \frac{p(x,y)}{D}$$
$$\nabla^2 w = M$$

Thus, the problem can be solved in two steps. First, solve for M so that

$$\nabla^2 M = \frac{p(x,y)}{D} \qquad \text{and} \qquad M = 0 \qquad \text{along the edges}$$

Then, solve for w so that

$$\nabla^2 w = M \qquad w = 0 \qquad \text{along the edges}$$

By such a transformation, instead of working with the biharmonic operator ∇^4, we need deal only with the much simpler Laplace operator ∇^2.

11.4. Bending of Rectangular Plates with Clamped Edges. Rayleigh-Ritz Method. In Chap. 7, we discussed the solution of elasticity problems by means of Rayleigh-Ritz methods. Let us now apply the Rayleigh-Ritz method to the solution of plate problems. The general

expression for strain energy stored in an elastic body is given by formula
(3.49), *viz.*,

$$U = \tfrac{1}{2} \iiint_V (\sigma_x \epsilon_x + \sigma_y \epsilon_y + \sigma_z \epsilon_z + \tau_{xy} \gamma_{xy} + \tau_{yz} \gamma_{yz} + \tau_{zx} \gamma_{zx})\, dx\, dy\, dz$$

In the case of thin plates, according to the assumptions made in Sec. 11.1,
σ_z, γ_{xz}, γ_{yz} are small quantities and can therefore be neglected. By
neglecting terms containing σ_z, γ_{xz}, γ_{yz} in the above expression and eliminating the strain components by using (11.4), we have

$$U = \iiint_V \left[\frac{1}{2E} (\sigma_x{}^2 + \sigma_y{}^2 - 2\nu\sigma_x\sigma_y) + \frac{1+\nu}{E} \tau_{xy}{}^2 \right] dx\, dy\, dz$$

where the relation $G = E/2(1 + \nu)$ has been used. Substituting into the
above formula Eqs. (11.6), which express σ_x, σ_y, and τ_{xy} in terms of w, we
obtain

$$U = \frac{D}{2} \iint_A \left[\left(\frac{\partial^2 w}{\partial x^2} \right)^2 + \left(\frac{\partial^2 w}{\partial y^2} \right)^2 + 2\nu \frac{\partial^2 w}{\partial x^2} \frac{\partial^2 w}{\partial y^2} + 2(1 - \nu) \left(\frac{\partial^2 w}{\partial x\, \partial y} \right)^2 \right] dx\, dy$$

$$= \frac{D}{2} \iint_A \left\{ \left(\frac{\partial^2 w}{\partial x^2} + \frac{\partial^2 w}{\partial y^2} \right)^2 - 2(1 - \nu) \left[\frac{\partial^2 w}{\partial x^2} \frac{\partial^2 w}{\partial y^2} - \left(\frac{\partial^2 w}{\partial x\, \partial y} \right)^2 \right] \right\} dx\, dy$$

$$(11.28)$$

where A is the area of the plate.

The above formula can be put in a much simpler form for plates of
any shape with all their edges built in and for rectangular plates with
$w = 0$ along the edges. Integrating by parts, we find

$$\iint_A \frac{\partial^2 w}{\partial x\, \partial y} \frac{\partial^2 w}{\partial x\, \partial y}\, dx\, dy = -\oint_s \frac{\partial^2 w}{\partial x\, \partial y} \frac{\partial w}{\partial x}\, dx - \iint_A \frac{\partial w}{\partial x} \frac{\partial^3 w}{\partial x\, \partial y^2}\, dx\, dy$$

$$= \oint_s \frac{\partial^2 w}{\partial x\, \partial y} \frac{\partial w}{\partial x}\, dx - \oint_s \frac{\partial w}{\partial x} \frac{\partial^2 w}{\partial y^2}\, dy$$

$$+ \iint_A \frac{\partial^2 w}{\partial x^2} \frac{\partial^2 w}{\partial y^2}\, dx\, dy$$

For plates with built-in edges, $\partial w/\partial n = \partial w/\partial s = 0$ and consequently $\partial w/\partial x = \partial w/\partial y = 0$ along the edges; for rectangular plates with
$w = 0$ along the edges, $\partial w/\partial x = 0$ along the edges $y = $ constant and
$\partial w/\partial y = \partial^2 w/\partial y^2 = 0$ along the edges $x = $ constant. Hence, the first
two integrals in the above expression become identically zero, and we have

$$\iint_A \left[\frac{\partial^2 w}{\partial x^2} \frac{\partial^2 w}{\partial y^2} - \left(\frac{\partial^2 w}{\partial x\, \partial y} \right)^2 \right] dx\, dy = 0 \qquad (11.29)$$

The bending-strain energy becomes then

$$U = \frac{D}{2} \iint\limits_{A} \left(\frac{\partial^2 w}{\partial x^2} + \frac{\partial^2 w}{\partial y^2} \right)^2 dx\, dy \qquad (11.30)$$

To illustrate the use of the Rayleigh-Ritz method, let us consider the bending of a rectangular plate with clamped edges. Take the coordinate axes as shown in Fig. 11.5. The boundary conditions are

$$w = 0, \frac{\partial w}{\partial x} = 0 \qquad \text{at } x = 0 \text{ and } a$$

$$w = 0, \frac{\partial w}{\partial y} = 0 \qquad \text{at } y = 0 \text{ and } b$$

These boundary conditions are satisfied if we assume w in the following form:

$$w = \sum_{m=1}^{\infty} \sum_{n=1}^{\infty} A_{mn} \left(1 - \cos \frac{2m\pi x}{a} \right) \left(1 - \cos \frac{2n\pi y}{b} \right) \qquad (11.31)$$

where the parameters A_{mn} are to be determined from the condition that the potential energy of the system

$$\Pi = U - W$$

is a minimum with respect to these parameters.

Substituting (11.31) into (11.30) and integrating, we find that

$$\Pi = \frac{D}{2} \int_0^a \int_0^b \left\{ \sum_{m=1}^{\infty} \sum_{n=1}^{\infty} 4\pi^2 A_{mn} \left[\frac{m^2}{a^2} \cos \frac{2m\pi x}{a} \left(1 - \cos \frac{2n\pi y}{b} \right) \right. \right.$$

$$\left. \left. + \frac{n^2}{b^2} \cos \frac{2n\pi y}{b} \left(1 - \cos \frac{2m\pi x}{a} \right) \right] \right\}^2 dx\, dy$$

$$= 2D\pi^4 ab \left\{ \sum_{m=1}^{\infty} \sum_{n=1}^{\infty} \left[3 \left(\frac{m^4}{a^4} \right) + 3 \left(\frac{n^4}{b^4} \right) + 2 \left(\frac{m^2}{a^2} \right) \left(\frac{n^2}{b^2} \right) \right] A_{mn}^{\ 2} \right.$$

$$\left. + \sum_{m=1}^{\infty} \sum_{\substack{r=1 \\ (r \neq s)}}^{\infty} \sum_{s=1}^{\infty} 2 \left(\frac{m^4}{a^4} \right) A_{mr} A_{ms} + \sum_{r=1}^{\infty} \sum_{\substack{s=1 \\ (r \neq s)}}^{\infty} \sum_{n=1}^{\infty} 2 \left(\frac{n^4}{b^4} \right) A_{rn} A_{sn} \right\}$$

If the plate is under the action of a uniformly distributed load of intensity p_0, the potential energy of the external force is

$$-W = - \int_0^a \int_0^b p_0 w \, dx\, dy$$

$$= -p_0 \int_0^a \int_0^b \left[\sum_{m=1}^{\infty} \sum_{n=1}^{\infty} A_{mn} \left(1 - \cos \frac{2m\pi x}{a} \right) \left(1 - \cos \frac{2n\pi y}{b} \right) \right] dx\, dy$$

$$= -p_0 ab \sum_{m=1}^{\infty} \sum_{n=1}^{\infty} A_{mn}$$

The condition $\partial\Pi/\partial A_{mn} = 0$ therefore gives

$$4D\pi^4 ab \left\{ \left[3\left(\frac{m^4}{a^4}\right) + 3\left(\frac{n^4}{b^4}\right) + 2\left(\frac{m^2}{a^2}\right)\left(\frac{n^2}{b^2}\right) \right] A_{mn} + \sum_{\substack{r=1 \\ (\text{except } r=n)}}^{\infty} 2\left(\frac{m^4}{a^4}\right) A_{mr} \right.$$

$$\left. + \sum_{\substack{r=1 \\ (\text{except } r=m)}}^{\infty} 2\left(\frac{n^4}{b^4}\right) A_{rn} \right\} - p_0 ab = 0 \quad (11.32)$$

For various values of m and n, the above condition gives the same number of equations for A_{mn} as the number of parameters taken. Solving these equations simultaneously, we can find these parameters and therefore the deflections, moments, and stresses everywhere in the plate. For example, if we take only one parameter A_{11}, then we have

$$A_{11} = \frac{p_0 a^4}{4D\pi^4} \frac{1}{3 + 3(a/b)^4 + 2(a/b)^2}$$

For a square plate, $A_{11} = p_0 a^4/32 D\pi^4$. Substituting this value into (11.31) and taking $\nu = 0.3$, we find the maximum deflection of the plate which occurs at $x = a/2$, $y = b/2 = a/2$ as

$$w_{\max} = \frac{0.0140 p_0 a^4}{Eh^3}$$

which is only 1.5 per cent greater than the value computed by a much longer method.[1] Now let us take a few more parameters, say A_{11}, A_{12}, A_{21}, A_{22}, A_{13}, A_{31}, A_{33}. Then the condition (11.32) becomes

$$\left[3 + 3\left(\frac{a}{b}\right)^4 + 2\left(\frac{a}{b}\right)^2 \right] A_{11} + 2A_{12} + 2\left(\frac{a}{b}\right)^4 A_{21} + 2A_{13}$$

$$+ 2\left(\frac{a}{b}\right)^4 A_{31} = \frac{p_0 a^4}{4D\pi^4}$$

$$2A_{11} + \left[3 + 48\left(\frac{a}{b}\right)^4 + 8\left(\frac{a}{b}\right)^2 \right] A_{12} + 2A_{13} + 32\left(\frac{a}{b}\right)^4 A_{22} = \frac{p_0 a^4}{4D\pi^4}$$

$$2\left(\frac{a}{b}\right)^4 A_{11} + \left[48 + 3\left(\frac{a}{b}\right)^4 + 8\left(\frac{a}{b}\right)^2 \right] A_{21} + 2\left(\frac{a}{b}\right)^4 A_{31}$$

$$+ 32A_{22} = \frac{p_0 a^4}{4D\pi^4}$$

$$32A_{21} + 16\left[3 + 3\left(\frac{a}{b}\right)^4 + 2\left(\frac{a}{b}\right)^2 \right] A_{22} + 32\left(\frac{a}{b}\right)^4 A_{12} = \frac{p_0 a^4}{4D\pi^4}$$

$$2A_{11} + 2A_{12} + \left[3 + 243\left(\frac{a}{b}\right)^4 + 18\left(\frac{a}{b}\right)^2 \right] A_{13} + 162\left(\frac{a}{b}\right)^4 A_{33} = \frac{p_0 a^4}{4D\pi^4}$$

---

[1] T. H. Evans, Tables of Moments and Deflections for a Rectangular Plate Fixed on All Edges and Carrying a Uniformly Distributed Load, *J. Applied Mech.*, Vol. 6, pp. A-7–A-10, 1939; see also S. Timoshenko, "Theory of Plates and Shells," p. 228, McGraw-Hill Book Company, Inc., New York, 1940.

$$2 \left(\frac{a}{b}\right)^4 A_{11} + 2 \left(\frac{a}{b}\right)^4 A_{21} + \left[243 + 3 \left(\frac{a}{b}\right)^4 + 18 \left(\frac{a}{b}\right)^2\right] A_{31}$$

$$+ 162 A_{33} = \frac{p_0 a^4}{4 D \pi^4}$$

$$162 \left(\frac{a}{b}\right)^4 A_{13} + 162 A_{31} + 81 \left[3 + 3 \left(\frac{a}{b}\right)^4 + 2 \left(\frac{a}{b}\right)^2\right] A_{33} = \frac{p_0 a^4}{4 D \pi^4}$$

For a square plate, $a = b$. The solution of the above equations gives the following values for the parameters,

$$A_{11} = 0.11774 p' \qquad A_{12} = A_{21} = 0.01184 p'$$
$$A_{22} = 0.00189 p' \qquad A_{13} = A_{31} = 0.00268 p'$$
$$A_{33} = 0.00020 p'$$

where $p' = p_0 a^4 / 4 D \pi^4$. Substituting these values into (11.31), we find that the maximum deflection is

$$w_{\max} = \frac{0.0138 p_0 a^4}{E h^3}$$

which is exactly the value obtained by Evans.

As a second example let us consider the bending of a rectangular plate by a concentrated load P perpendicular to the plate and applied at a point $x = x_1, y = y_1$. The potential energy of the external force in this case is

$$-W = -P(w)_{x=x_1, y=y_1}$$

$$= -P \sum_{m=1}^{\infty} \sum_{n=1}^{\infty} A_{mn} \left(1 - \cos \frac{2 m \pi x_1}{a}\right) \left(1 - \cos \frac{2 n \pi y_1}{b}\right)$$

The condition $\partial \Pi / \partial A_{mn} = 0$ becomes then

$$4 D \pi^4 ab \left\{\left[3 \left(\frac{m^4}{a^4}\right) + 3 \left(\frac{n^4}{b^4}\right) + 2 \left(\frac{m^2}{a^2}\right) \left(\frac{n^2}{b^2}\right)\right] A_{mn} + \sum_{\substack{r=1 \\ (\text{except } r = n)}}^{\infty} 2 \left(\frac{m^4}{a^4}\right) A_{mr} \right.$$

$$\left. + \sum_{\substack{r=1 \\ (\text{except } r = m)}}^{\infty} 2 \left(\frac{n^4}{b^4}\right) A_{rn} \right\} - P \left(1 - \cos \frac{2 m \pi x_1}{a}\right) \left(1 - \cos \frac{2 n \pi y_1}{b}\right) = 0 \quad (11.33)$$

from which the parameters A_{mn} can be solved.

In the particular case of a square plate with a concentrated load acting at its center, by taking seven parameters $A_{11}, A_{12}, A_{21}, A_{22}, A_{13}, A_{31}, A_{33}$, we find that

$$A_{11} = 0.12662 P' \qquad A_{12} = A_{21} = -0.00601 P'$$
$$A_{22} = 0.00301 P' \qquad A_{13} = A_{31} = 0.00278 P'$$
$$A_{33} = 0.00015 P'$$

where $P' = Pa^2/D\pi^4$. The maximum deflection at the center of the plate is then

$$w_{max} = \frac{0.0593Pa^2}{Eh^3}$$

which is 3 per cent smaller than the value obtained by Timoshenko.[1]

Problem 1. A rectangular plate is under a uniformly distributed load with intensity p_0 (Fig. 11.5). If the edges are simply supported, we may assume that

$$w = \sum_{m=1}^{\infty} \sum_{n=1}^{\infty} A_{mn} \sin \frac{m\pi x}{a} \sin \frac{n\pi y}{b}$$

Determine the parameters A_{mn} by the Rayleigh-Ritz method.

Ans. $A_{mn} = \dfrac{16p_0}{\pi^6 D} \dfrac{1}{mn[(m^2/a^2) + (n^2/b^2)]^2}$ for odd m and n

$A_{mn} = 0$ for even m or n

Problem 2. In the above problem, if the plate is under the action of a concentrated load P at $x = x_1$ and $y = y_1$, determine the parameters A_{mn}. Find the maximum deflection of a centrally loaded square plate.

Ans. $A_{mn} = \dfrac{4P}{\pi^4 abD} \dfrac{\sin (m\pi x_1/a) \sin (n\pi y_1/b)}{[(m^2/a^2) + (n^2/b^2)]^2}$

$(w_{max})_{a=b} = \dfrac{0.0115Pa^2}{D}$

Problem 3. For a rectangular plate with two sides clamped and the other sides simply supported, we may assume that

$$w = \sum_{m=1}^{\infty} \sum_{n=1}^{\infty} A_{mn} \left(1 - \cos \frac{2m\pi x}{a} \right) \sin \frac{n\pi y}{b}$$

Determine A_{mn} by the Rayleigh-Ritz method if the plate is under a uniformly distributed load of intensity p_0.

Problem 4. Solve the preceding problem if the plate is under the action of a concentrated load P at $x = x_1$ and $y = y_1$.

11.5. Bending of Circular Plates. In the discussion of bending of circular plates, it will be convenient to use polar coordinates. Let us take the coordinates as shown in Fig. 11.7.

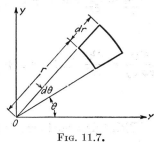

Fig. 11.7.

The relation between the polar and cartesian coordinates is given by the equations

$$r^2 = x^2 + y^2 \qquad \theta = \arctan \frac{y}{x}$$

[1] S. Timoshenko, "Theory of Plates and Shells," p. 231, McGraw-Hill Book Company, Inc., New York, 1940.

from which we find

$$\frac{\partial r}{\partial x} = \frac{x}{r} = \cos \theta \qquad \qquad \frac{\partial r}{\partial y} = \frac{y}{r} = \sin \theta$$

$$\frac{\partial \theta}{\partial x} = -\frac{y}{r^2} = -\frac{\sin \theta}{r} \qquad \qquad \frac{\partial \theta}{\partial y} = \frac{x}{r^2} = \frac{\cos \theta}{r}$$

Using these expressions, and considering w as a function of r and θ, we obtain

$$\frac{\partial w}{\partial x} = \frac{\partial w}{\partial r}\frac{\partial r}{\partial x} + \frac{\partial w}{\partial \theta}\frac{\partial \theta}{\partial x} = \frac{\partial w}{\partial r}\cos \theta - \frac{1}{r}\frac{\partial w}{\partial \theta}\sin \theta$$

$$= \left(\cos \theta \frac{\partial}{\partial r} - \frac{1}{r}\sin \theta \frac{\partial}{\partial \theta} \right) w$$

$$\frac{\partial w}{\partial y} = \frac{\partial w}{\partial r}\sin \theta + \frac{1}{r}\frac{\partial w}{\partial \theta}\cos \theta = \left(\sin \theta \frac{\partial}{\partial r} + \frac{1}{r}\cos \theta \frac{\partial}{\partial \theta} \right) w$$

To get the second derivatives, it is necessary only to repeat the above operation. Hence,

$$\frac{\partial^2 w}{\partial x^2} = \left(\cos \theta \frac{\partial}{\partial r} - \frac{1}{r}\sin \theta \frac{\partial}{\partial \theta} \right)\left(\frac{\partial w}{\partial r}\cos \theta - \frac{1}{r}\frac{\theta w}{\partial \theta}\sin \theta \right)$$

$$= \frac{\partial^2 w}{\partial r^2}\cos^2 \theta - 2\frac{\partial^2 w}{\partial \theta\,\partial r}\frac{\sin \theta \cos \theta}{r} + \frac{\partial w}{\partial r}\frac{\sin^2 \theta}{r}$$

$$+ 2\frac{\partial w}{\partial \theta}\frac{\sin \theta \cos \theta}{r^2} + \frac{\partial^2 w}{\partial \theta^2}\frac{\sin^2 \theta}{r^2}$$

Similarly,

$$\frac{\partial^2 w}{\partial y^2} = \frac{\partial^2 w}{\partial r^2}\sin^2 \theta + 2\frac{\partial^2 w}{\partial \theta\,\partial r}\frac{\sin \theta \cos \theta}{r} + \frac{\partial w}{\partial r}\frac{\cos^2 \theta}{r}$$

$$- 2\frac{\partial w}{\partial \theta}\frac{\sin \theta \cos \theta}{r^2} + \frac{\partial^2 w}{\partial \theta^2}\frac{\cos^2 \theta}{r^2}$$

$$\frac{\partial^2 w}{\partial x\,\partial y} = \frac{\partial^2 w}{\partial r^2}\sin \theta \cos \theta + \frac{\partial^2 w}{\partial r\,\partial \theta}\frac{\cos^2 \theta - \sin^2 \theta}{r} - \frac{\partial w}{\partial \theta}\frac{\cos^2 \theta - \sin^2 \theta}{r^2}$$

$$- \frac{\partial w}{\partial r}\frac{\sin \theta \cos \theta}{r} - \frac{\partial^2 w}{\partial \theta^2}\frac{\sin \theta \cos \theta}{r^2}$$

With this transformation of coordinates, we get

$$\nabla^2 w = \frac{\partial^2 w}{\partial x^2} + \frac{\partial^2 w}{\partial y^2} = \frac{\partial^2 w}{\partial r^2} + \frac{1}{r}\frac{\partial w}{\partial r} + \frac{1}{r^2}\frac{\partial^2 w}{\partial \theta^2} \tag{11.34}$$

Noting that

$$\nabla^2 = \frac{\partial^2}{\partial r^2} + \frac{1}{r}\frac{\partial}{\partial r} + \frac{1}{r^2}\frac{\partial^2}{\partial \theta^2}$$

and

$$\nabla^4 w = \left(\frac{\partial^2}{\partial x^2} + \frac{\partial^2}{\partial y^2} \right)\left(\frac{\partial^2 w}{\partial x^2} + \frac{\partial^2 w}{\partial y^2} \right)$$

we obtain the differential equation for the deflection surface of a laterally loaded thin plate in polar coordinates as

$$\left(\frac{\partial^2}{\partial r^2} + \frac{1}{r}\frac{\partial}{\partial r} + \frac{1}{r^2}\frac{\partial^2}{\partial \theta^2}\right)\left(\frac{\partial^2 w}{\partial r^2} + \frac{1}{r}\frac{\partial w}{\partial r} + \frac{1}{r^2}\frac{\partial^2 w}{\partial \theta^2}\right) = \frac{p}{D} \quad (11.35)$$

To derive the expressions for the moments and shearing forces in polar coordinates, let us consider an element of the plate bounded by two adjacent axial planes forming an angle $d\theta$ and by two cylindrical surfaces of radii r and $r + dr$, respectively (Fig. 11.8). Assume that the x axis coincides with the radius r. The moments M_r, M_t, M_{rt} and the shears Q_r, Q_t then have the same values as the moments M_x, M_y, M_{xy} and the shears Q_x, Q_y at the same point. By substituting $\theta = 0$ in the expressions for $\dfrac{\partial^2 w}{\partial x^2}, \dfrac{\partial^2 w}{\partial y^2}, \dfrac{\partial^2 w}{\partial x\,\partial y}$, we obtain

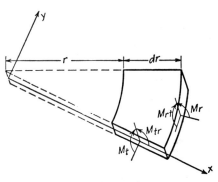

FIG. 11.8.

$$M_r = -D\left(\frac{\partial^2 w}{\partial x^2} + \nu \frac{\partial^2 w}{\partial y^2}\right)_{\theta=0}$$

$$= -D\left[\frac{\partial^2 w}{\partial r^2} + \nu\left(\frac{1}{r}\frac{\partial w}{\partial r} + \frac{1}{r^2}\frac{\partial^2 w}{\partial \theta^2}\right)\right]$$

$$M_t = -D\left(\frac{\partial^2 w}{\partial y^2} + \nu \frac{\partial^2 w}{\partial x^2}\right)_{\theta=0}$$

$$= -D\left(\frac{1}{r}\frac{\partial w}{\partial r} + \frac{1}{r^2}\frac{\partial^2 w}{\partial \theta^2} + \nu\frac{\partial^2 w}{\partial r^2}\right)$$

$$M_{rt} = M_{tr} = (1-\nu)D\left(\frac{\partial^2 w}{\partial x\,\partial y}\right)_{\theta=0} \qquad (11.36)$$

$$= (1-\nu)D\left(\frac{1}{r}\frac{\partial^2 w}{\partial r\,\partial \theta} - \frac{1}{r^2}\frac{\partial w}{\partial \theta}\right)$$

$$Q_r = -D\frac{\partial}{\partial x}\left(\frac{\partial^2 w}{\partial x^2} + \frac{\partial^2 w}{\partial y^2}\right)_{\theta=0}$$

$$= -D\frac{\partial}{\partial r}\left(\frac{\partial^2 w}{\partial r^2} + \frac{1}{r}\frac{\partial w}{\partial r} + \frac{1}{r^2}\frac{\partial^2 w}{\partial \theta^2}\right)$$

$$Q_t = -D\frac{\partial}{\partial y}\left(\frac{\partial^2 w}{\partial x^2} + \frac{\partial^2 w}{\partial y^2}\right)_{\theta=0}$$

$$= -D\frac{1}{r}\frac{\partial}{\partial \theta}\left(\frac{\partial^2 w}{\partial r^2} + \frac{1}{r}\frac{\partial w}{\partial r} + \frac{1}{r^2}\frac{\partial^2 w}{\partial \theta^2}\right)$$

The boundary conditions at the edge of a circular plate of radius a are as follows: If a part of the edge $r = a$ is simply supported, we have for that part of edge, $\theta_1 \leq \theta \leq \theta_2$,

$$w = 0 \qquad M_r = 0 \tag{11.37}$$

In the case of a clamped edge,

$$w = 0 \qquad \frac{\partial w}{\partial r} = 0 \tag{11.38}$$

In the case of a free edge,

$$M_r = 0 \qquad V = Q_r - \frac{\partial M_{rt}}{r\,\partial \theta} = 0 \tag{11.39}$$

If the load acting on a circular plate is symmetrically distributed about the axis perpendicular to the plate through its center and the boundary conditions are also symmetrical, the deflection surface of the plate will also be symmetrical.   In such cases, w will be independent of θ and is a function of r only.   Equation (11.35) becomes then

$$\left(\frac{d^2}{dr^2} + \frac{1}{r}\frac{d}{dr}\right)\left(\frac{d^2w}{dr^2} + \frac{1}{r}\frac{dw}{dr}\right) = \frac{p}{D} \tag{11.40}$$

Observing that

$$\frac{d^2w}{dr^2} + \frac{1}{r}\frac{dw}{dr} = \frac{1}{r}\frac{d}{dr}\left(r\frac{dw}{dr}\right)$$

we may rewrite Eq. (11.40) into the following form:

$$\frac{1}{r}\frac{d}{dr}\left\{r\frac{d}{dr}\left[\frac{1}{r}\frac{d}{dr}\left(r\frac{dw}{dr}\right)\right]\right\} = \frac{p}{D} \tag{11.41}$$

This equation can easily be integrated when $p(r)$ is given.

Consider the particular case of a circular plate with radius a under a uniformly distributed load p_0.   Multiplying both sides of (11.41) by r and carrying out the integration, we obtain

$$r\frac{d}{dr}\left[\frac{1}{r}\frac{d}{dr}\left(r\frac{dw}{dr}\right)\right] = \frac{p_0r^2}{2D} + C_1$$

or

$$\frac{d}{dr}\left[\frac{1}{r}\frac{d}{dr}\left(r\frac{dw}{dr}\right)\right] = \frac{p_0r}{2D} + \frac{C_1}{r} \tag{11.42}$$

where C_1 is a constant of integration.   Successive integrations can be carried out without any difficulty, and we obtain

$$\frac{1}{r}\frac{d}{dr}\left(r\frac{dw}{dr}\right) = \frac{p_0r^2}{4D} + C_1 \log r + C_2$$

$$r\frac{dw}{dr} = \frac{p_0r^4}{16D} + \frac{C_1r^2}{4}(2\log r - 1) + \frac{C_2r^2}{2} + C_3$$

$$w = \frac{p_0r^4}{64D} + \frac{C_1r^2}{4}(\log r - 1) + \frac{C_2r^2}{4} + C_3 \log r + C_4 \tag{11.43}$$

where C_2, C_3, C_4 are constants of integration.

From (11.36), we have, in the case of a symmetrically loaded plate,

$$\frac{d}{dr}\left[\frac{1}{r}\frac{d}{dr}\left(r\frac{dw}{dr}\right)\right] = \frac{d}{dr}\left(\frac{d^2w}{dr^2} + \frac{1}{r}\frac{dw}{dr}\right) = -\frac{Q}{D}$$

For a circular plate without a central hole, we find from (11.42) that Q becomes infinite at $r = 0$. As this is not possible, we must have $C_1 = 0$. Also, we observe from (11.43) that w becomes infinite at $r = 0$. To exclude this possibility, we must have $C_3 = 0$.

If the plate has its edge clamped, we have

$$w = 0 \qquad \frac{dw}{dr} = 0$$

at $r = a$. Hence,

$$\frac{p_0a^4}{64D} + \frac{C_2a^2}{4} + C_4 = 0$$

$$\frac{p_0a^3}{16D} + \frac{C_2a}{2} = 0$$

Solving, we find that

$$C_2 = -\frac{p_0a^2}{8D} \qquad C_4 = \frac{p_0a^4}{64D}$$

The deflection of such a plate is then

$$w = \frac{p_0}{64D}(a^2 - r^2)^2 \tag{11.44}$$

The maximum deflection occurs at the center of the plate and is

$$(w)_{r=0} = \frac{p_0a^4}{64D}$$

Substituting (11.44) into (11.36), we obtain

$$M_r = \frac{p_0}{16}[a^2(1 + \nu) - r^2(3 + \nu)] \qquad M_t = \frac{p_0}{16}[a^2(1 + \nu) - r^2(1 + 3\nu)]$$

$$\tag{11.45}$$

The maximum bending moment occurs at the edge of the plate and is

$$(M_r)_{r=a} = -\frac{p_0a^2}{8}$$

The maximum bending stress is therefore

$$(\sigma_r)_{max} = -\frac{6M_r}{h^2} = \frac{3p_0a^2}{4h^2}$$

Problem 1. A uniformly loaded circular plate with radius a has its edge simply supported. Assume that there is no hole in the plate. Find the maximum deflection, moment, and bending stress.

Ans. $w = \dfrac{p_0(a^2 - r^2)}{64D}\left(\dfrac{5 + \nu}{1 + \nu}a^2 - r^2\right)$

Problem 2. A circular plate with radius a is bent by a moment M uniformly distributed along the edge of the plate. Find the expression for the deflection w if the edge is assumed to be supported.

Ans. $w = \dfrac{M}{2D(1 + \nu)} (a^2 - r^2)$

Problem 3. Assume that the circular plate in Prob. 2 has a hole with radius b in the middle of the plate. Find the expression for the deflection of the plate.

Ans. $w = \dfrac{-b^2 M}{2(1 + \nu)D(a^2 - b^2)} (a^2 - r^2) + \dfrac{a^2 b^2 M}{(1 - \nu)D(a^2 - b^2)} \log \dfrac{r}{a}$

Problem 4. A circular plate with radius a has a hole with radius b at the middle of the plate. The plate is assumed to be under uniformly distributed load and has its inner edge clamped and external edge free. Find the maximum deflection, moment, and bending stress if $b = a/4$.

11.6. Combined Bending and Stretching of Rectangular Plates.

In the previous discussion the plate is assumed to be bent with small deflec-

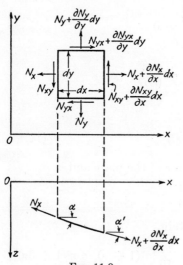

FIG. 11.9.

tion by lateral loads only. If there are forces acting in the middle plane of the plate in addition to the lateral loads, the governing differential equation must be modified to take into account the effects of these in-plane forces. Let us denote the in-plane stresses by σ_{x0}, σ_{y0}, and τ_{xy0}. Then the in-plane forces per unit length of plane are $N_x = h\sigma_{x0}$, $N_y = h\sigma_{y0}$, and $N_{xy} = N_{yx} = h\tau_{xy0}$. We shall assume that the deflection w of the plate is small enough so that the first two assumptions in Sec. 11.1 still hold, and yet large enough so that the products of the in-plane forces or their derivatives and the derivatives of w are of the same order of magnitude as the derivatives of the shear forces Q_x and Q_y. With this assumption, we find that the bending stresses in the plate will be again given by Eqs. (11.6) as derived in Sec. 11.1 and the moments and shear forces by Eqs. (11.8) and (11.13).

Consider the equilibrium of an element of the plate with sides dx and dy. In addition to the forces shown in Fig. 11.2, we have now the in-plane forces N_x, N_y and $N_{xy} = N_{yx}$. Since there are no resultant forces in the x or y directions in the group of forces shown in Fig. 11.2, when taking the summation of forces in the x and y directions, we need consider only the in-plane forces shown in Fig. 11.9. Considering the sum of x projections of the forces $N_x\, dy$ and $[N_x + (\partial N_x/\partial x)\, dx]\, dy$, we have

$$\left(N_x + \frac{\partial N_x}{\partial x}\, dx\right) dy \cos \alpha' - N_x\, dy \cos \alpha \qquad \textbf{(11.46)}$$

where $\alpha' = \alpha + (\partial\alpha/\partial x)\, dx$. But

$$\cos\alpha = (1 - \sin^2\alpha)^{1/2} = 1 - \tfrac{1}{2}\sin^2\alpha + \cdots$$
$$= 1 - \frac{\alpha^2}{2} + \cdots$$

For small α, $\alpha^2/2$ is much smaller than 1, and we have $\cos\alpha \cong 1$. Similarly, $\cos\alpha' \cong 1$. Expression (11.46) therefore becomes $(\partial N_x/\partial x)\, dx\, dy$. Likewise, we can show that the sum of the x components of the forces $N_{yx}\, dx$ and $[N_{yx} + (\partial N_{yx}/\partial y)\, dy]\, dx$ is $(\partial N_{xy}/\partial y)\, dx\, dy$. Summing up these components, we find that the condition $\Sigma F_x = 0$ gives

$$\frac{\partial N_x}{\partial x} + \frac{\partial N_{xy}}{\partial y} = 0 \tag{11.47}$$

Similarly, the condition $\Sigma F_y = 0$ leads to

$$\frac{\partial N_{xy}}{\partial x} + \frac{\partial N_y}{\partial y} = 0 \tag{11.48}$$

Now, let us find the equation of equilibrium in the z direction. In addition to the z components of the forces shown in Fig. 11.9, we have to consider also the z components of forces as shown in Fig. 11.2. The z components of the forces $N_x\, dy$ and $[N_x + (\partial N_x/\partial x)\, dx]\, dy$ give a resultant

$$-N_x\, dy \sin\alpha + \left(N_x + \frac{\partial N_x}{\partial x}\, dx\right) dy \sin\alpha'$$

For small α and α', we find $\sin\alpha \cong \alpha \cong \partial w/\partial x$ and

$$\sin\alpha' \cong \alpha' \cong \alpha + \frac{\partial\alpha}{\partial x}\, dx = \frac{\partial w}{\partial x} + \frac{\partial^2 w}{\partial x^2}\, dx$$

Thus, the above expression becomes

$$-N_x\, dy\, \frac{\partial w}{\partial x} + \left(N_x + \frac{\partial N_x}{\partial x}\, dx\right) dy \left(\frac{\partial w}{\partial x} + \frac{\partial^2 w}{\partial x^2}\, dx\right)$$
$$= N_x \frac{\partial^2 w}{\partial x^2}\, dx\, dy + \frac{\partial N_x}{\partial x}\frac{\partial w}{\partial x}\, dx\, dy$$

where higher-order terms are neglected. In a similar manner, the resultant of the z components of the forces $N_y\, dx$, $[N_y + (\partial N_y/\partial y)\, dy]\, dx$ can be shown to be

$$N_y \frac{\partial^2 w}{\partial y^2}\, dx\, dy + \frac{\partial N_y}{\partial y}\frac{\partial w}{\partial y}\, dx\, dy$$

To find the z components of the forces $N_{xy}\, dy$ and $[N_{xy} + (\partial N_{xy}/\partial x)\, dx]\, dy$, let us refer to Fig. 11.10. After bending, the deflection of O' is w and the deflection of B' is $w + (\partial w/\partial y)\, dy$. The line $O'B'$ is therefore inclined downward at an angle $\partial w/\partial y$ with the y axis. Similarly, we can show that the line $A'C'$ is inclined downward at an angle $(\partial w/\partial y) + [\partial^2 w/(\partial x\, \partial y)]\, dx$

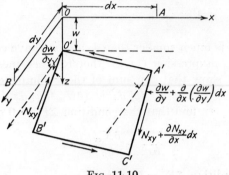

FIG. 11.10.

with the y axis. The shearing forces $N_{xy}\, dy$ and $[N_{xy} + (\partial N_{xy}/\partial x)\, dx]\, dy$ will therefore have a resultant force in the z direction equal to

$$-N_{xy}\, dy\, \frac{\partial w}{\partial y} + \left(N_{xy} + \frac{\partial N_{xy}}{\partial x}\, dx\right) dy \left(\frac{\partial w}{\partial y} + \frac{\partial^2 w}{\partial x\, \partial y}\, dx\right)$$

$$= N_{xy} \frac{\partial^2 w}{\partial x\, \partial y}\, dx\, dy + \frac{\partial N_{xy}}{\partial x} \frac{\partial w}{\partial y}\, dx\, dy$$

An analogous expression can be obtained for the z projection of the forces $N_{yx}\, dx$ and $[N_{yx} + (\partial N_{yx}/\partial y)\, dy]\, dx$ and is

$$N_{yx} \frac{\partial^2 w}{\partial x\, \partial y}\, dx\, dy + \frac{\partial N_{yx}}{\partial y} \frac{\partial w}{\partial x}\, dx\, dy$$

Adding these forces to the z component of forces shown in Fig. 11.2 and dividing by $dx\, dy$, we have

$$\frac{\partial Q_x}{\partial x} + \frac{\partial Q_y}{\partial y} + p + N_x \frac{\partial^2 w}{\partial x^2} + N_y \frac{\partial^2 w}{\partial y^2} + 2N_{xy} \frac{\partial^2 w}{\partial x\, \partial y}$$

$$+ \left(\frac{\partial N_x}{\partial x} + \frac{\partial N_{yx}}{\partial y}\right) \frac{\partial w}{\partial x} + \left(\frac{\partial N_{xy}}{\partial x} + \frac{\partial N_y}{\partial y}\right) \frac{\partial w}{\partial y} = 0$$

From Eqs. (11.47) and (11.48), we find that the terms inside the parentheses in the above equation are zero. Since the in-plane forces do not produce any moment along the edges of the element, the moment equations (11.11) and (11.12) and, consequently, formulas (11.13) will remain the same. Using these relations, we find that the equilibrium equation in the z direction becomes

$$\frac{\partial^4 w}{\partial x^4} + 2 \frac{\partial^4 w}{\partial x^2\, \partial y^2} + \frac{\partial^4 w}{\partial y^4} = \frac{1}{D}\left(p + N_x \frac{\partial^2 w}{\partial x^2} + N_y \frac{\partial^2 w}{\partial y^2} + 2N_{xy} \frac{\partial^2 w}{\partial x\, \partial y}\right)$$

$$(11.49)$$

Equations (11.47) to (11.49) are the governing differential equations for a thin plate under the combined action of bending and in-plane forces.

Let us now consider a rectangular plate with simply supported edges under the combined uniform lateral load and uniform tension N_x in the x direction. In such a case, we have

$$N_x = \text{constant} \qquad N_y = N_{xy} = 0$$

Equations (11.47) and (11.48) are satisfied identically, and we need consider only Eq. (11.49). It was shown in Sec. 11.3 that the uniform lateral load p_0 can be represented by the Fourier's series

$$p = \frac{16 p_0}{\pi^2} \sum_{m=1,3,5}^{\infty} \sum_{n=1,3,5}^{\infty} \frac{1}{mn} \sin \frac{m\pi x}{a} \sin \frac{n\pi y}{b}$$

Equation (11.49) thus becomes

$$\frac{\partial^4 w}{\partial x^4} + 2 \frac{\partial^4 w}{\partial x^2 \partial y^2} + \frac{\partial^4 w}{\partial y^4} - \frac{N_x}{D} \frac{\partial^2 w}{\partial x^2}$$
$$= \frac{16 p_0}{D\pi^2} \sum_{m=1,3,5}^{\infty} \sum_{n=1,3,5}^{\infty} \frac{1}{mn} \sin \frac{m\pi x}{a} \sin \frac{n\pi y}{b} \quad (11.50)$$

The boundary conditions are that at $x = 0$ and a, $w = \partial^2 w / \partial x^2 = 0$, and at $y = 0$ and b, $w = \partial^2 w / \partial y^2 = 0$.

The boundary conditions will be satisfied if we assume w in the following double series:

$$w = \sum_{m=1}^{\infty} \sum_{n=1}^{\infty} A_{mn} \sin \frac{m\pi x}{a} \sin \frac{n\pi y}{b}$$

Substituting into Eq. (11.50), we find that

$$A_{mn} = \frac{16 p_0}{D\pi^6 mn \left[\left(\dfrac{m^2}{a^2} + \dfrac{n^2}{b^2} \right)^2 + \dfrac{N_x m^2}{\pi^2 D a^2} \right]} \qquad \text{for odd } m \text{ and } n$$

$$A_{mn} = 0 \qquad \text{for even } m \text{ or } n$$

Therefore,

$$w = \frac{16 p_0}{\pi^6 D} \sum_{m=1,3,5}^{\infty} \sum_{n=1,3,5}^{\infty} \frac{1}{mn \left[\left(\dfrac{m^2}{a^2} + \dfrac{n^2}{b^2} \right)^2 + \dfrac{N_x m^2}{\pi^2 D a^2} \right]} \sin \frac{m\pi x}{a} \sin \frac{n\pi y}{b}$$

$$(11.51)$$

Comparing (11.51) with (11.25), we find that the presence of a tensile force will decrease the deflection of the plate. On the other hand, if the in-plane force N_x is compressive, the deflection of the plate will be increased.

Problem 1. A simply supported rectangular plate is under the action of hydrostatic pressure given by formula

$$p(x,y) = \frac{p_0 x}{a}$$

If the plate is also under a uniform tensile force N_x along the sides $x = 0$ and $x = a$, find the deflection, moments, and stresses in the plate.

Problem 2. A simply supported rectangular plate is under the combined action of uniform lateral pressure p_0 and uniform in-plane forces N along the four edges. Find the deflection, moments, and stresses in the plate.

11.7. Buckling of Simply Supported Rectangular Plates Uniformly Compressed in One Direction.

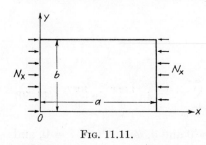

FIG. 11.11.

When a flat plate is compressed in its middle plane, just as in the case of columns, the flat form of equilibrium becomes unstable and the plate begins to buckle at a certain critical value of the in-plane force. Let us consider a simply supported rectangular plate (Fig. 11.11) compressed in its middle plane by a uniformly distributed force N_x along the sides $x = 0$ and $x = a$. In such a case, we have

$$N_x = -\text{constant} \qquad N_y = N_{xy} = p = 0$$

Equations (11.47) and (11.48) are satisfied identically, and Eq. (11.49) is the only one yet to be satisfied. By substituting $-N_x$ for N_x in (11.49), we have

$$D\nabla^4 w + N_x \frac{\partial^2 w}{\partial x^2} = 0 \tag{11.52}$$

The boundary conditions are satisfied if we take

$$w = \sum_{m=1}^{\infty} \sum_{n=1}^{\infty} A_{mn} \sin \frac{m\pi x}{a} \sin \frac{n\pi y}{b}$$

Substituting the above expression into Eq. (11.52), we find that

$$\sum_{m=1}^{\infty} \sum_{n=1}^{\infty} \left[D\pi^4 \left(\frac{m^2}{a^2} + \frac{n^2}{b^2} \right)^2 - N_x \pi^2 \frac{m^2}{a^2} \right] A_{mn} \sin \frac{m\pi x}{a} \sin \frac{n\pi y}{b} = 0$$

The trivial solution is that $A_{mn} = 0$ or $w = 0$. To find the nontrivial solution, we let

$$D\pi^4 \left(\frac{m^2}{a^2} + \frac{n^2}{b^2} \right)^2 - N_x \pi^2 \frac{m^2}{a^2} = 0$$

or
$$N_x = \frac{\pi^2 D \left(\frac{m^2}{a^2} + \frac{n^2}{b^2} \right)^2}{m^2/a^2} = \frac{\pi^2 D}{b^2} \left(\frac{mb}{a} + \frac{n^2 a}{mb} \right)^2 \qquad (11.53)$$

This means that when N_x reaches the value given by the right-hand side of the above formula, A_{mn} and consequently w may be different from zero, which indicates the buckling of the plate. The same conclusion can be reached by examining Eq. (11.51). We observe that, in the case of compressive force, N_x in (11.51) must be replaced by $-N_x$. When N_x reaches the value given by (11.53), the denominator in (11.51) becomes zero and

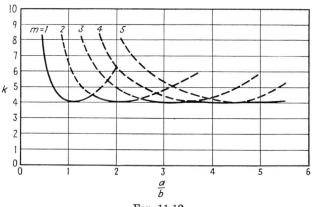

FIG. 11.12.

if p_0 is different from zero, w becomes infinity. The physical meaning of this is that no matter how small the lateral load is, the plate will have excessive deflections. In other words, the plate will buckle.

From Eq. (11.53), we find that the value of N_x is smallest if n is equal to 1. This indicates that, when such a plate buckles, there can be several half waves in the direction of compression but only one half wave in the perpendicular direction. The critical load is therefore

$$(N_x)_{cr} = \frac{\pi^2 D}{b^2} \left(\frac{mb}{a} + \frac{a}{mb} \right)^2 = k \frac{\pi^2 D}{b^2} \qquad (11.54)$$

where $k = [(mb/a) + (a/mb)]^2$ is a numerical factor the magnitude of which depends on m and the ratio a/b. The minimum value of $(N_x)_{cr}$ occurs when

$$\frac{d(N_x)_{cr}}{d(mb/a)} = \frac{2\pi^2 D}{b^2} \left(\frac{mb}{d} + \frac{a}{mb} \right) \left[1 - \frac{1}{(mb/a)^2} \right] = 0$$

or
$$\frac{mb}{a} = 1$$

This gives the minimum value of $(N_x)_{cr}$ as $4\pi^2D/b^2$. For various values of the integer m, the magnitude of k depends on the ratio a/b only. The values of k for $m = 1, 2, 3, 4, 5$ are plotted in Fig. 11.12 against a/b ratios. Having these curves, the magnitude of the critical load and the number of half waves for any value of a/b ratio can be determined by taking the ordinate of the curve which gives smallest k for the given ratio of a/b. For example, for $a/b = 2.5$, we find from Fig. 11.12 that $k = 4.133$ and $m = 3$. This indicates that the plate will buckle into three half waves in the direction of load under a buckling load of $(N_x)_{cr} = 4.133\pi^2D/b^2$.

Problem. A simply supported rectangular plate is under uniform compression in both directions. Find the buckling load.

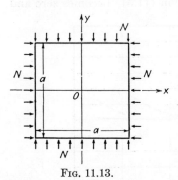

FIG. 11.13.

11.8. Buckling of a Simply Supported Square Plate Compressed in Two Perpendicular Directions. Finite-difference Approximation. The buckling load can also be calculated by the finite-difference approximation as was previously carried out in the case of columns. The application of the method can be most easily demonstrated by working out a numerical example.

Consider the buckling of a simply supported square plate under uniform compression. Let a be the length of the sides. Taking the coordinates as shown in Fig. 11.13, and noting that $N_x = N_y = -N$, $p = N_{xy} = 0$, the buckling equation (11.49) becomes

$$\nabla^4 w + \frac{N}{D} \nabla^2 w = 0$$

with the boundary conditions

$$w = \frac{\partial^2 w}{\partial x^2} = 0 \qquad \text{along } x = \pm \frac{a}{2}$$

$$w = \frac{\partial^2 w}{\partial y^2} = 0 \qquad \text{along } y = \pm \frac{a}{2}$$

Since $\partial^2 w/\partial y^2$ is identically zero along the edges $x = \pm a/2$ and $\partial^2 w/\partial x^2$ is identically zero along the edges $y = \pm b/2$, the boundary conditions may be written as

$$\nabla^2 w = 0 \qquad \text{along the edges}$$

Therefore we can rewrite the differential equation as follows:

$$\nabla^2 M + \frac{N}{D} M = 0 \tag{11.55}$$

with $M = 0$ on the boundary, and

$$\nabla^2 w = M \qquad (11.56)$$

with $w = 0$ on the boundary. From Eq. (11.56) together with the boundary condition on w, we observe that for the trivial solution $M = 0$ we also obtain the trivial solution $w = 0$. Consequently, to solve the buckling problem we only have to find the nontrivial solution of Eq. (11.55).

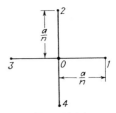

Referring to Fig. 11.14, we find that the corresponding difference equation at any point 0 becomes

$$M_1 + M_2 + M_3 + M_4 + C_n M_0 = 0 \qquad (11.57)$$

Fig. 11.14.

and, on the boundary, $M_i = 0$. In the above expressions, the subscript i indicates the boundary points and

$$C_n = \frac{N_n a^2}{n^2 D} - 4 = \frac{k_n}{n^2} - 4$$

where $k_n = N_n a^2 / D$. N_n denotes the approximate buckling load calculated when the sides of the plate are divided into n subdivisions.

Approximation $n = 2$. Because of symmetry, the nodal points are numbered as shown in Fig. 11.15. Apply Eq. (11.57) at $x = y = a/2$.

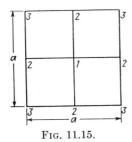

Fig. 11.15.

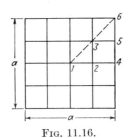

Fig. 11.16.

From the boundary condition, $M_2 = M_3 = 0$, we have therefore, from Eq. (11.57),

$$C_n M_1 = 0$$

which gives $C_n = 0$ or $k_n = 4n^2 = 16.00$ (error, -19 per cent).

Approximation $n = 4$. Because of symmetry we need to consider only one-eighth of the plate (Fig. 11.16). Applying Eq. (11.57) at the nodal points 1, 2, 3 and noting that $M_4 = M_5 = M_6 = 0$ because of the boundary condition, we have

$$C_4 M_1 + 4 M_2 = 0 \qquad M_1 + C_4 M_2 + 2 M_3 = 0 \qquad 2 M_2 + C_4 M_3 = 0$$

This equation admits a nonzero solution for M only if

$$\begin{vmatrix} C_4 & 4 & 0 \\ 1 & C_4 & 2 \\ 0 & 2 & C_4 \end{vmatrix} = 0$$

Therefore $C_4 = -2.8284$, and $k_4 = 18.75$ (error, -5.1 per cent). By extrapolation, $k_{2,4} = 19.67$ (error, -0.35 per cent). The exact value of k is 19.739.[1]

Problem 1. A simply supported rectangular plate with $a = 2b/3$ is under uniform compression along the edges. Calculate the buckling load by the finite-difference approximation.

Problem 2. A square plate with clamped edges is under uniform compression along two opposite edges. Calculate the buckling load by the finite-difference approximation.

Problem 3. A square plate has two opposite sides simply supported and the other two sides clamped. The plate is assumed to be under uniform compression along the two simply supported edges. Calculate the buckling load by the finite-difference approximation.

11.9. Buckling of Simply Supported Rectangular Plates under Shear. Energy Method. As in the case of columns, the buckling load of a plate

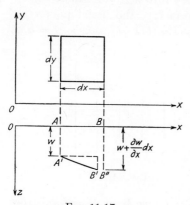

can also be calculated by the energy method. The plate is assumed to be under the action of constant in-plane forces just before the plate buckles, *i.e.*, the magnitudes of these in-plane forces are just equal to the critical values. Then, the plate is assumed to be subjected to some small disturbances, and buckling occurs. During this exchange of equilibrium forms, no energy is gained or lost, and the work done by these in-plane forces must be equal to the bending-strain energy stored in the plate.

Fig. 11.17.

Let us consider the element $dx\,dy$ as shown in Fig. 11.17. When the plate bends, the element AB is now displaced to the position $A'B'$. Since there is no change in the in-plane stresses or strains, the length of $A'B'$ will still be dx, but its horizontal projection will now be

$$\left[dx^2 - \left(\frac{\partial w}{\partial x} dx \right)^2 \right]^{1/2} = dx - \frac{1}{2} \left(\frac{\partial w}{\partial x} \right)^2 dx + \cdots$$

[1] S. Timoshenko, "Theory of Elastic Stability," pp. 333–337, McGraw-Hill Book Company, Inc., New York, 1936.

By neglecting small-order terms, the work done by the force $N_x\, dy$ is therefore

$$\frac{1}{2} \iint\limits_{A} N_x \left(\frac{\partial w}{\partial x}\right)^2 dx\, dy$$

Similarly, the work done by the force $N_y\, dx$ is

$$\frac{1}{2} \iint\limits_{A} N_y \left(\frac{\partial w}{\partial y}\right)^2 dx\, dy$$

where A is the area of the plate.

To calculate the work done by the shearing forces $N_{xy}\, dy$ and $N_{yx}\, dx$, let us find the change in the shearing strain due to the bending of the plate. Referring to Fig. 11.18, we find the direction cosines $l_1,\ m_1,\ n_1$ and $l_2,\ m_2,\ n_2$, of the elements O_1A_1 and O_1B_1, respectively, are as follows:

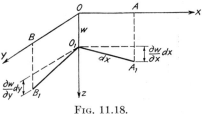

FIG. 11.18.

$$l_1 = \frac{\left[dx^2 - \left(\dfrac{\partial w}{\partial x}\, dx\right)^2\right]^{1/2}}{dx} \cong 1 - \frac{1}{2}\left(\frac{\partial w}{\partial x}\right)^2$$

$$m_1 = 0$$

$$n_1 = \frac{(\partial w/\partial x)\, dx}{dx} = \frac{\partial w}{\partial x}$$

$$l_2 = 0$$

$$m_2 = \frac{\left[dy^2 - \left(\dfrac{\partial w}{\partial y}\, dy\right)^2\right]^{1/2}}{dy} \cong 1 - \frac{1}{2}\left(\frac{\partial w}{\partial y}\right)^2$$

$$n_2 = \frac{(\partial w/\partial y)\, dy}{dy} = \frac{\partial w}{\partial y}$$

The shearing strain γ_{xy} is therefore

$$\gamma_{xy} = \frac{\pi}{2} - \angle A_1 O_1 B_1 = \sin\left(\frac{\pi}{2} - \angle A_1 O_1 B_1\right)$$

$$= \cos \angle A_1 O_1 B_1 = l_1 l_2 + m_1 m_2 + n_1 n_2$$

$$= \frac{\partial w}{\partial x}\frac{\partial w}{\partial y}$$

The work done by the shearing forces $N_{xy} = N_{yx}$ is therefore equal to

$$\iint\limits_{A} N_{xy} \frac{\partial w}{\partial x}\frac{\partial w}{\partial y}\, dx\, dy$$

The total work done by these in-plane forces is thus

$$\bar{W} = \frac{1}{2} \iint\limits_{A} \left[N_x \left(\frac{\partial w}{\partial x}\right)^2 + N_y \left(\frac{\partial w}{\partial y}\right)^2 + 2N_{xy} \frac{\partial w}{\partial x} \frac{\partial w}{\partial y} \right] dx\, dy \quad (11.58)$$

and the strain energy stored in the plate due to bending, from Sec. 11.4, is

$$U = \frac{D}{2} \iint\limits_{A} \left\{ \left(\frac{\partial^2 w}{\partial x^2} + \frac{\partial^2 w}{\partial y^2}\right)^2 - 2(1 - \nu) \left[\frac{\partial^2 w}{\partial x^2} \frac{\partial^2 w}{\partial y^2} - \left(\frac{\partial^2 w}{\partial x\, \partial y}\right)^2 \right] \right\} dx\, dy$$

At buckling, we have

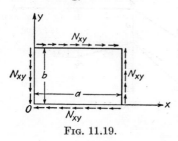

FIG. 11.19.

$$\bar{\Pi} = U - \bar{W} = 0 \qquad (11.59)$$

To illustrate the energy method, let us take as an example the buckling of simply supported rectangular plates under the action of shearing forces N_{xy} uniformly distributed along the edges (Fig. 11.19). To assume an expression for w satisfying the boundary conditions, we may take

$$w = \sum_{m=1}^{\infty} \sum_{n=1}^{\infty} A_{mn} \sin \frac{m\pi x}{a} \sin \frac{n\pi y}{b}$$

Since $N_x = N_y = 0$, the work done by the external forces during buckling of the plate is

$$\bar{W} = N_{xy} \int_0^a \int_0^b \frac{\partial w}{\partial x} \frac{\partial w}{\partial y} \, dx\, dy$$

Let us now substitute into the above expression the assumed series for w and integrate over the whole plate. Observing that

$$\int_0^a \sin \frac{m\pi x}{a} \cos \frac{p\pi x}{a} \, dx = 0 \qquad\qquad \text{if } m \pm p \text{ is an even number}$$

$$\int_0^a \sin \frac{m\pi x}{a} \cos \frac{p\pi x}{a} \, dx = \frac{2a}{\pi} \frac{m}{m^2 - p^2} \qquad \text{if } m \pm p \text{ is an odd number}$$

we obtain

$$\bar{W} = 4N_{xy} \sum_m \sum_n \sum_p \sum_q A_{mn} A_{pq} \frac{mnpq}{(m^2 - p^2)(q^2 - n^2)}$$

in which m, n, p, q are such integers that $m \pm p$ and $n \pm q$ are odd numbers.

The bending-strain energy of the buckled plate, after integration, is

$$U = \frac{D}{2} \frac{\pi^4 ab}{4} \sum_{m=1}^{\infty} \sum_{n=1}^{\infty} A_{mn}{}^2 \left(\frac{m^2}{a^2} + \frac{n^2}{b^2}\right)^2$$

Substituting into Eq. (11.59), we obtain

$$\bar{\Pi} = \frac{D\pi^4 ab}{8} \sum_{m=1}^{\infty} \sum_{n=1}^{\infty} A_{mn}{}^2 \left(\frac{m^2}{a^2} + \frac{n^2}{b^2}\right)^2 - 4N_{xy} \sum_m \sum_n \sum_p \sum_q$$
$$A_{mn}A_{pq} \frac{mnpq}{(m^2 - p^2)(q^2 - n^2)} = 0$$

To determine the critical value of the shearing forces, it is necessary to determine the parameters A_{mn} so that N_{xy} is a minimum. It was shown in Sec. 10.5 that this condition is equivalent to requiring that $\bar{\Pi}$ be a minimum. Carrying out differentiation with respect to A_{mn}, we find the condition $\partial\bar{\Pi}/\partial A_{mn} = 0$ leads to

$$\frac{D\pi^4 ab}{4} A_{mn} \left(\frac{m^2}{a^2} + \frac{n^2}{b^2}\right)^2 - 8N_{xy} \sum_p \sum_q A_{pq} \frac{mnpq}{(m^2 - p^2)(q^2 - n^2)} = 0 \quad (11.60)$$

where p and q must be such that $m \pm p$, $n \pm q$ are odd numbers.

Introducing the notation that

$$\alpha = \frac{a}{b} \qquad \phi = \frac{D\pi^4}{32\alpha b^2 N_{xy}}$$

Eq. (11.60) becomes

$$\phi A_{mn} \frac{(m^2 + n^2\alpha^2)^2}{\alpha^2} - \sum_p \sum_q A_{pq} \frac{mnpq}{(m^2 - p^2)(q^2 - n^2)} = 0 \quad (11.61)$$

We obtain thus a system of homogeneous linear equations in A_{mn}. The equation for calculating $(N_{xy})_{cr}$ is obtained by equating the determinant of these equations to zero. Since these equations are infinite in number, the exact solution will be obtained if we expand a determinant with an infinite number of rows and columns. As this is impossible, we shall obtain an approximate solution by taking a finite number of the parameters A_{mn}.

Let us begin with two parameters A_{11} and A_{22} and assume that all the other parameters are zero. In this case, Eq. (11.61) becomes

$$\frac{\phi(1 + \alpha^2)^2}{\alpha^2} A_{11} + \frac{4}{9} A_{22} = 0$$

$$\frac{16\phi(1 + \alpha^2)^2}{\alpha^2} A_{22} + \frac{4}{9} A_{11} = 0$$

The determinantal equation for ϕ is

$$\begin{vmatrix} \dfrac{\phi(1 + \alpha^2)^2}{\alpha^2} & \dfrac{4}{9} \\[3mm] \dfrac{4}{9} & \dfrac{16\phi(1 + \alpha^2)^2}{\alpha^2} \end{vmatrix} = 0$$

Expanding and solving, we find that

$$\phi = \pm \frac{1}{9} \frac{\alpha^2}{(1 + \alpha^2)^2}$$

or

$$(N_{xy})_{cr} = \pm \frac{9\pi^4 D}{32b^2} \frac{(1 + \alpha^2)^2}{\alpha^3} \qquad (11.62)$$

The plus or minus signs indicate that the critical value of the shearing forces does not depend on the direction of the forces. The approximate value of $(N_{xy})_{cr}$ given by Eq. (11.62) has an error of about 15 per cent for square plates and a larger value for larger a/b ratios.

To get a more satisfactory approximation, a larger number of these parameters must be taken. Let us now take six parameters A_{11}, A_{22}, A_{13}, A_{31}, A_{33}, A_{42}. Equation (11.62) thus becomes

A_{11}	A_{22}	A_{13}	A_{31}	A_{33}	A_{42}	
$\dfrac{\phi(1+\alpha^2)^2}{\alpha^2}$	$\dfrac{4}{9}$	0	0	0	$\dfrac{8}{45}$	$= 0$
$\dfrac{4}{9}$	$\dfrac{16\phi(1+\alpha^2)^2}{\alpha^2}$	$-\dfrac{4}{5}$	$-\dfrac{4}{5}$	$\dfrac{36}{25}$	0	$= 0$
0	$-\dfrac{4}{5}$	$\dfrac{\phi(1+9\alpha^2)^2}{\alpha^2}$	0	0	$-\dfrac{24}{75}$	$= 0$
0	$-\dfrac{4}{5}$	0	$\dfrac{\phi(9+\alpha^2)^2}{\alpha^2}$	0	$\dfrac{24}{21}$	$= 0$
0	$\dfrac{36}{25}$	0	0	$\dfrac{\phi(9+9\alpha^2)^2}{\alpha^2}$	$-\dfrac{72}{35}$	$= 0$
$\dfrac{8}{45}$	0	$-\dfrac{24}{75}$	$\dfrac{24}{21}$	$-\dfrac{72}{35}$	$\dfrac{\phi(16+4\alpha^2)^2}{\alpha^2}$	$= 0$

Setting the determinant of the coefficients of the above equations to zero and solving, we obtain

$$(N_{xy})_{cr} = k \frac{\pi^2 D}{b^2}$$

where k is a constant depending on the ratio a/b and is given in Table 11.1 for various values of a/b ratios.

TABLE 11.1

a/b	1.0	1.2	1.4	1.5	1.6	1.8	2.0	2.5	3
k	9.4	8.0	7.3	7.1	7.0	6.8	6.6	6.3	6.1

Problem 1. A simply supported rectangular plate is under uniform compression along two opposite sides. Calculate the buckling load by the energy method.

Problem 2. A simply supported rectangular plate is under uniform compression in two directions. Calculate the buckling load by the energy method.

Problem 3. A rectangular plate with all edges clamped is under uniform compression along two opposite sides. Calculate the buckling load by the energy method.

Problem 4. A rectangular plate has two opposite sides simply supported and the other two sides clamped. The plate is assumed to be under uniform compression along the two simply supported edges. Calculate the buckling load by the energy method.

CHAPTER 12

THEORY OF THIN SHELLS AND CURVED PLATES

12.1. Some Differential Geometry of a Surface. In the last chapter we have developed the theory of thin flat plates. Let us now extend our discussion to the case of thin shells. Since a curved plate can be regarded as part of a shell, the general equations for thin shells are also applicable to curved plates. Denote the thickness of the shell by h. For *thin* shells, h is small compared with the other dimensions of the shell and its radii of curvature. The surface that bisects the thickness of the shell is called the *middle* surface. The geometry of a shell is entirely defined by specifying the form of the middle surface and the thickness of the shell at each point.

Before we proceed to the discussion of the theory of thin shells, let us study some important geometrical properties of a surface. In the following discussion the notations of *vector analysis* are used. A surface is defined as the locus of a point whose position vector $\mathbf{r}$, relative to some fixed origin O, is a function of two independent parameters ξ_1, ξ_2. Thus, the cartesian coordinates (x,y,z) of a point on a surface are known functions of ξ_1, ξ_2 and can be written as

$$x = f_1(\xi_1,\xi_2) \qquad y = f_2(\xi_1,\xi_2) \qquad z = f_3(\xi_1,\xi_2) \tag{12.1}$$

Equations (12.1) are actually the parametric equations of a surface. If we eliminate ξ_1 and ξ_2 in these equations, then we obtain the familiar form of the equation of a surface, *viz.*,

$$F(x,y,z) = 0$$

Any relation between the parameters, say $g(\xi_1,\xi_2) = 0$, represents a curve on the surface. In this case, $\mathbf{r}$ becomes a function of only one independent parameter, and the locus is a curve. In particular, the curves on a surface along which one parameter remains constant are called *parametric curves*. The surface can be defined completely by a doubly infinite set of parametric curves. The parameters ξ_1, ξ_2 thus constitute a system of *curvilinear coordinates* for points on the surface, the position of any point on the surface being determined by the values of ξ_1 and ξ_2 at that point. This is illustrated in Fig. 12.1. As an example for this method of description, let us consider the surface of a sphere in terms of the usual spherical coordinates (r,φ,θ) as shown in Fig. 12.2. If R is the radius of the sphere, the cartesian coordinates of a point on the sphere are

$$x = R \sin \varphi \cos \theta \qquad y = R \sin \varphi \sin \theta \qquad z = R \cos \varphi$$

In this case, φ and θ may be taken as parameters which define the surface and may be identified with the general parameters ξ_1 and ξ_2.

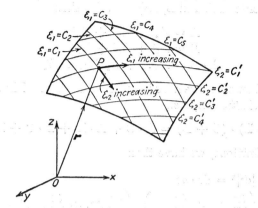

Fig. 12.1.

Consider, now, two neighboring points P, Q on the surface, with position vector $\mathbf{r}$, $\mathbf{r} + d\mathbf{r}$, respectively, corresponding to parametric coordinate values (ξ_1, ξ_2) and $(\xi_1 + d\xi_1, \xi_2 + d\xi_2)$ (Fig. 12.3).   Then, since $\mathbf{r}$ is a function of ξ_1 and ξ_2, we have

$$d\mathbf{r} = \frac{\partial \mathbf{r}}{\partial \xi_1} d\xi_1 + \frac{\partial \mathbf{r}}{\partial \xi_2} d\xi_2 \qquad (12.2)$$

Since the two points are adjacent points on a curve passing through them, the length ds of the elements of arc joining PQ is equal to the magnitude of $d\mathbf{r}$ or $|d\mathbf{r}|$ as Q approaches P as a limit.

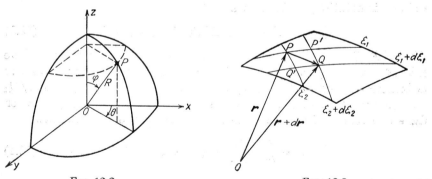

Fig. 12.2.   Fig. 12.3.

Let us define the *scalar product of two vectors* $\mathbf{A}$ and $\mathbf{B}$ as the product of the magnitudes of $\mathbf{A}$ and $\mathbf{B}$, viz., $|\mathbf{A}|$ and $|\mathbf{B}|$, and the cosine of the angle θ between these vectors.   Thus

$$\mathbf{A} \cdot \mathbf{B} = |\mathbf{A}||\mathbf{B}| \cos \theta$$

where the dot between two vectors indicates a scalar product. If $\mathbf{i}$, $\mathbf{j}$, $\mathbf{k}$ are unit vectors in the x, y, z directions and A_x, A_y, A_z, B_x, B_y, B_z are x, y, z components of $\mathbf{A}$ and $\mathbf{B}$, respectively, then

$$\mathbf{A} = A_x\mathbf{i} + A_y\mathbf{j} + A_z\mathbf{k}$$
$$\mathbf{B} = B_x\mathbf{i} + B_y\mathbf{j} + B_z\mathbf{k}$$

and
$$\mathbf{A} \cdot \mathbf{B} = A_xB_x + A_yB_y + A_zB_z$$

The scalar product of two vectors is a scalar quantity. The scalar product obeys the *distributive law*, viz.,

$$(\mathbf{A} + \mathbf{B}) \cdot (\mathbf{C} + \mathbf{D}) = \mathbf{A} \cdot \mathbf{C} + \mathbf{A} \cdot \mathbf{D} + \mathbf{B} \cdot \mathbf{C} + \mathbf{B} \cdot \mathbf{D}$$

With these definitions, we have then

$$(ds)^2 = |d\mathbf{r}|^2 = d\mathbf{r} \cdot d\mathbf{r}$$
$$= \left(\frac{\partial \mathbf{r}}{\partial \xi_1} d\xi_1 + \frac{\partial \mathbf{r}}{\partial \xi_2} d\xi_2\right) \cdot \left(\frac{\partial \mathbf{r}}{\partial \xi_1} d\xi_1 + \frac{\partial \mathbf{r}}{\partial \xi_2} d\xi_2\right)$$
$$= \frac{\partial \mathbf{r}}{\partial \xi_1} \cdot \frac{\partial \mathbf{r}}{\partial \xi_1} (d\xi_1)^2 + 2\frac{\partial \mathbf{r}}{\partial \xi_1} \cdot \frac{\partial \mathbf{r}}{\partial \xi_2} d\xi_1 d\xi_2 + \frac{\partial \mathbf{r}}{\partial \xi_2} \cdot \frac{\partial \mathbf{r}}{\partial \xi_2} (d\xi_2)^2$$

We define

$$E = \frac{\partial \mathbf{r}}{\partial \xi_1} \cdot \frac{\partial \mathbf{r}}{\partial \xi_1} = \left(\frac{\partial x}{\partial \xi_1}\right)^2 + \left(\frac{\partial y}{\partial \xi_1}\right)^2 + \left(\frac{\partial z}{\partial \xi_1}\right)^2$$
$$F = \frac{\partial \mathbf{r}}{\partial \xi_1} \cdot \frac{\partial \mathbf{r}}{\partial \xi_2} = \frac{\partial x}{\partial \xi_1}\frac{\partial x}{\partial \xi_2} + \frac{\partial y}{\partial \xi_1}\frac{\partial y}{\partial \xi_2} + \frac{\partial z}{\partial \xi_1}\frac{\partial z}{\partial \xi_2}$$
$$G = \frac{\partial \mathbf{r}}{\partial \xi_2} \cdot \frac{\partial \mathbf{r}}{\partial \xi_2} = \left(\frac{\partial x}{\partial \xi_2}\right)^2 + \left(\frac{\partial y}{\partial \xi_2}\right)^2 + \left(\frac{\partial z}{\partial \xi_2}\right)^2$$

Using this notation, we have then

$$(ds)^2 = E(d\xi_1)^2 + 2F\,d\xi_1\,d\xi_2 + G(d\xi_2)^2 \tag{12.3}$$

We call E, F, G the first *fundamental magnitudes* for the surface, and we call (12.3) the *quadratic differential form* for arc length. From the above definitions, we find that the magnitudes of the vectors $\partial \mathbf{r}/\partial \xi_1$ and $\partial \mathbf{r}/\partial \xi_2$ are equal to $\sqrt{E}$ and $\sqrt{G}$, respectively. Thus, if θ is the angle between these two vectors, from the definition of a scalar product, we have

$$F = \frac{\partial \mathbf{r}}{\partial \xi_1} \cdot \frac{\partial \mathbf{r}}{\partial \xi_2} = \sqrt{E}\,\sqrt{G}\cos\theta \tag{12.4}$$

Since $0 \leq \cos\theta \leq 1$, we find

$$F \leq \sqrt{EG}$$

which means that the quantity $EG - F^2$ cannot be negative and we may use the notation

$$H^2 = EG - F^2$$

Along the parametric curve $\xi_1 = $ constant, $d\xi_1 = 0$. From Eq. (12.2) we find that the vector PP' (Fig. 12.3) is equal to

$$(d\mathbf{r})_2 = \frac{\partial \mathbf{r}}{\partial \xi_2} d\xi_2$$

From (12.3) the length of the element PP' is then

$$(ds)_2 = \sqrt{G}\, d\xi_2$$

Similarly, along the parametric curve $\xi_2 = $ constant, $d\xi_2 = 0$. The vector PQ' is then given by

$$(d\mathbf{r})_1 = \frac{\partial \mathbf{r}}{\partial \xi_1} d\xi_1$$

and the length of PQ' is

$$(ds)_1 = \sqrt{E}\, d\xi_1$$

If the parametric curves form an orthogonal curvilinear coordinate system on a surface, the vectors PP' and PQ' must be perpendicular to each other. This means that the cosine of the angle between these two vectors must vanish. In other words, the scalar product of these two vectors must vanish; *viz.*,

$$(d\mathbf{r})_1 \cdot (d\mathbf{r})_2 = \frac{\partial \mathbf{r}}{\partial \xi_1} \cdot \frac{\partial \mathbf{r}}{\partial \xi_2} d\xi_1\, d\xi_2 = F\, d\xi_1\, d\xi_2 = 0$$

Thus, if $F = 0$, the parametric curves form an orthogonal curvilinear coordinate system on a surface; and (12.3) becomes in this case

$$(ds)^2 = \alpha_1{}^2 (d\xi_1)^2 + \alpha_2{}^2 (d\xi_2)^2$$

where $\qquad \alpha_1 = \sqrt{E} \qquad$ and $\qquad \alpha_2 = \sqrt{G}$

Let C and C' be two curves on a surface intersecting at P, and let s and σ be the arc length of C and C'. Then

$$\frac{d\mathbf{r}}{ds} = \frac{\partial \mathbf{r}}{\partial \xi_1} \frac{d\xi_1}{ds} + \frac{\partial \mathbf{r}}{\partial \xi_2} \frac{d\xi_2}{ds}$$

$$\frac{d\mathbf{r}}{d\sigma} = \frac{\partial \mathbf{r}}{\partial \xi_1} \frac{d\xi_1}{d\sigma} + \frac{\partial \mathbf{r}}{\partial \xi_2} \frac{d\xi_2}{d\sigma}$$

and if θ is the angle between C and C',

$$\cos\theta = \frac{d\mathbf{r}}{ds} \cdot \frac{d\mathbf{r}}{d\sigma} = E \frac{d\xi_1}{ds} \frac{d\xi_1}{d\sigma} + F \left(\frac{d\xi_1}{ds} \frac{d\xi_2}{d\sigma} + \frac{d\xi_1}{d\sigma} \frac{d\xi_2}{ds} \right) + G \frac{d\xi_2}{ds} \frac{d\xi_2}{d\sigma}$$

The necessary and sufficient condition that C and C' are orthogonal is

$$E \frac{d\xi_1}{ds} \frac{d\xi_1}{d\sigma} + F \left(\frac{d\xi_1}{ds} \frac{d\xi_2}{d\sigma} + \frac{d\xi_1}{d\sigma} \frac{d\xi_2}{ds} \right) + G \frac{d\xi_2}{ds} \frac{d\xi_2}{d\sigma} = 0 \qquad (12.6)$$

To eliminate s and σ from (12.6), let us write

$$\frac{d\xi_1}{ds} = \left(\frac{d\xi_1}{d\xi_2}\right)_c \frac{d\xi_2}{ds} \qquad \frac{d\xi_1}{d\sigma} = \left(\frac{d\xi_1}{d\xi_2}\right)_{c'} \frac{d\xi_2}{d\sigma}$$

where, for example, $(d\xi_1/d\xi_2)_c$ indicates that $d\xi_1/d\xi_2$ is to be computed along C. If we substitute these relations in (12.6) and then divide by $\dfrac{d\xi_2}{ds}\dfrac{d\xi_2}{d\sigma}$, we find that C and C' are orthogonal if

$$E\left(\frac{d\xi_1}{d\xi_2}\right)_c\left(\frac{d\xi_1}{d\xi_2}\right)_{c'} + F\left[\left(\frac{d\xi_1}{d\xi_2}\right)_c + \left(\frac{d\xi_1}{d\xi_2}\right)_{c'}\right] + G = 0 \qquad (12.7)$$

The plane containing three consecutive points, *i.e.*, two consecutive tangents, on a space curve is known as the *osculating plane at P*. The normal perpendicular to the tangent at P and lying in the osculating plane is called the *principal normal* to the curve at P.

A *normal section* of a surface at a given point P is defined as the section defined by a plane containing the normal to the surface at that point.

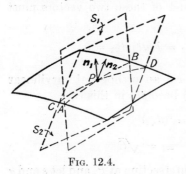

Fig. 12.4.

Such a section is a plane curve, whose principal normal is in the direction of the normal to the surface *at that one point P* but not necessary at any other point. Referring to Fig. 12.4, if n_1 is the normal to the surface at P, S_1 is the plane containing n_1, and AB is the intersection curve, then n_1 is also the principal normal of the curve AB at P. On the other hand, if the section made by the intersection of a plane such as S_2 in Fig. 12.4 and the surface is *not* a normal section, the resulting curve traced on the surface is still a plane curve but its principal normal is now in the direction of n_2, which lies in the plane of the curve. The curvature of a normal section such as AB in Fig. 12.4 is called the *normal curvature* of the surface at P in the direction of AB.

The normals at consecutive points on a surface do not, in general, intersect. However, we shall prove that at any point P there exist two directions on the surface such that the normal at a consecutive point in either of these directions cuts the normal from P. To show this, let $\mathbf{r}$ be the position vector of a point P on a surface, and let $\mathbf{n}$ be the unit normal there. Let $\mathbf{r} + d\mathbf{r}$ be a consecutive, or adjacent, point in a direction $d\xi_1$, $d\xi_2$ from P, and let $\mathbf{n} + d\mathbf{n}$ be the unit normal at this point. A necessary condition for these two adjacent normals to intersect is that the vectors $\mathbf{n}$, $d\mathbf{n}$, and $d\mathbf{r}$ are coplanar.

The *vector product* of two vectors **A** and **B**, that is, **A** × **B**, is defined as another vector **C** which is perpendicular to the plane determined by **A** and **B**, and whose magnitude is equal to the area of the parallelogram formed by **A** and **B**, that is, equal to $|\mathbf{A}||\mathbf{B}|\sin\theta$ where θ is the angle between these vectors. The sign, or sense, of **C** is determined by the right-hand rule, *i.e.*, sighting along **C**, the shortest rotation from **A** (the first vector), toward **B** (the second vector), is clockwise (Fig. 12.5).

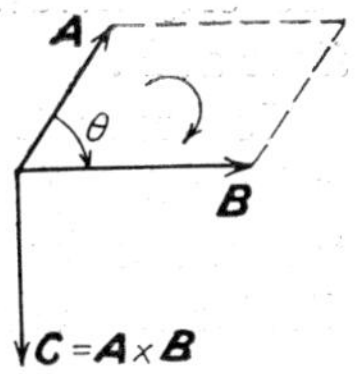

FIG. 12.5.

A normal to a surface S at a point **r** is perpendicular to $\partial\mathbf{r}/\partial\xi_1$ and $\partial\mathbf{r}/\partial\xi_2$ and hence is parallel to $(\partial\mathbf{r}/\partial\xi_1) \times (\partial\mathbf{r}/\partial\xi_2)$. We define the *unit normal* **n** to S at **r** by the relation

$$\mathbf{n} = \frac{(\partial\mathbf{r}/\partial\xi_1) \times (\partial\mathbf{r}/\partial\xi_2)}{|(\partial\mathbf{r}/\partial\xi_1) \times (\partial\mathbf{r}/\partial\xi_2)|}$$

where the quantity in the denominator indicates the magnitude of the vector product. But

$$\left|\frac{\partial\mathbf{r}}{\partial\xi_1} \times \frac{\partial\mathbf{r}}{\partial\xi_2}\right| = \left|\frac{\partial\mathbf{r}}{\partial\xi_1}\right|\left|\frac{\partial\mathbf{r}}{\partial\xi_2}\right|\sin\theta$$

Since $|\partial\mathbf{r}/\partial\xi_1| = \sqrt{E}$, $|\partial\mathbf{r}/\partial\xi_2| = \sqrt{G}$, and from (12.4)

$$\sin\theta = \sqrt{1 - \cos^2\theta} = \sqrt{\frac{(EG - F^2)}{EG}}$$

we have

$$\left|\frac{\partial\mathbf{r}}{\partial\xi_1} \times \frac{\partial\mathbf{r}}{\partial\xi_2}\right| = \sqrt{EG - F^2} = H$$

and

$$\mathbf{n} = \frac{(\partial\mathbf{r}/\partial\xi_1) \times (\partial\mathbf{r}/\partial\xi_2)}{H} \qquad (12.8)$$

The condition that **n**, $d\mathbf{n}$, $d\mathbf{r}$, are coplanar, in vector notation can be written as

$$\mathbf{n} \cdot d\mathbf{n} \times d\mathbf{r} = 0 \qquad (12.9)$$

But

$$d\mathbf{n} = \frac{\partial\mathbf{n}}{\partial\xi_1}d\xi_1 + \frac{\partial\mathbf{n}}{\partial\xi_2}d\xi_2 \qquad d\mathbf{r} = \frac{\partial\mathbf{r}}{\partial\xi_1}d\xi_1 + \frac{\partial\mathbf{r}}{\partial\xi_2}d\xi_2 \qquad (12.10)$$

Note that the distributive law holds for vector products, *i.e.*,

$$(\mathbf{A} + \mathbf{B}) \times (\mathbf{C} + \mathbf{D}) = \mathbf{A} \times (\mathbf{C} + \mathbf{D}) + \mathbf{B} \times (\mathbf{C} + \mathbf{D})$$
$$= \mathbf{A} \times \mathbf{C} + \mathbf{A} \times \mathbf{D} + \mathbf{B} \times \mathbf{C} + \mathbf{B} \times \mathbf{D}$$

Substituting (12.10) into (12.9) and expanding, we have

$$\left(\mathbf{n} \cdot \frac{\partial\mathbf{n}}{\partial\xi_1} \times \frac{\partial\mathbf{r}}{\partial\xi_1}\right)(d\xi_1)^2 + \left[\left(\mathbf{n} \cdot \frac{\partial\mathbf{n}}{\partial\xi_1} \times \frac{\partial\mathbf{r}}{\partial\xi_2}\right) + \left(\mathbf{n} \cdot \frac{\partial\mathbf{n}}{\partial\xi_2} \times \frac{\partial\mathbf{r}}{\partial\xi_1}\right)\right] d\xi_1\, d\xi_2$$
$$+ \left(\mathbf{n} \cdot \frac{\partial\mathbf{n}}{\partial\xi_2} \times \frac{\partial\mathbf{r}}{\partial\xi_2}\right)(d\xi_2)^2 = 0 \qquad (12.11)$$

This is a quadratic equation in $d\xi_1/d\xi_2$ or $d\xi_2/d\xi_1$, and two roots to this equation give the two directions on the surface for which the required property holds. These two directions are known as the *principal directions* at P.

To prove that the two principal directions are orthogonal, we shall write (12.11) in a more convenient form. Since the vector $\partial\mathbf{r}/\partial\xi_1$ is tangent to the parametric curve $\xi_2 =$ constant at the point $\mathbf{r}$, it is perpendicular to the normal $\mathbf{n}$. Hence

$$\mathbf{n} \cdot \frac{\partial \mathbf{r}}{\partial \xi_1} = 0 \qquad (12.12)$$

If we differentiate this relation with respect to ξ_1, we obtain

$$\frac{\partial \mathbf{n}}{\partial \xi_1} \cdot \frac{\partial \mathbf{r}}{\partial \xi_1} + \mathbf{n} \cdot \frac{\partial^2 \mathbf{r}}{\partial \xi_1{}^2} = 0$$

or
$$\frac{\partial \mathbf{n}}{\partial \xi_1} \cdot \frac{\partial \mathbf{r}}{\partial \xi_1} = -\mathbf{n} \cdot \frac{\partial^2 \mathbf{r}}{\partial \xi_1{}^2} = -L \qquad (12.13)$$

Similarly, if we differentiate Eq. (12.12) with respect to ξ_2 and differentiate the relation $\mathbf{n} \cdot (\partial\mathbf{r}/\partial\xi_2) = 0$ with respect to ξ_1 and ξ_2, we obtain, respectively,

$$\frac{\partial \mathbf{n}}{\partial \xi_2} \cdot \frac{\partial \mathbf{r}}{\partial \xi_1} = -\mathbf{n} \cdot \frac{\partial^2 \mathbf{r}}{\partial \xi_1\, \partial \xi_2} = -M$$

$$\frac{\partial \mathbf{n}}{\partial \xi_1} \cdot \frac{\partial \mathbf{r}}{\partial \xi_2} = -\mathbf{n} \cdot \frac{\partial^2 \mathbf{r}}{\partial \xi_1\, \partial \xi_2} = -M \qquad (12.14)$$

$$\frac{\partial \mathbf{n}}{\partial \xi_2} \cdot \frac{\partial \mathbf{r}}{\partial \xi_2} = -\mathbf{n} \cdot \frac{\partial^2 \mathbf{r}}{\partial \xi_2{}^2} = -N$$

The quantities L, M, N are the projection of the vectors $\partial^2\mathbf{r}/\partial\xi_1{}^2$, $\partial^2\mathbf{r}/(\partial\xi_1\,\partial\xi_2)$, $\partial^2\mathbf{r}/\partial\xi_2{}^2$ in the direction of the normal to the surface and are called the *fundamental magnitudes of the second order*. Since $\mathbf{n}$ is the unit normal or a vector of constant length, its first derivatives must be perpendicular to $\mathbf{n}$ and so parallel to the plane containing $\partial\mathbf{r}/\partial\xi_1$ and $\partial\mathbf{r}/\partial\xi_2$. It is therefore possible to express $\partial\mathbf{n}/\partial\xi_1$ and $\partial\mathbf{n}/\partial\xi_2$ in terms of $\partial\mathbf{r}/\partial\xi_1$ and $\partial\mathbf{r}/\partial\xi_2$. Let us write, then,

$$\frac{\partial \mathbf{n}}{\partial \xi_1} = a\, \frac{\partial \mathbf{r}}{\partial \xi_1} + b\, \frac{\partial \mathbf{r}}{\partial \xi_2} \qquad (12.15)$$

where a and b are unknowns to be determined. If we perform the scalar product of the above vector equation with the vector $\partial\mathbf{r}/\partial\xi_1$, there results

$$\frac{\partial \mathbf{n}}{\partial \xi_1} \cdot \frac{\partial \mathbf{r}}{\partial \xi_1} = a\, \frac{\partial \mathbf{r}}{\partial \xi_1} \cdot \frac{\partial \mathbf{r}}{\partial \xi_1} + b\, \frac{\partial \mathbf{r}}{\partial \xi_2} \cdot \frac{\partial \mathbf{r}}{\partial \xi_1}$$

From (12.13) and the definitions of E and F, we have

$$-L = aE + bF \tag{12.16}$$

Similarly, if we perform the scalar product of the vector equation (12.15) with the vector $\partial \mathbf{r}/\partial \xi_2$, we obtain

$$-M = aF + bG \tag{12.17}$$

Solving Eqs. (12.16) and (12.17) simultaneously, we have

$$a = \frac{FM - LG}{EG - F^2} = \frac{FM - LG}{H^2}$$

$$b = \frac{FL - EM}{H^2}$$

Hence,

$$\frac{\partial \mathbf{n}}{\partial \xi_1} = \frac{FM - LG}{H^2} \frac{\partial \mathbf{r}}{\partial \xi_1} + \frac{FL - EM}{H^2} \frac{\partial \mathbf{r}}{\partial \xi_2} \tag{12.18}$$

In a similar manner, we find

$$\frac{\partial \mathbf{n}}{\partial \xi_2} = \frac{FN - GM}{H^2} \frac{\partial \mathbf{r}}{\partial \xi_1} + \frac{FM - EN}{H^2} \frac{\partial \mathbf{r}}{\partial \xi_2} \tag{12.19}$$

With these relations and (12.8) it is easy to show that

$$\mathbf{n} \cdot \frac{\partial \mathbf{n}}{\partial \xi_1} \times \frac{\partial \mathbf{r}}{\partial \xi_1} = \frac{EM - FL}{H}$$

$$\mathbf{n} \cdot \frac{\partial \mathbf{n}}{\partial \xi_1} \times \frac{\partial \mathbf{r}}{\partial \xi_2} = \frac{FM - GL}{H}$$

$$\mathbf{n} \cdot \frac{\partial \mathbf{n}}{\partial \xi_2} \times \frac{\partial \mathbf{r}}{\partial \xi_1} = \frac{EN - FM}{H} \tag{12.20}$$

$$\mathbf{n} \cdot \frac{\partial \mathbf{n}}{\partial \xi_2} \times \frac{\partial \mathbf{r}}{\partial \xi_2} = \frac{FN - GM}{H}$$

Equation (12.11) can then be written as

$$(EM - FL)\left(\frac{d\xi_1}{d\xi_2}\right)^2 + (EN - GL)\left(\frac{d\xi_1}{d\xi_2}\right) + (FN - GM) = 0 \tag{12.21}$$

Let the two roots of Eq. (12.21) be $(d\xi_1/d\xi_2)_c$ and $(d\xi_1/d\xi_2)_{c'}$. From algebra, we find

$$\left(\frac{d\xi_1}{d\xi_2}\right)_c + \left(\frac{d\xi_1}{d\xi_2}\right)_{c'} = -\frac{EN - GL}{EM - FL}$$

$$\left(\frac{d\xi_1}{d\xi_2}\right)_c \left(\frac{d\xi_1}{d\xi_2}\right)_{c'} = \frac{FN - GM}{FM - FL}$$

Substituting these values into Eq. (12.7), we find that

$$E(FN - GM) - F(EN - GL) + G(EM - FL) \equiv 0$$

This means that the two directions on the surface as determined by the two roots of (12.11) or (12.21) are orthogonal. In other words, the two principal directions are orthogonal.

A curve C on a surface S, which possesses the property that normals to the surface at consecutive points on the curve intersect, is called a *line of curvature*. It follows that there are two families of lines of curvature on a surface, one curve of each family going through any given point P. As we shall see later in developing the shell theory, it is convenient to refer a surface to its lines of curvature as parametric curves. Along the parametric curves, we must have

$$d\xi_1/d\xi_2 = 0 \quad \text{and} \quad d\xi_2/d\xi_1 = 0$$

In order that they be the solutions of the following differential equation for the lines of curvature, (12.21),

$$(EM - FL)(d\xi_1)^2 + (EN - GL)\, d\xi_1\, d\xi_2 + (FN - GM)(d\xi_2)^2 = 0$$

we must have

$$EM - FL = 0 \qquad FN - GM = 0 \qquad EN - GL \neq 0 \quad (12.22)$$

Now if we multiply the first equation of (12.22) by N, the second by L, and add, we have

$$(EN - GL)M = 0$$

Similarly, if we multiply the first equation of (12.22) by G, the second by E and add, then

$$(EN - GL)F = 0$$

In view of the third equation of (12.22), we must have

$$M = 0 \qquad F = 0 \tag{12.23}$$

These are the conditions that the parametric curves are also lines of curvature.

The point of intersection of consecutive normals along a line of curvature at any point P on a surface S is called a *center of curvature* of the surface at P. Its distance from P, measured in the direction of the unit normal $\mathbf{n}$, is called a *principal radius of curvature* of S at P. The reciprocal of a principal radius of curvature is called a *principal curvature* of S at P. Thus, at each point on a surface there exist two principal curvatures, and these are the *normal* curvature of the surface in the direction of the lines of curvature. It can be proved that the principal directions at P are the directions of the maximum and minimum normal curvatures. It may be emphasized at this point that the principal normal of a line of curvature is in general not the normal to the surface, *i.e.*, the osculating plane of a line of curvature is not, as a rule, a normal section of the surface. Thus, the normal curvature of the surface in the direction of a 'line of curvature' is not in general the curvature of the 'line of curvature.'

To determine the principal curvatures, let $\mathbf{r}$ be the position vector of the surface at P, $\mathbf{n}$ be the unit normal there, and R a principal radius of

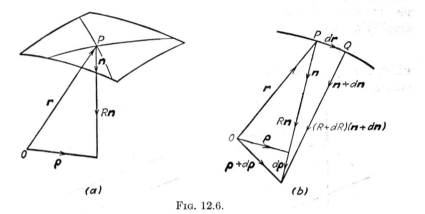

(a)   (b)

FIG. 12.6.

curvature at P. Then the corresponding center of curvature is given by ϱ, Fig. 12.6a.

$$\varrho = \mathbf{r} + R\mathbf{n}$$

Let Q be a point adjacent to P along a line of curvature of the surface, Fig. 12.6b; then

$$d\varrho = d\mathbf{r} + d(R\mathbf{n}) = (d\mathbf{r} + R\,d\mathbf{n}) + \mathbf{n}\,dR$$

But the vector $d\mathbf{r} + R\,d\mathbf{n}$ is tangential to the surface, whereas the condition that $d\mathbf{r}$ lie on a line of curvature is that $d\varrho$ be in the direction of $\mathbf{n}$. Hence, we must have

$$d\mathbf{r} + R\,d\mathbf{n} = 0$$

or, if κ is the corresponding principal curvature,

$$\kappa\,d\mathbf{r} + d\mathbf{n} = 0 \tag{12.24}$$

This is the vector form of Rodreques' formula. But

$$d\mathbf{r} = \frac{\partial \mathbf{r}}{\partial \xi_1}\,d\xi_1 + \frac{\partial \mathbf{r}}{\partial \xi_2}\,d\xi_2 \qquad d\mathbf{n} = \frac{\partial \mathbf{n}}{\partial \xi_1}\,d\xi_1 + \frac{\partial \mathbf{n}}{\partial \xi_2}\,d\xi_2$$

Substituting these relations into (12.24) and rearranging terms, we have

$$\left(\kappa\frac{\partial \mathbf{r}}{\partial \xi_1} + \frac{\partial \mathbf{n}}{\partial \xi_1}\right)d\xi_1 + \left(\kappa\frac{\partial \mathbf{r}}{\partial \xi_2} + \frac{\partial \mathbf{n}}{\partial \xi_2}\right)d\xi_2 = 0$$

Forming the scalar products of this equation with $\partial\mathbf{r}/\partial\xi_1$ and $\partial\mathbf{r}/\partial\xi_2$, respectively, we obtain

$$
\begin{aligned}
(\kappa E - L)\, d\xi_1 + (\kappa F - M)\, d\xi_2 &= 0 \\
(\kappa F - M)\, d\xi_1 + (\kappa G - N)\, d\xi_2 &= 0
\end{aligned}
\tag{12.25}
$$

These two equations determine the principal curvatures of a surface and also the directions of the lines of curvature. Eliminating $d\xi_1/d\xi_2$ and simplifying, we obtain

$$
H^2\kappa^2 - (EN - 2FM + GL)\kappa + (LN - M^2) = 0 \tag{12.26}
$$

which is a quadratic equation in κ and the two roots are the required values.

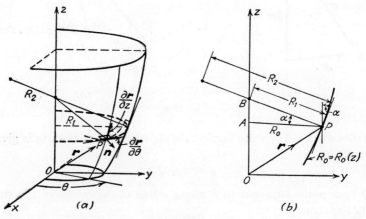

FIG. 12.7.

In the engineering application of thin shells, a shell whose medium surface is in the form of a surface of revolution has extensive usage. Let us therefore now consider some differential geometry of a surface of revolution. A surface of revolution is obtained by rotation of a plane curve about an axis lying in the plane of the curve. This curve is called the *meridian*, and its plane is a *meridian plane*. Referring to Fig. 12.7a and b, we take the axis of rotation as the z axis and let R_0 be the distance perpendicular to it to a point P on the surface. The position of a meridian is defined by the angle θ, measured from the xz plane. The equation of the meridian is $R_0 = R_0(z)$. The intersections of the surface with planes perpendicular to the z axis are parallel circles and are called *parallels*. The position of a parallel is defined by the equation $z = $ constant.

With these notations, we find that the cartesian coordinates of P are

$$
x = R_0(z)\cos\theta \qquad y = R_0(z)\sin\theta \qquad z = z
$$

Or the position vector $\mathbf{r}$ of P is

$$
\mathbf{r} = \mathbf{i}R_0(z)\cos\theta + \mathbf{j}R_0(z)\sin\theta + \mathbf{k}z
$$

Now let us take the meridians and the parallels as our parametric curves and identify ξ_1 with θ and ξ_2 with z. Then

$$\frac{\partial \mathbf{r}}{\partial \xi_1} = \frac{\partial \mathbf{r}}{\partial \theta} = -\mathbf{i}R_0 \sin \theta + \mathbf{j}R_0 \cos \theta + \mathbf{k}0$$

$$\frac{\partial \mathbf{r}}{\partial \xi_2} = \frac{\partial \mathbf{r}}{\partial z} = \mathbf{i}R_0' \cos \theta + \mathbf{j}R_0' \sin \theta + \mathbf{k}$$

where $R_0' = dR_0/dz$. The first fundamental magnitudes are

$$E = \frac{\partial \mathbf{r}}{\partial \xi_1} \cdot \frac{\partial \mathbf{r}}{\partial \xi_1} = R_0^2 \sin^2 \theta + R_0^2 \cos^2 \theta = R_0^2$$

$$F = \frac{\partial \mathbf{r}}{\partial \xi_1} \cdot \frac{\partial \mathbf{r}}{\partial \xi_2} = -R_0 R_0' \sin \theta \cos \theta + R_0 R_0' \sin \theta \cos \theta = 0$$

$$G = \frac{\partial \mathbf{r}}{\partial \xi_2} \cdot \frac{\partial \mathbf{r}}{\partial \xi_2} = R_0'^2 \cos^2 \theta + R_0'^2 \sin^2 \theta + 1 = 1 + R_0'^2$$

$$H = \sqrt{EG - F^2} = R_0 \sqrt{1 + R_0'^2}$$

Since $F = 0$, the parallels and the meridians are orthogonal.

To find the second fundamental magnitudes, let us calculate the second derivatives of $\mathbf{r}$ and the vector $\mathbf{n}$.

$$\frac{\partial^2 \mathbf{r}}{\partial \xi_1^2} = -\mathbf{i}R_0 \cos \theta - \mathbf{j}R_0 \sin \theta + \mathbf{k}0$$

$$\frac{\partial^2 \mathbf{r}}{\partial \xi_1 \partial \xi_2} = -\mathbf{i}R_0' \sin \theta + \mathbf{j}R_0' \cos \theta + \mathbf{k}0$$

$$\frac{\partial^2 \mathbf{r}}{\partial \xi_2^2} = \mathbf{i}R_0'' \cos \theta + \mathbf{j}R_0'' \sin \theta + \mathbf{k}0$$

$$\mathbf{n} = \frac{\dfrac{\partial \mathbf{r}}{\partial \xi_1} \times \dfrac{\partial \mathbf{r}}{\partial \xi_2}}{H} = \frac{1}{H} \begin{vmatrix} \mathbf{i} & \mathbf{j} & \mathbf{k} \\ -R_0 \sin \theta & R_0 \cos \theta & 0 \\ R_0' \cos \theta & R_0' \sin \theta & 1 \end{vmatrix}$$

$$= \frac{1}{H} (\mathbf{i}R_0 \cos \theta + \mathbf{j}R_0 \sin \theta - \mathbf{k}R_0 R_0')$$

Hence $L = \mathbf{n} \cdot \dfrac{\partial^2 \mathbf{r}}{\partial \xi_1^2} = \dfrac{1}{H} (-R_0^2 \cos^2 \theta - R_0^2 \sin^2 \theta) = -\dfrac{R_0^2}{H}$

$$M = \mathbf{n} \cdot \frac{\partial^2 \mathbf{r}}{\partial \xi_1 \partial \xi_2} = \frac{1}{H} (-R_0 R_0' \cos \theta \sin \theta + R_0 R_0' \cos \theta \sin \theta) = 0$$

$$N = \mathbf{n} \cdot \frac{\partial^2 \mathbf{r}}{\partial \xi_2^2} = \frac{1}{H} (R_0 R_0'' \cos^2 \theta + R_0 R_0'' \sin^2 \theta) = \frac{R_0 R_0''}{H}$$

Since F and M are both zero, the parametric curves are lines of curvature.

Substituting these values into Eq. (12.26), we find that the equation for the principal curvature becomes in this case

$$R_0(1 + R_0'^2)^{1/2}\kappa^2 - \left[\frac{R_0 R_0''}{(1 + R_0'^2)} - 1 \right]\kappa - \frac{R_0''}{(1 + R_0'^2)^{3/2}} = 0$$

Solving, we obtain

$$\kappa_1 = - \frac{1}{R_0 (1 + R_0'^2)^{1/2}} \qquad \kappa_2 = \frac{R_0''}{(1 + R_0'^2)^{3/2}}$$

We see immediately that κ_2 is the curvature of the plane generating curve $R_0 = R_0(z)$.

To interpret κ_1, let us consider the triangle APB, Fig. 12.7b. With an angle α defined as shown, we have

$$\tan \alpha = R_0'$$

But $\qquad AB = AP \tan \alpha = R_0 R_0'$

Hence $\qquad BP = \sqrt{(AP)^2 + (AB)^2} = R_0 \sqrt{1 + R_0'^2}$

so that κ_1 is the reciprocal of the length of the normal intercepted between the curve and the axis of rotation. The negative sign indicates that the radius of curvature and **n** are in opposite directions. It may be noted that for the generating curve as shown in Fig. 12.7, R_0'' is negative and κ_2 is therefore also negative, as it should be.

12.2. The Equilibrium Equations. Following our discussion in the previous section, we find that the location of any point on a shell can be determined by three parameters, two of which vary on the middle surface of the shell while the third varies along the normal to the middle surface. If we choose the lines of curvature at a point on the middle surface as the parametric curves, then we have a three-dimensional orthogonal coordinate system. Let us denote these parametric curves on the middle surface by $\xi_1 = $ constant and $\xi_2 = $ constant. Let z be the distance of the point from the middle surface. A point on the shell will then have the orthogonal curvilinear coordinates ξ_1, ξ_2, and z.

To analyze the internal forces, let us consider an element of the shell bounded by surfaces $\xi_1 = $ constant, $\xi_1 + d\xi_1 = $ constant, $\xi_2 = $ constant, $\xi_2 + d\xi_2 = $ constant, and $z = \pm h/2$. The sides of the element will have the lengths $\alpha_1 \, d\xi_1$ and $\alpha_2 \, d\xi_2$, where as defined before α_1 and α_2 are factors so that the square of a line element ds on the middle surface of the shell has the form

$$ds^2 = \alpha_1{}^2 \, d\xi_1{}^2 + \alpha_2{}^2 \, d\xi_2{}^2$$

Take, for instance, polar coordinates. In this case, the curvilinear coordinates are r and θ. Let $\xi_1 = r$ and $\xi_2 = \theta$. Then the square of a line element ds is

$$ds^2 = (dr)^2 + r^2 (d\theta)^2$$

We have therefore in this case

$$\alpha_1 = 1 \qquad \text{and} \qquad \alpha_2 = r$$

Let us denote by x and y the directions of the tangents to the curvilinear coordinates ξ_1 and ξ_2 at the point O (Fig. 12.8). Let R_1 and R_2 be the principal radii of curvature at O which lie in the xz and yz planes, respectively. The angle subtended by the arc length $\alpha_2 \, d\xi_2$ is then $(\alpha_2 \, d\xi_2)/R_2$, and the arc length of the element which is at a distance z from the middle surface in the yz plane is

$$\frac{(R_2 - z)\alpha_2 \, d\xi_2}{R_2} = \left(1 - \frac{z}{R_2}\right)\alpha_2 \, d\xi_2$$

The stresses acting on the plane faces of the element are $\sigma_1, \sigma_2, \tau_{12} = \tau_{21}, \tau_{1z}, \tau_{2z}$. If we denote the resultant normal force acting on the plane face yz

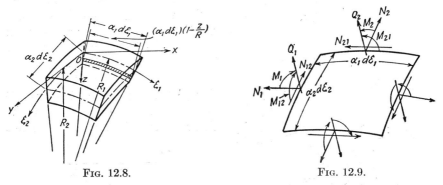

FIG. 12.8. FIG. 12.9.

per unit length by N_1, we have

$$N_1 \alpha_2 \, d\xi_2 = \int_{-h/2}^{+h/2} \sigma_1 \left(1 - \frac{z}{R_2}\right) \alpha_2 \, d\xi_2 \, dz$$

or

$$N_1 = \int_{-h/2}^{+h/2} \sigma_1 \left(1 - \frac{z}{R_2}\right) dz$$

In the same manner we obtain the expressions for the other resultant forces and moments per unit length of the normal sections shown in Figs. 12.8 and 12.9. Summing up, we have

$$N_1 = \int_{-h/2}^{+h/2} \sigma_1 \left(1 - \frac{z}{R_2}\right) dz \qquad N_2 = \int_{-h/2}^{+h/2} \sigma_2 \left(1 - \frac{z}{R_1}\right) dz$$

$$N_{12} = \int_{-h/2}^{+h/2} \tau_{12} \left(1 - \frac{z}{R_2}\right) dz \qquad N_{21} = \int_{-h/2}^{+h/2} \tau_{21} \left(1 - \frac{z}{R_1}\right) dz$$

$$Q_1 = \int_{-h/2}^{+h/2} \tau_{1z} \left(1 - \frac{z}{R_2}\right) dz \qquad Q_2 = \int_{-h/2}^{+h/2} \tau_{2z} \left(1 - \frac{z}{R_1}\right) dz$$

$$M_1 = \int_{-h/2}^{+h/2} \sigma_1 \left(1 - \frac{z}{R_2}\right) z \, dz \qquad\qquad (12.27)$$

$$M_2 = \int_{-h/2}^{+h/2} \sigma_2 \left(1 - \frac{z}{R_1}\right) z \, dz$$

$$M_{12} = - \int_{-h/2}^{+h/2} \tau_{12} \left(1 - \frac{z}{R_2}\right) z \, dz$$

$$M_{21} = - \int_{-h/2}^{+h/2} \tau_{21} \left(1 - \frac{z}{R_1}\right) z \, dz$$

From the above definitions, we find that, although $\tau_{12} = \tau_{21}$, N_{12} is not generally equal to N_{21} because R_1 is not generally equal to R_2. For the same reason, M_{12} is not in general equal to M_{21}. However, for *thin* shells, h is small in comparison with R_1 and R_2, and the terms z/R_1 and z/R_2 in the expressions (12.27) can be neglected compared with 1. In such cases, $N_{12} = N_{21}$, $M_{12} = M_{21}$, and the resultant forces and moments are given by the same expressions as in the case of thin plates.

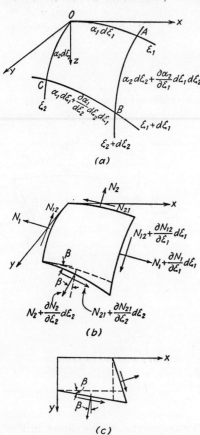

(a)

(b)

(c)

FIG. 12.10.

To derive the equilibrium equations, let us consider first the x components of forces acting on the element shown in Fig. 12.10. The x

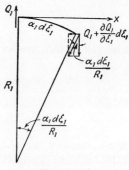

FIG. 12.11.

component of the forces N_1 and $N_1 + (\partial N_1/\partial \xi_1)\, d\xi_1$ is

$$-N_1 \alpha_2\, d\xi_2 + \left(N_1 + \frac{\partial N_1}{\partial \xi_1}\, d\xi_1 \right)\left(\alpha_2\, d\xi_2 + \frac{\partial \alpha_2}{\partial \xi_1}\, d\xi_1\, d\xi_2 \right)$$

$$= \left(\frac{\partial N_1}{\partial \xi_1}\, \alpha_2 + N_1 \frac{\partial \alpha_2}{\partial \xi_1} \right) d\xi_1\, d\xi_2 = \frac{\partial \alpha_2 N_1}{\partial \xi_1}\, d\xi_1\, d\xi_2$$

Similarly, the x component of the forces N_{21} and $N_{21} + (\partial N_{21}/\partial \xi_2)\, d\xi_2$ is

$$\left(\frac{\partial N_{21}}{\partial \xi_2}\, \alpha_1 + N_{21} \frac{\partial \alpha_1}{\partial \xi_2} \right) d\xi_1\, d\xi_2 = \frac{\partial \alpha_1 N_{21}}{\partial \xi_2}\, d\xi_1\, d\xi_2$$

Since α_2 varies from point to point, the force $N_2 + (\partial N_2/\partial \xi_2)\, d\xi_2$, which is normal to the surface BC, is inclined to the y direction by a small angle β. The change in direction can most easily be seen in Fig. 12.10c, where the curvature of the sides is neglected. Since β is small, we have

$$\beta \cong \left(\frac{(\partial \alpha_2 / \partial \xi_1)\, d\xi_1\, d\xi_2}{\alpha_1\, d\xi_1 + (\partial \alpha_1 / \partial \xi_2)\, d\xi_1\, d\xi_2} \right)$$

Thus, the x component of this force is

$$-\left(N_2 + \frac{\partial N_2}{\partial \xi_2}\, d\xi_2 \right)\left(\alpha_1\, d\xi_1 + \frac{\partial \alpha_1}{\partial \xi_2}\, d\xi_1\, d\xi_2 \right)\beta = -N_2 \frac{\partial \alpha_2}{\partial \xi_1}\, d\xi_1\, d\xi_2$$

Similarly, the x component of the force $N_{12} + (\partial N_{12} / \partial \xi_1)\, d\xi_1$ is

$$\left(N_{12} + \frac{\partial N_{12}}{\partial \xi_1}\, d\xi_1 \right)\left(\alpha_2\, d\xi_2 + \frac{\partial \alpha_2}{\partial \xi_1}\, d\xi_1\, d\xi_2 \right)\left(\frac{\partial \alpha_1}{\partial \xi_2}\, d\xi_1\, d\xi_2 \right) \Big/$$
$$\left(\alpha_2\, d\xi_2 + \frac{\partial \alpha_2}{\partial \xi_1}\, d\xi_1\, d\xi_2 \right) = N_{12} \frac{\partial \alpha_1}{\partial \xi_2}\, d\xi_1\, d\xi_2$$

From Fig. 12.11, we find that the shearing force $Q_1 + (\partial Q_1 / \partial \xi_1)\, d\xi_1$ has an x component equal to

$$-\left(Q_1 + \frac{\partial Q_1}{\partial \xi_1}\, d\xi_1 \right)\left(\alpha_2\, d\xi_2 + \frac{\partial \alpha_2}{\partial \xi_1}\, d\xi_1\, d\xi_2 \right)\frac{\alpha_1\, d\xi_1}{R_1} = -Q_1 \frac{\alpha_1 \alpha_2}{R_1}\, d\xi_1\, d\xi_2$$

If the lateral pressure has a component p_1 in the x direction, the total force is

$$p_1 \alpha_1 \alpha_2\, d\xi_1\, d\xi_2$$

Summing up these forces and dividing through by $d\xi_1\, d\xi_2$, we find that the condition $\Sigma F_x = 0$ requires that

$$\frac{\partial \alpha_2 N_1}{\partial \xi_1} + \frac{\partial \alpha_1 N_{21}}{\partial \xi_2} + N_{12} \frac{\partial \alpha_1}{\partial \xi_2} - N_2 \frac{\partial \alpha_2}{\partial \xi_1} - Q_1 \frac{\alpha_1 \alpha_2}{R_1} + \alpha_1 \alpha_2 p_1 = 0 \qquad (12.28)$$

In a similar manner, we find that the condition $\Sigma F_y = 0$ leads to

$$\frac{\partial \alpha_1 N_2}{\partial \xi_2} + \frac{\partial \alpha_2 N_{12}}{\partial \xi_1} + N_{21} \frac{\partial \alpha_2}{\partial \xi_1} - N_1 \frac{\partial \alpha_1}{\partial \xi_2} - Q_2 \frac{\alpha_1 \alpha_2}{R_2} + \alpha_1 \alpha_2 p_2 = 0 \qquad (12.29)$$

and the condition $\Sigma F_z = 0$ leads to

$$\frac{\partial \alpha_2 Q_1}{\partial \xi_1} + \frac{\partial \alpha_1 Q_2}{\partial \xi_2} + N_1 \frac{\alpha_1 \alpha_2}{R_1} + N_2 \frac{\alpha_1 \alpha_2}{R_2} + \alpha_1 \alpha_2 p_3 = 0 \qquad (12.30)$$

where p_1, p_2, and p_3 are, respectively, the x, y, and z components of the lateral load per unit area.

To find the equilibrium equations for the moments, let us represent the moments by vectors according to the right-hand rule as shown in Fig. 12.12. The components of the moments about the x axis can now be found by projecting these moment vectors on the x axis. Thus, we have

$$-M_{12}\alpha_2\,d\xi_2 + \left(M_{12} + \frac{\partial M_{12}}{\partial \xi_1}\,d\xi_1\right)\left(\alpha_2 + \frac{\partial \alpha_2}{\partial \xi_1}\,d\xi_1\right)d\xi_2$$

$$+ M_2\alpha_1\,d\xi_1 - \left(M_2 + \frac{\partial M_2}{\partial \xi_2}\,d\xi_2\right)\left(\alpha_1 + \frac{\partial \alpha_1}{\partial \xi_2}\,d\xi_2\right)d\xi_1$$

$$+ \left(M_1 + \frac{\partial M_1}{\partial \xi_1}\,d\xi_1\right)\left(\alpha_2 + \frac{\partial \alpha_2}{\partial \xi_1}\,d\xi_1\right)d\xi_2\,\frac{\partial \alpha_1}{\partial \xi_2}\,d\xi_2\,d\xi_1 \Big/ \left(\alpha_2 + \frac{\partial \alpha_2}{\partial \xi_1}\,d\xi_1\right)d\xi_2$$

$$+ \left(M_{21} + \frac{\partial M_{21}}{\partial \xi_2}\,d\xi_2\right)\left(\alpha_1 + \frac{\partial \alpha_1}{\partial \xi_2}\,d\xi_2\right)d\xi_1\,\frac{\partial \alpha_2}{\partial \xi_1}\,d\xi_1\,d\xi_2 \Big/ \left(\alpha_1 + \frac{\partial \alpha_1}{\partial \xi_2}\,d\xi_2\right)d\xi_1$$

$$= \left(\frac{\partial \alpha_2 M_{12}}{\partial \xi_1} - \frac{\partial \alpha_1 M_2}{\partial \xi_2} + M_1\frac{\partial \alpha_1}{\partial \xi_2} + M_{21}\frac{\partial \alpha_2}{\partial \xi_1}\right)d\xi_1\,d\xi_2$$

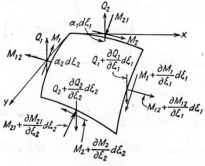

Fig. 12.12.

The shearing force Q_2 has a moment about the x axis of the magnitude

$$\left(Q_2 + \frac{\partial Q_2}{\partial \xi_2}\,d\xi_2\right)\alpha_1\,d\xi_1\,\alpha_2\,d\xi_2 = Q_2\alpha_1\alpha_2\,d\xi_1\,d\xi_2$$

Hence, the condition $\Sigma M_x = 0$ gives

$$\frac{\partial \alpha_2 M_{12}}{\partial \xi_1} - \frac{\partial \alpha_1 M_2}{\partial \xi_2} + M_1\frac{\partial \alpha_1}{\partial \xi_2} + M_{21}\frac{\partial \alpha_2}{\partial \xi_1} + Q_2\alpha_1\alpha_2 = 0 \quad (12.31)$$

Similarly, the condition $\Sigma M_y = 0$ gives

$$\frac{\partial \alpha_1 M_{21}}{\partial \xi_2} - \frac{\partial \alpha_2 M_1}{\partial \xi_1} + M_2\frac{\partial \alpha_2}{\partial \xi_1} + M_{12}\frac{\partial \alpha_1}{\partial \xi_2} + Q_1\alpha_1\alpha_2 = 0 \quad (12.32)$$

12.3. Membrane Theory of Shells in the Form of Surface of Revolution. In many problems of thin shells, the deformations are such that the stresses in the shell are mainly due to the middle surface forces N_1, N_2, N_{12} and the stresses due to bending are very small. In such cases, good approximations can be obtained by neglecting the bending stresses completely. By letting the moments and shearing forces go to zero, we find that there are three equilibrium equations with three unknown quantities N_1, N_2, and N_{12}. If the external forces acting on the shell are given, the problem becomes statically determinate, and these unknown forces can be determined without using the strain relations. The problem of stress analysis is therefore greatly simplified. The forces N_1, N_2, N_{12} obtained in this manner are sometimes called *membrane forces*. The theory of thin shells based on the assumption of no bending stresses is called *membrane theory*.

Let us first consider the membrane theory of shells in the form of surfaces of revolution. Such thin shells are used extensively in various kinds of containers, tanks, and domes. As explained in Sec. 12.1, a surface of revolution is obtained by the rotation of a meridian curve about an axis lying in the plane of the curve. We take in this case the curves $\xi_1 = $ constant along the meridians and $\xi_2 = $ constant along the circles in

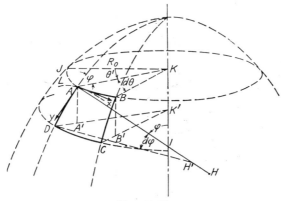

FIG. 12.13.

the planes perpendicular to the axis of revolution. From the notation as shown in Fig. 12.13, we have $\xi_1 = \theta$ and $\xi_2 = \varphi$. The tangents of the curvilinear coordinates θ and φ passing through the point A are denoted by x and y, respectively.

In the case of a surface of revolution, we have already shown that the meridian plane contains one of the principal radii of curvature, and the other principal radius of curvature will be that of the curve AL, which is the intersection of the plane xz and the middle surface of the shell. These two radii of curvature lie on the same line but have different lengths. We denote the radius of curvature of the curve AD at A, which is AH, by R_2 and the radius of curvature of the curve AL at A, which is AI, by R_1. Let R_0 be the radius of the intersecting circle at A, which is shown in Fig. 12.13 as JK. Thus, a line element ds on the middle surface of the shell will be given by the formula

$$ds^2 = R_0{}^2\, d\theta^2 + R_2{}^2\, d\varphi^2$$

from which we observe

$$\alpha_1 = R_0 \qquad \alpha_2 = R_2$$

If the bending stresses in the shell can be neglected, we may assume that

$$M_1 = M_2 = M_{21} = M_{12} = Q_1 = Q_2 = 0$$

Since $\xi_1 = \theta$ and $\xi_2 = \varphi$, let us use the notations

$$N_1 = N_\theta \qquad N_2 = N_\varphi \qquad N_{12} = N_{21} = N_{\varphi\theta}$$

If, furthermore, the shell is loaded symmetrically with respect to its axis, then $p_1 = 0$, $N_{\varphi\theta} = 0$, and N_θ, N_φ must be independent of θ (Fig. 12.14).

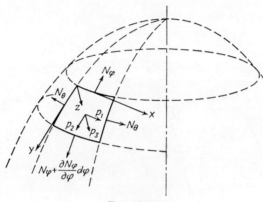

Fig. 12.14.

We find that in this case Eq. (12.28) is identically satisfied. From Eq. (12.29), we find that

$$\frac{d}{d\varphi} (R_0 N_\varphi) - N_\theta \frac{dR_0}{d\varphi} + R_0 R_2 p_2 = 0$$

Since the forces N_θ and N_φ are functions of φ only, total differentiation signs are used in the above equations. Now, from Fig. 12.13, we observe that

$$\frac{dR_0}{d\varphi} d\varphi = A'D \cong AD \cos \varphi = R_2 d\varphi \cos \varphi$$

or

$$\frac{dR_0}{d\varphi} = R_2 \cos \varphi$$

Therefore the condition $\Sigma F_y = 0$ becomes

$$\frac{d}{d\varphi} (R_0 N_\varphi) - R_0 N_\theta \cos \varphi + R_0 R_2 p_2 = 0 \qquad (12.33)$$

Since the radius of curvature in the plane xz is R_1, from Eq. (12.30), we find that the condition $\Sigma F_z = 0$ in the present case becomes

$$\frac{N_\theta}{R_1} + \frac{N_\varphi}{R_2} + p_3 = 0$$

By solving these two equations, N_θ and N_φ can be calculated.

Since $R_0 = R_1 \sin \varphi$, we may rewrite Eq. (12.34) as follows:

$$N_\theta = -\frac{R_0 N_\varphi}{R_2 \sin \varphi} - \frac{R_0 p_3}{\sin \varphi} \quad (12.34)$$

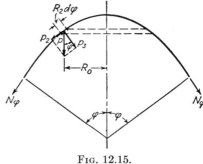

FIG. 12.15.

Substituting the above equation into (12.33) and multiplying the resulting equation by $\sin \varphi$, we find that

$$\sin \varphi \frac{d}{d\varphi} (R_0 N_\varphi) + R_0 N_\varphi \cos \varphi + R_0 R_2 (p_2 \sin \varphi + p_3 \cos \varphi) = 0$$

or

$$\frac{d}{d\varphi} (R_0 N_\varphi \sin \varphi) + R_0 R_2 (p_2 \sin \varphi + p_3 \cos \varphi) = 0$$

Integrating between the limits 0 and φ, we obtain

$$R_0 N_\varphi \sin \varphi + \int_0^\varphi R_0 R_2 (p_2 \sin \varphi + p_3 \cos \varphi) \, d\varphi = 0$$

But from Fig. 12.15, it can be seen that

$$p_2 \sin \varphi + p_3 \cos \varphi = p$$

and the annular area of the shell on which p acts is

$$2\pi R_0 R_2 \, d\varphi$$

Hence

$$\int_0^\varphi R_0 R_2 (p_2 \sin \varphi + p_3 \cos \varphi) \, d\varphi = \frac{F}{2\pi}$$

and

$$2\pi R_0 N_\varphi \sin \varphi + F = 0 \quad (12.35)$$

where F is the resultant of the total load acting on that portion of the shell corresponding to the angle φ. Instead of solving Eqs. (12.33) and (12.34) simultaneously, it is more convenient to solve N_φ from Eq. (12.35) and then to calculate N_θ from Eq. (12.34).

As a first example let us consider the case of a spherical dome of constant thickness under its own weight (Fig. 12.16). Let ρ be the gravitational density of the material from which the shell is made. The gravitational force per unit area of the shell is then ρh. If the radius of the sphere is a, the resultant of the total load on that portion of the spherical dome subtended by an angle φ is

$$F = \int_0^\varphi \rho h \cdot 2\pi a \sin \varphi \cdot a \, d\varphi$$

For spherical shells, $R_1 = R_2 = a$. Equations (12.35) and (12.34) then give

$$N_\varphi = -\frac{a^2 \rho h (1 - \cos \varphi)}{a \sin^2 \varphi} = -\frac{a \rho h}{1 + \cos \varphi}$$

$$N_\theta = -a \rho h \left(\cos \varphi - \frac{1}{1 + \cos \varphi} \right)$$

(12.36)

The negative signs in the above equations indicate compression. An examination of these equations shows that N_φ is compressive throughout the shell while N_θ becomes tensile when φ is greater than 51° 50′.

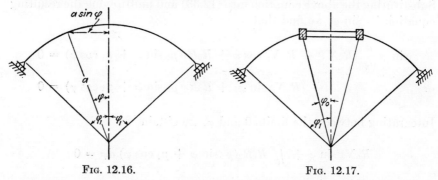

FIG. 12.16.   FIG. 12.17.

In the construction of the spherical dome, sometimes the upper portion of the dome is removed, and a reinforcing ring is used to support the upper structure (Fig. 12.17). If $2\varphi_0$ is the angle corresponding to the opening and P is the vertical load per unit length acting on the reinforcing ring, the resultant F corresponding to an angle φ is

$$F = \int_{\varphi_0}^\varphi \rho h \cdot 2\pi a \sin \varphi \cdot a \, d\varphi$$
$$= 2\pi a^2 \rho h (\cos \varphi_0 - \cos \varphi)$$

Now the integration of $\int_{\varphi_0}^\varphi 2\pi \dfrac{d}{d\varphi} (R_0 N_\varphi \sin \varphi) \, d\varphi$ becomes

$$[2\pi R_0 N_\varphi \sin \varphi]_{\varphi=\varphi} - [2\pi R_0 N_\varphi \sin \varphi]_{\varphi=\varphi_0}$$

Let P be the vertical load per unit length acting on the reinforcing ring. Then $[N_\varphi]_{\varphi=\varphi_0} = -P/\sin \varphi_0$. Equation (12.36) becomes in this case

$$2\pi a N_\varphi \sin^2 \varphi + 2\pi a P \sin \varphi_0 + 2\pi a^2 \rho h (\cos \varphi_0 - \cos \varphi) = 0$$

or

$$N_\varphi = -a \rho h \frac{\cos \varphi_0 - \cos \varphi}{\sin^2 \varphi} - P \frac{\sin \varphi_0}{\sin^2 \varphi}$$

From Eq. (12.34), we find

$$N_\theta = -a\rho h \left(\cos \varphi - \frac{\cos \varphi_0 - \cos \varphi}{\sin^2 \varphi} \right) + P \frac{\sin \varphi_0}{\sin^2 \varphi} \qquad (12.37)$$

As a second example, let us consider a shell in the form of an ellipsoid of revolution. We find the practical application of such shells in the construction of the ends of cylindrical boilers. For this purpose, only half of the ellipsoid such as that shown in Fig. 12.18 is used. Let a and b be the lengths of the major and minor axes of the ellipse, respectively. The equation of the ellipse is then

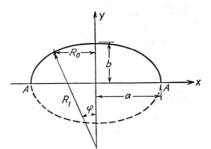

FIG. 12.18.

$$b^2 x^2 + a^2 y^2 = a^2 b^2$$

The principal radii of curvature can be computed by using formulas derived in Sec. 12.1. Noticing that R_0 is in this case x, we have

$$R_0' = \frac{dx}{dy} = -\frac{a^2}{b^2} \frac{y}{x}$$

$$R_0'' = \frac{d^2 x}{dy^2} = -\frac{a^4}{b^2 x^3}$$

Substituting into the formulas for principal curvatures (p. 322) and dropping the negative signs, we find

$$R_1 = \frac{1}{\kappa_1} = \frac{(a^4 y^2 + b^4 x^2)^{1/2}}{b^2}$$

$$R_2 = \frac{1}{\kappa_2} = \frac{(a^4 y^2 + b^4 x^2)^{3/2}}{a^4 b^4}$$

If p is the uniform steam pressure of the boiler, the resultant F corresponding to an angle φ is

$$F = -p \cdot \pi R_0^2 = -\pi p R_1^2 \sin^2 \varphi$$

Since $p_3 = -p$, Eqs. (12.35) and (12.34) then give

$$N_\varphi = \frac{pR_1}{2} = \frac{p(a^4 y^2 + b^4 x^2)^{1/2}}{2b^2}$$

$$N_\theta = R_1 p - \frac{R_1}{R_2} N_\varphi = \frac{p(a^4 y^2 + b^4 x^2)^{1/2}}{2b^2} \left(2 - \frac{a^4 b^2}{a^4 y^2 + b^4 x^2} \right)$$

(12.38)

At the top of the shell, $x = 0$ and $y = b$, Eqs. (12.38) give

$$N_\varphi = N_\theta = \frac{pa^2}{2b}$$

At the equator AA, $x = a$ and $y = 0$, we have

$$N_\varphi = \frac{pa}{2}$$

$$N_\theta = pa\left(1 - \frac{a^2}{2b^2}\right)$$

Problem 1. Find the stresses in a spherical tank filled with liquid of specific weight ρ and supported along a parallel circle AA (Fig. 12.19). Note that the pressure p_3 acting on the sphere for any angle φ is given by the expression

$$p_3 = -\rho a(1 - \cos\varphi)$$

Ans. $N_\varphi = \dfrac{\rho a^2}{6}\left(1 - \dfrac{2\cos^2\varphi}{1 + \cos\varphi}\right)$

$N_\theta = \dfrac{\rho a^2}{6}\left(5 - 6\cos\varphi + \dfrac{2\cos^2\varphi}{1 + \cos\varphi}\right)$, for $\varphi < \varphi_0$

$N_\varphi = \dfrac{\rho a^2}{6}\left(5 + \dfrac{2\cos^2\varphi}{1 - \cos\varphi}\right)$

$N_\theta = \dfrac{\rho a^2}{6}\left(1 - 6\cos\varphi - \dfrac{2\cos^2\varphi}{1 - \cos\varphi}\right)$, for $\varphi > \varphi_0$

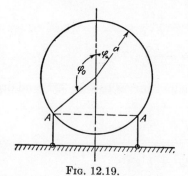

Fig. 12.19.

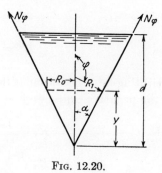

Fig. 12.20.

Problem 2. A conical shell is filled with liquid of specific weight ρ (Fig. 12.20). Find the stresses in the shell.

Ans. $N_\varphi = \dfrac{\rho y(3d - 2y)\tan\alpha}{6\cos\alpha}$

$N_\theta = \dfrac{\rho(d - y)y\tan\alpha}{\cos\alpha}$

12.4. Membrane Theory of Circular Cylindrical Shells. If we rotate a straight line around an axis parallel to it and follow a circle in a plane perpendicular to the axis, we obtain a circular cylindrical shell. This straight line is called the generator of the cylinder. Let us take the coordinate axis ξ_1 along the generator and ξ_2 along the circular arc in the plane perpendicular to the axis. Using the notation as shown in Fig. 12.21, we have $\xi_1 = x$ and $\xi_2 = \theta$. Let a be the radius of the circle. We find that in this case a line element ds on the middle surface of the shell is given by the formula

$$ds^2 = dx^2 + a^2\,d\theta^2$$

from which we obtain

$$\alpha_1 = 1 \qquad \text{and} \qquad \alpha_2 = a$$

The principal radii of curvature in this case are

$$R_1 = \infty \qquad R_2 = a$$

By letting the shearing forces and moments go to zero in the equilibrium

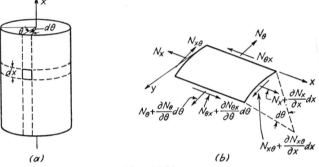

(a)   (b)

Fig. 12.21.

equations, we find from Eqs. (12.28) to (12.30) that these equations become

$$a\,\frac{\partial N_x}{\partial x} + \frac{\partial N_{x\theta}}{\partial \theta} + ap_1 = 0$$

$$a\,\frac{\partial N_{x\theta}}{\partial x} + \frac{\partial N_\theta}{\partial \theta} + ap_2 = 0 \tag{12.39}$$

$$N_\theta + ap_3 = 0$$

where we have used N_x, N_θ, and $N_{x\theta}$ in the place of N_1, N_2, and N_{12}, respectively. With the external load given, N_θ can be found from the third equation, and then by integration $N_{x\theta}$ and N_x are found from the second and first equation, respectively.

As an example, let us consider a horizontal circular cylindrical shell filled with liquid and rigidly built in at the ends (Fig. 12.22). The pressure at any point in the shell is equal to the weight of a unit column of the liquid at that point. If ρ is the weight of the liquid per unit volume and θ is measured from the vertical line as shown in Fig. 12.22, the pressure at point B, for example, is given by $\rho(AB) = \rho a(1 - \cos\theta)$. Since the pressure is directed outward, we have

$$p_3 = -\rho a(1 - \cos\theta) \qquad \text{and} \qquad p_1 = p_2 = 0$$

Substituting into Eqs. (12.39) and integrating, we find that

$$N_\theta = \rho a^2 (1 - \cos \theta)$$

$$N_{x\theta} = - \int \rho a \sin \theta \, dx + f_1(\theta) = -\rho a x \sin \theta + f_1(\theta)$$

$$N_x = \int \rho x \cos \theta \, dx - \frac{1}{a} \int \frac{df_1}{d\theta} \, dx + f_2(\theta) \qquad (12.40)$$

$$= \frac{\rho x^2}{2} \cos \theta - \frac{x}{a} \frac{df_1}{d\theta} + f_2(\theta)$$

where $f_1(\theta)$ and $f_2(\theta)$ are functions of θ to be determined from the boundary conditions.

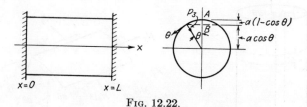

FIG. 12.22.

At the ends, the cylinder is assumed to be rigidly built in. Therefore, the strain component ϵ_θ must be zero. But

$$\epsilon_\theta = \frac{1}{Eh} (N_\theta - \nu N_x)$$

Substituting formulas (12.40) into the above expression, we find from the conditions $\epsilon_\theta = 0$ at $x = 0$ and $x = L$ that

$$f_2(\theta) = \frac{\rho a^2}{\nu} (1 - \cos \theta) \qquad f_1(\theta) = \frac{\rho a L}{2} \sin \theta + C$$

From the expression for $N_{x\theta}$, we observe that the constant C represents forces $N_{x\theta}$ uniformly distributed around the tube. If there is no torque applied, such a force cannot exist and C must therefore be zero. The solution of Eqs. (12.40) in this case is

$$N_\theta = \rho a^2 (1 - \cos \theta)$$

$$N_{x\theta} = -\rho a \left(\frac{L}{2} - x \right) \sin \theta \qquad (12.41)$$

$$N_x = -\frac{\rho x}{2} (L - x) \cos \theta + \frac{\rho a^2}{\nu} (1 - \cos \theta)$$

If the supports are rigid and cannot be moved in the x direction, there will be no change in the length of the generator. We find, however, that, corresponding to the forces given by (12.41), the change in the length of the generator

$$u = \int_0^L \epsilon_x \, dx = \frac{1}{Eh} \int_0^L (N_x - \nu N_\theta) \, dx$$

is not zero. This indicates that bending of the shell will occur, and the membrane theory will not be sufficient to describe the deformation in this case. A more complete solution of the problem can be obtained by taking into consideration the effect of bending as well as the membrane forces.

Problem 1. A horizontal thin circular cylinder is filled with steam at a constant pressure p. The cylinder is assumed to have a radius a, length L, and thickness h. Find the membrane forces in the cylinder if the ends are assumed to be rigidly built in.

Problem 2. A horizontal thin circular cylinder is under its own weight. Let ρ be the density of the material from which the cylinder is made, a the radius, L the length, and h the thickness. Find the membrane forces in the cylinder if the ends are assumed to be rigidly built in.

12.5. Determination of the Strain Components. Before we derive the expressions for the strain components for thin shells, we shall find the general expressions for the strain compo-

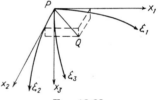

FIG. 12.23.

nents in any body referred to orthogonal curvilinear coordinates. Let ξ_1, ξ_2, and ξ_3 be the curvilinear coordinates. Consider two points $P(\xi_1, \xi_2, \xi_3)$ and $Q(\xi_1 + d\xi_1, \xi_2 + d\xi_2, \xi_3 + d\xi_3)$ at a short distance ds apart. Let the direction cosines of PQ, referred to the tangents at P to the curvilinear coordinates ξ_1, ξ_2, ξ_3, be l, m, n, respectively. These tangents are shown in Fig. 12.23 as x_1, x_2, and x_3. If A_1, A_2, A_3 are the factors at P which transform the curvilinear coordinates into linear distances, we find that the projections of ds on x_1, x_2, and x_3 are

$$l \, ds = A_1 \, d\xi_1 \qquad m \, ds = A_2 \, d\xi_2 \qquad n \, ds = A_3 \, d\xi_3 \qquad (12.42)$$

If we take the squares of the above expressions and then add them together, we obtain

$$ds^2 = (A_1 \, d\xi_1)^2 + (A_2 \, d\xi_2)^2 + (A_3 \, d\xi_3)^2$$

After deformation, let the particles which are at P, Q in the unstrained state be displaced to P', Q'. Let u_1, u_2, u_3 be the projections of the displacement PP' on x_1, x_2, x_3, and let $\xi_1' = \xi_1 + \mu_1$, $\xi_2' = \xi_2 + \mu_2$, $\xi_3' = \xi_3 + \mu_3$

be the curvilinear coordinates of P'. Assume that the displacement is small. Then

$$u_1 = A_1\mu_1 \qquad u_2 = A_2\mu_2 \qquad u_3 = A_3\mu_3 \qquad (12.43)$$

The curvilinear coordinates of $Q'(\xi_1'', \xi_2'', \xi_3'')$ can be expressed to the first order as

$$\xi_1'' = \xi_1' + d\xi_1 + d\mu_1 = \xi_1 + \mu_1 + d\xi_1 + \frac{\partial\mu_1}{\partial\xi_1}d\xi_1 + \frac{\partial\mu_1}{\partial\xi_2}d\xi_2 + \frac{\partial\mu_1}{\partial\xi_3}d\xi_3$$

$$\xi_2'' = \xi_2' + d\xi_2 + d\mu_2 = \xi_2 + \mu_2 + d\xi_2 + \frac{\partial\mu_2}{\partial\xi_1}d\xi_1 + \frac{\partial\mu_2}{\partial\xi_2}d\xi_2 + \frac{\partial\mu_2}{\partial\xi_3}d\xi_3$$

$$\xi_3'' = \xi_3' + d\xi_3 + d\mu_3 = \xi_3 + \mu_3 + d\xi_3 + \frac{\partial\mu_3}{\partial\xi_1}d\xi_1 + \frac{\partial\mu_3}{\partial\xi_2}d\xi_2 + \frac{\partial\mu_3}{\partial\xi_3}d\xi_3$$

Since the quantities A_1, A_2, A_3 vary from point to point, the quantities A_1', A_2', A_3' at P' can be expressed in terms of A_1, A_2, A_3 at P by the following formulas:

$$A_1' = A_1 + \frac{\partial A_1}{\partial\xi_1}\mu_1 + \frac{\partial A_1}{\partial\xi_2}\mu_2 + \frac{\partial A_1}{\partial\xi_3}\mu_3$$

$$A_2' = A_2 + \frac{\partial A_2}{\partial\xi_1}\mu_1 + \frac{\partial A_2}{\partial\xi_2}\mu_2 + \frac{\partial A_2}{\partial\xi_3}\mu_3$$

$$A_3' = A_3 + \frac{\partial A_3}{\partial\xi_1}\mu_1 + \frac{\partial A_3}{\partial\xi_2}\mu_2 + \frac{\partial A_3}{\partial\xi_3}\mu_3$$

Let ds' be the length of $P'Q'$ and l', m', n' be the direction cosines of $P'Q'$ referred to the tangents to the curvilinear coordinates ξ_1, ξ_2, ξ_3 which pass through P'. The projections of $P'Q'$ on these tangents can be expressed with sufficient accuracy by three formulas of the type

$$l'\,ds' = A_1'(\xi_1'' - \xi_1') = \left(A_1 + \frac{\partial A_1}{\partial\xi_1}\mu_1 + \frac{\partial A_1}{\partial\xi_2}\mu_2 + \frac{\partial A_1}{\partial\xi_3}\mu_3\right)$$
$$\left(d\xi_1 + \frac{\partial\mu_1}{\partial\xi_1}d\xi_1 + \frac{\partial\mu_1}{\partial\xi_2}d\xi_2 + \frac{\partial\mu_1}{\partial\xi_3}d\xi_3\right)$$

Neglecting higher-order terms, we have

$$l'\,ds' = A_1\,d\xi_1 + \frac{\partial A_1}{\partial\xi_1}\mu_1\,d\xi_1 + \frac{\partial A_1}{\partial\xi_2}\mu_2\,d\xi_1 + \frac{\partial A_1}{\partial\xi_3}\mu_3\,d\xi_1 + \frac{\partial\mu_1}{\partial\xi_1}A_1\,d\xi_1$$
$$+ \frac{\partial\mu_1}{\partial\xi_2}A_1\,d\xi_2 + \frac{\partial\mu_1}{\partial\xi_3}A_1\,d\xi_3$$

Substituting formulas (12.42) and (12.43) into the above equation and noting that

$$\frac{\partial A_1}{\partial\xi_1}\mu_1\,d\xi_1 + \frac{\partial\mu_1}{\partial\xi_1}A_1\,d\xi_1 = \frac{\partial A_1\mu_1}{\partial\xi_1}d\xi_1$$

we find that

$$l'\,ds' = l\,ds\left(1 + \frac{1}{A_1}\frac{\partial u_1}{\partial \xi_1} + \frac{u_2}{A_1 A_2}\frac{\partial A_1}{\partial \xi_2} + \frac{u_3}{A_1 A_3}\frac{\partial A_1}{\partial \xi_3}\right)$$
$$+ m\,ds\,\frac{A_1}{A_2}\frac{\partial}{\partial \xi_2}\left(\frac{u_1}{A_1}\right) + n\,ds\,\frac{A_1}{A_3}\frac{\partial}{\partial \xi_3}\left(\frac{\bar{u}_1}{A_1}\right)$$

Similarly, we find that

$$m'\,ds' = l\,ds\,\frac{A_2}{A_1}\frac{\partial}{\partial \xi_1}\left(\frac{u_2}{A_2}\right) + m\,ds\left(1 + \frac{1}{A_2}\frac{\partial u_2}{\partial \xi_2} + \frac{u_1}{A_1 A_2}\frac{\partial A_2}{\partial \xi_1}\right.$$
$$\left. + \frac{u_3}{A_2 A_3}\frac{\partial A_2}{\partial \xi_3}\right) + n\,ds\,\frac{A_2}{A_3}\frac{\partial}{\partial \xi_3}\left(\frac{u_2}{A_2}\right)$$

$$n'\,ds' = l\,ds\,\frac{A_3}{A_1}\frac{\partial}{\partial \xi_1}\left(\frac{u_3}{A_3}\right) + m\,ds\,\frac{A_3}{A_2}\frac{\partial}{\partial \xi_2}\left(\frac{u_3}{A_3}\right)$$
$$+ n\,ds\left(1 + \frac{1}{A_3}\frac{\partial u_3}{\partial \xi_3} + \frac{u_2}{A_2 A_3}\frac{\partial A_3}{\partial \xi_2} + \frac{u_1}{A_1 A_3}\frac{\partial A_3}{\partial \xi_1}\right)$$

If ϵ is the longitudinal strain of a linear element along PQ we have

$$\epsilon = \frac{P'Q' - PQ}{PQ} \quad \text{or} \quad P'Q' = PQ(1 + \epsilon) = ds\,(1 + \epsilon)$$

But
$$(P'Q')^2 = (l'\,ds')^2 + (m'\,ds')^2 + (n'\,ds')^2$$

The strain ϵ is therefore given by the equation

$$(1 + \epsilon)^2 = \left[l\left(1 + \frac{1}{A_1}\frac{\partial u_1}{\partial \xi_1} + \frac{u_2}{A_1 A_2}\frac{\partial A_1}{\partial \xi_2} + \frac{u_3}{A_1 A_3}\frac{\partial A_1}{\partial \xi_3}\right)\right.$$
$$\left. + m\,\frac{A_1}{A_2}\frac{\partial}{\partial \xi_2}\left(\frac{u_1}{A_1}\right) + n\,\frac{A_1}{A_3}\frac{\partial}{\partial \xi_3}\left(\frac{u_1}{A_1}\right)\right]^2 + \cdots + \cdots$$

Neglecting squares and products of u_1, u_2, u_3, we may write the result in the form

$$\epsilon = \epsilon_1 l^2 + \epsilon_2 m^2 + \epsilon_3 n^2 + \gamma_{12}lm + \gamma_{13}ln + \gamma_{23}mn \qquad (12.44)$$

in which

$$\epsilon_1 = \frac{1}{A_1}\frac{\partial u_1}{\partial \xi_1} + \frac{u_2}{A_1 A_2}\frac{\partial A_1}{\partial \xi_2} + \frac{u_3}{A_1 A_3}\frac{\partial A_1}{\partial \xi_3}$$

$$\epsilon_2 = \frac{1}{A_2}\frac{\partial u_2}{\partial \xi_2} + \frac{u_1}{A_1 A_2}\frac{\partial A_2}{\partial \xi_1} + \frac{u_3}{A_2 A_3}\frac{\partial A_2}{\partial \xi_3}$$

$$\epsilon_3 = \frac{1}{A_3}\frac{\partial u_3}{\partial \xi_3} + \frac{u_2}{A_2 A_3}\frac{\partial A_3}{\partial \xi_2} + \frac{u_1}{A_1 A_3}\frac{\partial A_3}{\partial \xi_1}$$

$$\gamma_{12} = \frac{A_2}{A_1}\frac{\partial}{\partial \xi_1}\left(\frac{u_2}{A_2}\right) + \frac{A_1}{A_2}\frac{\partial}{\partial \xi_2}\left(\frac{u_1}{A_1}\right) \qquad (12.45)$$

$$\gamma_{13} = \frac{A_1}{A_3}\frac{\partial}{\partial \xi_3}\left(\frac{u_1}{A_1}\right) + \frac{A_3}{A_1}\frac{\partial}{\partial \xi_1}\left(\frac{u_3}{A_3}\right)$$

$$\gamma_{23} = \frac{A_3}{A_2}\frac{\partial}{\partial \xi_2}\left(\frac{u_3}{A_3}\right) + \frac{A_2}{A_3}\frac{\partial}{\partial \xi_3}\left(\frac{u_2}{A_2}\right)$$

Comparing (12.44) with the first equation of (2.14), we see that ϵ_1, ϵ_2, ϵ_3 are the longitudinal strain components in the directions 1, 2, and 3 respectively, and γ_{12}, γ_{13}, γ_{23} are the shearing strain components.

In deriving the strain components for thin shells, we make the following assumptions:

1. The normals of the undeformed middle surface are deformed into the normals of the deformed middle surface.

2. The stress components normal to the middle surface are small compared with the other stress components and may be neglected in the stress-strain relations.

According to the coordinate system we took for thin shells, $\xi_3 = z$, while $\xi_1 = \xi_1$ and $\xi_2 = \xi_2$. Since the middle surface is not assumed to be unstrained as in the case of small bending of flat plates, the displacements at any point in the directions of ξ_1 and ξ_2 are, to the first order of z,

$$u_1 = u_{10} + z\left(\frac{\partial u_1}{\partial z}\right)_{z=0} \qquad u_2 = u_{20} + z\left(\frac{\partial u_2}{\partial z}\right)_{z=0} \qquad (12.46)$$

where u_{10} and u_{20} are the displacements u_1 and u_2 on the middle surface or at $z = 0$.

We have already explained in Sec. 11.1 that the first assumption is equivalent to assuming that $\gamma_{1z} = \gamma_{2z} = 0$. From (12.45), if we carry out the differentiation, we find that

$$\begin{aligned}
\gamma_{1z} &= \frac{1}{A_3}\frac{\partial u_1}{\partial z} - \frac{u_1}{A_1 A_3}\frac{\partial A_1}{\partial z} + \frac{A_3}{A_1}\frac{\partial}{\partial \xi_1}\left(\frac{u_3}{A_3}\right) \\
\gamma_{2z} &= \frac{A_3}{A_2}\frac{\partial}{\partial \xi_2}\left(\frac{u_3}{A_3}\right) + \frac{1}{A_3}\frac{\partial u_2}{\partial z} - \frac{u_2}{A_2 A_3}\frac{\partial A_2}{\partial z}
\end{aligned} \qquad (12.47)$$

If α_1, α_2 are the factors which transform the curvilinear coordinates to linear distances on the middle surface of the shell, we find then that

$$A_1 = \alpha_1\left(1 - \frac{z}{R_1}\right) \qquad A_2 = \alpha_2\left(1 - \frac{z}{R_2}\right) \qquad A_3 = 1$$

Substituting into formulas (12.47), at $z = 0$, we find that

$$\left(\frac{\partial u_1}{\partial z}\right)_{z=0} = -\frac{u_{10}}{R_1} - \frac{1}{\alpha_1}\frac{\partial w}{\partial \xi_1} \qquad \left(\frac{\partial u_2}{\partial z}\right)_{z=0} = -\frac{u_{20}}{R_2} - \frac{1}{\alpha_2}\frac{\partial w}{\partial \xi_2}$$

where w is the displacement u_3 on the middle surface. Hence

$$u_1 = u_{10} - z\left(\frac{u_{10}}{R_1} + \frac{1}{\alpha_1}\frac{\partial w}{\partial \xi_1}\right) \qquad u_2 = u_{20} - z\left(\frac{u_{20}}{R_2} + \frac{1}{\alpha_2}\frac{\partial w}{\partial \xi_2}\right) \qquad (12.48)$$

Neglecting z/R_1 and z/R_2 in the presence of 1, we find

$$A_1 = \alpha_1 \qquad A_2 = \alpha_2$$

Noting that

$$\frac{\partial A_1}{\partial z} = -\frac{\alpha_1}{R_1} \qquad \frac{\partial A_2}{\partial z} = -\frac{\alpha_2}{R_2} \qquad u_3 = w$$

we obtain the strain components in the following form:

$$
\epsilon_1 = \left(\frac{1}{\alpha_1}\frac{\partial u_{10}}{\partial \xi_1} + \frac{u_{20}}{\alpha_1\alpha_2}\frac{\partial \alpha_1}{\partial \xi_2} - \frac{w}{R_1} \right) - z\left[\frac{1}{\alpha_1}\frac{\partial}{\partial \xi_1}\left(\frac{u_{10}}{R_1} + \frac{1}{\alpha_1}\frac{\partial w}{\partial \xi_1} \right) \right.
$$
$$
\left. + \frac{1}{\alpha_1\alpha_2}\left(\frac{u_{20}}{R_2} + \frac{1}{\alpha_2}\frac{\partial w}{\partial \xi_2} \right)\frac{\partial \alpha_1}{\partial \xi_2} \right]
$$

$$
\epsilon_2 = \left(\frac{1}{\alpha_2}\frac{\partial u_{20}}{\partial \xi_2} + \frac{u_{10}}{\alpha_1\alpha_2}\frac{\partial \alpha_2}{\partial \xi_1} - \frac{w}{R_2} \right) - z\left[\frac{1}{\alpha_2}\frac{\partial}{\partial \xi_2}\left(\frac{u_{20}}{R_2} + \frac{1}{\alpha_2}\frac{\partial w}{\partial \xi_2} \right) \right.
$$
$$
\left. + \frac{1}{\alpha_1\alpha_2}\left(\frac{u_{10}}{R_1} + \frac{1}{\alpha_1}\frac{\partial w}{\partial \xi_1} \right)\frac{\partial \alpha_2}{\partial \xi_1} \right]
$$
$$
(12.49)
$$

$$
\gamma_{12} = \left[\frac{\alpha_2}{\alpha_1}\frac{\partial}{\partial \xi_1}\left(\frac{u_{20}}{\alpha_2} \right) + \frac{\alpha_1}{\alpha_2}\frac{\partial}{\partial \xi_2}\left(\frac{u_{10}}{\alpha_1} \right) \right] - z\left[\frac{\alpha_2}{\alpha_1}\frac{\partial}{\partial \xi_1}\left(\frac{u_{20}}{\alpha_2 R_2} + \frac{1}{\alpha_2{}^2}\frac{\partial w}{\partial \xi_2} \right) \right.
$$
$$
\left. + \frac{\alpha_1}{\alpha_2}\frac{\partial}{\partial \xi_2}\left(\frac{u_{10}}{\alpha_1 R_1} + \frac{1}{\alpha_1{}^2}\frac{\partial w}{\partial \xi_1} \right) \right]
$$

Formulas (12.49) may be written as

$$\epsilon_1 = \epsilon_{10} - z\chi_1 \qquad \epsilon_2 = \epsilon_{20} - z\chi_2 \qquad \gamma_{12} = \gamma_0 - 2z\chi_{12} \qquad (12.50)$$

where

$$\epsilon_{10} = \frac{1}{\alpha_1}\frac{\partial u_{10}}{\partial \xi_1} + \frac{u_{20}}{\alpha_1\alpha_2}\frac{\partial \alpha_1}{\partial \xi_2} - \frac{w}{R_1}$$

$$\epsilon_{20} = \frac{1}{\alpha_2}\frac{\partial u_{20}}{\partial \xi_2} + \frac{u_{10}}{\alpha_1\alpha_2}\frac{\partial \alpha_2}{\partial \xi_1} - \frac{w}{R_2}$$

$$\gamma_0 = \frac{\alpha_2}{\alpha_1}\frac{\partial}{\partial \xi_1}\left(\frac{u_{20}}{\alpha_2} \right) + \frac{\alpha_1}{\alpha_2}\frac{\partial}{\partial \xi_2}\left(\frac{u_{10}}{\alpha_1} \right)$$

$$\chi_1 = \frac{1}{\alpha_1}\frac{\partial}{\partial \xi_1}\left(\frac{u_{10}}{R_1} + \frac{1}{\alpha_1}\frac{\partial w}{\partial \xi_1} \right) + \frac{1}{\alpha_1\alpha_2}\left(\frac{u_{20}}{R_2} + \frac{1}{\alpha_2}\frac{\partial w}{\partial \xi_2} \right)\frac{\partial \alpha_1}{\partial \xi_2}$$

$$\chi_2 = \frac{1}{\alpha_2}\frac{\partial}{\partial \xi_2}\left(\frac{u_{20}}{R_2} + \frac{1}{\alpha_2}\frac{\partial w}{\partial \xi_2} \right) + \frac{1}{\alpha_1\alpha_2}\left(\frac{u_{10}}{R_1} + \frac{1}{\alpha_1}\frac{\partial w}{\partial \xi_1} \right)\frac{\partial \alpha_2}{\partial \xi_1}$$

$$\chi_{12} = \frac{1}{2}\left[\frac{\alpha_2}{\alpha_1}\frac{\partial}{\partial \xi_1}\left(\frac{u_{20}}{\alpha_2 R_2} + \frac{1}{\alpha_2{}^2}\frac{\partial w}{\partial \xi_2} \right) + \frac{\alpha_1}{\alpha_2}\frac{\partial}{\partial \xi_2}\left(\frac{u_{10}}{\alpha_1 R_1} + \frac{1}{\alpha_1{}^2}\frac{\partial w}{\partial \xi_1} \right) \right]$$

In the above expressions, ϵ_{10}, ϵ_{20}, γ_0 may be interpreted physically as strains in the middle surface of the shell, while χ_1, χ_2, χ_{12} are the changes in curvatures.

From the second assumption, the following expressions for the stress components are obtained:

$$\sigma_1 = \frac{E}{1 - \nu^2} [\epsilon_{10} + \nu\epsilon_{20} - z(\chi_1 + \nu\chi_2)]$$

$$\sigma_2 = \frac{E}{1 - \nu^2} [\epsilon_{20} + \nu\epsilon_{10} - z(\chi_2 + \nu\chi_1)] \qquad (12.51)$$

$$\tau_{12} = \frac{E}{2(1 + \nu)} (\gamma_0 - 2z\chi_{12})$$

Substituting these expressions into Eqs. (12.27) and neglecting z/R_1 and z/R_2 in the presence of 1, we obtain

$$N_1 = \frac{Eh}{1 - \nu^2} (\epsilon_{10} + \nu\epsilon_{20})$$

$$N_2 = \frac{Eh}{1 - \nu^2} (\epsilon_{20} + \nu\epsilon_{10})$$

$$N_{12} = N_{21} = \frac{Eh\gamma_0}{2(1 + \nu)} \qquad (12.52)$$

$$M_1 = -D(\chi_1 + \nu\chi_2)$$

$$M_2 = -D(\chi_2 + \nu\chi_1)$$

$$M_{12} = M_{21} = D(1 - \nu)\chi_{12}$$

The above method of derivation is due to Reissner.[1]

12.6. General Theory of Circular Cylindrical Shells. Let us consider the case of circular cylindrical shells. We choose the coordinate axes so that x is in the direction of the generatrix, θ is in the direction of the tangent to the circumference, and z is in the direction of the normal to the middle surface of the shell. Thus, $\xi_1 = x$, $\xi_2 = \theta$. Let a be the radius of the circular cylinder. A line element ds on the middle surface is given in this case by the formula

$$ds^2 = dx^2 + a^2 \, d\theta^2$$

Hence

$$\alpha_1 = 1 \qquad \alpha_2 = a$$

If we denote the tangent to the coordinate θ by y, we find that the radii of curvature in the xz and yz planes are the principal radii of curvature. Thus,

$$R_1 = \infty \qquad R_2 = a$$

Let $N_1 = N_x$, $N_2 = N_\theta$, $N_{12} = N_{x\theta}$, $M_1 = M_x$, $M_2 = M_\theta$, $M_{12} = M_{x\theta} = M_{21} = M_{\theta x}$, $Q_1 = Q_x$, $Q_2 = Q_\theta$. With these notations and the values of α and R given by the above formulas, we find from Eqs. (12.28) to (12.32) the following equilibrium equations for circular cylindrical shells:

---

[1] E. Reissner, A New Derivation of the Equations for the Deformation of Elastic Shells, *Am. J. Math.*, Vol. 63, No. 1, pp. 177–184, January, 1941.

$$a \frac{\partial N_x}{\partial x} + \frac{\partial N_{x\theta}}{\partial \theta} + ap_1 = 0$$

$$a \frac{\partial N_{x\theta}}{\partial x} + \frac{\partial N_\theta}{\partial \theta} - Q_\theta + ap_2 = 0$$

$$a \frac{\partial Q_x}{\partial x} + \frac{\partial Q_\theta}{\partial \theta} + N_\theta + ap_3 = 0 \qquad (12.53)$$

$$a \frac{\partial M_{x\theta}}{\partial x} - \frac{\partial M_\theta}{\partial \theta} + aQ_\theta = 0$$

$$\frac{\partial M_{x\theta}}{\partial \theta} - a \frac{\partial M_x}{\partial x} + aQ_x = 0$$

From the last two equations, we find that

$$Q_\theta = \frac{1}{a} \frac{\partial M_\theta}{\partial \theta} - \frac{\partial M_{x\theta}}{\partial x} \qquad Q_x = \frac{\partial M_x}{\partial x} - \frac{1}{a} \frac{\partial M_{x\theta}}{\partial \theta} \qquad (12.54)$$

Substituting these relations in the first three equations in (12.53), we obtain

$$a \frac{\partial N_x}{\partial x} + \frac{\partial N_{x\theta}}{\partial \theta} + ap_1 = 0$$

$$a \frac{\partial N_{x\theta}}{\partial x} + \frac{\partial N_\theta}{\partial \theta} + \frac{\partial M_{x\theta}}{\partial x} - \frac{1}{a} \frac{\partial M_\theta}{\partial \theta} + ap_2 = 0 \qquad (12.55)$$

$$a \frac{\partial^2 M_x}{\partial x^2} - 2 \frac{\partial^2 M_{x\theta}}{\partial x \, \partial \theta} + \frac{1}{a} \frac{\partial^2 M_\theta}{\partial \theta^2} + N_\theta + ap_3 = 0$$

To find the expressions for the strain components, let us denote

$$u_{10} = u \qquad u_{20} = v$$

$$\epsilon_1 = \epsilon_x \qquad \epsilon_2 = \epsilon_\theta \qquad \gamma_{12} = \gamma_{x\theta}$$

$$\chi_1 = \chi_x \qquad \chi_2 = \chi_\theta \qquad \chi_{12} = \chi_{x\theta}$$

From formulas (12.49) and (12.50), we obtain

$$\epsilon_x = \epsilon_{x0} - z\chi_x \qquad \epsilon_\theta = \epsilon_{\theta 0} - z\chi_\theta \qquad \gamma_{x\theta} = \gamma_0 - 2z\chi_{x\theta} \qquad (12.56)$$

where

$$\epsilon_{x0} = \frac{\partial u}{\partial x}$$

$$\epsilon_{\theta 0} = \frac{1}{a} \frac{\partial v}{\partial \theta} - \frac{w}{a}$$

$$\gamma_0 = \frac{\partial v}{\partial x} + \frac{1}{a} \frac{\partial u}{\partial \theta}$$

$$\chi_x = \frac{\partial^2 w}{\partial x^2} \qquad (12.57)$$

$$\chi_\theta = \frac{1}{a} \frac{\partial}{\partial \theta} \left(\frac{v}{a} + \frac{1}{a} \frac{\partial w}{\partial \theta} \right)$$

$$\chi_{x\theta} = \frac{1}{a} \left(\frac{1}{2} \frac{\partial v}{\partial x} + \frac{\partial^2 w}{\partial x \, \partial \theta} \right)$$

Substituting these expressions into formulas (12.52), we obtain

$$N_x = \frac{Eh}{1 - \nu^2} \left[\frac{\partial u}{\partial x} + \nu \left(\frac{1}{a} \frac{\partial v}{\partial \theta} - \frac{w}{a} \right) \right]$$

$$N_\theta = \frac{Eh}{1 - \nu^2} \left(\frac{1}{a} \frac{\partial v}{\partial \theta} - \frac{w}{a} + \nu \frac{\partial u}{\partial x} \right)$$

$$N_{x\theta} = \frac{Eh}{2(1 + \nu)} \left(\frac{\partial v}{\partial x} + \frac{1}{a} \frac{\partial u}{\partial \theta} \right)$$

$$M_x = -D \left[\frac{\partial^2 w}{\partial x^2} + \frac{\nu}{a^2} \left(\frac{\partial v}{\partial \theta} + \frac{\partial^2 w}{\partial \theta^2} \right) \right] \tag{12.58}$$

$$M_\theta = -D \left[\frac{1}{a^2} \left(\frac{\partial v}{\partial \theta} + \frac{\partial^2 w}{\partial \theta^2} \right) + \nu \frac{\partial^2 w}{\partial x^2} \right]$$

$$M_{x\theta} = D(1 - \nu) \frac{1}{a} \left(\frac{1}{2} \frac{\partial v}{\partial x} + \frac{\partial^2 w}{\partial x \, \partial \theta} \right)$$

In terms of the displacement components u, v, w, Eqs. (12.55) become

$$\frac{\partial^2 u}{\partial x^2} + \frac{1 - \nu}{2a^2} \frac{\partial^2 u}{\partial \theta^2} + \frac{1 + \nu}{2a} \frac{\partial^2 v}{\partial x \, \partial \theta} - \frac{\nu}{a} \frac{\partial w}{\partial x} + \frac{p_1(1 - \nu^2)}{Eh} = 0$$

$$\frac{1 + \nu}{2a} \frac{\partial^2 u}{\partial x \, \partial \theta} + \frac{1 - \nu}{2} \frac{\partial^2 v}{\partial x^2} + \frac{1}{a^2} \frac{\partial^2 v}{\partial \theta^2} - \frac{1}{a^2} \frac{\partial w}{\partial \theta} + \frac{h^2}{12a^2} \left(\frac{\partial^3 w}{\partial x^2 \, \partial \theta} \right.$$

$$\left. + \frac{\partial^3 w}{a^2 \, \partial \theta^3} \right) + \frac{h^2}{12a^2} \left(\frac{1 - \nu}{2} \frac{\partial^2 v}{\partial x^2} + \frac{\partial^2 v}{a^2 \, \partial \theta^2} \right) + \frac{p_2(1 - \nu^2)}{Eh} = 0 \tag{12.59}$$

$$\nu \frac{\partial u}{\partial x} + \frac{\partial v}{a \, \partial \theta} - \frac{w}{a} - \frac{h^2}{12} \left(a \frac{\partial^4 w}{\partial x^4} + \frac{2}{a} \frac{\partial^4 w}{\partial x^2 \, \partial \theta^2} + \frac{\partial w^4}{a^3 \, \partial \theta^4} \right)$$

$$- \frac{h^2}{12} \left(\frac{1}{a} \frac{\partial^3 v}{\partial x^2 \, \partial \theta} + \frac{1}{a^3} \frac{\partial^3 v}{\partial \theta^3} \right) + \frac{ap_3(1 - \nu^2)}{Eh} = 0$$

The problem of the circular cylindrical shell reduces thus in each particular case to the solution of this system of differential equations. Several examples of such solutions will be shown in the next two sections.

12.7. Circular Cylindrical Shell Loaded Symmetrically with Respect to Its Axis. For circular cylindrical shells loaded symmetrically with respect to their axes, the solution of Eqs. (12.59) can be very much simplified. Shells of this type have many practical applications, such as cylindrical boilers subjected to the action of steam pressure and vertical cylindrical containers subjected to internal liquid pressures. In such cases, because of symmetry, we find that $p_2 = 0$, $v = 0$, and u, w are functions of x only. If a is the radius of the cylinder, Eqs. (12.59) become

$$\frac{d^2 u}{dx^2} - \frac{\nu}{a} \frac{dw}{dx} + \frac{p_1(1 - \nu^2)}{Eh} = 0$$

$$\nu \frac{du}{dx} - \frac{w}{a} - \frac{h^2 a}{12} \frac{d^4 w}{dx^4} + \frac{ap_3(1 - \nu^2)}{Eh} = 0 \tag{12.60}$$

If the cylinder is loaded by lateral loading only, $p_1 = 0$ and the first equation can be integrated to give

$$\frac{du}{dx} - \frac{vw}{a} = C \tag{12.61}$$

where C is a constant of integration. From Eqs. (12.58), we find that

$$\frac{du}{dx} - \frac{vw}{a} = \frac{N_x(1 - v^2)}{Eh}$$

Equation (12.61) indicates that the forces N_x are constant.

Eliminating du/dx from the second equation in (12.60), we obtain

$$\frac{d^4w}{dx^4} + 4\beta^4 w = \frac{p_3}{D} + \frac{vN_x}{aD} \tag{12.62}$$

where $\beta^4 = 3(1 - v^2)/a^2h^2$. This is an ordinary differential equation with constant coefficients. The complementary solution of this equation is

$$w = C_1 e^{q_1 x} + C_2 e^{q_2 x} + C_3 e^{q_3 x} + C_4 e^{q_4 x}$$

where C_1, C_2, C_3, C_4 are constants and q_1, q_2, q_3, q_4 are the roots of the equation

$$q^4 + 4\beta^4 = 0$$

By adding and subtracting the terms $4q^2\beta^2$ in the above equation, we have

$$(q^2 + 2\beta^2)^2 - 4q^2\beta^2 = 0$$

Therefore
$$q^2 + 2\beta^2 = \pm 2q\beta$$

or
$$q = \pm\beta \pm i\beta$$

The complementary solution is

$$w = e^{-\beta x}(C_1 e^{i\beta x} + C_2 e^{-i\beta x}) + e^{\beta x}(C_3 e^{i\beta x} + C_4 e^{-i\beta x})$$

If the particular integral is $f(x)$, the general solution of Eq. (12.62) can be written in the following form,

$$w = e^{-\beta x}(C_1 \cos \beta x + C_2 \sin \beta x) + e^{\beta x}(C_3 \cos \beta x + C_4 \sin \beta x) + f(x) \tag{12.63}$$

where C_1, C_2, C_3, C_4 are arbitrary constants.

As a first example, let us consider a long circular pipe bent by a load uniformly distributed along a circular section. Let us take the coordinate axes as shown in Fig. 12.24 and consider the half cylinder at the right of the z axis.[1] In this case, there is no pressure p_3 distributed over the sur-

---

[1] For the other half cylinder at the left of the z axis, we shall take x in the opposite direction to that shown in Fig. 12.24.

face of the shell, and if the end condition is such that $N_x = 0$, then $f(x) = 0$. Since the cylinder is long, at the support, which is at a large

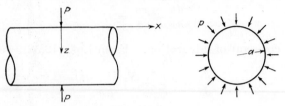

FIG. 12.24.

value of x, w must be zero. This is possible only if $C_3 = C_4 = 0$ in (12.63). We have therefore

$$w = e^{-\beta x}(C_1 \cos \beta x + C_2 \sin \beta x) \tag{12.64}$$

From Eqs. (12.58), we find that $N_{x\theta} = M_{x\theta} = 0$ and

$$N_\theta = \frac{Eh}{1 - \nu^2}\left(\nu \frac{du}{dx} - \frac{w}{a}\right)$$

$$M_x = -D\frac{d^2w}{dx^2} \tag{12.65}$$

$$M_\theta = -D\nu \frac{d^2w}{dx^2}$$

Since N_x is assumed to be zero, $du/dx = -\nu w/a$ and N_θ may be written in the following form:

$$N_\theta = -\frac{Ehw}{a}$$

From Eq. (12.54), we have

$$Q_x = \frac{dM_x}{dx} = -D\frac{d^3w}{dx^3} \tag{12.66}$$

In the present case, since each half of the cylinder will take one-half of the external load, at $x = 0$ we have $Q_x = -P/2$. For a long cylinder, w must be symmetrical about $x = 0$, which requires that $dw/dx = 0$ there. The integration constants C_1 and C_2 can be determined from these two conditions, viz.,

$$\left(\frac{dw}{dx}\right)_{x=0} = [-\beta C_1 e^{-\beta x}(\cos \beta x + \sin \beta x) + \beta C_2 e^{-\beta x}(\cos \beta x - \sin \beta x)]_{x=0}$$

$$= -C_1 + C_2 = 0$$

$$\left(\frac{d^3w}{dx^3}\right)_{x=0} = [2\beta^3 C_1 e^{-\beta x}(\cos \beta x - \sin \beta x) + 2\beta^3 C_2 e^{-\beta x}(\cos \beta x + \sin \beta x)]_{x=0}$$

$$= 2\beta^3(C_1 + C_2) = \frac{P}{2D}$$

Solving, we get

$$C_1 = C_2 = \frac{P}{8\beta^3 D}$$

The deflection w is therefore

$$w = \frac{Pe^{-\beta x}}{8\beta^3 D} (\sin \beta x + \cos \beta x) \tag{12.67}$$

Substituting into Eqs. (12.65), we find that

$$
\begin{aligned}
N_\theta &= -\frac{Ehw}{a} = -\frac{EhPe^{-\beta x}}{8\beta^3 Da} (\sin \beta x + \cos \beta x) \\
M_x &= -D \frac{d^2 w}{dx^2} = \frac{Pe^{-\beta x}}{4\beta} (\cos \beta x - \sin \beta x) \\
M_\theta &= -D\nu \frac{d^2 w}{dx^2} = \frac{\nu Pe^{-\beta x}}{4\beta} (\cos \beta x - \sin \beta x) \\
Q_x &= -D \frac{d^3 w}{dx^3} = -\frac{Pe^{-\beta x}}{2} \cos \beta x
\end{aligned}
\tag{12.68}
$$

From these formulas, we find that the maximum deflection and the maximum bending moment occur at $x = 0$ and are

$$w_{\max} = \frac{P}{8\beta^3 D} = \frac{Pa^2 \beta}{2Eh} \qquad M_{\max} = \frac{P}{4\beta}$$

We observe also that all the quantities computed from these formulas are negligible if $x > \pi/\beta$. This indicates that the bending is of local character and a cylinder with length $L = 2\pi/\beta$ loaded at the middle will have practically the same maximum deflection and bending moments as those for a long cylinder.

The bending stresses can be computed from formulas (12.51) and (12.52), *viz.*,

$$\sigma_x = \frac{12 M_x z}{h^3} \qquad \sigma_\theta = \frac{N_\theta}{h} + \frac{12 M_\theta z}{h^3}$$

The maximum bending stresses occur at $x = 0$ and $z = h/2$, and their values are

$$(\sigma_x)_{\max} = \frac{3P}{2\beta h^2} \qquad (\sigma_\theta)_{\max} = -\frac{Pa\beta}{2} - \frac{3\nu P}{2\beta h^2}$$

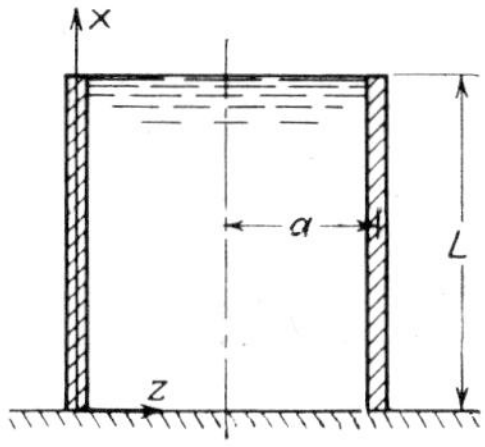

Fig. 12.25.

As a second example, let us consider a cylindrical tank filled with liquid of a specific weight ρ. Take the coordinate system as shown in Fig. 12.25. The pressure acting at any point x on the wall of the cylindrical tank is $p_3 = -\rho(L - x)$, where the negative sign indicates that p_3 is directed outward and is opposite to the positive z direction. Equation (12.62) becomes

$$\frac{d^4w}{dx^4} + 4\beta^4 w = -\frac{\rho(L - x)}{D}$$

The particular integral of this equation is

$$f(x) = -\frac{\rho(1 - x)}{4\beta^4 D} = -\frac{\rho(L - x)a^2}{Eh}$$

and the general solution is

$$w = e^{-\beta x}(C_1 \cos \beta x + C_2 \sin \beta x) + e^{\beta x}(C_3 \cos \beta x$$
$$+ C_4 \sin \beta x) - \frac{\rho(L - x)a^2}{Eh} \quad (12.69)$$

If L is large compared with $\sqrt{ah}$, we may regard the cylinder as infinitely long. The constants C_3 and C_4 are then equal to zero. At the bottom of the tank, we may assume that the tank is rigidly built in. In such a case, we have

$$w = 0 \text{ and } \frac{dw}{dx} = 0 \qquad \text{at } x = 0$$

From these conditions, we find that

$$(w)_{x=0} = C_1 - \frac{\rho a^2 L}{Eh} = 0$$

$$\left(\frac{dw}{dx}\right)_{x=0} = \beta(C_2 - C_1) + \frac{\rho a^2}{Eh} = 0$$

or

$$C_1 = \frac{\rho a^2 L}{Eh} \qquad C_2 = \frac{\rho a^2}{Eh}\left(L - \frac{1}{\beta}\right)$$

The deflection w then becomes

$$w = -\frac{\rho a^2}{Eh}\left\{L - x - e^{-\beta x}\left[L \cos \beta x + \left(L - \frac{1}{\beta}\right)\sin \beta x\right]\right\}$$

Substituting this expression into Eqs. (12.65), we find that

$$N_\theta = -\frac{Ehw}{a} = \rho a\left\{L - x - e^{-\beta x}\left[L \cos \beta x + \left(L - \frac{1}{\beta}\right)\sin \beta x\right]\right\}$$

$$M_x = -D\frac{d^2w}{dx^2} = \frac{\rho a L h}{\sqrt{12(1 - \nu^2)}}e^{-\beta x}\left[-\sin \beta x + \left(1 - \frac{1}{\beta L}\right)\cos \beta x\right]$$

$$M_\theta = -D\nu\frac{d^2w}{dx^2} = \frac{\nu\rho a L h}{\sqrt{12(1 - \nu^2)}}e^{-\beta x}\left[-\sin \beta x + \left(1 - \frac{1}{\beta L}\right)\cos \beta x\right]$$

With these expressions for N_θ, M_x, and M_θ, the maximum stresses can easily be calculated. The maximum bending moment occurs at the bottom of the tank, and its value is

$$(M_x)_{max} = \left(1 - \frac{1}{\beta L}\right)\frac{\rho a L h}{\sqrt{12(1 - \nu^2)}}$$

12.8. Cylindrical Shells under Unsymmetrical Loadings. In the general case of cylindrical shells under unsymmetrical loadings, we must solve the three equations in (12.59) simultaneously. Let us take as an example the case of a circular cylindrical shell filled with a liquid of specific weight ρ (Fig. 12.26). Assume that the edges of the shell can be

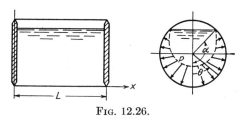

FIG. 12.26.

regarded as simply supported.[1] Then at the supports, $x = 0$ and $x = L$, we have

$$v = 0 \qquad w = 0 \qquad N_x = 0 \qquad M_x = 0$$

It can easily be verified that these conditions as well as the conditions of symmetry of deformation are satisfied if we take the components of displacement in the form of the following series,

$$u = \sum_{m=1}^{\infty} \sum_{n=0}^{\infty} A_{mn} \cos n\theta \cos \frac{m\pi x}{L}$$

$$v = \sum_{m=1}^{\infty} \sum_{n=0}^{\infty} B_{mn} \sin n\theta \sin \frac{m\pi x}{L} \qquad (12.70)$$

$$w = \sum_{m=1}^{\infty} \sum_{n=0}^{\infty} C_{mn} \cos n\theta \sin \frac{m\pi x}{L}$$

where L is the length of the cylinder and θ is the angle measured as shown in Fig. 12.26.

The intensity of the pressure p_3 is given by the following expressions,

$$\begin{aligned} p_3 &= -\rho a(\cos \theta - \cos \alpha) \qquad \text{when } 0 \leq \theta \leq \alpha \\ p_3 &= 0 \qquad\qquad\qquad\qquad\quad \text{when } \alpha \leq \theta \leq \pi \end{aligned} \qquad (12.71)$$

where the angle α defines the level of the liquid. It will be convenient to represent p_3 as given by (12.71) in the form of a Fourier's series as follows:

$$p_3 = -\sum_m \sum_n D_{mn} \cos n\theta \sin \frac{m\pi x}{L} \qquad (12.72)$$

[1] I. A. Wojtaszak, Deformation of Thin Cylindrical Shells Subjected to Internal Loading, *Phil. Mag.*, Ser. 7, Vol. 18, pp. 1099–1116, 1934.

The coefficients D_{mn} can be calculated in the usual way and are given by the following formulas,

$$D_{mn} = \frac{8\rho a}{mn\pi^2(n^2 - 1)} \;(\cos \alpha \sin n\alpha - n \cos n\alpha \sin \alpha) \qquad (12.73)$$

where $m = 1, 3, 5 \ldots$ and $n = 2, 3, 4 \ldots$, while

$$D_{m0} = \frac{4\rho a}{m\pi^2} \;(\sin \alpha - \alpha \cos \alpha) \qquad D_{m1} = \frac{2\rho a}{m\pi^2} \;(2\alpha - \sin 2\alpha) \quad (12.74)$$

In the case of a cylinder completely filled with liquid (Fig. 12.27), we denote by ρd the pressure at the axis of the shell.   Then

$$p_3 = -\rho(d + a \cos \theta)$$

and we obtain instead of (12.73) and (12.74)

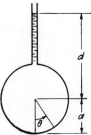

$$D_{mn} = 0 \qquad D_{m0} = \frac{4\rho d}{m\pi}$$

$$D_{m1} = \frac{4\rho a}{m\pi} \qquad m = 1, 3, 5, \ldots \quad (12.75)$$

For thin cylinders, $h^2/12a^2$ will be a small value, and the terms multiplied by that factor can be neglected in comparison with other terms in the second equation of (12.59).   Substituting (12.70) and (12.72) into Eqs. (12.59), and introducing the notation

$$\lambda = \frac{L}{a} \qquad \eta = \frac{h}{2L}$$

we obtain

$$A_{mn}[2m^2\pi^2 + (1 - \nu)\lambda^2n^2] - B_{mn}(1 - \nu)\lambda mn\pi + C_{mn}2\nu\lambda m\pi = 0$$
$$A_{mn}3(1 + \nu)\lambda mn\pi - B_{mn}[3(1 - \nu)m^2\pi^2 + 6\lambda^2n^2]$$
$$- C_{mn}2\lambda^2n[3 + \eta^2(m^2\pi^2 + \lambda^2n^2)] = 0 \qquad (12.76)$$
$$A_{mn}3\nu\lambda m\pi - B_{mn}\lambda^2n^2[3 + \eta^2(m^2\pi^2 + \lambda^2n^2)]$$
$$- C_{mn}[3\lambda^2 + \eta^2(m^2\pi^2 + \lambda^2n^2)^2] = -\frac{D_{mn}L^2h}{2D}$$

Since D_{mn} is known from Eqs. (12.73), (12.74), or (12.75) the coefficients A_{mn}, B_{mn}, C_{mn} can be calculated in each particular case from Eqs. (12.76) for any value of m and n, and therefore the resultant forces, moments, and components of displacement can be found for any point of the cylindrical shell by using Eqs. (12.58) and (12.70).

The above theoretical solution will now be applied to the case of a cylindrical shell full of liquid with the following numerical data:

$$a = d = 19.68 \text{ in.} \qquad L = 9.84 \qquad h = 2.76 \text{ in.} \qquad \nu = 0.3$$

Then $\quad \lambda = \dfrac{L}{a} = 0.5 \qquad \lambda^2 = 0.25 \qquad \eta = \dfrac{h}{2L} = 0.14 \qquad \eta^2 = 0.0196$

From (12.75), we obtain

$$D_{m0} = D_{m1} = \frac{4\rho a}{m\pi} \qquad \text{where } m = 1, 3, 5, \ldots$$

and
$$D_{mn} = 0 \qquad \text{for } n > 1$$

Using the notation $\varphi = 2a\rho L^2 h/\pi^2 D$ we find that, for $n = 0$, the solution of Eqs. (12.76) is

$$A_{m0} = \frac{\nu\varphi\lambda}{m^2[3\lambda^2(1 - \nu^2) + \eta^2 m^4\pi^4]}$$

$$B_{m0} = 0$$

$$C_{m0} = \frac{\varphi\pi}{m[3\lambda^2(1 - \nu^2) + \eta^2 m^4\pi^4]}$$

For $n = 1$ the expressions for the coefficients are too complicated to be put explicitly in terms of these parameters. For $m = 1, 3, 5$, the numerical values of the coefficients are given in Table 12.1. It is seen that the values of these coefficients diminish very rapidly so that only a few terms in the series (12.70) are necessary to represent the deformation with sufficient accuracy.

TABLE 12.1

m	$A_{m0}\varphi^{-1}h \times 10^3$	$C_{m0}\varphi^{-1}h \times 10^3$	$A_{m1}\varphi^{-1}h \times 10^3$	$B_{m1}\varphi^{-1}h \times 10^3$	$C_{m1}\varphi^{-1}h \times 10^3$
1	28.94	-606	24.38	-35.95	-593
3	0.0537	-3.371	0.0520	-0.0372	-3.352
5	0.00251	-0.263	0.00247	-0.00183	-0.263

Maximum values of w, N_x, N_θ, M_x, and M_θ occur at $x = L/2$, $\theta = 0$ and will now be computed. Taking $m = 1, 3, 5$ and $n = 0, 1$, we find that

$$w_{\max} = \frac{4,642\rho}{E} \qquad \text{in.}$$

$$(N_x)_{\max} = 0.1326\rho \qquad \text{lb per in.}$$
$$(N_\theta)_{\max} = 9.00\rho \qquad \text{lb per in.}$$
$$(M_x)_{\max} = 12.49\rho \qquad \text{lb}$$
$$(M_\theta)_{\max} = 3.885\rho \qquad \text{lb}$$

The maximum circumferential and longitudinal bending stresses are

$$(\sigma_\theta)_{\max} = \frac{(N_\theta)_{\max}}{h} + \frac{6(M_\theta)_{\max}}{h^2} = 6.335\rho \qquad \text{psi}$$

$$(\sigma_x)_{\max} = \frac{(N_x)_{\max}}{h} + \frac{6(M_x)_{\max}}{h^2} = 9.913\rho \qquad \text{psi}$$

Problem. In the numerical example worked out, if we take $h = 0.25$ in. but leave the other given data unchanged, calculate the maximum deflections and stresses.

12.9. Buckling of Circular Cylindrical Shell under Uniform Axial Compression. When a cylindrical shell is under uniform axial compression (Fig. 12.28), the cylindrical form of equilibrium becomes unstable at a certain value of the compressive load, and the cylinder buckles. Assume in this case that all middle surface forces except N_x are very small. The products of N_x and the derivatives of the displacements then become large enough to be included in the equilibrium equations, while the products of other forces and derivatives of displacements can still be neglected. In a calculation similar to that of Sec. 11.6, we find that the force N_x gives a y component $N_x(\partial^2 v/\partial x^2)\, dx\, a\, d\theta$ in the equation $\Sigma F_y = 0$ and a z component $N_x(\partial^2 w/\partial x^2)$ $dx\, a\, d\theta$ in the equation $\Sigma F_z = 0$. Dividing these components by $dx\, d\theta$ and adding them to Eq. (12.53), we find that in such a case the equilibrium equations are

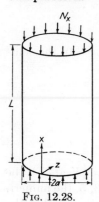

Fig. 12.28.

$$a\,\frac{\partial N_x}{\partial x} + \frac{\partial N_{x\theta}}{\partial \theta} = 0$$

$$\frac{\partial N_\theta}{\partial \theta} + a\,\frac{\partial N_{x\theta}}{\partial x} + aN_x\,\frac{\partial^2 v}{\partial x^2} - Q_\theta = 0$$

$$a\,\frac{\partial Q_x}{\partial x} + \frac{\partial Q_\theta}{\partial \theta} + aN_x\,\frac{\partial^2 w}{\partial x^2} + N_\theta = 0 \qquad (12.77)$$

$$a\,\frac{\partial M_{x\theta}}{\partial x} - \frac{\partial M_\theta}{\partial \theta} + aQ_\theta = 0$$

$$a\,\frac{\partial M_x}{\partial x} - \frac{\partial M_{x\theta}}{\partial \theta} - aQ_x = 0$$

where p_1, p_2, p_3 are taken as zero. If we eliminate the shearing forces Q_x and Q_θ from these equations, we obtain

$$a\,\frac{\partial N_x}{\partial x} + \frac{\partial N_{x\theta}}{\partial \theta} = 0$$

$$\frac{\partial N_\theta}{\partial \theta} + a\,\frac{\partial N_{x\theta}}{\partial x} + aN_x\,\frac{\partial^2 v}{\partial x^2} + \frac{\partial M_{x\theta}}{\partial x} - \frac{\partial M_\theta}{a\,\partial \theta} = 0 \qquad (12.78)$$

$$aN_x\,\frac{\partial^2 w}{\partial x^2} + N_\theta + a\,\frac{\partial^2 M_x}{\partial x^2} - 2\,\frac{\partial^2 M_{x\theta}}{\partial x\,\partial \theta} + \frac{\partial^2 M_\theta}{a\,\partial \theta^2} = 0$$

To solve these equations, let us express them in terms of the displacements u, v, w by using Eqs. (12.58). By taking compressive stress as positive and introducing the notations

$$\frac{h^2}{12a^2} = \alpha \qquad \frac{N_x(1 - \nu^2)}{Eh} = \varphi \qquad (12.79)$$

we finally obtain the following equations:

$$\frac{\partial^2 u}{\partial x^2} + \frac{1+\nu}{2a}\frac{\partial^2 v}{\partial x\,\partial\theta} - \frac{\nu}{a}\frac{\partial w}{\partial x} + \frac{1-\nu}{2}\frac{\partial^2 u}{a^2\,\partial\theta^2} = 0$$

$$\frac{1+\nu}{2a}\frac{\partial^2 u}{\partial x\,\partial\theta} + \frac{1-\nu}{2}\frac{\partial^2 v}{\partial x^2} + \frac{\partial^2 v}{a^2\,\partial\theta^2} - \frac{\partial w}{a^2\,\partial\theta}$$

$$+ \alpha\left(\frac{\partial^2 v}{a^2\,\partial\theta^2} + \frac{\partial^3 w}{a^2\,\partial\theta^3} + \frac{\partial^3 w}{\partial x^2\,\partial\theta} + \frac{1-\nu}{2}\frac{\partial^2 v}{\partial x^2}\right) - \varphi\frac{\partial^2 v}{\partial x^2} = 0 \quad (12.80)$$

$$-a\varphi\frac{\partial^2 w}{\partial x^2} + \nu\frac{\partial u}{\partial x} + \frac{\partial v}{a\,\partial\theta} - \frac{w}{a} - \alpha\left(\frac{\partial^3 v}{a\,\partial\theta^3} + a\frac{\partial^3 v}{\partial x^2\,\partial\theta}\right.$$

$$\left. + a^3\frac{\partial^4 w}{\partial x^4} + \frac{\partial^4 w}{a\,\partial\theta^4} + 2a\frac{\partial^4 w}{\partial x^2\,\partial\theta^2}\right) = 0$$

These equations are satisfied if

$$u = \frac{C_1}{\nu a}x + C_2 \qquad v = 0 \qquad w = C_1 \qquad (12.81)$$

where C_1 and C_2 are constants. This solution represents the cylindrical form of equilibrium in which the compressed shell expands uniformly in the lateral direction. If we take the origin of coordinates at one end of the shell and let L be the length of the cylinder, the general solution of Eqs. (12.54) can be expressed in terms of the following series:

$$u = \frac{C_1}{\nu a}x + C_2 + \sum_m\sum_n A_{mn}\sin n\theta\cos\frac{m\pi x}{L}$$

$$v = \sum_m\sum_n B_{mn}\cos n\theta\sin\frac{m\pi x}{L} \qquad (12.82)$$

$$w = C_1 + \sum_m\sum_n C_{mn}\sin n\theta\sin\frac{m\pi x}{L}$$

For *long* cylinders, the edge conditions have only a small effect on the magnitude of the critical load, and the solution given by (12.82) will give the critical load for such a cylinder under axial compression irrespective of the type of edge supports.

Substituting (12.82) into Eqs. (12.80) and introducing the notation

$$\lambda = \frac{m\pi a}{L}$$

we find that

$$A_{mn}\left(\lambda^2 + \frac{1-\nu}{2}n^2\right) + B_{mn}\frac{(1-\nu)\lambda n}{2} + C_{mn}\nu\lambda = 0$$

$$A_{mn}\frac{(1+\nu)\lambda n}{2} + B_{mn}\left[\frac{(1-\nu)(1+\alpha)\lambda^2}{2} + (1+\alpha)n^2 - \lambda^2\varphi\right] \quad (12.83)$$

$$+ C_{mn}[n + \alpha n(n^2 + \lambda^2)] = 0$$

$$A_{mn}\nu\lambda + B_{mn}[1 + \alpha(n^2 + \lambda^2)] + C_{mn}[1 - \lambda^2\varphi + \alpha(\lambda^2 + n^2)^2] = 0$$

A nontrivial solution is obtained if we equate to zero the determinant of the coefficients in the above equations. The quantities α and φ are usually very small so that the terms containing their squares can be neglected. By expanding the determinant, we find that the minimum value of φ occurs when λ^2 and n^2 are large numbers. Bearing these facts in mind, we shall neglect the small terms and finally obtain

$$\varphi = \alpha \frac{(n^2 + \lambda^2)^2}{\lambda^2} + \frac{(1 - \nu)\lambda^2}{(n^2 + \lambda^2)^2}$$

Let
$$\beta = \frac{(n^2 + \lambda^2)^2}{\lambda^2}$$

Then
$$\varphi = \alpha\beta + \frac{1 - \nu}{\beta}$$

φ is a minimum if $d\varphi/d\beta = 0$, or

$$\alpha - \frac{1 - \nu}{\beta^2} = 0$$

from which we find that

$$\beta = \sqrt{\frac{1 - \nu^2}{\alpha}}$$

Hence
$$\varphi_{\min} = 2 \sqrt{\alpha(1 - \nu^2)}$$

and, by using notations (12.79),

$$\sigma_{cr} = \frac{N_{cr}}{h} = \frac{Eh}{a \sqrt{3(1 - \nu^2)}} \tag{12.84}$$

Equation (12.84) gives the value of the critical stress for a long cylinder under axial compression. This theoretical value is, however, often three or four times that of the experimental values. To explain this discrepancy, a nonlinear theory of buckling has been advanced by von Kármán and Tsien,[1] who assume that the squares of the derivatives of the deflection w are now of the same order of magnitude as the derivatives of other displacements. Such calculations, however, are too long to be included in this volume.

[1] See Th. von Kármán and H. S. Tsien, The Buckling of Thin Cylindrical Shells under Axial Compression, *J. Aeronaut. Sci.*, Vol. 8, p. 303, June, 1941; D. M. A. Leggett and R. P. N. Jones, The Behavior of a Cylindrical Shell under Axial Compression when the Buckling Load Has Been Exceeded, *Brit. ARC Tech. Rept.*, *RLM* 2190, 1942; L. H. Donnell and C. C. Wan, Effect of Imperfections on Buckling of Thin Cylinders and Columns under Axial Compression, *J. Applied Mech.*, Vol. 17, No. 1, p. 173, 1951.

INDEX